APPLIED MATHEMATICS SERIES

Edited by

I. S. Sokolnikoff

FINITE-DIFFERENCE METHODS

FOR

PARTIAL

DIFFERENTIAL EQUATIONS

APPLIED MATHEMATICS SERIES

The Applied Mathematics Series is devoted to books dealing with mathematical theories underlying physical and biological sciences, and with advanced mathematical techniques needed for solving problems of these sciences.

FINITE-DIFFERENCE METHODS

FOR

PARTIAL
DIFFERENTIAL EQUATIONS

GEORGE E. FORSYTHE

PROFESSOR OF MATHEMATICS

STANFORD UNIVERSITY

WOLFGANG R. WASOW

PROFESSOR OF MATHEMATICS

UNIVERSITY OF WISCONSIN

JOHN WILEY & SONS, INC.

NEW YORK · LONDON

Library of Congress Catalog Card Number: 60–11721

PRINTED IN THE UNITED STATES OF AMERICA

PREFACE

The astonishingly rapid development of the technology of high-speed computing machines in recent years has been accompanied by a very substantial growth of the mathematical science of numerical analysis. It is no longer possible to do justice to all important aspects of this discipline in one volume. In fact, several branches of the theory, and especially the numerical aspects of differential equations, have become substantial enough to warrant accounts in more than one monograph.

There are many numerical methods for solving partial differential equations. Of these, only one stands out as being universally applicable to both linear and nonlinear problems—the method of finite differences—and we deal exclusively with that method. The literature on difference methods for partial differential equations is growing rapidly. It is widely scattered and differs greatly in viewpoint and character. A definitive presentation of this field will have to wait until the present period of intense development has come to at least a temporary halt. In the meantime, we believe that a connected account of many of the more important results and methods available at this time will serve a useful purpose.

We have tried to keep on a middle ground with respect to the choice of subject matter and the level of presentation. Most of the book ought to be understood by readers with a firm grasp of what is usually taught in a good course in advanced calculus and with some knowledge of matrix theory. Without this prerequisite no real understanding of any but the most elementary aspects of partial differential equations is possible. On the other hand, we do not presuppose a previous knowledge of the theory of partial differential equations, since this would have seriously limited the usefulness of the book. We have excluded topics that have no direct bearing on numerical analysis, such as existence and uniqueness proofs based on finite-difference approximations. At the other extreme, little attempt has been made to serve as a guide for programmers or to include many numerical examples. The numerical solution of partial differential equations is no easy matter. Almost every problem arising out of the physical sciences requires original thought and modifications of existing methods. A general knowledge of the theoretical background and the known

v

methods is almost indispensable for work on such problems, and this is what we have tried to give.

With minor exceptions, the numerical solution of difference equations corresponding to partial differential equations is so enormous a task that it is carried out only with automatic digital computers. For the reader who has had little experience with these machines, Sec. 3 provides some general background about them. In Sec. 25 we discuss in some detail certain algorithms for obtaining and solving difference equations on automatic computers.

The authors were colleagues for some years in the numerical analysis research program at the University of California, Los Angeles, a program founded by the National Bureau of Standards. The book originated in notes prepared by us for a graduate seminar at the university, and was finished at the encouragement of Professors C. B. Tompkins and I. S. Sokolnikoff. The book is directed to several groups of readers: (i) pure and applied mathematical analysts; (ii) programmers of automatic digital computing machines; (iii) engineers, physicists, meteorologists, and others with an interest in using machines to solve partial differential equations; and (iv) graduate students in these fields. Though this was not designed as a textbook, we have used drafts of the book in graduate lectures at our present universities.

Thanks are due the Office of Naval Research, the Office of Ordnance Research of the U. S. Army, the National Science Foundation, and the Mathematics Research Center of the U. S. Army at Madison, Wisconsin, who collectively have supported most of the work on this book at Stanford University, at the University of California, Los Angeles, and at the University of Wisconsin. We wish to thank three graduate students who read much of the manuscript and suggested innumerable improvements: William B. Gragg, Jr., James Ortega, and Betty Jane Stone. Finally, we wish to thank Mrs. Ruthanne Clark, Miss Barbara Spiering, and Mrs. Carolyn Young for their exceptionally responsible typing and other assistance.

GEORGE E. FORSYTHE
WOLFGANG R. WASOW

Stanford University,
University of Wisconsin,
December 10, 1959

CONTENTS

INTRODUCTION TO PARTIAL DIFFERENTIAL EQUATIONS AND COMPUTERS

1 HYPERBOLIC EQUATIONS IN TWO INDEPENDENT VARIABLES

4 INITIAL-VALUE PROBLEMS IN MORE THAN TWO INDEPENDENT VARIABLES

INTRODUCTION TO
PARTIAL DIFFERENTIAL EQUATIONS
AND COMPUTERS

SECTION 1. REMARKS ON THE CLASSIFICATION OF PARTIAL DIFFERENTIAL EQUATIONS

Let us consider, for the purpose of preliminary orientation, the three differential equations

$$u_{xx} + u_{yy} = 0, \tag{1.1}$$

$$u_{xx} - u_{yy} = 0, \tag{1.2}$$

$$u_{xx} - u_y = 0. \tag{1.3}$$

(The subscripts indicate partial differentiation.) They are the prototypes of many important partial differential equations met in the physical applications of mathematics.

As in the theory of ordinary differential equations, one might ask for the "general" solution of such a partial differential equation, but the general solution can be found even more rarely than for ordinary differential equations; and when found, it seldom helps much in answering the questions important to the mathematical physicist. In the applications one is usually concerned with the calculation of a solution which, in addition to the differential equation, satisfies certain subsidiary requirements, such as boundary or initial conditions. For linear (but generally not for nonlinear) ordinary differential equations the desired solution can frequently be found by appropriately determining the arbitrary constants occurring in the general solution. For partial differential equations this is only possible in exceptional cases, one reason being that the general solution now involves arbitrary functions instead of arbitrary constants.

The last remark can be illustrated with equation (1.1). This equation, which is known as *Laplace's equation* and commonly denoted by $\nabla^2 u = 0$ or $\Delta u = 0$, has a close relationship to the theory of analytic functions. Set $z = x + iy$ and let

$$f(z) = u(x, y) + i\, v(x, y)$$

1

be an analytic function of z. Then u and v are related by the Cauchy-Riemann differential equations

$$u_x - v_y = 0, \quad u_y + v_x = 0, \tag{1.4}$$

and possess partial derivatives of all orders (Knopp [1945], pp. 28–30). If the first of these equations is differentiated with respect to x and the second with respect to y, it is seen that

$$u(x, y) = \operatorname{Re} f(z) \tag{1.5}$$

is a solution of Laplace's equation. Conversely, we now show that every solution of Laplace's equation is the real part of some analytic function. Let a solution u be given; then equations (1.4) can be solved for v, since the compatibility condition of these two equations is precisely Laplace's equation for u. The quantity $u(x, y) + i\,v(x, y)$ is then (Knopp [1945], p. 30) an analytic function $f(z)$ of the complex variable $z = x + iy$; i.e., (1.5) is valid. Hence (1.5) is the general solution of (1.1).

The solutions of Laplace's equation are frequently called *harmonic* (or potential) functions, and two harmonic functions which are linked by the Cauchy-Riemann equations (1.4) are said to be *conjugate*.

The general solution of equation (1.2) can also be calculated without difficulty, for, if u_{xx} and u_{yy} are continuous, the change of variables

$$\xi = x + y, \quad \eta = x - y, \quad u(x, y) = \omega(\xi, \eta)$$

changes (1.2) into

$$\omega_{\xi\eta} = 0,$$

which is solved by

$$\omega = F(\xi) + G(\eta),$$

where F and G are arbitrary differentiable functions; if we require that $\omega_{\xi\eta} = \omega_{\eta\xi}$, there are no other solutions. Hence

$$u(x, y) = F(x + y) + G(x - y) \tag{1.6}$$

is a solution of (1.2), provided F and G are twice differentiable but otherwise arbitrary. [The second derivatives of F and G need not even be continuous for (1.6) to be a solution, as can be verified by inserting (1.6) into (1.2).]

The subsidiary conditions that are imposed on the solution of a differential equation in a problem of mathematical physics vary with the nature of the problem. We give a few extremely simple but typical examples.

(*a*) Consider a rigid wire whose orthogonal projection on the (x, y)-plane is a simple closed curve C. This frame is to contain an ideal elastic membrane of uniform density under uniform tension. Let $u(x, y)$ denote the deflection of this membrane measured from the (x, y)-plane. If u and its derivatives are so small that higher powers of u, u_x, u_y can be neglected by comparison with smaller ones, u can be shown to be a harmonic function in the interior R of C. The values of u on the boundary C are, of course, the prescribed deflection f of the wire frame. Hence u is a solution of the problem

$$\Delta u = 0 \text{ in } R, \qquad u = f \text{ on } C \tag{1.7}$$

(Courant and Hilbert [1953], p. 247). This is frequently called *Dirichlet's problem* for Laplace's equation. For this and other problems, it is important to keep in mind that the solution cannot be expected to have second derivatives, much less to satisfy the differential equation at the boundary points unless f is a rather smooth function. By saying that u *assumes the prescribed boundary values* one means that $u(x, y)$ tends to these values as the point (x, y) approaches the boundary from the interior.

  (b) A long, straight, narrow rod performs elastic longitudinal vibrations. In a mathematical idealization let the rod be represented by the x-axis, and denote by $u(x, t)$ the deflection from the rest position at time t of the point which, at rest, has the abscissa x. If $u(x, t)$ is small and the units are suitably chosen, u is a solution of the differential equation $u_{tt} - u_{xx} = 0$, the simplest form of the differential equation of wave propagation (Sokolnikoff and Sokolnikoff [1941], p. 367). On physical grounds we expect the values of u at any time to be uniquely determined if the initial deflection $u(x, 0)$ and the initial velocity $u_t(x, 0)$ are prescribed. We are thus led to the problem of finding $u(x, t)$ for $t > 0$, if

$$u_{tt} - u_{xx} = 0 \text{ for } t > 0, \qquad u(x, 0) = f(x), \qquad u_t(x, 0) = g(x), \tag{1.8}$$

where $f(x)$ and $g(x)$ are prescribed arbitrarily, except perhaps for certain smoothness requirements which we do not intend to discuss at this moment. This is an instance of an *initial-value problem*, or "Cauchy's problem," as it is sometimes called.

  (c) Again we consider a straight, narrow, infinite rod, but this time we let u denote its temperature, whose dependence on x and t we wish to study. We assume that the rod is thermally insulated and that we know the initial distribution of temperature $u(x, 0)$. It is physically plausible that the subsequent temperature distribution $u(x, t)$ is then uniquely determined. One shows easily that the differential equation that ideally governs the flow of heat in the rod is $u_t - u_{xx} = 0$, provided the units are defined properly (Churchill [1941], pp. 15 ff.). The natural initial-value problem in this context is therefore

$$u_t - u_{xx} = 0 \text{ for } t > 0, \qquad u(x, 0) = f(x).$$

In the theory of *ordinary* linear differential equations a given equation can usually be combined in many different ways with subsidiary conditions, which may consist in prescribing data at one, two, or more points. Within certain fairly wide limits such problems will generally have a unique solution, provided the number of conditions matches the order of the differential equation. It is a fact of fundamental importance that this is no longer true for partial differential equations. This had been emphasized and illustrated by Hadamard [1923], pp. 23–44.

He showed, for instance, that Cauchy's problem for Laplace's equation,

$$\Delta u = 0 \text{ for } t > 0, \qquad u(x, 0) = f(x), \qquad u_y(x, 0) = g(x) \qquad (1.9)$$

is, in a certain sense, not *well posed*. Let us consider, for example, the special case that $f(x) \equiv 0$, and assume that $u(x, y)$ solves (1.9) in some region bounded below by a segment of the x-axis. Then we can make use of two standard theorems on harmonic functions. The first states that a harmonic function $u(x, y)$ is an analytic function of each of the variables x and y (Sommerfeld [1949], pp. 47–48). The second is a simple consequence of the principle of reflection for analytic functions (Nehari [1952], pp. 183–187). It assures us that a function which is harmonic in a region bounded in part by a straight line segment and zero on this segment can be continued as a harmonic function onto and beyond this segment. Since the derivatives of a harmonic function are themselves harmonic, we conclude from these two facts that $u_y(x, y)$ is a regular analytic function of x for $y = 0$; i.e., $g(x)$ must be analytic. In other words, unless the prescribed function $g(x)$ belongs to the very special class of functions that are analytic, problem (1.9) with $f(x) \equiv 0$ has no solution. It is easy to show, but we shall not do this here, that, if $f(x)$ is not prescribed as identically zero, it also must be analytic if (1.9) is to have a solution.

This severe limitation in the permissible choice of initial values might at first glance be regarded as not very serious. For it is well known that by virtue of Weierstrass' approximation theorem any continuous function can be approximated as closely as we wish by analytic functions, even by polynomials (Courant and Hilbert [1953], pp. 65 ff.). This argument would be valid if close approximation of the boundary values always implied close approximation of the solution for $y > 0$. This, however, is not the case in our present problem. For a counterexample it suffices to consider the initial values

$$f(x) = e^{-\sqrt{n}} \sin nx, \qquad g(x) = 0,$$

where n is a positive integer. It can be easily verified that

$$u(x, y) = e^{-\sqrt{n}} \cosh ny \sin nx$$

is a harmonic function with these initial values. As $n \to \infty$, the initial data tend to zero with all their derivatives, while $u(x, y)$ diverges rapidly for $y \neq 0$.

According to Hadamard, the discontinuous dependence on the initial data precludes by itself any physical meaning for problem (1.9), because physical data are by their nature only approximate. More generally, Hadamard calls a problem of mathematical physics *well posed if its solution exists, is unique, and depends continuously on the data.* It can be shown that the problems (*a*), (*b*), and (*c*) are well posed. If a mathematical problem of physical origin turns out not to be well posed, this usually indicates that the formulation is incorrect or incomplete.

No permutation of the subsidiary conditions in problems (*a*), (*b*), and (*c*) leads to a well-posed problem. We consider one such permutation as a second example of a problem that is not well posed. Let

$$u_{xx} - u_{yy} = 0 \text{ in } R, \qquad u = f \text{ on } C, \tag{1.10}$$

where R is a rectangle whose sides have slopes ± 1. Using again the transformation $\xi = x + y$, $\eta = x - y$, we change the differential equation into $\omega_{\xi\eta} = 0$ and the rectangle R into a rectangle R^* with sides parallel to the ξ, η axes respectively. Suppose that (1.10) possesses a solution. Since ω_ξ does not depend on η, and since ω_η is independent of ξ, the boundary function f must be such that its tangential derivative has equal values at corresponding points on opposite sides of the bounding rectangle. In other words, for arbitrary f, even if severe smoothness restrictions are imposed, problem (1.10) has no solution.

Partial differential equations can be classified according to the type of subsidiary conditions that must be imposed to produce a well-posed problem. In the case of linear differential equations of the second order in two independent variables, this classification is easy to describe. The most general differential equation of this type is

$$Au_{xx} + 2Bu_{xy} + Cu_{yy} + Du_x + Eu_y + Fu + G = 0, \tag{1.11}$$

with coefficients that are functions of x and y. It is called *elliptic, hyperbolic,* or *parabolic* according as the determinant

$$\begin{vmatrix} A & B \\ B & C \end{vmatrix}$$

is positive, negative, or zero. This classification depends in general on the region of the (x, y)-plane under consideration. The differential equation $xu_{xx} + u_{yy} = 0$, for instance, is elliptic for $x > 0$, hyperbolic for $x < 0$, and parabolic for $x = 0$.

Each of the three simple equations we have been discussing in this section is an example of one of these types: Laplace's equation is elliptic, the equation of wave propagation is hyperbolic, and the equation of heat flow is parabolic. It can be shown that the subsidiary conditions imposed by us in each case will generate well-posed problems also when combined with more general differential equations of the respective type but not when combined with differential equations of any other type.

For differential equations in more than two variables, for systems, and for nonlinear differential equations, useful definitions of the concepts of elliptic, hyperbolic, and parabolic character can also be given. We shall introduce these as the need arises.

Recently, Hadamard's position that only well-posed problems are physically relevant has been questioned by several mathematicians. In the case of certain initial-value problems for elliptic differential equations of physical origin, numerical schemes have been suggested which should approximate the exact solution even though the latter depends in discontinuous fashion on the initial values. But these investigations are as yet too incomplete to warrant a description herein.

SECTION 2. SYSTEMS AND SINGLE EQUATIONS

Every single differential equation of order higher than one can be written as a system of first-order equations. This is rather obvious. One way of doing it is to introduce all derivatives of the dependent variable, except those of highest order, as new unknown functions. Thus $u_{xx} - u_{yy} = 0$ is equivalent to the system

$$u_x = p, \qquad u_y = q, \qquad p_x - q_y = 0$$

for the three functions u, p, q.

For ordinary differential equations a converse of this statement is also true: From a system of n first-order equations for n functions satisfying certain mild regularity conditions one can derive one differential equation of order n containing only one of these unknown functions. For instance, from the two simultaneous equations $f(x, u, v, u', v') = 0, g(x, u, v, u', v') = 0$, the unknown function v and its derivatives can be eliminated by first solving for v and v', which leads to two equations of the form

$$v = \phi(x, u, u'), \qquad v' = \psi(x, u, u').$$

The function u must then satisfy the second-order differential equation

$$\frac{d}{dx}\,\phi(x, u, u') - \psi(x, u, u') = 0.$$

This elimination is possible provided f and g have the necessary differentiability properties and provided the Jacobian $f_v g_{v'} - f_{v'} g_v$ does not vanish for the solution in question.

For partial differential equations such an elimination is not generally possible. The reason is that successive differentiations may introduce more new unknowns than new equations. Let there be given a system of n partial differential equations of order one, involving n unknown functions and $p > 1$ independent variables. Then we have to eliminate $n - 1$ unknown functions and their $p(n - 1)$ first derivatives. This is, in general, not possible. If we add the np new equations obtained by differentiating each given equation once with respect to each of the p independent variables, we introduce the $\frac{1}{2}p(p + 1)$ second derivatives of each of the $n - 1$ functions we wish to eliminate. Thus, whenever $\frac{1}{2}p(p + 1)(n - 1) > np$, the number of quantities to be eliminated has been increased more than the number of equations. This is the case, for instance, for $n = p = 3$. More differentiations will only make the situation worse.

SECTION 3. PROPERTIES OF DIGITAL COMPUTING SYSTEMS

Machines for scientific computation can be reasonably divided into *analog* and *digital* types. Analog machines include devices which, like planimeters and electronic differential analyzers, model physical variables by continuously varying shaft rotations, voltages, etc. Their over-all accuracy is of the range of magnitude from 0.1 to 5%. Various practical tolerances limit the size of analog machines and, hence, of the problems which they can treat. Their accuracy and size suffice for many applications, and analog machines are widely used; those interested may consult Soroka [1954] or Huskey and Korn [1960].

In digital computation all numbers are *quantized*; i.e., like the integers, they are integral multiples of some unit which can be given an arbitrary scaling. For digital machines, unlike analog machines, there is no clear bound on the accuracy obtainable nor on the size of problems which can be attacked. For these reasons, digital machines are being used for an increasing variety of problems, even where great accuracy is not required in the ultimate answer. For example, suppose one wants, with 1% accuracy, the gradient of the solution of a large elliptic boundary-value problem. The complexity of the region alone may demand digital computation. Moreover, since differentiation usually magnifies small errors, it is important to have a considerable margin of precision in the function to be differentiated, a margin which itself demands the precision of digital computers.

Let us now examine the common digital computing systems, and characterize their applicability to scientific computation. Our purpose is to develop some background with which to consider the computational problems raised by the solution of partial differential equations.

3.1. Desk Computation

Until the 1940's most computation was performed by a person with pencil and paper, assisted by books of tables, and, later, especially in the United States, by a keyboard desk calculator. Let us give a sort of machine's eye view of this computing system. It can perform one multiplication (a typical arithmetic operation) in 10 to 60 seconds on the average, including entering the factors (*input*) and posting the results (*output*). Call this the typical *operation time*. The person has access to data sheets (the *high-speed memory*) on his desk, from which any of perhaps 10^3 numbers can be copied into the keyboard in about 10 seconds (called the *fast-access time*). The person can choose a book out of about 100 in his room, scan its 500 pages of perhaps 200 tabulated 10-decimal numbers on each page, and enter the desired number into his keyboard in around 10^2 seconds. Thus the *intermediate-speed memory* is about 10^7 numbers, with an access time near 10^2 seconds. (It is possible also to define an access time of 10^4 to 10^6 seconds to much of the world's relevant information.)

The immediate *control* of the one-person computing system is the person's mind. The control ordinarily follows a *program*, which is a sequence of simple *instructions* laid out earlier by a *programmer* who may be the same or a different person (e.g., add the entry in column 1 to that in column 2, divide the result by the number in column 4, and post the answer in column 3). The computer is personally at the center of each step of the computation, and he has the chance to learn immediately of various difficulties not anticipated in the program. Examples of such difficulties include division by zero, exceeding capacity of a register, loss of significant digits, bad interval choice, etc. Thus, if intelligent and well trained, the computer is capable of extraordinarily valuable judgment on many vital matters, and this judgment is ordinarily available without having even to be mentioned in the program. Offsetting this, however, is the fact that the computer's control must be expected to deviate from the program relatively frequently: the person may, for example, occasionally and without warning subtract instead of add.

The fact that the high-speed memory of the one-person computing system is on paper means that there is a written record of almost every significant step in the calculation. This makes it possible for the computer or any one else to trace troubles to their source with a minimum of difficulty. This possibility and the available judgment of the computer are characteristics of the one-person computing system which are absent from modern automatic computers.

3.2. Punched-Card Computers

In the late 1930's people began to use punched-card equipment for scientific computation (Eckert [1940]). Throughout the 1940's this movement spread widely, and it reached its climax around 1950 in such systems as the Card-Programmed Calculator (C.P.C.) of the International Business Machines Corporation. The program and an almost unlimited intermediate storage are on punched cards. The high-speed storage is mainly electro-mechanical, holding 25 to 100 numbers. The operation time is about 0.5 second, including access to the high-speed memory. Because the arithmetic organ of the C.P.C. is electronic, it is possible to perform such complicated operations as finding a square root or cosine in a few operation times. This machine can make a written record of every operation while operating at about half-speed, and thus mistakes are easily traced. Since the program is contained on a deck of punched cards, it will normally be followed in a linear order, without much branching or scrambling of the order. Thus this system is practically devoid of even routine judgment.

Punched-card computation is able to produce and make a complete record of a straightforward *marching* (linearly ordered) computation something like 100 times faster than a one-person computing system. A good example of a problem well suited to the C.P.C. is an initial-value problem for an ordinary differential equation, linear or not. A more intricately ordered computation is also possible, but is much less economical unless a large number of cases of such a computation are done in parallel, or unless a long iteration is to be repeated many times. Thus the C.P.C. has been used to solve the Dirichlet problem of Sec. 18, but only rather awkwardly (Yowell [1951]).

3.3. Automatic Digital Computers

In spite of the revolution they created in the late 1940's, such punched-card computers as the C.P.C. have been rendered obsolete by the rapid development of still more revolutionary devices—internally programmed electronic digital computers, which we shall refer to simply as *automatic computers*. These machines seem to the authors to be one of the most significant technological developments of the present decade, and perhaps of a longer period. Any one who would understand the elements of modern computing must first become quite familiar with the preparation of problems for these automatic computers.

Like the one-person computing system mentioned above, the automatic computer has one or more memories to store the data. But in the automatic computers the program is also stored in a memory in the form of a numerical *code* which can be interpreted by the control of the machine. As in all computing systems, there is an arithmetic organ to operate on the numbers. The novel feature of the automatic computers is that, since the instructions are themselves numbers, the arithmetic organ can operate on them to create new instructions. This constitutes the fascinating *internal programming* feature, which seems to have been inaugurated on ENIAC about 1945 at the suggestion of the late J. von Neumann.

There are input and output devices on the automatic computers, and usually a variety of them with different speeds and purposes. Finally, there are one or more controls to interpret the coded program and, following it, to regulate and synchronize the flow of information among the memories, arithmetic organ, and outside world.

The automatic computers are now developing so rapidly in size and speed that any precise characterization is bound to be obsolete soon. It will surely be many years before mathematicians close the gap between what engineers are designing and what we know how to use efficiently. As an example of a modern computing system, we shall sketch the IBM electronic computer type 709 which became available in late 1958. The IBM 709 has a high-speed memory of up to 32,768 *words*, i.e., numbers, coded instructions, or other coded data. Each word has a sign digit and 35 binary digits, the equivalent of over 10 decimal digits. The access time is 12 microseconds.* For an intermediate-speed memory there are magnetic tapes which hold around 10^6 words each; these can be read from or written on at about 2500 words per second in a linear order. Buffer units make it possible for linearly stored information to be transferred between the magnetic tapes and the high-speed memory without interrupting the computations. Such a buffer had proved itself exceedingly useful in the Sperry-Rand UNIVAC computer. Other forms of intermediate storage are available.

With a fixed binary point the IBM 709 adds in 24 microseconds and multiplies in from 24 to 240 microseconds. Like many modern computers, the IBM 709 has provision for an automatic scaling feature called *floating*

* A million microseconds make one second.

(binary) *point*. In this, the word of 36 binary digits is divided into a sign (one digit), an exponent P between -128 and 127 (8 digits), and 27 significant digits Q. Here the word is to be interpreted as $\pm Q \cdot 2^P$. Floating-point addition takes at least 84 microseconds and floating-point multiplication takes 24 to 208 microseconds.

Besides the floating-point operations, the IBM 709 has other devices to simplify coding. Nevertheless, coding and code checking are pretty strenuous operations on substantial problems, and are likely to take from a week to many months. The preparation of such a sequence of instructions is a very formidable problem in itself, since a single error is likely to ruin the entire code. For this reason it is highly desirable to use the machine itself to carry out the routine aspects of assembling the instructions, assigning memory locations, etc. (*automatic coding*). A great deal of the current effort in programming for the new machines consists in preparing routines for automatic coding. The desired end result is that an engineer or other user should be able to input a small number of parameters into an automatic computer, whereupon the computer itself should use these data to prepare a program for running a problem. There are many approaches to the problem of automatic coding, and the interested reader should consult such journals as the *Journal* or the *Communications of the Association for Computing Machinery*. A new international algebraic language called ALGOL gives promise of becoming an excellent medium for describing algorithms to an automatic digital computer.

It should be mentioned once more that the IBM 709 represents merely the current state of a rapidly changing development. In addition to growth in pure memory capacity and speed, automatic computers are evolving an internal organization of a complexity rivaling that of a large corporation! It is expected that the 1960's will see computers whose high-speed memories may be 50 or 100 times as large, and whose arithmetic may be performed up to 100 times as fast as the IBM 709. However, there are technical considerations (such as the velocity of light!) suggesting that, at that stage, computer development will level off, and that machine users will begin to have an opportunity to catch up with the engineers.

The reader interested in current developments might consult, for example, the annual review article in the *Transactions of the Professional Group on Electronic Computers* of the Institute of Radio Engineers.

3.4. Demands of Partial Differential Equations

Among common scientific problems, the greatest demands on both memory space and arithmetic speed are made by partial differential equations. To understand these demands, let us consider the solution by finite-difference methods (see below) of a boundary-value problem which is elliptic with respect to s space dimensions ($s = 1$, 2, or 3). If there is a time dependence, assume it enters in such a way that the problem must be marched off in time by the successive solution of elliptic boundary-value problems. This is characteristic, for example, of the meteorological equations of Sec. 28. Suppose that each space dimension is given N subdivisions in a cubical lattice. The storage of the solution will therefore

TABLE 3.1. Rough storage requirements for a typical problem with N subdivisions in each of s space dimensions

	$N = 10$	$N = 10^2$	$N = 10^3$
$s = 1$	10	10^2	10^3
$s = 2$	10^2	10^4	10^6
$s = 3$	10^3	10^6	10^9

require N^s numbers for each instant of time represented. As a great simplification, let us suppose that the coefficients of the equation need not be stored in the memory. (They may be constant, or easily generated.)

Let us assume that the value $N = 10$ gives a sketchy detail, that $N = 10^2$ is moderately adequate in detail, and $N = 10^3$ is needed for great detail. Table 3.1 shows the number of data values to be stored for the values of

TABLE 3.2. Rough number of arithmetic operations required for the problem of Table 3.1

	$N = 10$	$N = 10^2$	$N = 10^3$
$s = 1$	10^3	10^5	10^7
$s = 2$	10^4	10^7	10^{10}
$s = 3$	10^5	10^9	10^{13}

N and s considered. It is possible in principle to pack 2 or 3 numbers in one machine word, but packing and unpacking them greatly increases the computing time.

Now let us consider the demands on the arithmetic unit to solve one boundary-value problem. The principal methods used in practice and described below require sweeping through the entire field many times. As a working hypothesis, suppose that N sweeps are required; the justification of such a value independent of s is implicit in Sec. 22. Let us assume that 2 multiplications and 8 additions are used for each point in the sweep; this low number is reasonable for a simple equation like Poisson's. Table

3.2 shows the number of arithmetic operations per boundary-value problem solved; the values are $10N$ times those of Table 3.1.

Now for the above operations the IBM 709 computer will average about 50 microseconds each, a rate of about 7×10^7 operations per hour. Allowing for various logical operations, we should discount this to, say, 10^7 arithmetic operations per hour. At this rate, assuming no essential loss of time for getting data from intermediate storage, we obtain the

TABLE 3.3. **Approximate length of time for computation of one time step for the problem of Table 3.1**

	$N = 10$	$N = 10^2$	$N = 10^3$
$s = 1$	1 sec	1 min	1 hr
$s = 2$	3 sec	1 hr	6 wk
$s = 3$	1 min	1 wk	100 yr

times of Table 3.3 for solving each boundary-value problem. For time-dependent problems, we assume we will need about 10^2 time steps, and Table 3.4 gives the approximate total length of time for a time-dependent problem.

The following crude assessments apply to these difference methods only, and assume that computing times up to the order of magnitude of a few

TABLE 3.4. **Approximate length of time to compute 100 time steps for the problem of Table 3.1**

	$N = 10$	$N = 10^2$	$N = 10^3$
$s = 1$	1 min	1 hr	1 wk
$s = 2$	6 min	1 wk	10 yr
$s = 3$	1 hr	1 yr	10^4 yr

weeks are now possible but that those of a week or more would be very expensive.

It is clear that problems with one space dimension are entirely possible with a modern machine, although a need for great geometrical detail ($N = 10^3$) will make time-dependent problems quite expensive.

Problems with two space dimensions are now possible only in moderate detail ($N = 10^2$), and time-dependent problems are very expensive unless geometrical detail is sacrificed. The computers of the 1960's should have enough speed and storage to attack two-dimensional time-dependent problems with great detail ($N = 10^3$).

Problems with three space dimensions cannot possibly be solved in great detail ($N = 10^3$) now, and probably will not be solvable in great detail with the machines of the forseeable future. They are currently possible in moderate detail ($N = 10^2$) if there is no time dependence, and are now very easy in sketchy detail ($N = 10$) even if they depend on time. The machines of the 1960's should permit time-dependent problems in three dimensions to be attacked in moderate detail ($N = 10^2$).

1

HYPERBOLIC EQUATIONS
IN TWO INDEPENDENT VARIABLES

SECTION 4. A FINITE-DIFFERENCE APPROXIMATION
TO THE EQUATION $u_{tt} - u_{xx} = 0$

4.1. Solution of the Simplest Initial-Value Problem for $u_{tt} - u_{xx} = 0$

The solution of the problem defined by the formulas (1.8) is almost trivial, thanks to the general relation (1.6), provided f and g are twice differentiable. For we find immediately (replacing y by t) that a solution of the form (1.6) will satisfy the initial conditions if

$$F(x) + G(x) = u(x, 0) = f(x),$$

$$F'(x) - G'(x) = u_t(x, 0) = g(x).$$

We differentiate the first of these equations and thus obtain two linear algebraic equations for $F'(x)$ and $G'(x)$. Solving these and integrating, we see that

$$F(x) = \frac{1}{2}\left[f(x) + \int_0^x g(\xi)\, d\xi\right] + C_1,$$

$$G(x) = \frac{1}{2}\left[f(x) - \int_0^x g(\xi)\, d\xi\right] + C_2,$$

where C_1 and C_2 are unknown constants of integration. Hence, again using formula (1.6),

$$u(x, t) = \frac{1}{2}\left[f(x + t) + f(x - t) + \int_{x-t}^{x+t} g(\xi)\, d\xi\right] + C_3.$$

15

For $t = 0$, this reduces to $f(x) = f(x) + C_3$, showing that $C_3 = 0$. The solution of the problem defined by equations (1.8) is therefore

$$u(x, t) = \frac{1}{2}\left[f(x + t) + f(x - t) + \int_{x-t}^{x+t} g(\xi)\, d\xi \right]. \tag{4.1}$$

This is almost the only initial-value or boundary-value problem of any interest that can be solved in such an explicit and elementary manner.

The following observations can immediately be read from formula (4.1): The value of the solution at a point (x_0, t_0) depends only on the initial data on the segment of the x-axis cut out by the lines $x + t = \text{const.}$, $x - t = \text{const.}$ that pass through (x_0, t_0). This segment is called the *interval of dependence* of the point (x_0, t_0). Conversely, the set of points (x, t) at which the solution is influenced by the initial data at a point $(x_0, 0)$ on the x-axis is the sector that is bounded by the lines $x + t = x_0$ and $x - t = x_0$. This sector is the *region of influence* of the point $(x_0, 0)$. The lines $x \pm t = \text{const.}$ are called the *characteristics* of the differential equation $u_{tt} - u_{xx} = 0$.

We shall see later that these concepts of domains of dependence and influence and of characteristics are capable of generalization to all hyperbolic problems, and that they are of decisive importance there.

Formula (4.1) is valid for negative as well as for positive t. If the initial values are prescribed on the interval $a \leq x \leq b$ only, the solution is determined in the square bounded by the four characteristics through the points $(a, 0)$, $(b, 0)$, and formula (4.1) represents a solution of the differential equation at every point of that square.

4.2. An Approximating Difference Equation

Since the initial-value problem (1.8) has been completely solved by formula (4.1), there is no direct computational reason for studying finite-difference approximations to the differential equation $u_{tt} - u_{xx} = 0$. But, on the other hand, it is precisely the simplicity of this problem which makes it an excellent object for the first introduction and discussion of concepts important also in many more complicated situations. The present section is therefore to be understood as serving an illustrative purpose, not a computational one.

The simplest finite-difference approximation to the equation $u_{tt} = u_{xx}$ is

$$\frac{U(x, t + k) - 2U(x, t) + U(x, t - k)}{k^2}$$
$$= \frac{U(x + h, t) - 2U(x, t) + U(x - h, t)}{h^2}. \tag{4.2}$$

It is obtained by replacing the partial derivatives by central finite-difference quotients, using the increments h and k in the x and t directions respectively. If we replace the initial conditions in (1.8) by

$$U(x, 0) = f(x), \qquad \frac{U(x, k) - U(x, 0)}{k} = g(x), \qquad (4.3)$$

equations (4.2) and (4.3) constitute a formal finite-difference approximation to the problem (1.8) in the following sense: For any function $U(x, t)$ with second partial derivatives, the difference quotients in (4.2) and (4.3) will tend to the corresponding derivatives figuring in the differential problem as h and k tend to zero. We call this a *formal* approximation because it does not imply that the solution of the difference problem for U will always tend to the solution of the differential problem, as $h \to 0$, and $k \to 0$. This point will be amply illustrated in the sequel. If a formal finite-difference approximation to a differential equation problem is to be computationally useful, it is, of course, necessary that the solution of the former approach the solution of the latter.

The problem of solving a difference equation can always be interpreted in two different ways: We may think of x and t in (4.2) and (4.3) as continuous variables and try to satisfy the equations identically in x and t, or we may limit the variables to a suitable discrete set such as $(x_0 + rh, sk)$, where $r, s = 0, \pm 1, \pm 2, \cdots$, which has the property that, if x and t belong to this set, only values of U at points of the set occur in the difference equation. Explicit solution in the first sense is usually difficult or impossible. We shall, however, carry it out in the present problem where it is comparatively easy. For purposes of computation it is always the second interpretation that is intended.

The numerical solution of (4.2), (4.3) in this second sense is a simple matter. We have

$$U(x, 0) = f(x),$$

$$U(x, k) = kg(x) + f(x),$$

$$U(x, t + k) = 2U(x, t) - U(x, t - k)$$
$$+ \lambda^2[U(x + h, t) - 2U(x, t) + U(x - h, t)], \qquad (4.4)$$

where

$$\lambda = \frac{k}{h}.$$

Beginning with the grid points $(x_0 + rh, 0)$ on the initial line, the values at the grid points on the lines $t = k, 2k, 3k$, can be successively calculated from these equations. The situation is schematically illustrated by Fig. 4.1, in which circles show the "stencil" or "star" of net points that enter into one application of the recursion formula.

If the initial values are given in an interval $a \leq x \leq b$ (which, for simplicity, we suppose to be bounded by grid points), then the recursion formula (4.4) enables us to calculate $U(x, t)$ at the grid points inside a triangle bounded by this interval and two sides with slopes $\pm \lambda$. We recognize the analogy with the situation met in the discussion of the differential problem: Every grid point in this triangle has an interval of dependence on the x-axis which lies in the interval $a \leq x \leq b$.

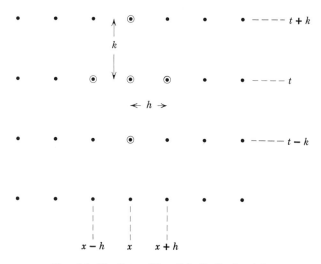

Fig. 4.1. The "stencil" or "star" of net points.

The analogy is, however, not complete, and this is an observation of great importance. For the interval of dependence for the difference equation depends on λ, the ratio of the increments k and h. From this simple fact there follows immediately an important negative statement.

THEOREM 4.1. *Let $U(x, t)$ and $u(x, t)$ be respectively the solutions of the initial-value problems* (4.4) *and* (1.8). *Let h and k tend to zero in such a manner that $k/h \geq \lambda_0 > 1$. Then there exist infinitely many initial functions $f(x)$, $g(x)$ for which $U(x, t)$ does not converge to $u(x, t)$.*

Proof. As we have seen, the interval of dependence for the difference equation lies in the interior of the interval of dependence of the differential equation if $k/h \geq \lambda_0 > 1$. If at a point (x, t) the function U tends to u for some choice of the initial functions, we can change these functions in a way that modifies the value of the expression (4.1) at (x, t), but leaves the initial values in the interval of dependence of the difference equation the same as before. For the modified initial functions the solution u is then different from the limit of U.

As this proof indicates, convergence of U to u is to be regarded as an exception when $k/h > 1$.

4.3. Explicit Solution of the Difference Equation for $\lambda < 1$

The most useful method for the explicit solution of initial-value problems for linear partial differential equations is based on the technique of separation of variables and the superposition of solutions, i.e., the formation of linear combinations of solutions. As an illustration, we treat problem (1.8) in this manner.

By separation of variables one means the construction of particular solutions of the form

$$u(x, t) = \phi(x)\, \psi(t). \tag{4.5}$$

Insertion into $u_{tt} - u_{xx} = 0$ leads to a relation that can be written in the form

$$\frac{\phi''(x)}{\phi(x)} = \frac{\psi''(t)}{\psi(t)}.$$

Since the two members of this equation are functions of different independent variables, it follows that both must be equal to the same constant c. For any value of c, every solution of the pair of equations

$$\phi''(x) - c\,\phi(x) = 0, \qquad \psi''(t) - c\,\psi(t) = 0, \tag{4.6}$$

when inserted into (4.5), leads to a solution of the differential equation $u_{tt} - u_{xx} = 0$.

The principle of superposition enables us to construct a solution satisfying the prescribed initial conditions by adding a finite or infinite number of solutions of the form (4.5). To find such a sum, we represent the initial functions as Fourier series. Let us treat the special case where $g(x) \equiv 0$ and assume, for the sake of simplicity, that $f'(x)$ is continuous. To deal with Fourier series of conveniently strong convergence, we extend the function $f(x)$ into a larger interval $a' \le x \le b'$ such that $f'(x)$ is continuous in the larger interval and such that, in addition, $f(a') = f(b') = 0$. Finally, we may assume without loss of generality that $a' = 0$, $b' = \pi$, since this can be brought about, without changing the differential equation, by the linear transformation

$$x' = \frac{(x - a')\pi}{(b' - a')}, \qquad t' = \pi t.$$

Then $f(x)$ is representable by a uniformly convergent Fourier sine series of the form

$$f(x) = \sum_{n=1}^{\infty} a_n \sin nx, \tag{4.7}$$

where

$$a_n = \frac{2}{\pi} \int_0^\pi f(x) \sin nx \, dx. \tag{4.8}$$

Moreover, the series

$$\sum_{n=1}^\infty |a_n| \tag{4.9}$$

converges (Courant [1934], p. 439). The extension of the initial values into a larger interval has no influence on the solution at any point whose interval of dependence lies in the original smaller interval.

Now consider one arbitrary term of the series in (4.7) and let us try to find a solution of $u_{xx} - u_{tt} = 0$ which has the form (4.5) and reduces to this term for $t = 0$. In view of (4.6) this is possible if and only if

$$c = -n^2,$$

and we can then set

$$\phi(x) = a_n \sin nx, \qquad \psi(t) = \cos nt.$$

Hence the solution of our initial-value problem is

$$u(x, t) = \sum_{n=1}^\infty a_n \cos nt \sin nx, \tag{4.10}$$

at least if this series can be twice differentiated termwise. This series itself converges uniformly and absolutely because series (4.9) is convergent. It is, of course, nothing but the Fourier series of the function $\frac{1}{2}[f(x + t) + f(x - t)]$ to which the solution of problem (1.8) reduces for $g(x) \equiv 0$. This can easily be verified explicitly.

The solution to the initial-value problem for $f(x) \equiv 0$, $g(x) \not\equiv 0$ can be obtained from the solution to the problem just treated, as follows. Let $G''(x) = g(x)$. If $u(x, t)$ solves (1.8) with $u(x, 0) = G(x)$ and with $u_t(x, 0) = 0$, then $v(x, t) = u_t(x, t)$ solves (1.8) with $v(x, 0) = 0$, $v_t(x, 0) = u_{tt}(x, 0) = u_{xx}(x, 0) = g(x)$. (In this last chain of equalities we have made use of the fact that in our special problem the differential equation is satisfied on the initial line itself, a fact which can either be deduced from (4.1) or verified after the series has been calculated.)

The preceding detailed discussion of a problem solved once before in a different manner is justified by the fact that the difference problem (4.2), (4.3) can be treated in strictly analogous fashion, whereas the argument leading to formula (4.1) has no such analog.

Let us therefore assume again that $g(x) \equiv 0$ and that $f(x)$ is represented by series (4.7). If

$$U(x, t) = \Phi(x) \Psi(t)$$

is to be a solution of (4.2), separation of variables leads to the difference equations

$$\frac{\Phi(x + h) - 2\Phi(x) + \Phi(x - h)}{h^2} - c\,\Phi(x) = 0, \tag{4.11}$$

$$\frac{\Psi(t + k) - 2\Psi(t) + \Psi(t - k)}{k^2} - c\,\Psi(t) = 0. \tag{4.12}$$

The function $\sin nx$ is a solution of (4.11) if

$$c = 2\,\frac{\cos nh - 1}{h^2} = -\frac{4}{h^2}\sin^2\frac{nh}{2}. \tag{4.13}$$

Pursuing the analogy with the differential equation, we must now find $\Psi(t)$ from the difference equation

$$\frac{\Psi(t + k) - 2\Psi(t) + \Psi(t - k)}{k^2} + \frac{4}{h^2}\sin^2\frac{nh}{2}\,\Psi(t) = 0 \tag{4.14}$$

and the initial conditions

$$\Psi(0) = \Psi(k) = 1. \tag{4.15}$$

The theory of such linear difference equations with constant coefficients much resembles the better known theory of the analogous differential equations. In general, there exists a fundamental system of two solutions of the form $e^{r_1 t}$, $e^{r_2 t}$, where r_1 and r_2 can be determined by insertion into the difference equation. The general solution is obtained by linear combination of these two solutions. The coefficients of this combination are arbitrary constants or, more generally, arbitrary periodic functions of t of period k. These coefficients must then be determined from the boundary conditions.

In the present case the manipulations are somewhat simplified if we make use of the fact, already employed in the derivation of formula (4.13), that the second central difference quotient of $\sin \mu t$ is equal to

$$-\frac{4}{k^2}\sin^2\frac{\mu k}{2}\sin \mu t.$$

Hence, if $\sin(nh/2) \neq 0$, the function $\sin \mu t$ satisfies (4.14) if μ is a solution of the equation

$$\sin\frac{\mu k}{2} = \pm\lambda\sin\frac{nh}{2}. \tag{4.16}$$

The same is true of $\cos \mu t$. No generality is lost by taking only the positive sign in (4.16). When $\lambda \leq 1$, the solutions $\mu = \mu_n$ of (4.16) are all real and we may assume that $-\pi < \mu k/2 \leq \pi$. A short trigonometric calculation, which need not be reproduced here, then shows that the linear combination of $\sin \mu_n t$ and $\cos \mu_n t$ that satisfies the boundary conditions (4.15) can be written in the form

$$\Psi(t) = \gamma_n(t) = \frac{\cos \mu_n(t - k/2)}{\cos (\mu_n k/2)},\qquad (4.17)$$

provided the denominator is different from zero. If $\sin (nh/2) = 0$, equation (4.14) is satisfied by any linear function of t, and therefore $\gamma_n(t) \equiv 1$ is a suitable choice for $\Psi(t)$ in this exceptional case.

Collecting our results, we see that for $\lambda \leq 1$ the solution of the difference equation problem can be written as the Fourier series

$$U(x, t) = \sum_{n=1}^{\infty} a_n \, \gamma_n(t) \sin nx,\qquad (4.18)$$

provided this series converges.

When $\lambda < 1$ we have, thanks to (4.16),

$$|\gamma_n(t)| = \left| \frac{\cos \mu_n(t - k/2)}{\cos (\mu_n k/2)} \right| \leq \frac{1}{\sqrt{1 - \sin^2 (\mu_n k/2)}} \leq \frac{1}{\sqrt{1 - \lambda^2}}.$$

Since the series $\sum_{n=1}^{\infty} |a_n|$ is known to converge, we conclude that the series (4.18) converges uniformly and absolutely. Incidentally we have shown that $\cos (\mu_n k/2) \neq 0$, if $\lambda < 1$.

The solution of (4.2) satisfying the general initial condition (4.3) is the sum of (4.18) and the particular solution $V(x, t)$ with the initial values

$$V(x, 0) = 0, \qquad V(x, k) = k \, g(x).$$

It can also be expressed as a Fourier series, at least if t is an integral multiple of k. In fact, $g(x)$ can be expanded in the Fourier series

$$g(x) = \sum_{n=1}^{\infty} b_n \sin nx$$

and, if we introduce the abbreviation

$$\delta_n(t) = k \sum_{s=1}^{t/k} \gamma_n(sk),$$

it can be shown that

$$V(x, t) = \begin{cases} \sum_{n=1}^{\infty} b_n \, \delta_n(t) \sin nx, & t > 0 \\ 0, & t = 0 \end{cases}\qquad (4.19)$$

is the desired solution. To prove this, we first observe that, if a function $V(x, t)$ is the solution for $t > 0$, and if we set $V(x, -t) = -V(x, t)$, the difference equation is satisfied for $t \leq 0$ also. The function $W(x, t) = V(x, t) - V(x, t - k)$ is then the solution of the difference equation with the initial values $W(x, 0) = V(x, 0) - V(x, -k) = V(x, 0) + V(x, k) = k\,g(x)$, $W(x, k) = V(x, k) - V(x, 0) = k\,g(x)$. Hence

$$W(x, t) = k \sum_{n=1}^{\infty} b_n\, \gamma_n(t) \sin nx.$$

Since, by the definition of $W(x, t)$,

$$V(x, t) = \sum_{\nu=0}^{t/k-1} W(x, t - \nu k) = k \sum_{n=1}^{\infty} b_n \sum_{\nu=0}^{t/k-1} \gamma_n(t - \nu k) \sin nx$$

$$= \sum_{n=1}^{\infty} b_n k \sum_{s=1}^{t/k} \gamma_n(sk) \sin nx, \qquad t > k, \tag{4.20}$$

the proof of (4.19) is at hand.

The convergence of the series in (4.19) can be proved in the same way as that of the series in (4.18), using the fact that, for $\lambda < 1$, $|\delta_n(t)| < |t|/\sqrt{1 - \lambda^2}$.

For $\lambda \geq 1$, the representation of the solution by the series (4.18) and (4.19) is awkward to discuss since $\delta_n(t)$, $\gamma_n(t)$ may fail to depend in a bounded fashion on n.

4.4. Solution of the Difference Equation by a Finite Fourier Series

Series (4.18), if it converges, solves the difference equation for all t and all x, and (4.19) is a solution for all x and for $t = sk$, $s = 0, 1, \cdots$. If we relax our requirements by asking only for a function $U(x, t)$ that satisfies the problems in the grid points $x = rh$ ($r = 0, 1, \cdots, \pi/h$), $t = sk$ ($s = 0, 1, 2, \cdots$), it is easy to find a solution also when $\lambda \geq 1$. (We assume that $\pi/h = N$ is an integer.)

This solution can be considered a still stricter analog to the continuous case than series (4.18). It is based on the theory of trigonometric interpolation (Milne [1949], pp. 294 ff.), and more particularly on the orthogonality relations

$$\sum_{r=0}^{N-1} \begin{Bmatrix} \cos \\ \sin \end{Bmatrix} nrh \begin{Bmatrix} \cos \\ \sin \end{Bmatrix} mrh = 0, \qquad n \neq m, \qquad n, m < N,$$

$$\sum_{r=0}^{N-1} \cos^2 nrh = \sum_{r=0}^{N-1} \sin^2 nrh = \frac{N}{2}, \qquad 0 < n < N,$$

where $N = \pi/h$ is an integer (Milne [1949], p. 301). They lead in a simple manner to the result that the trigonometric representation

$$f(x) = \sum_{n=1}^{N-1} A_n \sin nx, \tag{4.21}$$

with

$$A_n = \frac{2}{N} \sum_{r=1}^{N-1} f(rh) \sin nrh, \qquad (4.22)$$

is valid at all grid points $x = rh$ $(r = 0, 1, \cdots, \pi/n)$ (but generally not elsewhere).

By the same argument as before it now follows that

$$U^*(x, t) = \sum_{n=1}^{N-1} A_n \gamma_n(t) \sin nx \qquad (4.23)$$

solves the difference problem (4.2), (4.3) with $g(x) \equiv 0$ at all grid points. This formula is valid for all $\lambda > 0$, since it contains a finite number of terms only.

The function

$$V^*(x, t) = \begin{cases} \sum_{n=1}^{N-1} B_n \delta_n(t) \sin nx, & t > 0 \\ 0, & t = 0, \end{cases} \qquad (4.24)$$

where

$$B_n = \frac{2}{N} \sum_{r=1}^{N-1} g(rh) \sin nrh,$$

also solves the difference equation at the grid points and assumes the initial values $V^*(x, 0) = 0$, $V^*(x, k) = k\, g(x)$. It is the analog of the function $V(x, t)$ in (4.19). If the right member of (4.16) is numerically greater than unity, the solution μ_n of (4.16) is complex. However, $\gamma_n(t)$ and $\delta_n(t)$ are always real, at least for $t = sk$, since their values can be calculated step by step from the data by rational operations.

4.5. The Convergence to the Solution of the Differential Problem

Formula (4.18) gives rise to a particularly short proof that $U(x, t) \to u(x, t)$ as $h \to 0$, provided λ is a constant less than unity.

In fact, we see from (4.16) that $\mu_n \to n$ as $h \to 0$ (and, therefore, as $k \to 0$) for every fixed n. Hence

$$\lim_{h \to 0} \gamma_n(t) = \cos nt;$$

i.e., every term of series (4.18) tends to the corresponding term of the series representation (4.10) for $u(x, t)$. This implies that every term of (4.18) is a continuous function of h at $h = 0$. A uniformly convergent series of terms which are continuous functions represents a continuous function; therefore $U(x, t)$ is a continuous function of h whose value at $h = 0$ is the sum of series (4.10), i.e., $u(x, t)$.

A similar argument proves the convergence of $V(x, t)$, as $h \to 0$, provided $\lambda < 1$: For fixed n, the quantity $\gamma_n(sk) - \cos nsk$ tends to zero, as $k \to 0$, uniformly for $1 \le s \le t/k$. This follows from (4.16) and (4.17). If we write $\delta_n(t)$ in the form

$$\delta_n(t) = k \sum_{s=1}^{t/k} \cos nsk + k \sum_{s=1}^{t/k} [\gamma_n(sk) - \cos nsk]$$

we can conclude that $\delta_n(t)$ tends to $\int_0^t \cos n\tau \, d\tau$, as $h \to 0$ through values such that $t/k = t/h\lambda$ is always an integer. Therefore

$$\lim_{h \to 0} V(x, t) = v(x, t),$$

where

$$
\begin{aligned}
v(x, t) &= \int_0^t \sum_{n=1}^{\infty} b_n \cos n\tau \sin nx \, d\tau \\
&= \frac{1}{2} \int_0^t \left[\sum_{n=1}^{\infty} b_n \sin n(x + \tau) + \sum_{n=1}^{\infty} b_n \sin n(x - \tau) \right] d\tau \\
&= \frac{1}{2} \int_0^t \left[g(x + \tau) + g(x - \tau) \right] d\tau = \frac{1}{2} \int_{x-t}^{x+t} g(\xi) \, d\xi
\end{aligned}
$$

is the solution of the differential problem (1.8) with $f(x) \equiv 0$.

For $\lambda > 1$, the solution of the difference problem will, in general, not converge to $u(x, t)$, as we have seen. But there are special classes of initial functions $f(x)$ for which convergence does take place. For instance, it has been proved by Dahlquist [1954] that, if $f(x)$ is *analytic*, $U(x, t)$ converges to $u(x, t)$ for all λ, at least on a subinterval of $a \le x \le b$. This is not implausible, for the essential argument of our proof of Theorem 4.1 consisted in a change of $f(x)$ in only a part of the interval (a, b). For analytic functions such a change is not possible, since the values of $f(x)$ in an arbitrarily small interval determine its value everywhere else.

The limit case $\lambda = 1$ is not easily handled by the methods described in this section. We use instead an argument given in Courant, Friedrichs, and Lewy [1928], p. 59.

For $\lambda = 1$ the difference equation (4.4) becomes

$$U(x, t + h) - U(x - h, t) = U(x + h, t) - U(x, t - h).$$

In words, the difference of the values of U from a grid point to the adjacent one in one diagonal direction is constant for all grid points on a diagonal in the other direction.

Hence, if $(x, t) = (rh, sh)$,

$$U(rh, (s+1)h) - U((r-1)h, sh) = U((r+s)h, h) - U((r+s-1)h, 0).$$

If we sum this equation along the diagonal segment in Fig. 4.2 joining $(rh, (s+1)h)$ to $((r-s-1)h, 0)$, we obtain

$$U(rh, (s+1)h) - U((r-s-1)h, 0)$$

$$= \sum_{\sigma=0}^{s} [U((r-s+2\sigma)h, h) - U((r-s-1+2\sigma)h, 0)], \quad \text{for } s \geq 1.$$

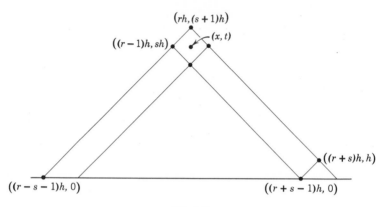

Fig. 4.2.

Now, if we impose the initial conditions in the form of the first two equations in (4.4), this becomes

$$U(x, t+h) - f(x-t-h) = \sum_{\sigma=0}^{s} [hg(x-t+2\sigma h)$$

$$+ f(x-t+2\sigma h) - f(x-t-h+2\sigma h)].$$

(4.25)

If $g(x)$ is continuous and $f(x)$ is continuously differentiable, a simple calculation shows that $U(x, t)$ tends to the expression (4.1) for $u(x, t)$, as $h \to 0$. In fact, $f(x-t+2\sigma h) - f(x-t-h+2\sigma h) = hf'(x-t-h+2\sigma h + \theta)$, $0 < \theta < h$, and the right member of (4.25) therefore tends to

$$\frac{1}{2} \int_0^{2t} g(x-t+\tau)\, d\tau + \frac{1}{2} \int_0^{t} f'(x-t+\tau)\, d\tau$$

$$= \frac{1}{2} \int_{x-t}^{x+t} g(\alpha)\, d\alpha + \frac{1}{2} [f(x+t) - f(x-t)].$$

4.6. Stability

The result of Dahlquist [1954] quoted in Sec. 4.5 seems to indicate that, when dealing with analytic initial functions, one could use any ratio λ in the recursive approximate computation of $u(x, t)$ by means of the difference scheme (4.4). This is, however, not true, since all numerical calculations are subject to round-off errors, whose effect destroys the precarious convergence in the analytic case. The situation has some resemblance to the discontinuous dependence on the initial values discussed in Sec. 1 in a different context.

To understand more clearly the effect of such round-off errors, let us assume that the problem to be solved is the one corresponding to $f(x) \equiv 0$, $g(x) \equiv 0$, whose solution is, of course, $U(x, t) \equiv 0$, $u(x, t) \equiv 0$, for the difference and differential equation respectively. Now suppose that there has been introduced only *one* round-off error, which consists in taking, say, $U(0, k) = \epsilon$ instead of zero. The propagation of this round-off error is governed by the difference equation (4.2) and the initial functions

$$ f(x) \equiv 0, \qquad g(x) \equiv \begin{cases} 0, & x \neq 0 \\ \epsilon/k, & x = 0 \end{cases} \qquad (4.26) $$

in (4.3). By means of formulas (4.4) the effect of this round-off error can be followed through the grid. The table of $U(x, t)$ below, taken from Dahlquist [1954], p. 100, gives an idea of the rapid growth of the error for $\lambda = 2$ and $\epsilon = 1$:

t									
$5k$	256	−1536	4432	−7920	9541	−7920	4432	−1536	256
$4k$	0	64	−288	616	−780	616	−288	64	0
$3k$	0	0	16	−48	67	−48	16	0	0
$2k$	0	0	0	4	−6	4	0	0	0
k	0	0	0	0	1	0	0	0	0
0	0	0	0	0	0	0	0	0	0
	$-4h$	$-3h$	$-2h$	$-h$	0	h	$2h$	$3h$	$4h$ → x

To arrive at an estimate for the rate of growth of this single error, we prove the following lemma, which is plausible in view of the table above.

LEMMA 4.2. *Let $U(x, t)$ denote the solution of the difference equation problem (4.2), (4.3) with the initial functions defined by (4.26), and assume $\lambda > 1$. Then:*

1. The sign of $U(x, t)$ in the grid alternates; i.e., $U(x, t)$ has the form $U(rh, sk) = (-1)^{r+s-1} c_{rs}$, where $c_{rs} \geq 0$.

2. $|U(x \pm h, t)| \leq |U(x, t + k)|$ in the grid; i.e., $|U(x, t)|$ is non-decreasing along the diagonals.

Proof. We use induction with respect to the discrete variable t. The statements are trivially true for $t = 0, k$. Assume that they have been proved for all grid points with $t \leq t_n = nk$, and, to fix the ideas, let us take a grid point (x, t_n) where $U(x, t_n) \geq 0$. Writing the recursion formula in (4.4) in the form

$$U(x, t_n + k) = 2(1 - \lambda^2)\, U(x, t_n) + [\lambda^2\, U(x + h, t_n)$$

$$- U(x, t_n - k)] + \lambda^2\, U(x - h, t_n), \quad (4.27)$$

we see that the three terms in the right member are all nonpositive by virtue of the inductive assumptions. Hence

$$U(x, t_n + k) \leq 0.$$

The argument for $U(x, t_n) \leq 0$ is analogous. This proves statement 1 for $t = t_{n+1} = t_n + k$ and, hence, generally. To prove statement 2, observe that, when $\lambda > 1$ and $U(x, t_n) \geq 0$, then $U(x, t_n + k) - U(x - h, t_n) \leq U(x, t_n + k) - \lambda^2 U(x - h, t_n)$, because our inductive assumptions imply that $U(x - h, t_n)$ is nonpositive. In view of (4.27), the right member of the last inequality is nonpositive. With statement 1, this proves one of the two relations contained in statement 2. The other is proved analogously.

With the help of this lemma, we deduce readily that, for $\lambda > 1$, the absolute value of an isolated error of amount ϵ at the point $(0, k)$ grows to at least the value $\epsilon\lambda^{2(t/k-1)}$ at every second grid point (x, t) of the domain of influence $|x| < t/\lambda$ of the error. This is true because (4.27) implies, in view of the fact that the three right-hand terms have the same sign, the inequality

$$|U(x, t_n + k)| \geq \lambda^2 |U(x - h, t_n)|.$$

Similarly one can prove

$$|U(x, t_n + k| \geq \lambda^2 |U(x + h, t_n)|.$$

The lower bound $\epsilon\lambda^{2(t/k-1)}$ for $U(x, t_n)$ is now obtained from these inequalities by linking the point (x, t_n) to $(0, k)$ through a sequence of diagonal segments in the grid. Such a linking is possible for every second point of the grid in the domain of influence.

The foregoing result shows that the modulus of an isolated error grows exponentially, for fixed t, as k tends to zero. In computational practice round-off errors are introduced at every step. The total effect of these errors is difficult to analyze (see Sec. 5 for some results), but it is extremely plausible that they will, in general, not cancel each other to the extent of making the difference equation useful for the approximate numerical solution of the differential equation.

This behavior of the difference equation for $\lambda > 1$ is an instance of what is called *instability* in the theory of finite-difference approximations to differential equations. It is of sufficient importance to devote a whole section to its discussion.

SECTION 5.   FURTHER ASPECTS OF THE CONCEPT OF STABILITY

5.1. Definitions and Simple Examples

Although the stability of difference equations has been amply discussed in the literature, one rarely meets precise definitions. The subject is therefore in need of further clarification. The same can be said, by the way, of the general theory of round-off errors, of which the present topic is an important chapter.

To facilitate the explanations, it is convenient to distinguish in our terminology between two concepts that are often both called "error." Let $Y(x, t)$ be the solution of a given difference problem that can be solved step by step in the t direction, and assume that we replace the value $Y(x_0, t_0)$ by $Y(x_0, t_0) + \epsilon$ at a single grid point (x_0, t_0). In practice this may be the effect of a round-off procedure or of a mistake. We shall refer to ϵ as the *error* at (x_0, t_0). If the solution procedure is continued with the value $Y(x_0, t_0) + \epsilon$ without introducing new errors, and if we obtain at the subsequent points the values $Y^*(x, t)$, then $Y^*(x, t) - Y(x, t)$ will be called the *departure* of the solution caused by the error ϵ at (x_0, t_0). If errors are committed at more than one point, we can speak of the *cumulative* departure caused by these errors. In linear problems, and only in those, the departure caused by two errors is always the sum of the departures caused by each error alone.

In principle, the departure can be kept under control even in a case exhibiting the unstable situation discussed in Sec. 4. There always exist certain bounds for the rate of growth of the departure, for given increments h, k, and for a given (x, t)-region. Hence, by carrying out the calculations with sufficient precision, we can make the result agree as closely as we wish with the theoretical one that is free from errors. The precision necessary in the situation of Sec. 4 would undoubtedly far exceed the practical possibilities of any computing machine now in existence, but it is nevertheless true that the distinction between "stable" and "unstable" problems has not yet been defined here in mathematical terms. It is natural to look for criteria of stability that involve bounds on the departure.

The ideal behavior of a finite-difference approximation with respect to round-off errors might be described as that in which the greatest possible departure produced in the solution by errors committed at every step tends to zero with the maximum of these errors, uniformly with respect to the mesh length h. It is a sad fact that this ideal is unattainable for linear problems, and very likely for nonlinear problems as well. The reason is that in a linear problem the effects of the errors introduced at each step superimpose themselves in the solution. We give an example which, although almost trivial in itself, serves to illustrate this concept.

The ordinary differential equation problem

$$y' = -y, \qquad y(0) = 1 \tag{5.1}$$

is to be solved numerically for $x \geq 0$ by the difference approximation

$$Y(x + h) - Y(x) = -h\, Y(x), \qquad Y(0) = 1.$$

The error introduced at every step is a quantity $\epsilon(x)$, of which nothing is assumed except that

$$|\epsilon(x)| \leq \delta.$$

Thus, the problem solved in actual computation is

$$Y^*(x + h) - Y^*(x) = -h\, Y^*(x) + \epsilon(x + h), \qquad Y^*(0) = 1 + \epsilon(0),$$

and the departure in the solution,

$$w(x) = Y^*(x) - Y(x),$$

solves the problem

$$w(x + h) = (1 - h)\, w(x) + \epsilon(x + h), \qquad w(0) = \epsilon(0).$$

The absolute value $|w(x)|$ satisfies the inequalities

$$|w(x + h)| \leq (1 - h)\, |w(x)| + \delta, \qquad |w(0)| \leq \delta.$$

Hence the solution of the problem

$$\omega(x + h) = (1 - h)\, \omega(x) + \delta, \qquad \omega(0) = \delta, \tag{5.2}$$

furnishes an upper bound for $|w(x)|$. The last difference equation can be solved by using the same technique as for linear differential equations with constant coefficients: The constant $\omega_p = \delta/h$ is seen by inspection to be a particular solution. The homogeneous equation $\omega(x + h) = (1 - h)\, \omega(x)$ is solved by $(1 - h)^{x/h}$; hence

$$\omega(x) = C(1 - h)^{x/h} + \frac{\delta}{h}$$

is the general solution of the difference equation in (5.2). We determine the constant C by means of the initial condition and find

$$\omega(x) = \frac{\delta}{h} \left[1 - (1 - h)^{x/h+1} \right].$$ (5.3)

If nothing else is known about the error $\epsilon(x)$, the function $\omega(x)$ is the best possible upper bound for the total departure. This quantity does, indeed, tend to zero with δ. But it deteriorates linearly as h tends to zero. Such a behavior is typical: The choice of a small mesh size, although desirable for a good approximation of the solution of the differential equation, increases the possible maximum of the departure in the solution of the difference equation.

If the differential equation (5.1) is replaced by $y' = y$, the bound for the departure becomes

$$\omega(x) = \frac{\delta}{h} \left[(1 + h)^{x/h+1} - 1 \right] \leq \frac{\delta}{h} \left[e^x (1 + h) - 1 \right].$$ (5.4)

In the literature one sometimes meets definitions which would compel us to speak of instability in this case, because the round-off error may grow exponentially with x, but this is a misleading terminology. For this exponential growth is shared by the solution $y = e^x$ of the differential problem itself, so that the *relative departure* $\omega(x)/y$ is small for all $x \geq 0$ in (5.3) as well as in (5.4), as long as δ/h is small.

The exponential rate of increase of $\omega(x)$ in (5.4) must not be confused with the unstable growth of the departure met in Sec. 4.6 and appraised there by the function $\epsilon\lambda^{2(t/k-1)}$, $\lambda > 1$. There, λ was independent of k and, therefore, this expression grew *exponentially* for any positive fixed value of the variable t, as the mesh length k tended to zero. The function $\omega(x)$ in (5.4), on the other hand, grows only *linearly* with the reciprocal of the mesh length. An additional difference is that $\omega(x)$ refers to the departure caused by the cumulative effect of the round-off errors committed at every step, whereas $\epsilon\lambda^{2(t/k-1)}$ was a lower bound for the departure caused by just *one* error in the initial value. It is easy to see that, for the differential equation $y' = y$, the effect of one single error is bounded as $h \to 0$.

For difference equations of order higher than the first, even the effect of a *single* error is frequently unbounded with respect to h^{-1}. The difference equation

$$Y(x + h) - 2Y(x) + Y(x - h) = h^2 Y(x),$$ (5.5)

which approximates the differential equation $y'' = y$, may serve as a simple example. By substituting $r^{x/h}$ for Y, with r to be determined, it is easily shown that $r_1^{x/h}$, $r_2^{x/h}$ are two linearly independent solutions if

$$r_1 = 1 + \frac{h^2}{2} + \frac{1}{2}\sqrt{4h^2 + h^4} = 1 + h + O(h^2),$$

$$\text{(5.6)}$$

$$r_2 = 1 + \frac{h^2}{2} - \frac{1}{2}\sqrt{4h^2 + h^4} = 1 - h + O(h^2).$$

Let us assume that at $x = 0$ an error ϵ is introduced. The corresponding departure (we now call it Y) is the solution of (5.5) with initial values

$$Y(0) = \epsilon, \qquad Y(h) = 0.$$

If we write it in the form $c_1 r_1^{x/h} + c_2 r_2^{x/h}$, we can calculate the departure with the help of (5.6). A calculation, which we will not reproduce here, shows it to be equal to

$$-\epsilon[h^{-1} \sinh x + O(1)] \qquad (h \to 0).$$

The greatest possible cumulative departure caused by errors at *all* grid points is therefore of the order $O(\delta h^{-2})$, where δ is, as before, an upper bound for the errors. For difference equations of higher order, still higher powers of h^{-1} may appear in the expression for the departure.

In the light of this discussion, it seems natural to consider stability and instability to be quantitative rather than qualitative concepts, i.e., to speak only of greater or lesser stability, and not of stability as such. The order of magnitude of the cumulative departure might be used as a natural measure of the degree of stability. In more precise terms, we mean by this the order of magnitude of the maximum departure in a given domain with respect to the mesh size h (or mesh sizes) and to the maximum absolute error δ, as both quantities tend to zero.

We may still ask which are the orders of magnitude that are usually referred to as stable behavior in the literature. It seems that *most authors call a procedure stable if the cumulative departure tends to zero with δ and does not grow faster than some power of h^{-1}, as h tends to zero.* This is the definition of stability that will be adopted in this book. It is justified by the fact that, in all problems that have been mathematically analyzed so far, the order of magnitude of the departure is either a low power of h^{-1} or else an exponential function of h^{-1}, so that there is a genuine gap between the nature of stable and unstable methods. It is the exponential growth in $1/h$ which is commonly considered unmanageable in actual computations.

Unfortunately, the order of magnitude of the cumulative departure can rarely be exactly determined. One usually either uses an experimental approach such as testing a difference procedure by means of some problems whose solutions are known or one relies on the theoretical study of the departure corresponding to some special type of errors. In Sec. 4 we have shown that even an error at a single point grows exponentially with $1/h$, if $k/h > 1$ in problem (4.2). This indicates very strong cumulative instability.

For certain types of linear partial difference equations, it is easy to study the departure corresponding to a line of errors of the form $\epsilon \sin \alpha x$, $\epsilon \cos \alpha x$ or, more generally, $\epsilon e^{i\alpha x}$. If the corresponding departure grows fast with $1/h$, we conclude that the total departure for any type of error grows at least at the same rate. If the rate of growth is slow, or if the error is even bounded in $1/h$, it is likely that the total departure grows at a rate that can be kept under control.

These statements are not very precise, but this lies in the nature of the problem. It is frequently stated that the departure corresponding to a line of errors of the form $\epsilon e^{i\alpha x}$ indicates the behavior of the total departure caused by arbitrary errors at all points of this line, since any line of errors in a grid can be written as a finite trigonometric series of the form (4.21) (or as a Fourier integral). But this is an oversimplification. Even for unstable methods it is usually true that the departure caused by one line of errors of the special form $\epsilon e^{i\alpha x}$ does not grow faster than some power of h^{-1}, as $h \to 0$ (see Sec. 12.1). But in the unstable cases, the maximum size of the departure may grow rapidly with α, so that the cumulative departure due to all terms of the Fourier series (or integral) may be of a higher order of magnitude in h^{-1} than any power. It is important to remember that our definition of stability requires that the departure have the indicated behavior for all possible errors that are numerically less than δ and not only for certain special functions.

Before closing this general discussion, it should be pointed out that there is a phenomenon, different from the one considered here, which is sometimes also referred to as computational instability. The difference equation

$$Y(x + 2h) - Y(x) = -2h\ Y(x + h),$$

which formally approximates the differential equation $y' = -y$, may serve as an illustration of this point. Since this difference equation is of order two, its solution is not uniquely determined by its initial value at $x = 0$. The value of $Y(h)$ must also be prescribed. For an illustration of the growth of errors in this case, let us assume that the value at $x = 0$ is the correct one, but that at $x = h$ the single error δ has been introduced. Then the departure caused by this error is the solution of the difference equation corresponding to the initial data $Y(0) = 0$, $Y(h) = \delta$. The departure is easily found to be

$$\frac{\delta}{2\sqrt{1+h^2}}\left[(\sqrt{1+h^2}-h)^{x/h}-(-\sqrt{1+h^2}-h)^{x/h}\right],$$

which is approximately equal to

$$\frac{\delta}{2}\left[e^{-x}-(-1)^{x/h}e^{x}\right].$$

At a fixed point x the cumulative departure is therefore $O(\delta h^{-1})$, which is associated with stable behavior according to our definition. Nevertheless, the presence of the "extraneous" term $(-1)^{x/h}e^{x}$ will make the relative departure large, unless either high precision is used or the calculation is limited to small x intervals. Although not as catastrophic as instability in our sense, this phenomenon may destroy the usefulness of otherwise plausible numerical procedures, particularly for ordinary differential equations. The appearance of the "extraneous" error term is related to the fact that we are approximating the differential equation by a difference equation of higher order.

The error bounds discussed so far are highly pessimistic in that they take into account the possibility that the effects of all the various round-off errors reinforce each other systematically. In reality, the distribution of round-off errors has many features of a random process, and the effects of the errors will therefore generally cancel each other in part. Hence it may be reasonable to use ideas from the theory of probability in this context. We may, for instance, consider the round-off errors introduced at each step as random variables. Then the departure is also a random variable, and we may regard the standard deviation of the latter as a realistic measure of the effect of round-off errors.

The simplest assumption is that the error at every grid point has the mean zero and the constant variance σ^2, and that the errors are uncorrelated. The last of these hypotheses is less satisfactory than the other two (see Forsythe [1950]) and might be replaced by a more complicated one.

In linear homogeneous problems in one dimension, the departure $e_r(x, h)$ generated at the point $x = sh$ by a single error ϵ_r at the point $x = rh$ is of the form

$$e_r(x, h) = M_r(x, h)\epsilon_r.$$

For the variance $V[e(x, h)]$ of the total departure $e(x, h) = \Sigma_{r=0}^{s}\, e_r(x, h)$ at $x = sh$, we find then, with the aforegoing statistical assumptions, that

$$V[e(x, h)] = V\left[\sum_{r=0}^{s}e_r(x, h)\right] = \sigma^2\sum_{r=0}^{s}M_r^{\,2}(x, h).$$

The standard deviation s.d. $[e(x, h)]$ is

$$\text{s.d. } [e(x, h)] = \sigma \sqrt{\sum_{r=0}^{x/h} M_r^2(x, h)}.$$

On the other hand, if δ is the maximum possible error at every point, the greatest possible cumulative departure is

$$\max |e(x, h)| = \delta \sum_{r=0}^{x/h} |M_r(x, h)|.$$

If we are dealing with a stable situation, $M_r(x, h)$ is $O(h^{-\alpha})$, where α is some nonnegative number. Then s.d. $[e(x, h)] = \sigma\, O(h^{-\alpha-1/2})$, while max $|e(x, h)| = \delta\, O(h^{-\alpha-1})$. These formulas set in evidence the effect of partial cancellation of round-off errors. We emphasize that this argument is valid for linear problems only.

The same argument can be applied to linear homogeneous problems in two independent variables. The departure $e_{rs}(x, t, h)$ at (x, t) caused by an error ϵ_{rs} at $x = rh$, $t = sk$ is of the form $e_{rs}(x, t, h) = M_{rs}(x, t, h)\epsilon_{rs}$. This leads to the equation

$$\text{s.d. } [e(x, t, h)] = \sigma \sqrt{\sum_{r,s} M_{rs}^2(s, t, h)}$$

for the total departure $e(x, t, h) = \Sigma_{r,s}\, e_{rs}(s, t, h)$. The summation is extended over all grid points where errors can produce nonzero departure at (x, t). However, replacing all $M_{rs}(x, t, h)$ in this formula by some common bound, as we did in one dimension, is now a somewhat wasteful appraisal. This point will be illustrated later.

5.2. Application to the Wave Equation

If, in the numerical solution of problem (4.2), errors $\epsilon(x)$ are committed at the grid points of one line only, say, on $t = 0$, the departure $e(x, t)$ is the solution of problem (4.2), (4.3) with $f(x) = \epsilon(x), g(x) = -(1/k)\,\epsilon(x)$. If

$$\epsilon(x) = \sum_{n=1}^{N-1} \alpha_n \sin nx, \tag{5.7}$$

with

$$\alpha_n = \frac{2}{N} \sum_{r=1}^{N-1} \epsilon(rh) \sin nrh, \tag{5.8}$$

is the finite Fourier series for $\epsilon(x)$, then the formulas (4.23), (4.24) yield, after a short calculation, the representation

$$e(x, t) = -\sum_{n=1}^{N-1} \alpha_n \left[\sum_{s=1}^{t/k-1} \gamma_n(sk) \right] \sin nx \qquad (t > 0). \tag{5.9}$$

By inserting the expression for α_n from (5.8), we can change formula (5.9) into

$$e(x, t) = \sum_{r=1}^{N-1} g_r(x, t)\, \epsilon(rh) \qquad (t > 0), \tag{5.10}$$

where

$$g_r(x, t) = -\frac{2}{N} \sum_{n=1}^{N-1} \left[\sum_{s=1}^{t/k-1} \gamma_n(sk) \right] \sin nx \sin nrh \qquad (t > 0). \tag{5.11}$$

Now, as we have seen, $|\gamma_n(t)| \leq (1 - \lambda^2)^{-1/2}$ for $\lambda < 1$ and, hence,

$$\left| \sum_{s=1}^{t/k-1} \gamma_n(sk) \right| < (t/k)(1 - \lambda^2)^{-1/2} = O(h^{-1}).$$

It therefore follows from (5.11) that

$$g_r(x, t) = O(h^{-1}), \qquad \text{as } h \to 0,$$

uniformly in any finite x interval. In conjunction with (5.10) this is seen to imply that an error δ at each point of a line $t = sk$ causes a departure of order $O(\delta h^{-2})$, as in the case of the ordinary linear difference equation of order two discussed in Sec. 5.1. From this we can conclude immediately that the total departure caused by errors not exceeding δ at all grid points is $O(\delta h^{-3})$ at worst. However, this is not the best possible appraisal, as we shall see.

For $\epsilon(x) = \delta \sin nx$ the departure $e(x, t)$ of (5.9) equals $-\delta\Sigma_{s=1}^{t/k-1} \gamma_n(sk)$ $\sin nx$, and is, therefore, $O(\delta h^{-1})$; i.e., $e(x, t)$ has the same order as the departure caused by a single error. The departure caused by an arbitrary line of errors is, however, smaller than $O(\epsilon h^{-2})$, the order that one might expect in view of the fact that series (5.9) has π/h terms.

A proof of the last statement can be based on Parseval's identity for discrete Fourier series,

$$\frac{2}{N} \sum_{r=1}^{N-1} f^2(rh) = \sum_{n=1}^{N-1} A_n^2,$$

which follows from the identity $f(x) - \Sigma_{n=1}^{N-1} A_n \sin nx = 0$ by squaring it, summing over the grid points and using the orthogonality relations for sums of products of sines and cosines. Since the right member of (5.9) is the discrete Fourier series for $e(x, t)$, two applications of Parseval's identity, one to (5.9) and one to (5.8), and a reference to the inequality $|\gamma_n(t)| \leq (1 - \lambda^2)^{-1/2}$ yield

$$\frac{1}{N} \sum_{r=1}^{N-1} e^2(rh, t) = \frac{1}{2} \sum_{n=1}^{N-1} \alpha_n^2 \left[\sum_{s=1}^{t/k-1} \gamma_n(sk) \right]^2$$

$$\leq \frac{t^2}{k^2(1 - \lambda^2)N} \sum_{r=1}^{N-1} \epsilon^2(rh) \leq \frac{t^2\delta^2}{h^2\lambda^2(1 - \lambda^2)}.$$

Hence the mean square of the departure on a line $t = $ const. due to a line of errors at $t = 0$ is of the order $O(\delta^2 h^{-2})$. Therefore the order of magnitude of the departure at one point caused by errors on the line $t = 0$ cannot exceed $O(\delta h^{-3/2})$ for $\lambda < 1$, and the cumulative departure for all errors is at worst $O(\delta h^{-5/2})$.

For $\lambda = 1$ the cumulative departure is only $O(\delta h^{-2})$. In this case, we use formula (4.25), which shows that for the line of errors $\epsilon(x)$ at $t = 0$, i.e., for $f(x) = \epsilon(x)$, $g(x) = -h^{-1} \epsilon(x)$, with $|\epsilon(x)| \le \delta$, we have

$$|e(x, t)| \le (s + 2)\delta = \left(\frac{t}{h} + 1\right)\delta.$$

This proves our statement. In this case $O(\delta h^{-2})$ is the best possible result, as can be seen by taking $\epsilon(\sigma h) = (-1)^\sigma \delta$ and calculating the departure at a point where $x = t$. It would be interesting to investigate whether this is a special property of $\lambda = 1$ or whether our appraisals for $\lambda < 1$ can be improved.

We conclude with some remarks on the statistical error. If the values of $\epsilon(rh)$ for $r = \pm 1, \pm 2, \cdots$ are assumed to be independent random variables with mean zero and variance σ^2, the Fourier coefficients α_n in (5.8), as well as the departure (5.9) due to this line of errors at $t = 0$, are also random variables. Their variances are respectively

$$V(\alpha_n) = \frac{4}{N^2} \sigma^2 \sum_{r=1}^{N-1} \sin^2 nrh = \frac{2\sigma^2}{N}$$

and

$$V[e(x, t)] = \frac{2}{N} \sigma^2 \sum_{n=1}^{N-1} \left[\sum_{s=1}^{t/k-1} \gamma_n(sk)\right]^2 \sin^2 nx.$$

Now

$$\left|\sum_{s=1}^{t/k-1} \gamma_n(sk)\right| = O(h^{-1}),$$

as was shown before, and we therefore find that

$$V[e(x, t)] = O(\sigma^2 h^{-2}).$$

By summing over the grid lines $t = 0, k, \cdots$, each of which contributes an amount of the same order to the variance of the cumulative departure, we see that the latter has the order $O(\delta^2 h^{-3})$. Its standard deviation is therefore $O(\delta h^{-3/2})$. This implies that the actual departure will in general be considerably smaller than the order $O(\delta h^{-5/2})$ obtained for the maximum possible departure seems to indicate.

SECTION 6. SYSTEMS OF HYPERBOLIC DIFFERENTIAL EQUATIONS AND THEIR CHARACTERISTICS

6.1. The Normal Form

It was shown in Sec. 2 that every partial differential equation can be transformed into an equivalent system of first-order differential equations. In a general theory such a system is easier to manipulate, and even for computational purposes it has certain advantages. Also, most differential equations of mathematical physics are originally formulated as systems, from which single equations of higher order are then obtained by elimination. We shall therefore give a very brief sketch of some of the most important concepts concerning hyperbolic systems. Our sources in this section are primarily Courant and Friedrichs [1948] and Courant and Lax [1949]. We refer to them for a more thorough treatment of these equations.

The theory of hyperbolic differential equations is essentially simpler for two independent variables than in more dimensions. In this section we therefore restrict ourselves to the two-dimensional case, considering systems of differential equations of the form

$$\sum_{i=1}^{n} (a^{vi}u_x{}^i + b^{vi}u_y{}^i) + d^v = 0, \qquad v = 1, \cdots, n \qquad (6.1)$$

for the n unknown functions $u^i(x, y)$. We use the letter u to denote the (column) vector with components $u^1, u^2, \cdots, u^n$. The coefficients a^{vi}, b^{vi}, d^v may be functions of x, y, u. If they are independent of u, the system is linear. The system (6.1) is special in that it is linear in the derivatives, and is called *quasilinear*. This is no essential restriction, for an initial-value problem for a general nonlinear system can always be transformed into a quasilinear one containing a larger number of equations and unknowns (Courant and Hilbert [1937], p. 35).

The system (6.1) looks particularly simple in matrix notation. Let us introduce the matrices

$$A = [a^{vi}], \qquad B = [b^{vi}]$$

and the column vector

$$d = [d^v];$$

then (6.1) reads

$$Au_x + Bu_y + d = 0. \qquad (6.2)$$

If the system of equations (6.1) is subjected to a linear transformation with nonvanishing determinant, a new system of similar form is obtained which is equivalent to the original one in the sense that every solution of one is a solution of the other. The coefficients of the transformation may even depend on x, y, and u (but not on u_x, u_y). If $T = [t^{ri}]$ is such a transformation, the new system is

$$TAu_x + TBu_y + Td = 0. \tag{6.3}$$

We can take advantage of this remark to transform (6.2) into some suitable normal form. A particularly convenient form is one in which

$$TA = CTB, \tag{6.4}$$

where C is a diagonal matrix. Before we discuss the possibility of such a transformation, let us take a look at its advantages. If we set $TB = A^* = [a^{*vi}]$, $Td = d^* = [d^{*i}]$, the system (6.3) can be written

$$CA^*u_x + A^*u_y + d^* = 0. \tag{6.5}$$

Its vth equation is

$$\sum_{i=1}^{n} a^{*vi}(c^v u_x{}^i + u_y{}^i) + d^{*v} = 0, \tag{6.6}$$

where c^v $(v = 1, \cdots, n)$ are the diagonal elements of the matrix C. Now, if (ξ, η) is the vector of unit length for which

$$c^v = \xi/\eta,$$

the expression

$$c^v u_x{}^i + u_y{}^i = (u_x{}^i\xi + u_y{}^i\eta)/\eta$$

represents, except for the factor $1/\eta$, the directional derivative of u^i in the direction defined by the vector (ξ, η), which, of course, depends on v. Hence every equation of (6.5) contains differentiations in one direction only. This direction depends, of course, on x, y, and u. It is plausible that this fact will permit great simplifications of the theoretical, and perhaps also of the computational, study of the differential system. For the system (6.2) is more complicated than a system of ordinary differential equations in two respects: it contains more than one unknown function in every equation, and also more than one differential operator. By our transformation we have eliminated the second of these complications and thereby brought the theory that much closer to the simpler one of ordinary differential equations.

To calculate C, we observe that the condition of equality of the vth rows in the two members of (6.4), i.e.,

$$\sum_{\mu=1}^{n} t^{v\mu}a^{\mu i} = \sum_{\mu=1}^{n} c^v t^{v\mu}b^{\mu i}, \qquad i = 1, \cdots, n, \tag{6.7}$$

represents a system of n homogeneous linear algebraic equations for $t^{\nu 1}$, $t^{\nu 2}, \cdots, t^{\nu n}$, so that we must have

$$\det(A - c^\nu B) = 0. \tag{6.8}$$

This is an algebraic equation for c^ν. We now make the explicit assumption that *the equation*

$$\det(A - \lambda B) = 0 \tag{6.9}$$

possesses n distinct real roots. It is important to remember that A and B depend on u as well as on x and y. Therefore, whether condition (6.9) is satisfied depends not only on the equation itself and on the region under consideration but also on the function $u(x, y)$. If the condition is satisfied in a region R for a solution $u(x, y)$ of the equation, we shall say that the differential equation is of *hyperbolic type* for this solution in the region R.

This definition of hyperbolic type is more special than necessary. We might have generalized it by permitting multiple roots of (6.9) (Courant and Lax [1949], p. 256, or Courant and Hilbert [1937], p. 142), but it is general enough for our purpose and simplifies the discussion.

In the hyperbolic case we can choose the n roots of equation (6.9) as the values of $c^1, c^2, \cdots, c^n$ and then determine the elements $t^{\nu\mu}$ of the transformation matrix T from (6.7).

The definition as given here implies that $\det B \neq 0$ for a hyperbolic system since otherwise the equation (6.9) would have fewer than n roots. Since these roots are distinct, the matrix T is also nonsingular (Hildebrand [1952], pp. 76–77). Hence A^* is nonsingular.

From now on we assume that the differential system is hyperbolic for the solution to be investigated and that it has already been transformed into the normal form (6.5). We therefore omit the asterisks and write the system in the *normal form*

$$CAu_x + Au_y + d = 0, \quad C \text{ diagonal}, \quad \det A \neq 0. \tag{6.10}$$

The direction of a vector (ξ, η) for which

$$\frac{\xi}{\eta} = c^\nu$$

is called the νth *characteristic direction.* It depends on x, y and on the solution $u(x, y)$ of the system. The n differential equations

$$\frac{dx}{dy} = c^\nu, \quad \nu = 1, \cdots, n \tag{6.11}$$

define, for given $u(x, y)$, n one-parameter families of curves whose directions at every point are precisely the characteristic directions there. They are called the *characteristics* of the system for that solution. If the coefficients A, C are independent of u, the characteristics are the same for all solutions.

6.2. Examples

(a) The simplest wave equation $u_{xx} - u_{yy} = 0$ is equivalent to the system

$$u_x^1 - u_y^2 = 0,$$
$$u_x^2 - u_y^1 = 0. \tag{6.12}$$

Therefore the coefficients A, B, d of (6.2) are in this case

$$A = \begin{bmatrix} 1 & 0 \\ 0 & 1 \end{bmatrix}, \qquad B = \begin{bmatrix} 0 & -1 \\ -1 & 0 \end{bmatrix}, \qquad d = \begin{bmatrix} 0 \\ 0 \end{bmatrix},$$

and equation (6.9) becomes

$$\begin{vmatrix} 1 & \lambda \\ \lambda & 1 \end{vmatrix} = 0.$$

Its roots are $c^1 = 1$, $c^2 = -1$, and the matrix T can be chosen to be

$$T = \begin{bmatrix} 1 & -1 \\ 1 & 1 \end{bmatrix}.$$

The normal form turns out to be

$$(u_x^1 + u_y^1) - (u_x^2 + u_y^2) = 0,$$
$$(u_x^1 - u_y^1) + (u_x^2 - u_y^2) = 0. \tag{6.13}$$

The characteristics are the straight lines $x \pm y = $ const. For this special case they had already been introduced in Sec. 4.1.

(b) The differential equations of one-dimensional isentropic flow are

$$\rho_t + u\rho_x + \rho u_x = 0,$$
$$\rho(u_t + uu_x) + c^2\rho_x = 0. \tag{6.14}$$

(See Courant and Friedrichs [1948], pp. 28–29, for explanation and derivation.) Here u is the velocity, ρ the density, and $c = c(\rho)$ the speed of sound. In the notation of our general theory, (6.14) can be rewritten as

$$u^2 u_x^1 + u^1 u_x^2 + u_y^2 = 0,$$
$$u^1 u^2 u_x^1 + c^2 u_x^2 + u^2 u_y^1 = 0,$$

where $u^1 = u$, $u^2 = \rho$, $y = t$.

The coefficients of (6.2) are here

$$A = \begin{bmatrix} u^2 & u^1 \\ u^1 u^2 & c^2 \end{bmatrix}, \qquad B = \begin{bmatrix} 0 & 1 \\ u^2 & 0 \end{bmatrix}, \qquad d = \begin{bmatrix} 0 \\ 0 \end{bmatrix},$$

and equation (6.9) is

$$\begin{vmatrix} u^2 & u^1 - \lambda \\ u^1 u^2 - \lambda u^2 & c^2 \end{vmatrix} = 0,$$

whose roots are

$$c^{(1)} = u^1 + c, \qquad c^{(2)} = u^1 - c. \tag{6.15}$$

(We temporarily write $c^{(1)}$, $c^{(2)}$ instead of the c^1, c^2 used before to avoid confusion with the powers of the sound velocity c.)

The characteristics are therefore, in the original notation, the solutions of the differential equations

$$\frac{dx}{dt} = u^1 + c, \qquad \frac{dx}{dt} = u^1 - c$$

respectively.

If λ takes the values $c^{(1)}$ or $c^{(2)}$ given by (6.15), the matrix $A - \lambda B$ in the present example becomes

$$\begin{bmatrix} u^2 & -c \\ -cu^2 & c^2 \end{bmatrix} \quad \text{or} \quad \begin{bmatrix} u^2 & c \\ cu^2 & c^2 \end{bmatrix},$$

respectively (c is the sound velocity). From (6.7) we see then that a suitable corresponding matrix T is

$$T = \begin{bmatrix} t^{11} & t^{12} \\ t^{21} & t^{22} \end{bmatrix} = \begin{bmatrix} c & 1 \\ -c & 1 \end{bmatrix}.$$

Therefore

$$TB = A^* = [a^{*vi}] = \begin{bmatrix} u^2 & c \\ u^2 & -c \end{bmatrix}. \tag{6.16}$$

The vector d^* is zero in this example, and hence (6.16) determines the normal form (6.6) for the equations (6.14), if $u^1 = u$, $u^2 = \rho$, $y = t$.

6.3. The Canonical Differential System for $n = 2$

In general the characteristic directions are unknown until we know the solution of the differential problem. It is remarkable that for a system of two equations the concept of characteristics can nevertheless be used to transform the given system (6.10) into a simpler system. It is true that the new system will consist of four rather than two equations, but this is frequently a price one is willing to pay, inasmuch as the new system lends itself particularly well to the study of existence and uniqueness questions (Lewy [1928]) and can also be used for numerical computation of the solution.

The starting point for this transformation is the observation that, in a system of two equations, the characteristics corresponding to a solution form two one-parameter families of curves such that through every point of the region R where the system is hyperbolic there passes exactly one curve of each family. These curves have different directions at that point, because our definition of hyperbolic character included the condition that the c's are distinct. This suggests the idea of using these curves as coordinate lines for a new coordinate system. Of course, there are infinitely many transformations

$$x = x(\alpha, \beta), \qquad y = y(\alpha, \beta) \qquad (6.17)$$

of the independent variables which will do this, since we may follow any such change of variables by transformations of α or β *separately* without changing the families of curves $\alpha = $ const., $\beta = $ const. In terms of the new variables the differential equations (6.11) of the characteristics become

$$x_\alpha = c^1 y_\alpha, \qquad x_\beta = c^2 y_\beta. \qquad (6.18)$$

The quantities $c^\nu u_x{}^i + u_y{}^i$, $(i, \nu = 1, 2)$ therefore become

$$c^1 u_x{}^i + u_y{}^i = u_\alpha{}^i / y_\alpha, \qquad c^2 u_x{}^i + u_y{}^i = u_\beta{}^i / y_\beta, \qquad (6.19)$$

and the differential system (6.10) takes the form

$$
\begin{aligned}
a^{11} u_\alpha{}^1 + a^{12} u_\alpha{}^2 + d^1 y_\alpha = 0, \\
a^{21} u_\beta{}^1 + a^{22} u_\beta{}^2 + d^2 y_\beta = 0.
\end{aligned}
\qquad (6.20)
$$

So far in this argument we have assumed that we start from some given particular solution $u(x, y)$ of the differential equation, which determines the characteristics and knowledge of which is therefore necessary for the introduction of the new coordinate system. Now, however, we change our point of view and regard the four equations (6.18), (6.20) as a system of four partial differential equations in the independent variables α, β for the four unknown functions x, y, u^1, u^2. These equations can be constructed from the original system (6.10) without solving it beforehand. They are sometimes called the *canonical equations*.

In the simple example (a), Sec. 6.2, the canonical equations become

$$x_\alpha = y_\alpha, \qquad x_\beta = -y_\beta, \qquad u_\alpha{}^1 = u_\alpha{}^2, \qquad u_\beta{}^1 = -u_\beta{}^2,$$

the last two of which imply $u_{\alpha\beta}{}^1 = 0$. In this case the transformation to characteristic parameters is essentially the transformation used in Sec. 1 for the general solution of the equation $u_{xx} - u_{yy} = 0$.

To find the canonical equations for example (b), Sec. 6.2—the equations of isentropic flow—we refer to formulas (6.15) and see that (6.18) becomes, in the notation of (6.14),

$$x_\alpha = (u + c)y_\alpha, \qquad x_\beta = (u - c)y_\beta. \qquad (6.21)$$

Furthermore, if we return to the notation of (6.14) in (6.16) and recall that (6.16) is, in this example, the matrix A of (6.10), we see that the equations (6.20) are in this case

$$\rho u_\alpha + c\rho_\alpha = 0, \qquad \rho u_\beta - c\rho_\beta = 0. \qquad (6.22)$$

The canonical system shares with the normal form the property that each equation contains differentiations in one direction only, but now these directions coincide with the two coordinate directions, which is a considerable improvement. Furthermore, the system does not contain the independent variables α, β explicitly.

6.4. Remarks on the Initial-Value Problem

The simplest subsidiary conditions which produce a well-posed problem when added to a differential system of the form (6.1) consist in prescribing the values of the functions $u^i(x, y)$ on an arc of some curve. In the case $n = 2$ the canonical form (6.18), (6.20) is very convenient for the proof of theorems that establish precise conditions under which such a problem is actually well posed (Lewy [1928]). If $n > 2$, the concept of characteristics and the normal form are still extremely helpful for such existence proofs (Courant and Lax [1949]).

Probably the best methods to this end are those based on some variant of Picard's iteration procedure. We sketch very briefly the outline of a proof in the case $n = 2$ (Courant and Hilbert [1937], pp. 317–323; Courant and Friedrichs [1948], pp. 49–55; Sauer [1952], Chap. III).

If each of the differential equations (6.18), (6.20) is differentiated so as to introduce the mixed second derivatives with respect to α and β, there result four equations that are linear in $u_{\alpha\beta}{}^1$, $u_{\alpha\beta}{}^2$, $x_{\alpha\beta}$, $y_{\alpha\beta}$. The coefficients of these four quantities form the matrix

$$\begin{bmatrix} a^{11} & a^{12} & 0 & d^1 \\ a^{21} & a^{22} & 0 & d^2 \\ 0 & 0 & 1 & -c^1 \\ 0 & 0 & 1 & -c^2 \end{bmatrix},$$

whose determinant

$$\begin{vmatrix} a^{11} & a^{12} \\ a^{21} & a^{22} \end{vmatrix} (c^1 - c^2)$$

is different from zero, thanks to our definition of hyperbolic systems. We may therefore solve the system for these second derivatives, and are thus led to a system of the form

$$x_{\alpha\beta} = f_1, \qquad y_{\alpha\beta} = f_2, \qquad u_{\alpha\beta}{}^1 = f_3, \qquad u_{\alpha\beta}{}^2 = f_4, \qquad (6.23)$$

where the f_j ($j = 1, \cdots, 4$) depend on x, y, u^i, $u_\alpha{}^i$, $u_\beta{}^i$ ($i = 1, 2$).

Let there now be prescribed in the (x, y)-plane an initial curve Γ and on it values of u^1 and u^2. The curve Γ may be represented by two parametric equations $x = f(s)$, $y = g(s)$, and we assume that x_s, y_s are piecewise continuous (i.e., that these derivatives are continuous except for a finite number of jump discontinuities). Also, Γ should have no singular points; i.e., $f_s{}^2 + g_s{}^2 \neq 0$. The initial values are assumed to be given parametrically by continuously differentiable functions $u^i = u^i(s)$ ($i = 1, 2$). These data permit us to calculate at every point of Γ the characteristic directions which are determined by the $c^i(x, y, u)$. We shall need the decisive hypothesis that Γ *has nowhere a characteristic direction* or, analytically, that

$$(f_s - c^1 g_s)(f_s - c^2 g_s) \neq 0. \qquad (6.24)$$

There now arises the question of finding the equation of Γ in the (α, β)-plane. This may seem an insoluble problem, since the relation between x, y and α, β is governed by equations (6.18), which are part of the system we wish to solve. But we may now take advantage of the fact that our original condition on the transformation (6.17), which stated that it change the characteristics into the coordinate lines $\alpha = $ const., $\beta = $ const., does not determine them uniquely. In a sufficiently narrow strip about Γ in the (x, y)-plane every characteristic intersects Γ in exactly one point because Γ has nowhere a characteristic direction. A convenient labeling of the characteristics consists in ascribing to the characteristic of the family $\alpha = $ const. that intersects Γ at, say, $s = s_0$ the equation $\alpha = s_0$. If we do the same with the other family, the point P at the intersection of the characteristics $\alpha = \alpha_0$, $\beta = \beta_0$ lies on Γ if and only if $\alpha_0 = \beta_0$. Hence Γ has the equation $\alpha - \beta = 0$ in the (α, β)-coordinate system. Following a time-honored tradition that goes back to Riemann, we perform the trivial additional transformation of replacing β by $-\beta$ and write the equation of the initial curve in the form $\alpha + \beta = 0$.

The initial values of the first derivatives x_α, y_α, $u_\alpha{}^i$, x_β, y_β, $u_\beta{}^i$ ($i = 1, 2$) that figure in the functions f_j of (6.23) can be determined directly from the differential equations (6.18), (6.20) and the initial conditions for x, y, and u^i. The condition that the differential equations themselves are to be satisfied on Γ represents four linear equations for the eight initial values of the derivatives. By virtue of our construction, α is identical with the parameter s along the initial curve in the (x, y)-plane. Hence $x(\alpha, -\alpha) = f(\alpha)$, $y(\alpha, -\alpha) = g(\alpha)$ identically in α. This gives us the two equations on Γ,

$$x_\alpha - x_\beta = f'(\alpha), \qquad y_\alpha - y_\beta = g'(\alpha). \qquad (6.25)$$

The remaining two equations are obtained similarly from the initial conditions on u^i. It is easy to verify that these eight simultaneous linear algebraic equations possess a unique solution.

The formalisms of the existence proof are particularly simple if all initial data are zero. This can always be brought about by subtracting from x, y, u^i functions $x^*(\alpha, \beta)$, $y^*(\alpha, \beta)$, $u^{*i}(\alpha, \beta)$ that have the same initial data and are sufficiently smooth for the new differential equations in $x - x^*$, $y - y^*$, $u^i - u^{*i}$ to satisfy the same requirements as those necessary for the discussion of (6.23) (see Courant and Hilbert [1937], p. 318, for the construction of such functions). The new differential equations depend explicitly on α, β.

Following the general plan of the iteration method for differential equations, we convert system (6.23) into a system of integral equations by integrating it twice. The initial conditions that all unknown functions and their first derivatives vanish for $\alpha + \beta = 0$ are satisfied if the lower limits of integration are chosen so that the repeated integral can be written as a double integral over the triangle D in the (α, β)-plane that is bounded by the initial line $\alpha + \beta = 0$ and the lines $\alpha = \text{const.}$, $\beta = \text{const.}$ through the point at which the solution is to be found. Let σ, τ be the variables of integration; then the integral equations are

$$x(\alpha, \beta) = \int\!\!\!\int_D f_1(\sigma, \tau, x(\sigma, \tau), y(\sigma, \tau), u^1(\sigma, \tau), \cdots) \, d\sigma \, d\tau, \text{ etc.,} \qquad (6.26)$$

where the domain D is illustrated in Fig. 6.1. The solutions of (6.26), if they exist and are sufficiently regular, obviously satisfy the differential equations (6.23) and all initial conditions.

To prove the existence and uniqueness of a solution of (6.26), it must be supposed that the functions f_j satisfy Lipschitz conditions in all variables, uniformly in some neighborhood S of the origin in the space of all the variables occurring in f_j, i.e., x, y, u^i and the first partial derivatives of these quantities with respect to α and β.

We recall that a function $\phi(x)$ satisfies a *Lipschitz condition* (or is *Lipschitzian*) uniformly in an interval I, if

$$|\phi(x_1) - \phi(x_2)| \leq M|x_1 - x_2| \qquad \text{for} \qquad x_1 \in I, \qquad x_2 \in I,$$

where M is independent of x_1 and x_2. Since f_j was obtained by differentiation of the original canonical system, the coefficients of the former must possess continuous partial derivatives satisfying a Lipschitz condition. As we are assuming that our system had been obtained from another one by subtracting functions $x^*(\alpha, \beta)$, $y^*(\alpha, \beta)$, etc., that satisfy the original initial conditions from x, y, etc., this smoothness condition makes it necessary that we impose also on the initial values the condition that their derivatives be Lipschitzian.

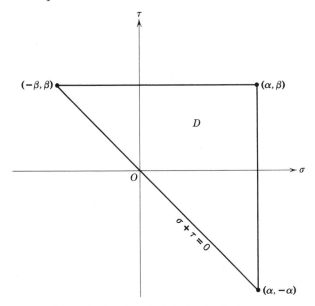

FIG. 6.1. The domain D in the (α, β)-plane.

To construct a solution of the integral equations, one defines sequences of functions $x^{(n)}$, $y^{(n)}$, $u^{i,(n)}$ by setting

$$x^{(0)} = y^{(0)} = u^{i,(0)} = 0,$$

$$x^{(n+1)} = \int\!\!\!\int_D f_1^{(n)} \, d\sigma \, d\tau, \text{ etc.,}$$

where $f_j^{(n)}$ denotes the function f_j with all arguments x, y, etc., replaced by the nth iterants $x^{(n)}$, $y^{(n)}$, etc.

The convergence in D of these sequences to limit functions $x(\alpha, \beta)$, $y(\alpha, \beta)$, etc., is proved by the usual pattern of Picard's method (see, e.g., Courant and Hilbert [1937], pp. 317 ff., for the details). This method proves also that the first derivatives are continuous and Lipschitzian and that the mixed second derivatives exist.

The solution of the system (6.23) with the prescribed initial values also solves the canonical equations (6.18) and (6.20), for the latter equations can be regained from (6.23) by inverting the linear transformation that led to them, and then integrating. This integration introduces an arbitrary function of one variable; for instance, instead of $x_\alpha = c^1 y_\alpha$ as in (6.18), one obtains $x_\alpha = c^1 y_\alpha + k(\alpha)$ [$k(\alpha)$ arbitrary]. However, the solution of (6.26) has, by construction, initial values for x_α and y_α that satisfy the relation $x_\alpha = c^1 y_\alpha$ on Γ, i.e., for $\beta = -\alpha$. Hence $k(\alpha) \equiv 0$. The same argument holds for the other three equations (6.18), (6.20).

The return from the canonical equations (6.18), (6.20) to the original differential system (6.10), where x and y are the independent variables, requires the inversion of the transformation (6.17). This is possible if the Jacobian $x_\alpha y_\beta - x_\beta y_\alpha$ does not vanish. For the points on Γ this can be directly verified by calculating x_α, x_β, y_α, y_β on Γ from (6.18) and (6.25), and making use of (6.24) and the assumption $c^1 \neq c^2$. By continuity, the Jacobian must then also be different from zero in some neighborhood of Γ. It may occur that the solution of the canonical system can be uniquely extended beyond a curve on which the Jacobian vanishes. In such a case the resulting existence and uniqueness theorem for the *original* system with x and y as independent variables can be asserted only in a smaller domain where the Jacobian does not vanish. It can be shown that this is not a shortcoming of our method of proof but that these boundaries for the unique existence are inherent in the problem (see Sec. 10).

Our main reason for sketching the foregoing proof is that it gives us a clearer understanding of the role played by the characteristics. We see, for example, that again only the subarc of the initial curve that is bounded by the characteristics through a point influences the solution at that point, for in the (α, β)-plane the characteristics and the initial curve are the straight lines bounding D. Thus the concepts of interval of dependence and domain of influence apply also in the present general case.

As usual, the iteration procedure can also be employed to prove the uniqueness of the solution. This uniqueness is established only in D and subject to the smoothness requirements imposed on the initial functions. The fact that the initial line is not a characteristic is essential for the uniqueness. If the initial values are changed in a subinterval of the interval of dependence, without destroying the smoothness properties of the initial functions, the solution is changed in a subregion of D bounded by characteristics. This shows that no uniqueness statement can be made if the initial curve is a characteristic. In fact, there exist infinitely many solutions corresponding to the same initial values on an arc of a characteristic. Conversely, it follows from the uniqueness that, if two solutions $u_1(x, y)$, $u_2(x, y)$ of the differential system in a domain R "meet" along a curve Γ in R, i.e., if $u_1(x, y) = u_2(x, y)$ on Γ (we recall that $u_1(x, y)$, $u_2(x, y)$ are vectors), then Γ must be a characteristic.

The results of this section—but not the method—are valid for differential systems in more than two dependent variables also. (See Courant and Lax [1949] for a comparatively simple proof.) There are then n characteristics through every point, and the domain of dependence is the interval cut out on the initial curve by the two extreme characteristics.

If there are more than two independent variables, the theory is considerably more complicated since the characteristics are then surfaces or hypersurfaces. An account can be found in Sauer [1952], for example.

SECTION 7. FINITE-DIFFERENCE METHODS FOR SYSTEMS OF QUASILINEAR HYPERBOLIC EQUATIONS

7.1. Description of the Procedure

Of the numerous methods for the numerical solution of the initial-value problem in the hyperbolic case we single out one for a more detailed discussion. It is described and analyzed in Courant, Isaacson, and Rees [1952], which is our main source for this section. There exist more refined methods for the treatment of the ordinary initial-value problem and many special procedures for other problems, such as solutions characterized by prescribed values on two characteristics and problems involving shock waves. But the technique to be described here is both simple and general and, therefore, serves well as an illustration.

We shall deal with a hyperbolic system in the normal form (6.10). In Secs. 7.1 through 7.3 the initial curve is assumed to be a segment L of the x-axis. On the initial values and on the coefficients of the differential system we impose the smoothness requirements of the existence and uniqueness theorem discussed in Sec. 6. We assume that the initial functions $g^i(x, y)$ and the coefficients $C(x, y, z)$, $A(x, y, z)$, $d(x, y, z)$ have partial derivatives that uniformly satisfy a Lipschitz condition as long as (x, y) lies in some strip containing the initial segment, and provided that

$$|z^i - g^i(x, y)| < K^i,$$

where the K^i are suitable constants. Then the initial-value problem will possess in a (possibly narrower) strip S a solution $u(x, y)$ whose derivatives also satisfy a uniform Lipschitz condition.

We introduce capital letters P, Q, etc., as abbreviations for the points of the (x, y)-plane. Then our initial-value problem can be written in the vectorial form

$$C(P, u(P)) A(P, u(P)) u_x(P) + A(P, u(P)) u_y(P) + d(P, u(P)) = 0, \qquad P \in S, \tag{7.1}$$

$$u(P) = g(P), \qquad P \in L,$$

where $g(P)$ is the vector formed by the initial values.

Now we introduce a rectangular net of mesh lengths h, k, and construct a difference equation problem that approximates (7.1) in the formal sense. Let Q', Q, Q'' be three consecutive net points on a line $y = $ const. > 0, in the order of increasing x, and let P be the net point above Q in the direction of increasing y, as follows:

$$P$$
$$Q' \quad Q \quad Q''$$

As in the simpler problem of Secs. 1 and 4, we hold the ratio

$$\lambda = k/h \tag{7.2}$$

fixed. It seems natural to choose as a difference equation for the approximation U to u an equation obtained from (7.1) by replacing the derivatives there by the finite-difference quotients in the net. But with respect to x there are two possibilities: We can choose the forward or the backward difference at Q. Now it turns out that it is not irrelevant which of these differences we use. To understand this, we give a somewhat differently motivated derivation of the difference equation to be used. This argument has the advantage that it applies to a more general method as well, which uses nonrectangular grids and is explained in Sec. 7.4.

The νth component equation of (7.1) can be written

$$\sum_{i=1}^{n} a^{\nu i}(P, u(P))[c^{\nu}(P, u(P)) u_x^{i}(P) + u_y^{i}(P)] + d^{\nu}(P, u(P)) = 0. \tag{7.3}$$

Now, $c^{\nu}(P, u(P)) u_x^{i}(P) + u_y^{i}(P)$ is proportional to the derivative of $u^i(P)$ in the νth characteristic direction; i.e., if we denote this directional derivative by $D_\nu u^i$,

$$D_\nu u^i(P) = \rho^\nu(P, u(P))[c^\nu(P, u(P)) u_x^i(P) + u_y^i(P)], \tag{7.4}$$

where $1/\rho^\nu$ is the length of the vector with components c^ν, 1. Let Q_ν be the intersection of the line $y = $ const. through Q with the line through P having the νth characteristic direction there. Then

$$\frac{\overline{Q_\nu Q}}{\overline{PQ}} = \frac{c^\nu(P, u(P))}{1}$$

and, therefore, by geometrical considerations involving similar triangles, we see that

$$\rho^v(P, u(P)) = \frac{1}{\sqrt{1 + [c^v(P, u(P))]^2}} = \frac{k}{\overline{PQ_v}} .$$

Hence

$$c^v(P, u(P)) \, u_x{}^i(P) + u_y{}^i(P) = \frac{\overline{PQ_v}}{k} \, D_v \, u^i(P), \qquad (7.5)$$

or, replacing the derivative by the corresponding finite-difference quotient, which introduces an error of order $O(h)$,

$$c^v(P, u(P)) \, u_x{}^i(P) + u_y{}^i(P) = \frac{1}{k} [u^i(P) - u^i(Q_v)] + O(h). \qquad (7.6)$$

Since Q_v is in general not a net point, the finite difference in the right member is not yet a very convenient expression to use in our difference scheme. It is more natural to use only grid points in the difference formula. So far no restriction has been imposed on λ in (7.2), but now we have to make sure that the interval of dependence for the difference equation does not turn out smaller than the one for the differential equation. Since we wish to approximate the derivatives by differences employing Q and one of its nearest neighbors only, this forces us to impose the following restriction on λ in (7.2): It must be so small that all points Q_v $(v = 1, \cdots, n)$ lie between Q' and Q''. This is equivalent to the condition that $1/\lambda$ *be greater than the maximum of all* $|c^v(P, u(P))|$ *in the region under consideration.*

This condition has the drawback that it depends on the as yet unknown solution of our problem. It is unfortunately true that many, perhaps most, of the known conditions describing the applicability of finite-difference procedures are expressed in terms of the solution of the differential problem. This remark applies particularly to nonlinear problems. The practical computer usually meets this situation by trusting his experience and his intuition, and by testing the criterion in an approximate manner after the computation is finished, using U instead of u for this purpose. Hence we content ourselves with the remark that max $|c^v(P, u(P))|$ exists as long as (x, y) remains in the region S.

There then exists a certain constant m such that all Q_v lie between Q' and Q'', if

$$\lambda \leq 1/m. \qquad (7.7)$$

We recall that Q was an arbitrary grid point in S, and that m must be large enough to meet the condition at all these points.

To fix the ideas, assume, for a given v, that the point Q_v lies between Q' and Q. See Fig. 7.1. Then it is natural to approximate the left member of (7.6) by a finite-difference expression based on P, Q, and Q' rather than on Q''. This can be done, for example, by replacing the derivatives $u_x{}^i(P)$, $u_y{}^i(P)$ by the forward difference quotients based on Q' and Q respectively. The error thus introduced is $O(h)$. To show more clearly the relation between this method and the formula (7.6), we show that the same result is obtained if (7.6) is modified by replacing $u^i(Q_v)$ in it by the

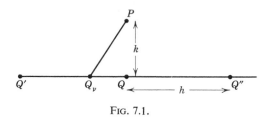

FIG. 7.1.

value obtained through linear interpolation between Q' and Q. The interpolated value is

$$\frac{1}{h}\left[\overline{QQ_v}\, u(Q') + \overline{Q_vQ}'\, u(Q)\right] = \frac{1}{h}\left[(h - c^v(P, u(P))k)\, u(Q')\right.$$
$$\left. + c^v(P, u(P))k\, u(Q')\right]. \quad (7.8)$$

This expression differs from $u(Q_v)$ by $O(h^2)$ because of our smoothness assumptions, as one can see by expanding the left member by Taylor's formula about Q_v up to terms containing second derivatives.

Hence, if we replace $u^i(Q_v)$ in (7.6) by the right member of (7.8) and compensate for the error introduced by adding a term $O(h^2k^{-1}) = O(h)$, we find, after some rearrangement,

$$c^v u_x{}^i(P) + u_y{}^i(P) = c^v\, \frac{u^i(Q) - u^i(Q')}{h} + \frac{u^i(P) - u^i(Q)}{k} + O(h),$$

$$c^v = c^v(P, u(P)). \quad (7.9)$$

This relation could, of course, have been written down almost immediately, but the preceding discussion serves to bring out two points: First, it clarifies the relation between (7.9) and the formula (7.6), which is going to form the basis for the adaptation of our method to nonrectangular nets; second, it explains why it is natural to use the backward x difference at Q, when Q_v lies between Q' and Q, i.e., when $c^v(P, u(P))$ is positive. If $c^v(P, u(P))$ is negative, the forward difference at P must be employed.

Following our plan, we use as the finite-difference system to approximate $u(P)$ the equations

$$\sum_{i=1}^{n} a^{vi}(Q, U(Q))\left[\frac{U^i(P) - U^i(Q)}{k} + c^v(Q, U(Q))\frac{U^i(Q) - U^i(Q')}{h}\right]$$

$$+ d^v(Q, U(Q)) = 0, \quad \text{for } c^v(Q, U(Q)) \geq 0. \quad (7.10)$$

For values of v with $c^v(Q, U(Q)) < 0$, we take the forward x difference at Q instead. From now on it will be assumed that $c^v(Q, U(Q)) \geq 0$. The modifications of the proof when $c^v(Q, U(Q)) < 0$ are straightforward. The initial values are

$$U(P) = g(P), \quad P \in L. \quad (7.11)$$

Equation (7.10) differs from the differential equation not only in the replacement of derivatives by finite-difference quotients but also in the substitution of Q for P in all but one place. This is necessary if we wish to deal with a difference equation that can easily be solved at every point for the value of U at the next grid point where it is to be calculated. This can be done with (7.10) by solving a system of n linear algebraic equations for the $U^i(P)$. We must, of course, assume that the determinant of $A(Q, U(Q))$ in (7.10) does not vanish. The (x, y)-domain for which this is true depends on the solution U. Its size will be discussed at the end of the proof.

Formula (7.10) is, in its context, just as naturally motivated as the difference equation (4.2) for the simple wave equation. One might therefore expect that the present method, when applied to system (6.13), which is the normal form of system (6.12), which, in turn, is the natural equivalent of the wave equation, would yield a difference scheme equivalent to (4.2). This is not so, however, as is already obvious from the fact that the general difference formula of the present section is based on four grid points and not on five, and that it requires, at every step, the solution of a simultaneous system of n equations.

7.2. A General Scheme for Proving the Convergence of Difference Approximations

In Sec. 4 the convergence of U to u was proved by means of rather special representations based on Fourier series. Actually, there exists a powerful general technique for this purpose, which we shall now explain and then apply to the difference scheme (7.10), (7.11).

Let

$$F(u) = 0 \quad \text{in} \quad S, \quad u = g \quad \text{on} \quad L \quad (7.12)$$

be some differential equation or system of differential equations for an unknown vector function u. We do not specify the number of independent variables nor the nature of the regions S and of the initial set L. Even in this form this formulation is too special, since frequently not the function u, but some combination of its derivatives, is prescribed at the boundary. Our arguments can be extended to cover such problems too.

We associate with (7.12) a finite-difference problem whose network, no matter what its configuration, depends on one parameter h:

$$F_h(U) = 0 \quad \text{in} \quad S, \qquad U = g_h \quad \text{on} \quad L. \tag{7.13}$$

Again, this difference problem is not sufficiently general to include all schemes actually occurring, since frequently S and L depend on h also. We wish to investigate whether or not the difference

$$v = U - u \tag{7.14}$$

tends to zero with h. The term *truncation error* is frequently used for v, conveying the idea that U can be represented by a series in powers of h of which u is the first term. The first term is then the result of cutting off or "truncating" the series after it. But this is a misleading idea since, as often as not, such a series expansion does not exist. *Discretization error* is a more descriptive designation for the quantity v, and we shall use it.

By means of (7.14) we can eliminate U from (7.13) and obtain thus a difference equation for v itself. The analogous idea of eliminating u in favor of v from (7.12) is generally not feasible since U is usually defined at the net points only, so that the differentiations contained in $F(u)$ cannot be applied to U.

The most common way of performing this elimination is to form first the expression $F_h(u)$ and to show that

$$F_h(u) = F(u) + \omega_h^1(u), \tag{7.15}$$

where $\omega_h^1(u)$ tends to zero with h. Unless (7.15) is true, the operator F_h cannot well be called an approximation to the operator F. Now $F(u) = 0$, by assumption, and therefore we find, subtracting (7.15) from (7.13), that

$$F_h(U) - F_h(u) = -\omega_h^1(u). \tag{7.16}$$

If the coefficients of F_h are sufficiently smooth, it can usually be shown without much difficulty that there exists a function $G_h(v)$ such that

$$F_h(U) - F_h(u) = G_h(v) + \omega_h^2(u, v), \tag{7.17}$$

where ω_h^2 tends to zero with h as well as with v. If F_h is linear, $G_h = F_h$ and $\omega_h^2 = 0$, so that this part of the argument is trivial. Combining (7.12), (7.13), (7.16), and (7.17), we derive for v the difference equation

$$G_h(v) = -\omega_h^1(u) - \omega_h^2(u, v) \quad \text{in} \quad S, \qquad v = g_h - g \quad \text{on} \quad L. \tag{7.18}$$

Again, g_h can be considered an approximation to g only if $g_h \to g$, as $h \to 0$. The proof is now reduced to showing that problem (7.18) has a unique solution v that tends to 0 with h, and that its solution depends continuously on h at $h = 0$.

Frequently the same argument also yields some explicit appraisal for the discretization error v. Such appraisals are, of course, much sought after in actual computations. But it is usually very difficult to formulate them in such a way that they contain only quantities explicitly known to the computer. As to the solution u of the differential problem, for instance, we are assuming here that it exists and is sufficiently smooth for our need. This is sufficient for a convergence proof but, to the computer, u is precisely the quantity he wants to know, so that its presence in an appraisal of the discretization error is very undesirable.

There exists a somewhat different approach to the convergence problem, which is described in some of the most ingenious papers on this subject. There, the existence of the solution u is not *assumed*, but, on the contrary, is *proved* by showing that $\lim_{h \to 0} U$ exists. These proofs are much more intricate and less useful to the numerical analyst, inasmuch as they are usually nonconstructive and give no indication whatever of the size of v.

We illustrate these generalities by the simple example of the scalar differential equation problem

$$u' - f(x, u) = 0, \qquad x > 0, \qquad u(0) = \alpha, \qquad (7.19)$$

with the finite-difference approximation

$$\frac{U(x + h) - U(x)}{h} - f(x, U) = 0, \qquad U(0) = \alpha. \qquad (7.20)$$

If, as we shall assume, $f(x, u)$ is continuous in $0 \le x \le a$, $|\alpha - u| \le b$, and satisfies the Lipschitz condition

$$|f(x, u_1) - f(x, u_2)| < M|u_1 - u_2| \qquad (7.21)$$

in this domain, then it is known that problem (7.19) possesses a continuously differentiable solution in some interval $0 \le x \le a' \le a$, and that $|\alpha - u| < b$ there (Ford [1933], Chap. 4).

We insert u for U into the left member of (7.20) and find

$$\frac{u(x + h) - u(x)}{h} - f(x, u) = u'(x) + \omega_h(x) - f(x, u) = \omega_h(x),$$

where $\omega_h(x)$ indicates a function of x and h that tends to zero with h, uniformly for $0 \le x \le a'$. Subtraction of this equation from (7.20) yields

$$\frac{v(x + h) - v(x)}{h} - f(x, U) + f(x, u) = -\omega_h(x),$$

with $v = U - u$, or, using (7.21),

$$\frac{v(x + h) - v(x)}{h} = -\omega_h(x) + O(v(x)), \qquad v(0) = 0. \qquad (7.22)$$

This is equation (7.18) for the present problem.

The use of the inequality (7.21) in this step implies the assumption that not only $|\alpha - u| \leq b$ but also $|\alpha - U| \leq b$. Since $U(0) = \alpha$, this is certainly true for $x = 0$, but at the end of our proof we must investigate the size of the x interval in which this inequality can still be guaranteed. Beyond that interval, U is no longer necessarily an approximation to u.

To show that $v(x)$ is small for small h, we derive from (7.22) the relation

$$|v(x + h)| \leq |v(x)| + h(|\omega_h(x)| + M|v(x)|), \qquad v(0) = 0. \qquad (7.23)$$

Let β_h be a quantity, independent of x, such that $|\omega_h(x)| \leq \beta_h$ in $0 \leq x \leq a'$, and such that β_h tends to zero with h. The inequality in (7.23) shows that, if $m(x)$ is the solution of the difference equation problem

$$m(x + h) = m(x) + h(\beta_h + M\, m(x)), \qquad m(0) = 0, \qquad (7.24)$$

then $m(x)$ dominates $v(x)$ at all net points; i.e.,

$$|v(x)| \leq m(x).$$

The linear difference equation (7.24) can be solved explicitly since it has constant coefficients. The result of this routine calculation is

$$m(x) = \frac{\beta_h}{M} [(1 + hM)^{x/h} - 1].$$

The ensuing inequality for $v(x)$,

$$|v(x)| \leq \frac{\beta_h}{M} [(1 + hM)^{x/h} - 1], \qquad (7.25)$$

shows not only that U does indeed tend to u as $h \to 0$ but it also indicates the order of magnitude of the discretization error. If we have some *a priori* bound on β_h, (7.25) constitutes an effective appraisal of the discretization error.

We must still investigate the interval of validity of (7.25). To this end we first observe that in our proof we have assumed the validity of $|U - \alpha| \leq b$ in the interval from 0 to the net point x under consideration, and that we obtained from that the inequality (7.23), which restricts the size of $v(x)$ at the *next* net point $v(x + h)$. Under this assumption, the inequality (7.25) can therefore be applied at the net point $x + h$. Now, since $|u - \alpha| < b$ in $0 \leq x \leq a$, there exists a positive number ϵ such that

$$|u - \alpha| < b - \epsilon \qquad \text{for} \qquad 0 \leq x \leq a'. \qquad (7.26)$$

If we assume that the condition $|U(x) - \alpha| \leq b$ has already been proved for $0 \leq x \leq x_1$, where x_1 is a net point in $0 \leq x \leq a' - h$, we obtain from (7.25) the inequality

$$|U(x_1 + h) - u(x_1 + h)| \leq \beta_h M_1,$$

in which M_1 is some constant depending on a'. If we combine this with inequality (7.26), which is valid at $x_1 + h$ also, we find that

$$|U(x_1 + h) - \alpha| \leq b - \epsilon + \beta_h M.$$

Hence, if h is so small that

$$\beta_h \leq \frac{\epsilon}{M}, \tag{7.27}$$

the validity of $|U(x) - \alpha| \leq b$ is proved for the point $x_1 + h$ also. Since $|U(0) - \alpha| = 0$, the inequality is proved by induction to be valid in the whole interval $0 \leq x \leq a'$, i.e., in the interval in which the differential equation itself is known to be solvable. This is true provided h satisfies the inequality (7.27).

7.3. The Convergence of the Difference Scheme for Hyperbolic Systems

The proof that $U(P)$ as defined by (7.10) and (7.11) converges to the solution $u(P)$ of (7.3) with the same initial values, as $h \to 0$, differs from the argument in the preceding section only by a greater complexity of the details.

Substitution of (7.9) into (7.3) yields

$$\sum_{i=1}^{n} a^{vi}(P, u(P)) \left[\frac{u^i(P) - u^i(Q)}{k} + c^v(P, u(P)) \frac{u^i(Q) - u^i(Q')}{h} \right]$$
$$+ d^v(P, u(P)) = O(h).$$

Here we must replace P by Q in a^{vi}, c^v, and d^v, since, according to our program, we have to apply the difference operator in (7.10) to the function u, and the coefficients were taken at Q in (7.10). Because of the Lipschitzian character of the coefficients and the continuous differentiability of u, this introduces changes that are $O(h)$, and therefore

$$\sum_{i=1}^{n} a^{vi}(Q, u(Q)) \left[\frac{u^i(P) - u^i(Q)}{k} + c^v(Q, u(Q)) \frac{u^i(Q) - u^i(Q')}{h} \right]$$
$$+ d^v(Q, u(Q)) = O(h). \tag{7.28}$$

Before we subtract this from (7.10) to obtain a difference equation for the discretization error

$$v = U - u,$$

we replace $u(Q)$ by $U(Q)$ in the coefficients of (7.28) to simplify the resulting expression. The change produced by this substitution is $O(|v(Q)|) + O(v^2(Q))$, provided the value of $U(Q)$ is in a range where the coefficients are Lipschitzian. The analysis of this hypothesis will be postponed to the end of the proof. The difference equation for v that results by the indicated subtraction is of the form

$$\sum_{i=1}^{n} a^{vi}(Q, U(Q))\left[\frac{v^i(P) - v^i(Q)}{k} + c^v(Q, U(Q))\frac{v^i(Q) - v^i(Q')}{h}\right]$$

$$= O(h) + O(|v(Q)|) + O(|v(Q)|^2), \quad (7.29)$$

where $|v|$ designates the length of the vector v. Also,

$$v = 0 \quad \text{on} \quad L. \quad (7.30)$$

Instead of aiming directly at an appraisal of $|v|$, it is now convenient to introduce the auxiliary vector V with the components

$$V^v(P) = \sum_{i=1}^{n} a^{vi}(Q, U(Q)) v^i(P) \quad (7.31)$$

into (7.29). Since the determinant of this linear transformation is by assumption bounded and bounded away from zero in a certain neighborhood of the prescribed initial values, any appraisal of $V(P)$ leads to an appraisal of $v(P)$ as long as $U(P)$ is in that neighborhood.

In formula (7.31) the point Q is the grid point directly below P. We now wish to multiply out the expressions in brackets in (7.29) and to eliminate v^i in favor of V^i. But in several terms of the resulting sum the point occurring in the argument of a^{vi} is not the one below the grid point in the v^i that multiplies it. This fact makes necessary some further modification of (7.29). We have, for instance,

$$a^{vi}(Q, U(Q)) v^i(Q') = a^{vi}(\tilde{Q}, U(\tilde{Q})) v^i(Q')$$

$$+ [a^{vi}(Q, U(Q)) - a^{vi}(\tilde{Q}, U(\tilde{Q}))] v^i(Q'),$$

where $\tilde{Q}$ is the grid point below Q', provided Q' is on a grid line $t > 0$. For $t = 0$ this expression is zero. The second term in the right member is equal to

$$v^i(Q')[O(h) + O(|U(\tilde{Q}) - U(Q)|)].$$

But

$$U(\tilde{Q}) - U(Q) = [U(\tilde{Q}) - u(\tilde{Q})] + [u(\tilde{Q}) - u(Q)] + [u(Q) - U(Q)]$$

$$= v(\tilde{Q}) + O(h) + v(Q).$$

Therefore

$$\sum_{i=1}^{n} a^{vi}(Q, U(Q))\, v^{i}(Q') = V^{v}(Q') + O(v(Q')\, v(\tilde{Q}))$$
$$+ O(|v(Q')|h) + O(v(Q')\, v(Q)).$$

An analogous formula holds for a sum involving the $v^{i}(Q)$. Replacing $O(|v(Q)|)$ by $O(|V(Q)|)$, etc., and substituting into (7.29), after some rearrangements we obtain

$$V^{v}(P) = [1 - \lambda c^{v}(Q, U(Q))]\, V^{v}(Q) + \lambda c^{v}(Q, U(Q))\, V^{v}(Q') + \omega(P),$$
$$\text{(7.32)}$$

where

$$\omega(P) = O(h^{2}) + O(|V(Q)|h) + O(V(Q)^{2}h) + O(V(Q')\, V(\tilde{Q})) + O(|V(Q')|h)$$
$$+ O(V(Q')\, V(Q)) + O(V(Q)\, V(\tilde{\tilde{Q}})) + O(|V(Q)|h) + O(V(Q)^{2}),$$
$$\text{for } t > k. \quad \text{(7.33)}$$

Here $\tilde{\tilde{Q}}$ is the grid point below Q. The initial values of $V^{v}(P)$ are zero. For $t = k$, we have $\omega(P) = O(h^{2})$, as can be seen directly from (7.29).
If $c^{v}(Q, U(Q)) < 0$, formula (7.32) has to be replaced by

$$V^{v}(P) = [1 + \lambda c^{v}(Q, U(Q))]\, V^{v}(Q) - \lambda c^{v}(Q, U(Q))\, V^{v}(Q^{v}) + \omega. \quad \text{(7.32a)}$$

Let us assume that the points Q, Q', and Q'' are on the jth line of the grid, and denote by E_{j} the maximum of $|V^{i}(R)|$ for $i = 1, \cdots, n$ and for all grid points R on the jth line. From the fact that $1 - \lambda|c^{v}(Q, U(Q))| > 0$, thanks to the definition of m in (7.7), it follows that in (7.32) as well as in (7.32a) the coefficients of V^{v} are nonnegative. Hence these two equations and (7.33) yield

$$E_{j+1} \leq E_{j} + \alpha(h^{2} + hE_{j} + E_{j}E_{j-1} + E_{j}^{2}), \quad j \geq 1, \quad \text{(7.34)}$$

where α is a positive constant that depends on U, on the Lipschitz constants of the coefficients, and on the upper bound of h. As initial conditions for the difference inequality (7.34) we have

$$E_{0} = 0, \quad E_{1} = O(h^{2}).$$

Our next aim is to show that the solutions of this inequality problem are $O(h)$. To facilitate this task, we replace (7.34) temporarily by the simpler linear difference equation problem

$$F_{j+1} = (1 + 3\alpha h)F_{j} + \alpha h^{2}, \quad j > 1, \quad F_{1} = mh^{2}, \quad \text{(7.35)}$$

where $m > 0$ is a constant so large that $E_1 \leq mh^2$. The relation between (7.34) and (7.35) will become apparent shortly. The solution of (7.35) is

$$F_{j+1} = mh^2(1 + 3\alpha h)^j + \frac{h}{3}[(1 + 3\alpha h)^j - 1], \qquad (7.36)$$

whence

$$F_{j+1} \leq mh^2 e^{3\alpha h j} + \frac{h}{3}(e^{3\alpha h j} - 1) \leq e^{3\alpha h j}(mh + \alpha j h)h_0. \qquad (7.37)$$

Let $h \leq 1/2m$, and denote by ξ some positive number such that $(\frac{1}{2} + \alpha\xi)e^{3\alpha\xi} < 1$. Then $F_{j+1} \leq h$ for all $j \leq \xi/h$. Now, as long as F_j and F_{j-1} do not exceed h,

$$3hF_j \geq hF_j + F_j F_{j-1} + F_j^2, \qquad (7.38)$$

so that comparison of (7.34) and (7.35) yields

$$E_{j+1} \leq F_{j+1} \leq h, \qquad 0 \leq j \leq \xi/h. \qquad (7.39)$$

This establishes the convergence of U to u for $0 \leq y < k/\xi h = \lambda/\xi$ and shows at the same time that the discretization error is $O(h)$. But this is true only under the hypothesis that the point $x, y, z^i = U^i(x, y)$ remains inside a finite region of the $(n + 2)$-dimensional space of the variables $x, y, z^1, \cdots, z^n$, where the coefficients of the differential equations satisfy the Lipschitz conditions that we have used in our argument. More precisely, let z be the vector with components z^i, and let S be a neighborhood of $x = 0$ in the (x, y)-plane. Then we must investigate, for (x, y) in S and with $z = U(x, y)$, whether the coefficients $a^{\nu i}(x, y, z)$, $c^\nu(x, y, z)$, $d^\nu(x, y, z)$ have the smoothness properties required in the existence and uniqueness theorem of Sec. 6. Furthermore, the condition $\det [a^{\nu i}(x, y, z)] \neq 0$ has been used with $z = U$ and must now be verified.

We know that these conditions are satisfied for $z = u$ as long as (x, y) is in S. In fact, the existence and uniqueness theorems for u employed here assume, as was stated before, that the conditions are true for (x, y) in S and

$$|g^i(x) - z^i| < K^i, \qquad (7.40)$$

where K is a suitable positive constant vector.

Now an inspection of our proof will show that the smoothness properties have been used only at t levels *below* P. We can therefore repeat almost literally the argument given at the end of Sec. 7.2. The inequality (7.38) is trivially satisfied for $z^i = U^i(x, 0)$. Let it be supposed to be true with

$z^i = U^i(Q)$ for all net points Q below the line $y = (j + 1)k$, and assume that P is on the line $y = (j + 1)k$. By assumption,

$$|g^i(x) - u^i| < K^i$$

in S. Hence there exists a positive constant ϵ such that in a closed sub-domain S^* of S containing the initial segment,

$$|g^i(x) - u^i| < K^i - \epsilon \qquad \text{for } i = 1, \cdots, n.$$

Let P be in S^* and also in the strip $0 \le y < \lambda/\xi$. Then

$$|g^i(x) - u^i(P)| < K^i - \epsilon,$$

and, because of (7.39),

$$|U^i(P) - u^i(P)| \le h.$$

Hence

$$|g^i(x) - U^i(P)| < K^i - \epsilon + h\beta.$$

Thus, if

$$h \le \epsilon,$$

the coefficients of the differential equation have the necessary smoothness properties for $z^i = U^i(P)$ also. This completes the convergence proof.

7.4. Differences in a Curvilinear Net

For initial curves that are not segments of the x-axis, the article by Courant, Isaacson, and Rees [1952] contains a generalization of the method described here that uses an irregular, not a rectangular, net. Such nets have actually been used in computations on high-speed computing machines. We content ourselves with a brief description here.

Let I_0 be the initial curve. We construct a family of smooth curves $\{I\}$, one of which is I_0, which have nowhere in the region under consideration a characteristic direction, and which cover this region simply. To start the calculation, we choose a curve I_1 near I_0 from this family and select net points on I_0 and I_1 in such a way that the following condition is satisfied: If straight lines are drawn through a net point P of I_1 in the n characteristic directions, then their intersections ($j = 1, \cdots, n$) with I_0 all lie on an arc that contains only one net point Q. Since $u(P)$ is not known, the characteristic directions at P are unknown in nonlinear problems. The ensuing uncertainty in the construction has already been discussed in Sec. 7.1. See Fig. 7.2.

Let Q', Q'' be the net points on I_0 nearest to Q, and denote by Q_j the point where the ray through P in the jth characteristic direction intersects the chord $Q'Q$ (or $Q''Q$, as the case may be).

We now define $U(Q_j)$ as the linearly interpolated average of the prescribed values $U(Q')$, $U(Q)$, and then calculate $U^i(P)$ $(i = 1, \cdots, n)$ from the n difference equations

$$\sum_{i=1}^{n} a^{ji}(Q, U(Q)) \frac{U^i(P) - U^i(Q_j)}{k_j} + d^j(Q, U(Q)) = 0, \qquad j = 1, \cdots, n,$$

in which k_j is the difference between the ordinates of P and Q_j. The choice of this difference approximation is motivated by formula (7.6). The arguments leading to (7.6) can readily be generalized to the present situation. There the curves $\{I\}$ were the lines $y = $ const.

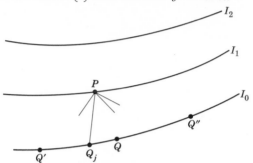

FIG. 7.2. Differences in a curvilinear net.

After the values of U at all net points on I_1 are calculated, a curve I_2 beyond I_1 is chosen from the family $\{I\}$, and on it net points are chosen that bear the same relationship to the net points on I_1 as the latter did to those on I_0. Then U can be calculated in the same manner at these new net points, and the procedure is repeated.

To study mathematically the difference $U - u$ for this method, we must think of the distances between any two adjacent net points P_1, P_2 as being of the form $h \, \phi(P_1, P_2, h)$, where $\phi(P_1, P_2, h)$ remains bounded as $h \to 0$. By an almost straightforward adaptation of the proof given in the rectangular case, it can again be shown that $|U - u| = O(h)$ in a suitable neighborhood of the initial curve. The details can be found in Courant, Isaacson, and Rees [1952].

7.5. The Round-Off Errors

The propagation of round-off errors can be appraised by a slight modification of the method that gave us the convergence and the order of the discretization error.

Formula (7.10) and the corresponding formula for $c^\nu(Q, U(Q)) < 0$ permit us to calculate $U(P)$ as a function of $U(Q)$, $U(Q')$, $U(Q'')$, say

$$U(P) = F(U(Q), U(Q'), U(Q''), Q). \tag{7.41}$$

The effect of the round-off errors can be expressed by replacing (7.41) with a slightly different equation

$$\bar{U}(P) = \bar{F}(\bar{U}(Q), \bar{U}(Q'), \bar{U}(Q''), Q). \tag{7.42}$$

The difference between F and $\bar{F}$ is caused by the rounding off in the arithmetic operations. For equal arguments, the values of the functions F and $\bar{F}$ differ by an amount that depends on the nature of the arithmetic operations involved in carrying out the computations and on the precision, as well as on the program used on the computing machine. Let us assume that

$$|F - \bar{F}| \le \epsilon$$

for equal arguments, uniformly in the region under consideration. Then the reasoning leading to an appraisal of the discretization error v can be applied to the quantity $\bar{v} = \bar{U} - u$, and the only difference is the appearance of an additional term $O(\epsilon)$ among the correction terms. Let $\bar{V}$ be the thus modified quantity V, and $\bar{E}_j$ the analog of E_j for $\bar{U}$ instead of for U. Then $\bar{E}_j$ satisfies a difference inequality of the form

$$\bar{E}_{j+1} \le \bar{E}_j + \alpha(h^2 + \epsilon + h\bar{E}_j + \bar{E}_j\bar{E}_{j-1} + \bar{E}_j^2), \qquad j \ge 1$$
$$E_0 = 0, \qquad E_1 = O(h^2 + \epsilon), \tag{7.43}$$

provided there is no error in the initial data.

Hence, if $\epsilon = O(h^2)$, our results will not be essentially affected; i.e., $\bar{U} - u = O(h)$.

It must be kept in mind that (7.39) is an inequality of unknown wastefulness since ξ depends on the unknown constant α. It has a precise meaning only as a statement concerning the orders of magnitude involved in the passage to the limit as $h \to 0$. In actual computations one cannot pass to the limit, and the value of these appraisals is therefore limited. Nevertheless, in the absence of any better information, it is interesting to know that the precision of the computations should be multiplied by m^2 when the mesh length is divided by m, if we wish to preserve the order of magnitude of $|\bar{U} - u|$. This is the concrete implication of the requirement that $\epsilon = O(h^2)$. If we fail to do this, the round-off error may destroy the usefulness of the method completely.

It is interesting to compare these results with our discussion of the stability of the wave equation $u_{xx} - u_{tt} = 0$ in Sec. 5.2. In the case $\lambda = 1$ we were able to give the exact order of the departure due to round-off errors, namely $O(\epsilon h^{-2})$. Hence we must take $\epsilon = O(h^3)$ in that problem, if we wish to have $|\bar{U} - u| = O(h)$. Therefore the method introduced in this section is better, as far as round-off is concerned, than that of Sec. 4.

SECTION 8. INTEGRATION ALONG CHARACTERISTICS

8.1. The Method of Massau

When the given system consists of two quasilinear hyperbolic equations in two dependent variables u^1, u^2, and two independent variables x, y, a modified version of the integration method explained in Sec. 7.4 can be used, which goes back to a monograph by Massau [1899] (see also Sauer [1952], pp. 83 ff.). Its starting point is the canonical system (6.18), (6.20).

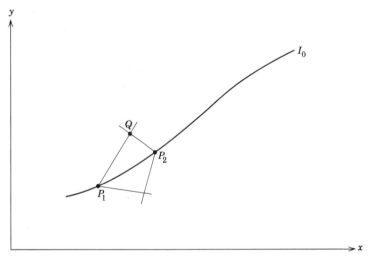

FIG. 8.1.

As before, let I_0 be the initial curve in the (x, y)-plane and assume that I_0 has nowhere a characteristic direction. On I_0 we choose a sequence of approximately equally spaced points. Let P_1, P_2 be two adjacent grid points on I_0, and denote by Q that one of the two points of intersection of the four straight lines with characteristic directions through P_1 and P_2 which lies on the side of I_0 on which we want to find the solutions u^1, u^2 (see Fig. 8.1). To fix the ideas, assume that Q is the intersection of the line with slope $1/c^1$ through P_1 and the line with slope $1/c^2$ through P_2. The finite-difference equations

$$X(Q) - X(P_1) = c^1(X(P_1), Y(P_1), U^1(P_1), U^2(P_1))[Y(Q) - Y(P_1)], \quad (8.1)$$

$$X(Q) - X(P_2) = c^2(X(P_2), Y(P_2), U^1(P_2), U^2(P_2))[Y(Q) - Y(P_2)] \quad (8.2)$$

are then formal finite-difference approximations to the differential equations (6.18). Similarly, (6.20) can be replaced by

$$a^{11}(P_1)[U^1(Q) - U^1(P_1)] + a^{12}(P_1)[U^2(Q) - U^2(P_1)]$$
$$+ d^1(P_1)[Y(Q) - Y(P_1)] = 0, \quad (8.3)$$
$$a^{21}(P_2)[U^1(Q) - U^1(P_2)] + a^{22}(P_2)[U^2(Q) - U^2(P_2)]$$
$$+ d^2(P_2)[Y(Q) - Y(P_2)] = 0. \quad (8.4)$$

In the interest of conciseness we have replaced the full expressions for the coefficients by obvious abbreviations. From the first two of these four equations we can find $X(Q)$, $Y(Q)$. The second pair then gives us $U^1(Q)$ and $U^2(Q)$.

It is clear that by successive applications of this method we can find the values of X, Y, U^1, U^2 in a system of irregularly spaced grid points. We expect this method to yield an approximation of order $O(h)$ to the true values of u^1, u^2 at these points. Here h is some number indicating the order of magnitude of the distances of the initial grid points on I_1, for instance the maximum distance of two adjacent grid points. No restrictive conditions to ensure stability and convergence, such as were necessary in previous methods, are to be expected for this procedure since it is based on a net that approximates the net of characteristic curves. A proof of the convergence can be found in Sauer [1952], Sec. 16.

Experience has shown that the results so obtained can be improved by repeating the application of formulas (8.1) to (8.4), taking as arguments of the coefficients the mean values

$$\tfrac{1}{2}[X(P_1) + X(Q)], \quad \tfrac{1}{2}[X(P_2) + X(Q)], \quad \tfrac{1}{2}[Y(P_1) + Y(Q)], \text{ etc.}$$

In fact, it may be useful to carry out such improvements several times in succession. It is plausible that this will increase the smallness, if not necessarily the order of magnitude, of the discretization error, but no theoretical analysis of this point seems to exist.

8.2. Quasilinear Equations of Order Two

A single differential equation of order two can be replaced (in more than one way) by a system of two first-order equations. For instance, the equation

$$aw_{xx} + 2bw_{xy} + cw_{yy} = f, \quad (8.5)$$

where $a, b, c,$ and f are functions of x, y, u, u_x, u_y, is equivalent to the system

$$au_x + b(u_y + v_x) + cv_y = f,$$
$$u_y - v_x = 0, \quad (8.6)$$

where $u = w_x, v = w_y$.

The most common initial data that accompany an equation like (8.5) are the values of w and of its normal derivative w_n on an initial arc I_0. The initial values of u and v are related to these by the equations

$$u = w_t \cos \theta - w_n \sin \theta, \qquad v = w_t \sin \theta + w_n \cos \theta,$$

in which θ is the directional angle of the curve I_0, and w_t is the tangential derivative of w. The latter can be calculated from the given values of w on I_0.

The characteristic directions of the system (8.6) can easily be found by the theory of Sec. 6.1. We obtain

$$\left. \begin{array}{c} c^1 \\ c^2 \end{array} \right\} = \frac{1}{c}(b \pm \sqrt{b^2 - ac}).$$

They are usually referred to directly as the characteristic directions of equation (8.5). The corresponding transformation matrix T of (6.4) is

$$T = \begin{bmatrix} -1 & \sqrt{b^2 - ac} \\ -1 & -\sqrt{b^2 - ac} \end{bmatrix},$$

and the normal form (6.6) becomes

$$cc^2(c^1 u_x + u_y) + c(c^1 v_x + v_y) = f,$$
$$cc^1(c^2 u_x + u_y) + c(c^2 v_x + v_y) = f.$$

Hence the canonical equations (6.20) are, in this case,

$$\begin{aligned} cc^2 u_\alpha + cv_\alpha &= fy_\alpha, \\ cc^1 u_\beta + cv_\beta &= fy_\beta. \end{aligned} \tag{8.7}$$

We may now again apply the method of Massau.

To find w from u and v, one has once more to solve a system of partial differential equations, but a very simple one, namely,

$$w_x = u, \qquad w_y = v.$$

However, since u and v are known only at the points of an irregular grid, this may represent a by no means negligible part of the total amount of work required.

8.3. Another Integration Method for n Dependent Variables

The schemes of Secs. 7.4 and 7.1 can be modified and improved in various ways. Consider again the initial-value problem (7.1) with an initial curve I_0 instead of the initial segment L. As in Sec. 7.4 we embed

I_0 in a family of curves $\{I\}$, a sequence $I_0, I_1, I_2, \cdots$ of which divides the region under consideration into a number of narrow strips $J_1, J_2, \cdots$. Now, instead of using a simple finite-difference scheme to step from I_r to I_{r+1}, we approximate the differential equation in every strip by a suitable *linear* differential equation which can be solved more easily. The result obtained can then be improved by an iteration scheme.

The following arrangement for such a procedure is suggested in Courant and Friedrichs [1948], pp. 74–75 (see also Sauer [1952], pp. 124–126). Let us study first the case of a linear differential system. Here the characteristics are independent of the solution and can be found by integrating the n ordinary first-order differential equations (6.11). Each characteristic is then given by a function $x = \phi_i(y)$ for which we possess a table of values. The hyperbolic system (7.1), which in scalar notation reads

$$\sum_{i=1}^{n} a^{\nu i}(c^\nu u_x{}^i + u_y{}^i) + d^\nu = 0, \qquad \nu = 1, 2, \cdots, n,$$

can be written

$$\sum_{i=1}^{n} a^{\nu i}(x, y)\, du^i + d^\nu(x, y)\, dy = 0, \qquad \nu = 1, 2, \cdots, n, \qquad (8.8)$$

where du^i, dy in the νth equation are differentials along the νth characteristic. This follows from the argument between formulas (6.1) and (6.5). To solve (8.8) numerically, we perform an integration by parts along an arc of the νth characteristic through a point P, from its intersection P_ν with I_0 to P. Then we obtain the integral equations

$$\sum_{i=1}^{n} a^{\nu i}(P)\, u^i(P) = -\int_P^{P_\nu} d^\nu \, dy + \sum_{i=1}^{n} a^{\nu i}(P_\nu)\, u^i(P_\nu) - \sum_{i=1}^{n} \int_{P_\nu}^{P} u^i \, da^{\nu i}$$
$$\nu = 1, \cdots, n,$$

in which the integrations are extended along the νth characteristic. They can be solved numerically, either by an iteration scheme of the Picard type (usually a method of slow convergence) or by some finite-difference method.

If the system is nonlinear, iterative procedures are possible: First, in the coefficients $a^{\nu i}$, c^ν, d^ν replace the unknown functions u^i by an approximation $v_1{}^i$. This operation produces a linear hyperbolic system, which can be solved as indicated above. Let $u_1{}^i$ be its solution. Then we set $v_2{}^i = u_1{}^i$, replace u^i in the coefficients of the original system by $v_2{}^i$, and again solve the resulting linear system, etc. But this is probably a very cumbersome process. It can be speeded up by applying it only in a narrow strip, for instance in J_1 between I_0 and I_1. In such a narrow region a good first approximation $v_1{}^i$ can be constructed by extending the initial data as constants along some family of curves that intersect each curve of $\{I\}$ once. With a good first approximation, the number of necessary iterations becomes smaller. In the next strip, J_2, the values obtained on I_1 are to be used as initial data, etc.

The method of Sec. 7.4 may be regarded as a very simplified variant of this technique, in which the strips J_r are so narrow that no iterations are necessary and the integration of the linear differential equations is done in one step.

SECTION 9. INTEGRATION BY ADAMS' METHOD

Most of the finite-difference approximations used so far are very crude when compared with the methods available for the integration of *ordinary* differential equations. A simple replacement of the derivative by a difference quotient is hardly ever considered sufficiently accurate when dealing with ordinary differential equations. Since each of the differential equations of a hyperbolic system in normal form contains differentiations in one direction only, some of the methods developed for ordinary differential equations can be adapted to such hyperbolic systems. We illustrate this point by the example of Adams' method, which was used for hyperbolic problems by Thomas [1954].

If the ordinary differential equation

$$y' = f(x, y) \tag{9.1}$$

is integrated over the interval $(x, x + h)$, one obtains the integral equation

$$y(x + h) - y(x) = \int_{x}^{x+h} f(t, y(t))\, dt, \tag{9.2}$$

which is the starting point for numerous discrete integration schemes for (9.1). The simplest finite-difference approximation to (9.1) is obtained when $f(t, y(t))$ in (9.2) is replaced by its value at x. The use of more refined quadrature formulas leads to better integration schemes for (9.1).

To obtain one such formula, we assume that $y(x)$—and therefore $f(x, y(x))$—is already known at $x - ph, x - (p - 1)h, \cdots, x - h, x$. Then we can expect that the polynomial of degree p which coincides with $f(x, y(x))$ at those $p + 1$ points will supply us with a good approximation for $f(x, y(x))$ in the interval $(x, x + h)$. If this polynomial is inserted in

(9.2), Adams' formula results. The details of this program, including appraisals of the error, can be found in many texts on numerical analysis, e.g., Milne [1949] or Collatz [1955]. The final formula can be written in the form

$$y(x + h) = y(x) + h \sum_{r=0}^{p} \beta_r \nabla^r f(x, y(x)) + R_{p+1}, \qquad (9.3)$$

where

$$\beta_r = \frac{1}{r!} \int_0^1 t(t + 1) \cdots (t + r - 1)\, dt, \qquad \beta_0 = 1,$$

and ∇ is the backward-difference operator corresponding to the mesh length h, i.e.,

$$\nabla \phi(x) = \phi(x) - \phi(x - h).$$

The error R_{p+1} can be appraised (see Collatz [1955], p. 9) by the inequality

$$|R_{p+1}| \leq h^{p+2} \beta_{p+1} \max_{x \leq t \leq x+h} |f(t)| \left| \frac{d^{p+1}}{dt^{p+1}} f(t, y(t)) \right|.$$

For some computational schemes it is preferable to replace the differences of f by their explicit expressions and collect terms according to the values of f at the net points occurring in the formula. For $p = 2$, for instance, one finds the approximate equality

$$y(x + h) \doteq y(x) + h\left[\tfrac{23}{12} f(x, y(x)) - \tfrac{16}{12} f(x - h, y(x - h)) + \tfrac{5}{12} f(x - 2h, y(x - 2h))\right]. \quad (9.4)$$

In (9.3) or (9.4) we may replace $f(x, y(x))$, $f(x - h, y(x - h))$, etc., by $dy(x)/dx$, $dy(x - h)/dx$, etc. The formulas can then be interpreted as giving approximate expressions for the difference quotient in terms of the first derivatives at the preceding net points.

It is clear that the formulas (9.3), (9.4) can be used only after the values of $y(x)$ at the first $p + 1$ net points have been calculated by some other method. One way of doing this is to use the simplest difference approximation, namely the one based on $p = 0$, with a mesh fine enough to give the required accuracy.

Adams' method has been adapted by Thomas [1954] to the solution of hyperbolic systems in canonical form. A brief illustration will suffice for our present purpose. Let us say that we wish to integrate the system (6.18), (6.20) when the initial values of u and v are prescribed on the line $\alpha + \beta = 0$, as in Sec. 6.4. We use the square grid formed by the lines $\alpha + nh$, $\beta + mh$ ($n, m = 0, \pm 1, \pm 2, \cdots$), and propose to calculate u and v successively on the parallels to $\alpha + \beta = 0$ whose distance from the initial line is a multiple of $h/\sqrt{2}$. Let these lines be denoted by $L_1, L_2, \cdots$, and assume that the calculation of u^1 and u^2 has progressed to the line L_n. We suppose, likewise, that the first partial derivatives of u^1, u^2, x, and y with respect to α and β are known at all grid points up to L_{n-1} inclusive. Consider a point P on L_{n+1} with coordinates $(\alpha + h, \beta + h)$, and the points $Q_0, Q_1, \cdots, Q_p$ with coordinates $(\alpha, \beta + h), (\alpha - h, \beta + h), \cdots, (\alpha - ph, \beta + h)$, as well as the points $R_0, R_1, \cdots, R_p$ with coordinates $(\alpha + h, \beta)$, $(\alpha + h, \beta - h), \cdots, (\alpha + h, \beta - ph)$. The position of these points is indicated in Fig. 9.1.

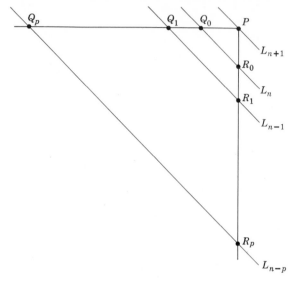

FIG. 9.1.

Now we apply the approximation formula

$$u^j(P) = u(Q_0) + h \sum_{r=0}^{p} \beta_r \nabla_\alpha^r u_\alpha{}^j(Q_0), \qquad j = 1, 2, \qquad (9.5)$$

in which ∇_α is the backward-difference operator in the α-direction. This formula is simply (9.3) without remainder term, applied to $u^j(P)$ with respect to α. Similarly, in the β-direction we use

$$u^j(P) = u(R_0) + h \sum_{r=0}^{p} \beta_r \nabla_\beta^r u_\beta{}^j(R_0), \qquad j = 1, 2. \qquad (9.6)$$

These four equations involve the values of $u_\alpha{}^j$ at the points Q_ν and the values of $u_\beta{}^j$ $(j = 1, 2)$ at the points R_ν $(\nu = 0, 1, \cdots, p)$. Of these, the values at Q_0 and R_0 are still unknown, so that (9.5) and (9.6) cannot be solved by themselves.

Analogous equations can be set up for $x(P)$ and $y(P)$. Thus we obtain eight relations, which we may interpret as a system of simultaneous linear equations for the twelve unknowns $u^j(P)$, $u_\alpha{}^j(Q_0)$, $u_\beta{}^j(R_0)$, ($j = 1, 2$), $x(P)$, $y(P)$, $x_\alpha(Q_0)$, $y_\alpha(Q_0)$, $x_\beta(R_0)$, $y_\beta(R_0)$. It is obvious that the number of unknowns must exceed the number of equations since the differential equations themselves have not been used yet. If we now add the four equations (6.18), (6.20) to the eight we have, taking those equations that involve differentiations with respect to α at the point Q_0, and taking the others at R_0, we arrive at a linear system—fortunately of a simple structure —of twelve simultaneous equations in twelve unknowns. Employing the fact that $\beta_0 = 1$, one can show that the determinant of this system does not vanish.

Taking in this manner successively all the grid points P on L_{n+1}, one calculates at the same time the values of u^1, u^2, x, y on L_{n+1} and the values of all their first derivatives on L_n. If $p > 0$, the first $p + 1$ lines $L_1, \cdots,$ L_{p+1} must be treated by some different method.

According to Thomas, the complications inherent in this method are more than offset by the possibility of taking h much larger than in the simpler methods discussed previously. It must also be borne in mind that even these simpler methods require the solution of a linear algebraic system of order four at every point.

The flexibility of finite-difference methods is greatly enhanced if they can be adapted to variable step length. Let us discuss this point first in connection with the ordinary differential equation (9.1). The basic idea of our integration scheme was to replace $f(t, y(t))$ in (9.2) by a polynomial which coincides with f at the $p + 1$ net points preceding the point $x + h$. If these points are not evenly spaced, (9.3) and (9.4) are no longer valid. There are, however, convenient methods available (e.g., Milne [1949], p. 207) for calculating Lagrange's interpolation polynomials in an irregular grid by means of divided differences.

In two dimensions the distance between the diagonal lines L_j introduced above may be varied analogously. However, it is advisable to maintain the arrangement of the grid points on parallel diagonal lines since otherwise the interpolating problem would become impossibly complicated.

SECTION 10. SHOCK WAVES

10.1. The Concept of Shock Waves

The existence theorem for the solution of the initial-value problem as discussed in Sec. 6.4 is a *local* theorem only; i.e., it guarantees the existence of the solution only in a certain strip along the initial curve. This strip is usually only a part of the complete domain in which the solution exists as a continuously differentiable function, but even the complete domain of existence is in general smaller than the region in which the coefficients of the differential equation satisfy the necessary regularity conditions. For ordinary nonlinear differential equations this fact can be easily illustrated by any number of elementary examples, and there exists a well-developed theory which deals with the singularities of the solutions.

For hyperbolic partial differential equations the corresponding problem is more complex. To give a more concrete idea of the phenomena to be expected, we shall discuss a simple problem of one-dimensional isentropic flow in some detail without, however, giving any proofs. A fuller treatment is contained in Courant and Friedrichs [1948], Chap. 3.

Consider a thermally insulated tube along the x-axis filled with a gas. The left end of the tube is closed by a movable piston, while at the right the tube extends to infinity. Assume that the piston, starting from rest at the point $x = 0$ and at the time $t = 0$, is moved into the tube with a small continuous positive acceleration. The resulting disturbance propagates into the gas according to the differential equation (6.14). (We assume that in first approximation the problem can be treated as one-dimensional.) The initial conditions are not quite of the type discussed in Sec. 6. Let $x = X(t)$ be the law of motion of the piston; then the gas has at the piston at any time t the same velocity as the piston, i.e., $dX(t)/dt$. For $t = 0$ the velocity and density are supposed to be prescribed everywhere. Thus the system (6.14) must be solved subject to the conditions $u = dX/dt$ for $x = X(t)$; $u = u_0(x)$, $\rho = \rho_0(x)$ for $t = 0$. Figure 10.1 illustrates this situation. We wish to find the functions $u(x, t)$, $\rho(x, t)$ in the region between the curve $x = X(t)$ and the x-axis. By methods similar to those of Sec. 7 it can be proved that this problem possesses a unique solution if we remain sufficiently close to the point $x = t = 0$.

A further analysis shows that one of the two families of characteristics consists of straight lines, and that the extension of these straight lines forms an envelope with a cusp, as indicated in Fig. 10.2. The other family of characteristics covers the region simply. It is seen that inside this envelope there pass through every point not one, but three, straight lines. This fact alone makes it plausible that the theorem of unique existence does not extend into the region in the interior of the envelope. This can be seen more clearly by the following argument. Consider some curve having nowhere a characteristic direction and lying in the interior of the domain where a unique solution exists. If we take the values of u and ρ on this cur e as new initial values, our existence theorem of Sec. 6 permits us to continue the solution. This process of continuation can be repeated, and it can be shown that it will not be interrupted as long as the coefficients of the differential equation are sufficiently regular. The straight characteristics of each continuation are the extensions of the

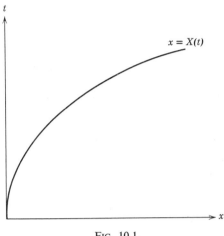

FIG. 10.1.

straight characteristics in the preceding region. In this manner it is possible to continue the solution beyond one branch of the envelope. Another sequence of continuations will take us across the other arc of the envelope.

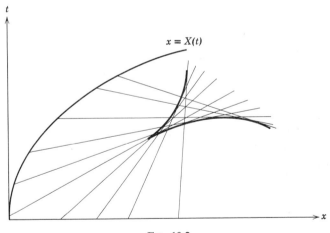

FIG. 10.2.

Since this second sequence of continuations has a different family of straight characteristics, the two solutions cannot be identical inside the envelope. Each of the two solutions can be connected in a continuously differentiable manner with the initial data by moving along suitable paths in the (x, t)-plane. This example is typical for many problems in fluid dynamics.

There remains, however, the physical question as to what happens to the flow after t has reached the value at the cusp of the envelope. Experimental evidence shows that the flow continues to satisfy the differential equations of hydrodynamics even for larger values of t, except along a certain curve in the (x, t)-plane, where a discontinuous change of states takes place. In other words, after a certain value of t has been reached, a discontinuous disturbance—a so-called *shock*—arises in the flow and travels through the gas as a "shock wave." These shock waves are of fundamental importance in the theory of flows, particularly fast flows.

To continue the solution after the shock starts, we must know its position in the (x, t)-plane and the size of the jumps of u and ρ (or of some other variables) at the shock. This information can clearly not be obtained from the original initial-value problem, but requires some analysis of the physical nature of the phenomenon. The "jump conditions" are obtained from the conservation laws of fluid dynamics: An element of mass that crosses the shock must conserve its mass, its momentum, and its energy. A detailed description of these conditions can be found in more specialized treatises, such as Courant and Friedrichs [1948].

Physically, the occurrence of shocks is closely related to the viscosity of the moving fluid. The differential equations (6.14) do not take into account the viscosity, i.e., the inner friction of the fluid. In most practical problems the terms which are thus neglected would cause only a very small change in the solution except in certain narrow regions, such as boundary layers and shock waves, where the influence of viscosity is decisive. Inside the shock wave the fluid is subject to highly complicated changes of state, which are *irreversible* in the sense in which this term is used in thermo-dynamics. Irreversible changes of state are always accompanied by an increase of the entropy. To the jump conditions mentioned above one must therefore add the rule that the specific entropy of the fluid increases on crossing a shock wave.

10.2. Numerical Solution of Problems Involving Shock Waves

It is impossible to give a complete account of the numerical techniques used in the solution of shock-wave problems without going more deeply into the hydrodynamic background than would be suitable here. We limit ourselves therefore to brief descriptions of the purely computational aspects of a few methods, illustrated by examples. The problem discussed in this section is taken from Courant and Friedrichs [1948], Sec. 83.

It concerns a shock wave in one space dimension which moves into a fluid in which the velocity u and the sound speed c are constant (so-called constant state). The fluid is assumed to be an ideal gas. The simplest such problem can be solved by purely analytic means (see Courant and Friedrichs [1948], Secs. 65–70). A somewhat more complicated situation arises when the shock wave is being overtaken by a so-called simple wave (Courant and Friedrichs [1948], Sec. 29). The user of this terminology must bear in mind that for the nonlinear differential equations under consideration no superposition principle holds. The conceptual splitting of the solution into two components is therefore a procedure that has to be defined with care. However, we shall need here only a purely mathematical description of the boundary-value problem to be solved.

The flow in question is not isentropic, and therefore requires three differential equations for its description, instead of the two equations (6.14). This precludes the use of the canonical form described in Sec. 6.3. But it is still possible to introduce a new coordinate system (α, β) in which two of the three families of characteristics are the coordinate lines. Since the characteristics are not known *a priori*, we must again add $x(\alpha, \beta)$, $y(\alpha, \beta)$ as unknown functions to the three unknown functions in the original system. The differential equations (6.18) of the two families of characteristics $\alpha = \text{const.}$, $\beta = \text{const.}$, then complete the differential system, which consists now of five equations for five functions in two unknowns. In the present case it turns out that this system can be written

$$x_\alpha = (u + c)t_\alpha,$$

$$x_\beta = (u - c)t_\beta,$$

$$u_\alpha + \frac{2}{\gamma - 1} c_\alpha = \frac{c\eta_\alpha}{\gamma(\gamma - 1)},$$

$$u_\beta - \frac{2}{\gamma - 1} c_\beta = \frac{-c\eta_\beta}{\gamma(\gamma - 1)}, \qquad (10.1)$$

$$\eta_\alpha t_\beta - \eta_\beta t_\alpha = 0$$

(see Courant and Friedrichs [1948], p. 199). Here $\eta = \eta(\alpha, \beta)$ is proportional to the entropy and γ is a physical constant ($\gamma = 1.4$ for air). Observe that this system is not quasilinear since the last equation is quadratic in the derivatives.

In the problem to be discussed, these flow equations are to be solved in a domain R of the (α, β)-plane bounded by a straight line $L_0: \alpha = \alpha_0$ and a curve S intersecting L_0 at the given point (α_0, β_0) (see Fig. 10.3). The curve S is, however, not known in advance. It represents the moving shock front. On L_0 the values of x, t, u, c, η are prescribed. Beyond the shock front the state of the fluid is supposed to be constant (i.e., it has constant velocity, sound speed, and entropy).

The jump conditions can be written as three functional relations between the values of c, u, η on the inner (left) side of S, the shock velocity U and quantities referring to the constant flow to the right of S. This constant flow is assumed to be known. The shock velocity is $U = dX/dt$, where

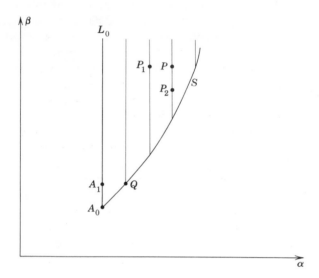

FIG. 10.3.

$x = X(t)$ is the unknown equation of motion of the shock. Hence, we have at our disposal three relations

$$H_i\left(c, u, \eta, \frac{dX}{dt}\right) = 0, \qquad i = 1, 2, 3. \tag{10.2}$$

These equations are fairly involved. To give an idea of the type of expressions encountered, we write them down explicitly for a polytropic ideal gas. For such a substance the specific volume τ, the pressure p, and the specific internal energy e can be expressed in terms of c and η by the equations

$$\tau = (\gamma A)^{\gamma-1} c^{2(\gamma-1)},$$

$$p = (\gamma A)^{(\gamma-1)\gamma} c^{2(1-\gamma)\gamma},$$

$$e = \frac{c^2}{(\gamma - 1)\gamma},$$

(10.3)

where

$$A = (\gamma - 1) \exp \frac{\eta - \eta^*}{c_v^2(\gamma - 1)}, \qquad (\eta^*, c_v \text{ are constants}).$$

For a derivation of these formulas see Courant and Friedrichs [1948], Secs. 2–5. We use subscripts 0 to denote the values of the variables encountered on the right side of S. These are part of the data of the problem. Then

$$H_1 \equiv (1 - \mu^2) \left(\frac{dX/dt - u_0}{c_0} - \frac{c_0}{dX/dt - u_0} \right) - \frac{u - u_0}{c_0}, \qquad \text{with } \mu^2 = \frac{\gamma - 1}{\gamma + 1},$$

$$H_2 \equiv (\tau_0 - \tau) \frac{p + p_0}{2} - (e - e_0), \qquad (10.4)$$

$$H_3 \equiv (1 + \mu^2) \left(u_0 - \frac{dX}{dt} \right)^2 c_0^{-2} - \mu^2 - \frac{p}{p_0}.$$

The derivation of these relations requires a deeper analysis of the hydrodynamics of shock waves and will not be discussed here.

The simplest finite-difference approximation to (10.1) is obtained by replacing the derivatives by forward-difference quotients and by taking the values of the coefficients at one of the grid points where the solution has already been computed. More precisely, let P be a grid point with coordinates α, β and assume that the solution of the difference problem is already known at the points P_1: $(\alpha - \Delta\alpha, \beta)$, P_2: $(\alpha, \beta - \Delta\beta)$ in R. Then we replace the first equation in (10.1) by

$$\frac{x(P) - x(P_1)}{\Delta\alpha} = [u(P_1) + c(P_1)] \frac{t(P) - t(P_1)}{\Delta\alpha},$$

and the second by

$$\frac{x(P) - x(P_2)}{\Delta\beta} = [u(P_2) - c(P_2)] \frac{t(P) - t(P_2)}{\Delta\beta}, \qquad \text{etc.}$$

This gives us five simultaneous equations for the values of the five unknown functions at P. Except for the last, these equations are linear. Greater accuracy—although probably not in the order of magnitude—can be achieved if the coefficients $u(P_1)$, etc., are replaced by the averages $[u(P_1) + u(P)]/2$, etc., but this complicates the computations considerably. The equations are then best solved by an iterative process.

Near the shock front the procedure is more complex. Let A_1 be, for instance, the first grid point above the vertex A_0: (α_0, β_0), and denote by Q the point where the line $\beta = \text{const.}$ through A_1 intersects S. (See

Fig. 10.3.) Not only are the solutions of the differential equations unknown at Q but also the position of Q itself has to be determined.

The first and third of the differential equations (10.1) yield difference equations that link the values of the unknown functions at Q with the known values at A_1. To these equations we must add three difference equations obtained by replacing dX/dt by $[x(Q) - x(A_0)]/[t(Q) - t(A_0)]$ in (10.4). The solution of these five equations gives us the five functions to be determined at Q and, therefore, in particular, the position of Q in the (x, t)-plane. The curve S in the (α, β)-plane is not directly obtained in this manner. But, as it is an auxiliary construction without physical relevance, it can be dispensed with.

In this way the differential problem can be approximately solved at the points of a rectangular grid of irregular (and unknown) increments $\Delta\alpha$.

The difference method can be refined by using an adaptation of Adams' method to irregular mesh size, as was mentioned in Sec. 9. See Thomas [1954] for more details.

10.3. Calculation of Shock Fronts by Means of Simulated Viscosity Terms

It was mentioned in Sec. 10.1 that the phenomenon of shock waves is related to the viscosity of the fluid. If the viscosity is taken into consideration, the differential equations of the flow become more complicated (see Courant and Friedrichs [1948], Sec. 63), and, in particular, the *order* of the differential equations is increased. For, while the system (10.1) contains only first partial derivatives, the terms due to viscosity contain second derivatives. It is a well-known fact that the solutions of differential equations in which the highest derivatives are multiplied by a small parameter are apt to change very rapidly in certain regions. If the solutions converge at all, as the parameter goes to zero, these regions become increasingly narrow, and the limit is a discontinuous function. Therefore we may expect that a numerical solution of a viscous flow problem with a small viscosity coefficient will indicate clearly the position and strength of the shocks. However, such a treatment is, in general, not feasible because of the complexity of the differential equations (see, however, Sec. 10.4).

Von Neumann and Richtmyer [1950] have suggested that the same aim can frequently be obtained by inserting a "pseudoviscosity" term into the differential equations of nonviscous flows, i.e., a term of higher order of differentiation that is multiplied by a small parameter, but which is simpler than the true viscosity terms would be. Naturally, this term must be chosen to conform with certain conditions. Von Neumann and Richtmyer illustrate this idea by the example of a one-dimensional shock wave separating two regions of constant state. This is the situation that arises if a piston is pushed at constant velocity into a tube containing a gas at rest (or in uniform motion). This problem is simple enough to permit an analytic treatment (see Courant and Friedrichs [1948], Sec. 69), but the method is also applicable to more complicated situations.

Von Neumann and Richtmyer start from a form of the differential equations which is somewhat different from (10.1). As independent variables they use t and the abscissa ξ of a gas particle at time $t = 0$. (This is the so-called Lagrangian representation.) The dependent variables are the specific volume τ, the flow velocity u, and the pressure p. The system of differential equations then becomes

$$\rho_0 u_t + p_\xi = 0,$$

$$e_t + p\tau_t = 0, \qquad (10.5)$$

$$\rho_0 \tau_t - u_\xi = 0,$$

where ρ_0 is the initial density, and

$$e = \frac{p\tau}{\gamma - 1}$$

for an ideal polytropic gas. As the modified differential system they introduce

$$\rho_0 u_t + (p + q)_\xi = 0,$$

$$e_t + (p + q)\tau_t = 0, \qquad (10.6)$$

$$\rho_0 \tau_t - u_\xi = 0,$$

where the artificial additional pressure term is given by

$$q = \begin{cases} \dfrac{\epsilon^2}{\tau} u_\xi^2, & u_\xi < 0, \qquad \epsilon = \text{a small constant} \\[2mm] 0, & u_\xi > 0. \end{cases}$$

The choice of q is probably not unique. The function q must, of course, have the physical dimension of a pressure and there are other physical considerations which make such a form as the one used here plausible. From the mathematical viewpoint the following conditions are decisive.

1. The equations (10.6) together with the boundary conditions imposed by the physical nature of the problem must possess a continuous solution for all $t > 0$ and all $\xi > 0$ (we assume that the piston moves to the right from the initial position $\xi = 0$).

2. If $\epsilon \to 0$, the solution must approach a state with a jump discontinuity at which the known jump relations prescribed by the physical conservation laws hold.

For the problem under consideration, i.e., a piston moving at constant speed into an infinite tube containing a gas in a constant state, these conditions can be verified by solving system (10.6) for the appropriate boundary conditions explicitly (see von Neumann and Richtmyer [1950]). These authors suggest, however, that the same method is applicable to more general one-dimensional problems. For instance, the initial density ρ_0 may depend on ξ, or the tube may be closed at one end or both.

For the numerical procedure by finite differences they propose a method which yields formally a second-order approximation in the increments h, k. To attain this accuracy without complicating the numerical solution of the difference equations unduly, they use central differences which are skillfully staggered, as explained below.

We observe first that by inserting the explicit expression $e = p\tau/(\gamma - 1)$ into the second of equations (10.6), we can bring it into the form

$$[\gamma p + (\gamma - 1)q]\tau_t + \tau p_t = 0.$$

The basic grid is rectangular with mesh lengths $\Delta\xi = h$, $\Delta t = k$. The use of central differences to approximate first derivatives forces us to introduce also the mid-points of the mesh segments; in other words, we actually operate in a grid of mesh lengths $h/2$, $k/2$. However, the unknown functions will be found only at points of one of the two coarser nets that are obtained from each other by a parallel shift through the vector $(h/2, k/2)$ whose superposition produces the finer net. This makes it necessary to replace the values of most of the coefficients in the differential equation by the averages of their values at the two net points half a mesh length away; otherwise the resulting difference equations would not lend themselves to an explicit computational procedure.

For abbreviation we introduce the notation

$$\mu_\xi f(\xi) = \frac{1}{2}\left[f\left(\xi + \frac{h}{2}\right) + f\left(\xi - \frac{h}{2}\right)\right], \quad \delta_\xi f(\xi) = \frac{1}{h}\left[f\left(\xi + \frac{h}{2}\right) - f\left(\xi - \frac{h}{2}\right)\right].$$

The operators μ_t, δ_t are defined similarly. The proposed finite-difference equations are

$$\rho_0\,\delta_t\,u(\xi, t) + \delta_\xi\,p(\xi, t) + \delta_\xi\,q\left(\xi, t - \frac{k}{2}\right) = 0, \tag{10.7}$$

$$\left[\gamma\mu_t\,p\left(\xi + \frac{h}{2}, t + \frac{k}{2}\right) + (\gamma - 1)\,q\left(\xi + \frac{h}{2}, t + \frac{k}{2}\right)\right]\delta_t\,\tau\left(\xi + \frac{h}{2}, t + \frac{k}{2}\right)$$

$$+ \mu_t\,\tau\left(\xi + \frac{h}{2}, t + \frac{k}{2}\right)\delta_t\,p\left(\xi + \frac{h}{2}, t + \frac{k}{2}\right) = 0, \tag{10.8}$$

$$\rho_0\,\delta_t\,\tau\left(\xi + \frac{h}{2}, t + \frac{k}{2}\right) - \delta_\xi\,u\left(\xi + \frac{h}{2}, t + \frac{k}{2}\right) = 0. \tag{10.9}$$

The artificial viscosity term is given by

$$q\left(\xi + \frac{h}{2}, t + \frac{k}{2}\right) = \frac{\epsilon^2}{\mu_t \tau(\xi + (h/2),\, t + (k/2))}\left[\delta_\xi u\left(\xi + \frac{h}{2}, t + \frac{k}{2}\right)\right]^2,$$

or

$$q\left(\xi + \frac{h}{2}, t + \frac{k}{2}\right) = 0, \tag{10.10}$$

depending on whether $\delta_\xi u(\xi + \frac{1}{2}h, t + \frac{1}{2}k)$ is negative or not. The last three formulas are centered about the point $(\xi + h/2, t + k/2)$, and therefore yield formal approximations of second order in h and k to the corresponding differential equation when expanded about that point. Except for the term in q, equation (10.7) is centered at (ξ, t). Since in the practical applications ϵ is taken to be of the order of magnitude of h, this equation is formally a second-order approximation when expanded about (ξ, t).

To describe the arrangement of the numerical work, let us denote the two coarser grids mentioned above by L_1 and L_2, and suppose that the grid points of L_1 are $\xi = lh$, $t = nk$, so that the points of L_2 are $\xi = (l + \frac{1}{2})h$, $t = (n + \frac{1}{2})k$. The computation will give us successively, for increasing n, the values of u at the points $[lh, (n + \frac{1}{2})k]$; the values of q at $[(l + \frac{1}{2})h, (n + \frac{1}{2})k]$ and those of p and τ at $[(l + \frac{1}{2})h, nk]$, for all positive integers n and l that correspond to points in the region where the differential equations are to be integrated. To see this, let us assume that the calculation has already progressed to the line $n = m$, for all l. Then we can compute u on the line $(m + \frac{1}{2})k$ from (10.7). This done, we find τ on the line $(m + 1)k$ from (10.9). After this, q can be calculated [from (10.10)] on the line $(m + \frac{1}{2})k$, and, finally, p is found on the line $(m + 1)k$, by means of (10.8).

Because of the use of two staggered nets the proper approximation of the boundary conditions may require special care. This point will not be discussed here, but it is given some attention in a similar context in Sec. 17, Chap. 2.

Von Neumann and Richtmyer [1950] make no attempt to discuss the discretization error. There is included, however, a heuristic analysis of the stability of the difference equations. Since we are not operating in the plane of the characteristic variables, we expect to find only conditional stability; i.e., stability will obtain only for certain combinations of the increments h and k. The stability is investigated by studying the growth—or decay—of small errors of sinusoidal form introduced on a line $t = $ const. This technique was already mentioned in Sec. 5.1, and is suitable only for linear differential equations with constant coefficients.

Therefore the first task is to approximate the given system of difference equations by one of this special type, making use of the assumed smallness of the errors.

We must refer to von Neumann and Richtmyer [1950] for the details of this argument, but the following observation is important. As was mentioned before, for small ϵ, we expect the solution of the differential system—and therefore also of the difference system—to approximate a flow with a shock front. In other words, the solutions, although continuous, will contain a narrow interval where the derivatives $\partial\tau/\partial\xi$, $\partial u/\partial\xi$, etc., are increasingly large, as ϵ shrinks to zero. All order-of-magnitude arguments must therefore be modified in this shock layer. (This, incidentally, applies also to the formal order of approximation of the difference equation to the differential equation.) Accordingly, there result two different stability conditions, one valid in the region of steady flow, the other in the shock layer. However, if ϵ is of the order of magnitude of h, say $\epsilon = \alpha h$ (α a constant), then both conditions have the effect of limiting the size of k/h, just as in the problems dealt with previously. By means of a somewhat vague argument, in which the fact that the coefficients of the difference equations are variable is simply ignored, the explicit sufficient stability condition

$$\frac{k}{h} \leq \frac{\rho_0}{2\alpha} \sqrt{\min \frac{\tau}{p}}$$

is obtained.

In the simplest case, when the shock wave separates two constant states, $\min(\tau/p)$ can be found from the known analytic solution of the problem. Experiments carried out on a UNIVAC by Richtmyer with $1.5 < \alpha < 2.0$ indicate that the calculations are stable for such values of h/k. Indeed, even somewhat larger values are permissible.

10.4. Integration of the True Equations of Viscous Flow

Ludford, Polachek, and Seeger [1953] have shown that the true differential equations of viscous flow can be integrated by a finite-difference method which differs somewhat from the one used in von Neumann and Richtmyer [1950]. We report here very briefly the principal ideas of this paper.

The equations of motion of an ideal viscous gas may be written, in terms of u, p, and ρ as dependent variables, as

$$\rho\dot{u} + (p - \sigma)_x = 0, \tag{10.11}$$

$$\dot{\rho} + \rho u_x = 0, \tag{10.12}$$

$$\sigma u_x - \rho T\dot{S} = 0, \tag{10.13}$$

where the temperature T and the entropy S are given by

$$p = c_v(\gamma - 1)\rho T, \qquad S = c_v \log \frac{p}{\rho^\gamma}, \qquad (10.14)$$

and

$$\sigma = \tfrac{4}{3}\mu u_x. \qquad (10.15)$$

The symbol c_v denotes, as usual, the specific heat; μ is the coefficient of viscosity. The dot indicates the rate of change of the quantity below it if we move with a gas particle (Lagrangian viewpoint). Observe that the viscosity term σu_x is linear in u_x, whereas the corresponding term q in Sec. 10.3 is quadratic.

By means of (10.12) and (10.14) the variable ρ can be eliminated from (10.13), changing it into

$$\dot{p} + [\gamma p - (\gamma - 1)\sigma]u_x = 0. \qquad (10.16)$$

For the integration of these differential equations Ludford et al. use "Lagrangian" coordinates; i.e., the independent variables are the initial position ξ of the gas particle and the time t, just as in von Neumann and Richtmyer [1950]. Their dependent variables are x, p, and σ. Now $u_\xi(\xi, t) = u_x(x, t) \, \partial x(\xi, t)/\partial \xi$, $\dot{u} = \ddot{x} = x_{tt}(\xi, t)$, etc., and $\rho x_\xi = \rho_0(\xi)$ is the initial density of the fluid. Hence equations (10.11), (10.16), and (10.15) become, in Lagrangian form,

$$\rho_0 x_{tt} + (p - \sigma)_\xi = 0, \qquad (10.17)$$

$$x_\xi p_t + [\gamma p - (\gamma - 1)\sigma]x_{\xi t} = 0, \qquad (10.18)$$

$$x_\xi \sigma - \tfrac{4}{3}\mu x_{\xi t} = 0. \qquad (10.19)$$

Equation (10.12), which was used in the derivation of (10.16), is no longer needed explicitly.

For the computations it is convenient to eliminate $x_{\xi t}$ from (10.18) by means of (10.19). This yields the equation

$$\frac{4p_t\mu}{3\sigma} p_t + \gamma p - (\gamma - 1)\sigma = 0. \qquad (10.18a)$$

The finite-difference approximations of (10.17), (10.18a), (10.19) used by Ludford, Polachek, and Seeger [1953] are—with the abbreviations introduced in Sec. 10.3—essentially as follows:

$$\rho_0 \, \delta_t^2 \, x(\xi, t) + \delta_\xi[p(\xi, t) - \sigma(\xi, t)] = 0, \qquad (10.20)$$

$$\frac{4\mu}{3\sigma} \delta_t \, p\left(\xi + \frac{h}{2}, t + \frac{k}{2}\right) + \left[\gamma\mu_t \, p\left(\xi + \frac{h}{2}, t + \frac{k}{2}\right)\right.$$

$$\left. - (\gamma - 1) \, \sigma\left(\xi + \frac{h}{2}, t + \frac{k}{2}\right)\right] = 0, \quad (10.21)$$

$$\sigma\left(\xi + \frac{h}{2}, t + \frac{k}{2}\right) \delta_\xi \mu_t \, x\left(\xi + \frac{h}{2}, t + \frac{k}{2}\right)$$

$$- \frac{4\mu}{3} \delta_\xi \, \delta_t \, x\left(\xi + \frac{h}{2}, t + \frac{k}{2}\right) = 0. \quad (10.22)$$

These equations differ superficially from those found in Ludford, Polachek, and Seeger [1953]. There the variables are first multiplied by suitable constants to simplify the computations.

The system (10.20), (10.21), (10.22) cannot be solved explicitly, since σ occurs at the points $(\xi \pm \frac{1}{2}h, t)$ in the first equation, and at the points $(\xi + \frac{1}{2}h, t + \frac{1}{2}k)$ in the other two. It is therefore necessary to solve these equations at every t-level by an iterative method. We must refer to Ludford, Polachek, and Seeger [1953] for a description of the finite-difference treatment of the boundary conditions. The stability of the difference equations, according to an analysis that resembles that given in von Neumann and Richtmyer [1950], is subject to the same restriction as the method of that earlier paper.

Ludford, Polachek, and Seeger [1953] emphasize another condition on the mesh lengths: If h is larger than the thickness of the shock layer, it cannot be expected that the finite-difference solutions will be good approximations beyond the shock front. Rather than to employ an inconveniently fine grid, the authors carried out their calculations with an unrealistically high viscosity coefficient μ. It is very likely that the results outside the shock front are little affected by this change.

The article by Ludford, Polachek, and Seeger [1953] contains a successful treatment of the following two problems by this method: (1) Flow of a gas in a stationary closed tube for initially constant values of velocity, pressure, and density; (2) flow in a stationary closed tube when the initial velocity is zero, and when a membrane which separates two gases of the same density but at different pressures is removed at time $t = 0$.

10.5. The Difference Method of Lax

An interesting, quite different, method was developed by Lax [1954]. He starts from the observation that the quasilinear systems of fluid dynamics in one space dimension all enjoy a certain special feature, which stems from the fact that they express the conservation of physical quantities such as mass, momentum, and energy. Any quasilinear hyperbolic system of differential equations of the form (6.10) can be written, after multiplication by A^{-1} and an obvious change of notation, in the form

$$w_t + Gw_x + b = 0, \tag{10.23}$$

where w is a column vector, G is a square matrix, and b a vector depending on x, t, and w. The systems (10.23) occurring in hydrodynamics can generally be brought into the special form

$$w_t + F_x + b = 0, \tag{10.24}$$

where $F = F(x, t, w)$, and w is to be treated as a function of x in the indicated differentiation of F. Such differential equations are called by Lax *conservation laws*.

The equations (6.14) of isentropic flow, for example, can be written in the form

$$\rho_t + (u\rho)_x = 0, \qquad u_t + \left(\frac{u^2}{2} + i\right)_x = 0,$$

where

$$i = i(\rho) = \int \frac{c^2(\rho)}{\rho} \, d\rho.$$

The differential equations of nonisentropic flow of an ideal gas may serve as another example. If ρ, $m = \rho u$, and E, the total specific energy per unit volume, are used as dependent variables, they can be brought into the form

$$\rho_t + m_x = 0,$$

$$m_t + \left[(\gamma - 1)E + \frac{3 - \gamma}{2}\frac{m^2}{\rho}\right]_x = 0, \tag{10.25}$$

$$E_t + \left(\gamma \frac{m}{\rho} E - \frac{\gamma - 1}{2}\frac{m^3}{\rho^2}\right)_x = 0.$$

Lax discovered that, if the differential equations are conservation laws and if the differentiations are replaced by finite-difference operations according to the scheme

$$f_x(x, t) \rightarrow \frac{1}{2h}[f(x + h, t) - f(x - h, t)], \tag{10.26}$$

$$f_t(x, t) \rightarrow \frac{1}{2k}\left[f(x, t + k) - \frac{f(x + h, t) + f(x - h, t)}{2}\right], \tag{10.27}$$

a system of finite-difference equations is obtained whose solutions approximate the physical solution of the differential problem, including the shock-wave jump with the correct jump sizes, in the *whole* region of the flow and not only on one side of the shock front. In other words, the solution will change very rapidly in certain narrow subregions, so as to be there almost discontinuous.

The introduction of the mean value of f in (10.27) is necessary if instability is to be avoided. Even with the more complicated formula (10.27), the difference equations can be stable for certain mesh ratios k/h only. We shall not enter upon a discussion of the theory underlying this method. It is as yet incomplete, and the arguments are largely heuristic.

Instead, we reproduce the numerical results obtained by Lax [1954] in one of the several exploratory calculations reported in that paper. Rather than imposing continuous initial conditions and continuing the solution until after a shock has formed, Lax supposes that at the time $t = 0$ there already exists a shock front. More particularly, he assumes that the initial values of the velocity, pressure, and density are piecewise constant, having one set of values (u_i, p_i, ρ_i) for negative values of x and another, (u_f, p_f, ρ_f), for positive x. Let, for instance,

$$u_i = 1, \qquad p_i = 50, \qquad \rho_i = 50,$$

$$u_f = 0, \qquad p_f = 0, \qquad \rho_f = 10,$$

$$\gamma = 1.5,$$

$$\frac{k}{h} = 0.25.$$

With the help of the jump conditions, we can solve equations (10.25) analytically for these initial conditions. From the existence-and-uniqueness theory for continuously differentiable solutions, it follows immediately that there must exist a region of the (x, t)-plane above the negative x-axis where the solution is $u = u_i, p = p_i, \rho = \rho_i$, and a region above the positive x-axis where $u = u_f, p = p_f, \rho = \rho_f$. But for a complete solution the jump conditions are needed. It can be shown analytically that the solution has the following structure:

Constant state (i), for $x/t < -0.225$;
rarefaction wave, for $-0.225 < x/t < 1.47$;
constant state (s), for $1.47 < x/t < 1.84$;
constant state (f), for $1.84 < x/t$.

The symbols (i) and (f) refer to the states characterized by the values (u_i, p_i, ρ_i) and (u_f, p_f, ρ_f) respectively. The state (s) is given by $u_s = 1.47$,

$p_s = 27.1$, $\rho_s = 50$. For the concept of rarefaction wave see, for example, Courant and Friedrichs [1948], Chap. 3, B. The line $x/t = 1.84$ is therefore a discontinuity of the solution, i.e., a shock front. The rays bounding the sector of nonconstant flow are characteristics. The solutions are there continuous, but not continuously differentiable.

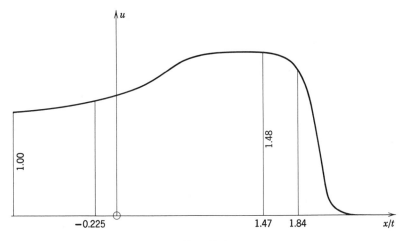

FIG. 10.4.

It can furthermore be shown that the solution of the problem is a function of x/t. In Fig. 10.4 the value of u obtained in one of the computations described in Lax [1954] is plotted against x/t. The curve was obtained by calculating 99 time steps. Qualitatively the four different regions of the flow are recognizable. The speed $u_s = 1.48$ behind the shock, in the region where u is almost constant, agrees quite well with the correct value 1.47. The values of x/t corresponding to the separations between the four regions are, however, only vaguely defined. A smaller value of k, or, what is the same in this example, more time steps, are indicated if these quantities are to be determined with reasonable accuracy.

2

PARABOLIC EQUATIONS

SECTION 11. THE SIMPLEST HEAT FLOW PROBLEM

11.1. Preliminary Remarks

The simplest initial-value problem of parabolic type is probably that of determining a function $u(x, t)$ such that

$$u_t = u_{xx} \quad (t > 0), \qquad u(x, 0) = f(x) \qquad (-\infty < x < \infty). \quad (11.1)$$

Its physical interpretation in terms of heat flow was briefly mentioned in Sec. 1.

The concept of characteristics defined in Sec. 6.1 does not apply here in the strict sense. This can be seen by replacing (11.1) by the equivalent problem

$$u_x - v = 0, \qquad v_x - u_t = 0,$$

$$u(x, 0) = f(x), \qquad v(x, 0) = f'(x).$$

In the notation of Sec. 6, this system of differential equations is of the form (6.2) with

$$A = \begin{bmatrix} 1 & 0 \\ 0 & 1 \end{bmatrix}, \qquad B = \begin{bmatrix} 0 & 0 \\ -1 & 0 \end{bmatrix}, \qquad d = \begin{bmatrix} -v \\ 0 \end{bmatrix}.$$

The equation for the characteristic directions $\lambda = c^v$,

$$\det (A - \lambda B) = 0,$$

becomes

$$\begin{vmatrix} 1 & 0 \\ \lambda & 1 \end{vmatrix} = 0,$$

which has no solution.

Nevertheless, one frequently hears the statement that the differential equation $u_t = u_{xx}$ has the lines $t = \text{const.}$ as characteristics. One of several ways of justifying this assertion is to regard $u_t = u_{xx}$ as the limit of a hyperbolic equation, say of

$$u_{xx} - \epsilon^2 u_{tt} = u_t,$$

as ϵ tends to zero. For the corresponding system

$$u_x - \epsilon^2 v_t - v = 0,$$
$$v_x - u_t = 0,$$

the equation

$$\det (A - \lambda B) \equiv 1 - \lambda^2 \epsilon^2 = 0,$$

yields the characteristic directions $dx/dt = \pm 1/\epsilon$.

Hence both families of characteristics approach the lines $t = \text{const.}$, as $\epsilon \to 0$. We therefore expect that the solution of problem (11.1) will depend on the full extent of the initial function and not only on a finite segment of dependence. This fact in turn implies that we must expect the stability problem for approximating difference equations to be much more burdensome than for hyperbolic equations.

11.2. Solution of the Initial-Value Problem

If the interval of dependence for problem (11.1) is the whole x-axis, we cannot hope to solve (11.1) by means of Fourier series, as we solved the simplest wave equation. The analogous tool in the present situation is the theory of the Fourier *integral*.

A convenient form of the main theorem on Fourier integrals is the following: Let $f(x)$ be piecewise continuous and have a piecewise continuous derivative (i.e., the function and its derivative are continuous except possibly for a finite number of jump discontinuities in every finite interval), and assume that $\int_{-\infty}^{\infty} |f(x)|\, dx$ is finite. Then $f(x)$ can be represented as the integral

$$f(x) = \int_{-\infty}^{\infty} e^{isx}\, \phi(s)\, ds, \tag{11.2}$$

with

$$\phi(s) = \frac{1}{2\pi} \int_{-\infty}^{\infty} e^{-is\xi} f(\xi)\, d\xi. \tag{11.3}$$

(See Courant and Hilbert [1953], p. 77, for a proof.) The conditions on $f(x)$ can be considerably weakened (see Courant and Hilbert [1937], Chap. 10), but the version given here suffices for our purposes.

The complex notation used in (11.2) and (11.3) simplifies the calculations, but is not essential. Since $f(x)$ is by assumption real, we obtain the entirely real representation

$$f(x) = \frac{1}{2\pi} \int_{-\infty}^{\infty} ds \int_{-\infty}^{\infty} f(\xi) \cos \left[s(x - \xi) \right] d\xi$$

by inserting (11.3) into (11.2) and making use of the fact that $f(x) = \frac{1}{2}[f(x) + \overline{f(x)}]$. However, we prefer to operate with the complex formulas, which resemble in structure more closely the Fourier series formulas from which they can be formally derived by letting the period of the periodic function to be represented tend to infinity (see Courant and Hilbert [1953], p. 78). Equality (11.2) is the analog of the Fourier series: $\phi(s)$ corresponds to the Fourier coefficients, and (11.3) gives these "coefficients" in terms of the function to be represented.

On the basis of these analogies it is clear how we have to proceed if we wish to solve (11.1) by means of (11.2) and (11.3). Let $f(x)$ be the function occurring in (11.1). Then we must first solve $u_t - u_{xx} = 0$ for the initial values e^{isx}. By tentatively inserting $e^{isx} \psi(t)$ for u into the differential equation, we find for $\psi(t)$ the differential equation

$$\psi'(t) + s^2 \psi(t) = 0.$$

Hence $e^{isx} e^{-s^2 t}$ is the solution of $u_t - u_{xx} = 0$ that reduces to e^{isx} for $t = 0$. The integral

$$u(x, t) = \int_{-\infty}^{\infty} e^{isx - s^2 t} \phi(s) \, ds, \tag{11.4}$$

where $\phi(s)$ is defined by (11.3), is then a solution of the differential equation, provided it is legitimate to differentiate inside the integral sign, once with respect to t, and twice with respect to x. Also, the integral reduces to $f(x)$, as t tends to zero.

If we ignore questions about the validity of formal operations with improper integrals, we can simplify (11.4) by inserting $\phi(s)$ from (11.3) into it and by interchanging the order of the integrations. Then we find that

$$u(x, t) = \frac{1}{2\pi} \int_{-\infty}^{\infty} \left(\int_{-\infty}^{\infty} e^{is(x - \xi) - s^2 t} \, ds \right) f(\xi) \, d\xi.$$

The inner integral can be calculated by completing the square with respect to s in the exponent. The value of the inner integral is then seen to be

$$\sqrt{\frac{\pi}{t}} \, e^{-(x - \xi)^2/(4t)}.$$

Hence

$$u(x, t) = \frac{1}{2\sqrt{\pi t}} \int_{-\infty}^{\infty} e^{-(x-\xi)^2/(4t)} f(\xi) \, d\xi. \tag{11.5}$$

It is easier to prove directly that this integral may be differentiated under the integral sign and that $u(x, t) \to f(x)$, as $t \to 0$, than to justify the interchanges of limits that led to it. We omit these simple arguments (see Carslaw and Jaeger [1947], p. 34). The function $(4\pi t)^{-1/2} e^{-(x-\xi)^2/(4t)}$ is itself a solution of the heat equation, and hence formula (11.5) solves our initial-value problem.

The particular solution

$$\frac{1}{2\sqrt{\pi t}} e^{-(x-\xi)^2/(4t)} \tag{11.6}$$

is often called the *fundamental solution* of problem (11.1). It can be interpreted as the probability density of a random variable ξ that is normally distributed with mean x and standard deviation $\sqrt{2t}$. This interpretation is by no means artificial. The flow of heat is governed by the same law as the diffusion of molecules in a solution. The equation $u_t = u_{xx}$ and similar parabolic equations are frequently called the differential equations of diffusion. In fact, heat flow can be regarded as the diffusion of kinetic energy. Now, diffusion processes are the result of the motions of very large numbers of particles which can be adequately described by assuming that each particle moves at random according to some probability law. The actual motion of an elementary particle is then a *random walk*, i.e., a sequence of rectilinear motions with abrupt changes of direction at each collision which are governed by certain probability laws. In our present example we are dealing with one-dimensional flow, and hence there are only two possible directions. In the theory of stochastic processes (Khintchine [1933], p. 16; Chandrasekhar [1943]) it is proved rigorously that, under fairly mild conditions on the nature of this random walk, the probability distribution of the position at time t for a particle known to have started from $\xi = x$ at time $t = 0$ is precisely given by (11.6), provided the time scale is chosen appropriately. Conversely, (11.6) is also the probability density that a particle known to be at ξ at time t was at x at time $t = 0$. The function $u(x, t)$ of (11.5) is the expected value of $f(\xi)$ with respect to the probability distribution (11.6); i.e., it is the temperature (or specific kinetic energy) to be expected statistically at x at the time t if the initial temperature at $t = 0$ is given by $f(\xi)$.

From this interpretation or directly from (11.5), if we prefer, there follows immediately the following extreme value principle for the solution $u(x, t)$ of problem (11.1): *If* $m \leq f(x) \leq M$ *in* $-\infty < x < \infty$, *then* $m \leq u(x, t) \leq M$.

SECTION 12.   THE SIMPLEST FINITE-DIFFERENCE
APPROXIMATION

12.1. The Stability Condition

The most natural finite-difference problem for the approximation of
the differential problem (11.1) is

$$\frac{U(x, t+k) - U(x, t)}{k} - \frac{U(x+h, t) - 2U(x, t) + U(x-h, t)}{h^2} = 0, \quad (12.1)$$

$$U(x, 0) = f(x).$$

If we set

$$\lambda = \frac{k}{h^2}, \quad (12.2)$$

the difference equation can be written

$$U(x, t+k) = \lambda U(x+h, t) + (1 - 2\lambda) U(x, t) + \lambda U(x-h, t). \quad (12.3)$$

Starting with the initial values $U(x, 0) = f(x)$, the values of U at the
grid points on $t = k, 2k, \cdots$ can be successively calculated from (12.3).
If

$$\lambda \leq \tfrac{1}{2}, \quad (12.4)$$

the right member of (12.3) is a weighted average of $U(x, t)$ with nonnegative weight factors. It follows that $U(x, t)$, just like $u(x, t)$, satisfies
at all grid points the inequalities

$$m \leq U(x, t) \leq M \quad \text{if} \quad \lambda \leq \tfrac{1}{2}, \quad (12.5)$$

provided $m \leq f(x) \leq M$.

This extreme-value principle ensures the stability of the difference
equation, if $\lambda \leq \tfrac{1}{2}$. For the departure due to round-off errors on the
initial line satisfies the difference equation. Hence the maximum departure
cannot increase numerically with t without contradicting (12.5). The
cumulative departure due to round-off errors at all lines is then $O(\delta h^{-1})$,
where δ is the least upper bound of the single round-off errors. According
to our definition of stability in Sec. 5.1, this is a stable behavior.

If $\lambda > \tfrac{1}{2}$, the preceding argument does not hold any more. In fact,
the difference equation is then unstable. The proof can be given by the
same kind of reasoning as in Sec. 4.6.

Let

$$U(x, 0) = \begin{cases} \epsilon, & x = 0 \\ 0, & x \neq 0. \end{cases}$$

Then the solution of (12.1) corresponding to these initial values represents the departure due to a single error of size ϵ at $x = 0$. If $\lambda > \frac{1}{2}$, we prove by induction that the sign of $U(x, t)$ in the grid alternates; i.e., if $U(x, t)$ is different from zero at two adjacent grid points, then it has opposite signs there.

This statement is immediately verified for $t = 0$ and $t = k$. Assume now that it has already been proved for all grid points below and on the level t, and consider a grid point (x, t) at which $U(x, t) \geq 0$. Then the right member of (12.3) is nonpositive; i.e., $U(x, t + k) \leq 0$. The argument is analogous when $U(x, t) \leq 0$. This completes the induction.

By virtue of the alternating sign of $U(x, t)$, the relation (12.3) implies that

$$|U(x, t + k)| = \lambda|U(x + h, t)| + \lambda|U(x - h, t)| + (2\lambda - 1)|U(x, t)|. \quad (12.6)$$

Let

$$S(t) = \sum_x |U(x, t)|,$$

where the sum is extended over all grid points at the level t. Since at most $2t/k + 1$ of these terms are different from zero, $S(t)$ is finite. By (12.6) we have

$$S(t + k) = (4\lambda - 1) S(t) = (4\lambda - 1)^{(t/k)+1}\epsilon.$$

On the other hand, there must be at least one grid point (x_0, t) on the level t at which

$$|U(x_0, t)| \geq \left(2\frac{t}{k} + 1\right)^{-1} S(t).$$

Therefore

$$|U(x_0, t)| \geq \left(2\frac{t}{k} + 1\right)^{-1} (4\lambda - 1)^{t/k}\epsilon.$$

The right member grows exponentially as $k \to 0$, because $4\lambda - 1 > 1$. In other words, the difference equation (12.1) is unstable for $\lambda > \frac{1}{2}$.

The conclusion that $\lambda > \frac{1}{2}$ means instability is frequently reached in the literature by a plausibility argument based on the behavior of the solution $U(x, t)$ of (12.1) corresponding to the initial function $f(x) = e^{isx}$, s arbitrary [or $f(x) = \sin sx$, if one prefers to deal with real quantities only]. By inserting

$$U(x, t) = e^{isx} \psi(t)$$

into the difference equation (12.1), the equation

$$\psi(t + k) - \psi(t) = 2\lambda \psi(t)(\cos sh - 1)$$

or

$$\psi(t + k) = \left(1 - 4\lambda \sin^2 \frac{sh}{2}\right) \psi(t)$$

for $\psi(t)$ is obtained. Since we must also have $\psi(0) = 1$, it follows that

$$\psi(t) = \left(1 - 4\lambda \sin^2 \frac{sh}{2}\right)^{t/(h^2\lambda)}.$$

It is easy to show (we omit the proof) that the resulting solution

$$U(x, t) = e^{isx}\left(1 - 4\lambda \sin^2 \frac{sh}{2}\right)^{t/(h^2\lambda)} \tag{12.7}$$

of (12.1) converges to the solution

$$u(x, t) = e^{isx - s^2 t} \tag{12.8}$$

of the corresponding differential problem (Sec. 11.2), as $h \to 0$. This is true for *all* $\lambda > 0$, and for all fixed values of x. But when $\lambda > \frac{1}{2}$, there exist values of h, for instance $h = \pi/s$, for which $|1 - 4\lambda \sin^2 (sh/2)| > 1$. For such values of h, the solution $U(x, t)$ grows exponentially with t. If s is large, $h = \pi/s$ is small, and the growth of $U(x, t)$ with t is exceedingly rapid. For such values of h and s the function (12.7) is in no way an approximation to (12.8). If we now consider initial functions $f(x)$ which are representable by an infinite Fourier integral or Fourier series, the solution $U(x, t)$ of (12.1) is the sum (or perhaps an integral) of infinitely many terms of the form (12.7) with different values of s. No matter how h is chosen, there will be values of s for which the corresponding Fourier component in the solution shows the rapid exponential growth with t, thus destroying the stability of the differential equation.

On the other hand, if $\lambda \leq \frac{1}{2}$, the solution (12.7) remains uniformly bounded for all h, and this makes it plausible that the solution of the difference equation corresponding to any initial function representable by a convergent Fourier series or integral is similarly bounded. From this one infers stability for $\lambda \leq \frac{1}{2}$.

This reasoning is very convincing, and it has the advantage that it can be very easily adapted to almost any linear difference equation with constant coefficients, but it is not so easy to convert it into a complete proof. One method for doing this is contained in John [1952] and will be used in Secs. 14 and 15 to study the stability or instability of various difference equations.

For equations with constant coefficients and periodic initial conditions, a very general version of this approach has been given by Lax and Richtmyer [1956] (see Sec. 29).

The condition $\lambda \leq \frac{1}{2}$ ensures that the interval of dependence on the

x-axis, corresponding to a point (x, t), expands into the domain of dependence for the differential problem, viz., the whole x-axis, as $h \to 0$, but the condition cannot be derived from this requirement, which is fulfilled as long as $\lim_{h \to 0} k/h = 0$.

12.2. The Convergence and the Discretization Error

The convergence of $U(x, t)$ to $u(x, t)$ could be investigated by the method of Fourier analysis employed previously for the simple wave equation. To carry this out, one would first have to prove the formula

$$U(x, t) = \int_{-\infty}^{\infty} e^{isx} \left(1 - 4\lambda \sin^2 \frac{sh}{2}\right)^{t/(h^2\lambda)} \phi(s) \, ds \qquad (12.9)$$

for the solution of problem (12.1), where $\phi(s)$ is defined by equation (11.3). The representation (12.9) is the discrete analog of (11.4), obtained by superposition of particular solutions of the form (12.7). Then one would let h tend to zero inside the integral sign in (12.9), an interchange of limits which can be justified if $\lambda \leq \frac{1}{2}$ and if $f(x)$ is sufficiently regular. This passage to the limit changes (12.9) into the corresponding integral (11.4) for the solution $u(x, t)$ of the continuous problem.

Rather than carry out the details of this program, we shall apply the method explained in Sec. 7.2 to the study of the convergence of U to u. Let us first assume that, for $0 \leq t \leq T$, $-\infty < x < \infty$, u possesses continuous bounded partial derivatives up to order three with respect to t and up to order six with respect to x. Since $u_t = u_{xx}$, these two conditions are identical for the present simple differential equation. In fact, many of the formulas below can and will be simplified by substituting u_{xx} for u_t. This is no longer possible for other simple differential equations that could be treated by the same argument. Let $(1/k) L_h(U)$ denote the left member of (12.1). The factor $1/k$ is extracted in this definition to simplify the notation of later sections. Then we find by means of Taylor's formula and because $u_t - u_{xx} = 0$ that

$$\frac{1}{k} L_h(u) \equiv \frac{k}{2} u_{tt} - \frac{h^2}{12} u_{xxxx} + O(k^2) + O(h^4). \qquad (12.10)$$

Subtracting this from $(1/k) L_h(U) = 0$, we see that the discretization error $v = U - u$ solves the difference equation problem

$$\frac{1}{k} L_h(v) = \omega(x, t), \qquad v(x, 0) = 0, \qquad (12.11)$$

where

$$\omega(x, t) = -\frac{k}{2} u_{tt} + \frac{h^2}{12} u_{xxxx} + O(k^2) + O(h^4). \qquad (12.12)$$

The difference equation in (12.11) can be written

$$v(x, t + k) = \lambda v(x + h, t) + (1 - 2\lambda) v(x, t) + \lambda v(x - h, t) + k \omega(x, t).$$
(12.13)

If $m(t)$ denotes an upper bound for $|v(x, \tau)|$ for $0 \leq \tau \leq t$, $-\infty < x < \infty$, and if $\mu(t)$ is a similar bound for $|\omega(x, t)|$, equation (12.13) is seen to imply, for $\lambda \leq \frac{1}{2}$, the inequality

$$m(t + k) \leq m(t) + k\mu(t), \qquad t = 0, k, 2k, \cdots.$$

Since $m(0) = 0$, and since $\mu(t)$ is a nondecreasing function of t, it follows by induction that

$$m(t) \leq t \, \mu(t),$$

and therefore

$$|v(x, t)| \leq t \, \mu(t).$$
(12.14)

This bound for the discretization error can be used, no matter what the form of $\omega(x, t)$. On the basis of (12.12) we can conclude that *the discretization error is strictly $O(h^2)$ under the assumptions made, except for $\lambda = \frac{1}{6}$, when the error is $O(h^4)$.* This proves, *a fortiori*, the convergence of U to u.

The form (12.12) for $\omega(x, t)$ was chosen here because it exhibits the special advantage of the value $\lambda = \frac{1}{6}$. However, such exceptionally favorable net ratios exist only for a few types of parabolic difference equations that possess high symmetry and constant coefficients. Moreover, the benefit of this special choice of λ does not necessarily extend to the round-off errors. It is true that the departure due to round-off satisfies an equation of the form (12.11), but $\omega(x, t)$ does not have the form (12.12) then, because the round-off errors cannot be regarded as the values at the grid points of a smooth function independent of h and k. By means of our analysis of the round-off errors in Sec. 5, or, if we prefer, independently by the methods of this section, it is readily seen that the round-off errors must be $O(h^6)$ if the departure caused by them is to be of the same order as the discretization error when $\lambda = \frac{1}{6}$. This puts a rather heavy burden on the precision of the computations.

The hypothesis that u possesses continuous derivatives of rather high order, which underlies the formula (12.10), will be satisfied only if $f(x)$ is a very smooth function. If we are not interested in the special case $\lambda = \frac{1}{6}$, it suffices to assume only the continuity and boundedness of u_{tt} and u_{xxxx} and to replace the expression (12.12) for $\omega(x, t)$ by

$$\omega(x, t) = -\frac{k}{2} \tilde{u}_{tt} + \frac{h^2}{12} \tilde{u}_{xxxx},$$
(12.15)

where the tilde indicates that the derivatives are to be taken at certain points in the domain R defined by $0 \leq t \leq T$, $-\infty < x < \infty$. This expression is derived by expanding u in $L_h(u)$ with respect to k and h, up to terms of order k and h^2. In this manner we obtain from (12.14) the inequality

$$|v(x, t)| \leq t\left(M_2 \frac{k}{2} + N_4 \frac{h^2}{12}\right), \qquad (12.16)$$

where M_2 is the least upper bound of $|u_{tt}|$ in R, and N_4, the least upper bound of $|u_{xxxx}|$ in R. In John [1952], Sec. 6.1, a sufficient (but probably not necessary) condition for the continuity and boundedness of u_{tt} and u_{xxxx} is shown to be that $f(x)$ possesses bounded and continuous derivatives up to order six.

The strong regularity assumptions used in the derivation of (12.16) can be relaxed if we wish to prove only that $\lim_{h \to 0} v(x, t) = 0$. It suffices to know that the derivatives u_t, u_{xx} are uniformly continuous and bounded in $0 \leq t \leq T$, $-\infty < x < \infty$. In fact, by means of Taylor's formula we then obtain, instead of (12.10), the relation

$$\frac{1}{k} L_h(u) = u_t(x, t + \theta_1 k) - u_{xx}(x + \theta_2 h, t) = \gamma(x, t, h),$$

where θ_1 and $|\theta_2|$ lie between 0 and 1, and $\lim_{h \to 0} \gamma(x, t, h) = 0$. The argument which led to the appraisal (12.16) before now shows that $\lim_{h \to 0} v = 0$, but it does not yield an appraisal for v.

The explicit bound on the discretization error given in (12.16) suffers from the same disadvantage as similar appraisals met previously: it depends on the derivatives of the unknown solution $u(x, t)$ of the differential problem itself.

For certain problems of parabolic type, including the one under discussion, it is possible to transform (12.16) into an appraisal in terms of the data alone. This transformation is based on the fact that the partial derivatives of u also solve a parabolic differential equation, in the present instance even the same as u itself. Furthermore, by virtue of the differential equation $u_t = u_{xx}$, we have

$$u_{tt} = u_{xxt} = u_{txx} = u_{xxxx}.$$

Now, since u_{xxxx} is by assumption continuous in R, it is the solution of our differential equation corresponding to the initial value $f^{(4)}(x)$. Since the solutions of this differential equation do not exceed their initial values in magnitude, (12.16) can be converted into

$$|U(x, t) - u(x, t)| \leq t\left(\frac{\lambda}{2} + \frac{1}{12}\right)h^2 \text{ l.u.b.} \quad |f^{(4)}(x)| \qquad (12.17)$$
$$-\infty < x < \infty$$

(l.u.b. means "least upper bound" here), which is as explicit a global appraisal as can be desired when $f^{(4)}(x)$ is bounded.

However, the degree of smoothness required of $f(x)$ in this argument is not warranted by the physical origin of the differential problem. Take, for instance, an infinite insulated rod whose temperature at time $t = 0$ is $u = 0$ except for an interval of length 2, where it is equal to unity, in the units of measurement chosen. It is physically perfectly legitimate to ask for the distribution of the temperature in the rod at time t, and it is not difficult to show that

$$u(x, t) = \frac{1}{2\sqrt{\pi t}} \int_{-1}^{1} e^{-(x-\xi)^2/(4t)} \, d\xi$$

is the solution of this problem. The question as to the discretization error of the finite-difference method for such a simple problem does not seem to have been studied in the literature. For the closely related problem of a rod of finite length whose ends are kept at constant temperature, it has however been examined in great detail in Juncosa and Young [1953], and the method of proof as well as the results can probably be carried over to the present case without serious difficulty. If $f(x)$ is a step function, the discretization error turns out to be $O(h^2)$ except in the immediate neighborhood of the initial line, provided h tends to zero in such a way that the jump discontinuities of $f(x)$ are grid points for all h.

Unfortunately, results of this sort have so far been obtained only for very simple differential equations that can be solved by the methods of Fourier analysis. The present situation—not only with respect to parabolic equations but also to hyperbolic and elliptic ones—may be roughly summarized as follows: (1) It can be proved, with a generality amply sufficient for computational purposes, that the discretization error $v(x, t)$ tends to zero with the mesh length, but only by methods which do not yield appraisals of $|v|$. (2) If the solution u of the differential problem is very smooth in the interior *and on the boundary* of the region under consideration, then appraisals of $|v|$ in terms of u and its derivatives can be found by various methods. (3) In certain, all too few, cases these bounds are even expressible in terms of the data alone.

SECTION 13.　LINEAR PROBLEMS IN A FINITE INTERVAL

13.1.　Differential Problems

More realistic, in the physical sense, than the problem (11.1) are parabolic problems in which the differential equation is to be satisfied in a finite interval only—for example, heat flow in a rod of finite length.

The following is a typical problem of that sort:

$$u_t = u_{xx} \quad \text{for} \quad a < x < b, \quad t > 0,$$
$$u(x, 0) = f(x), \quad u(a, t) = g(t), \quad u(b, t) = h(t). \tag{13.1}$$

Observe that in order to deal with a well-posed problem we now have to prescribe boundary conditions at $x = a$, $x = b$ for $t > 0$, in addition to the initial condition at $t = 0$. Many other problems of this kind have been studied (Churchill [1941] and Carslaw and Jaeger [1947]). We again choose (13.1) for a more detailed discussion, not for its own sake but as an illustrative example.

In general, $f(a)$ is not given as equal to $g(0)$ and, similarly, $f(b) \neq h(0)$. The requirement that $u(x, t)$ assume the boundary values is understood to mean that

$$\lim_{t \to 0} u(x, t) = f(x) \quad \text{for constant } x \text{ in } a < x < b,$$

$$\lim_{x \to a} u(x, t) = g(t) \quad \text{for constant } t > 0, \text{ and for } x > a,$$

$$\lim_{x \to b} u(x, t) = h(t) \quad \text{for constant } t > 0, \text{ and for } x < b.$$

The corners $(a, 0)$, $(b, 0)$ are therefore, in general, discontinuities of the function $u(x, t)$, and this is a cause of new difficulties in such combined boundary- and initial-value problems.

Problem (13.1) can be solved explicitly by means of Fourier series. In the case that $g(x) \equiv 0$, $h(x) \equiv 0$, the argument is almost the same as that for the wave equation in Sec. 4.3. Without loss of generality we assume that $a = 0$, $b = \pi$. Under suitable regularity assumptions $f(x)$ can be expanded into a convergent Fourier sine series

$$f(x) = \sum_{r=1}^{\infty} a_r \sin rx.$$

The product $\sin rx \, \psi(t)$ is a solution of the differential equation which reduces to $\sin rx$ for $t = 0$ if

$$\psi'(t) = -r^2 \psi(t), \quad \psi(0) = 1.$$

Hence the series

$$u(x, t) = \sum_{r=1}^{\infty} a_r e^{-r^2 t} \sin rx \tag{13.2}$$

is a solution if it converges and if termwise differentiation, once with respect to t and twice with respect to x, is permissible. That this is the case follows readily from standard theorems, thanks to the presence of the factor $e^{-r^2 t}$ (see, e.g., Carslaw and Jaeger [1947], p. 77). When $t > 0$ this factor causes the series to be *uniformly* convergent in the *closed* interval $0 \leq x \leq \pi$, so that $u(x, t)$ is a continuous function of x at $x = 0$ and $x = \pi$. Therefore the boundary conditions are satisfied.

The passage to the limit, as $t \to +0$ in (13.2), may also be performed termwise. This is obvious if $\Sigma_{r=1}^{\infty} |a_r|$ converges. For (13.2) is then a uniformly convergent series. But $\Sigma_{r=1}^{\infty} |a_r|$ is in general infinite, unless $f(0) = f(\pi) = 0$, since only then is the function that is represented by $\Sigma_{r=1}^{\infty} a_r \sin rx$ continuous beyond the interval $0 < x < \pi$. If the Fourier series is only conditionally convergent, one must refer instead to a somewhat stronger theorem on series (Abel's theorem; see Carslaw [1930], Sec. 73 and Carslaw and Jaeger [1947], Sec. 34).

13.2. A Finite-Difference Approximation

The reasoning of Sec. 12.1 carries over to problems in finite intervals almost without any change. The finite-difference method is again stable for $\lambda \leq \frac{1}{2}$. The maximum-minimum principle (12.5) remains valid if m and M are replaced by

$$m(t) = \min_{\substack{a \leq x \leq b \\ 0 \leq \tau \leq t}} \left[f(x), g(\tau), h(\tau) \right],$$

$$M(t) = \max_{\substack{a \leq x \leq b \\ 0 \leq \tau \leq t}} \left[f(x), g(\tau), h(\tau) \right].$$

There is a slight modification in the argument that establishes instability for $\lambda > \frac{1}{2}$. The departure caused by a single error at a grid point in the interval $a < x < b$, $t = 0$, is a solution of (12.3) for all grid points in $a < x < b, t > 0$. It is characterized by the boundary values $g(t) = h(t) = 0$, and the initial value is zero except for one point, where it is equal to ϵ. This time the summation in the definition of $S(t)$ need only be extended over the grid points in $a < x < b$. Hence the resulting inequality for $|U(x_0, t)|$ becomes

$$|U(x_0, t)| \geq \frac{h}{b - a} (4\lambda - 1)^{t/k} \epsilon,$$

which again proves the instability of the procedure.

For $g(t) \equiv 0$, $h(t) \equiv 0$, $a = 0$, $b = \pi$, the difference equation problem is solved by the function

$$U(x, t) = \sum_{n=1}^{N-1} A_n \left(1 - 4\lambda \sin^2 \frac{nh}{2} \right)^{t/(h^2\lambda)} \sin nx, \tag{13.3}$$

with $N = \pi/h$. This result is analogous to formula (4.23) for the difference equation of wave propagation. It is obtained by expanding $f(x)$ in a finite Fourier sine series that represents $f(x)$ at the grid points and by separating variables, as in the derivation of formula (12.7).

Starting from formula (13.3), numerous theorems about the convergence, stability, and discretization error can be proved under much milder assumptions than are necessary if the method of Sec. 12.2 is adapted to this problem. We content ourselves with a brief description of some of these results due to Juncosa, Young, and Leutert.

Juncosa and Young [1953], [1954] show that piecewise continuity as well as bounded variation are conditions on $f(x)$ sufficient for convergence of $U(x, t)$ to $u(x, t)$, for $t > 0$, provided $\lambda \leq \frac{1}{2}$. These seem to be the most general existing convergence statements concerning the function (13.3). In the article by Juncosa and Young [1953], the order of the discretization error in domains that are bounded away from the initial segment is investigated under varying assumptions on $f(x)$. We mention here only that the discretization error is $O(h)$ if $f(x)$ is of bounded variation.

If $\lambda > \frac{1}{2}$, expression (13.3) may still converge to $u(x, t)$ for exceptional types of initial values. Convergence is very easily established when the Fourier series of $f(x)$ has only a finite number of terms. If the Fourier series has infinitely many terms, it is possible to replace $f(x)$ by a particular function $f(x, h)$ depending on h such that $\lim_{h \to 0} f(x, h) = f(x)$, and such that the solution $U_h(x, t)$ corresponding to $U(x, t)$ in (13.3) but having $f(x, h)$ as initial function tends to $u(x, t)$, as $h \to 0$, even if $\lambda > \frac{1}{2}$ (Leutert [1951]).

These results are mathematically interesting but probably of little value in actual computation. In this connection one might be tempted to conjecture that the result of Dahlquist [1954] for hyperbolic equations (see Sec. 5.4) is true for the parabolic difference equation (12.1) as well, i.e., that convergence obtains even for unstable mesh ratios whenever the initial function is analytic. However, this conjecture is false, at least in this generality. F. John, in a set of unpublished lecture notes, has observed that the solution $U(x, t)$ of (12.1) with the initial values

$$f(x) = \sum_{r=0}^{\infty} e^{-3^r} \cos(\pi 2^r x)$$

on the whole x-axis diverges for $\lambda > \frac{1}{2}$, as $h \to 0$, even though $f(x)$ is an entire analytic function.

13.3. An Implicit Method

The stability restriction $\lambda \leq \frac{1}{2}$ (or similar inequalities for more complicated differential equations to be studied later) is much more irksome than the corresponding inequalities in hyperbolic problems, because it forces the computer to use very small steps in the time direction. There is therefore considerable interest in the so-called *implicit difference methods*, in which stability for all $\lambda > 0$ is ensured at the price of greater computational complexity.

Such implicit methods seem to have been used for the first time by Crank and Nicolson [1947]. We illustrate them again by means of the simple equation $u_t - u_{xx} = 0$. If u_{xx} is replaced by the second difference quotient, not at the level t as in (12.1), but at $t + k$, the difference equation

$$\frac{U(x, t+k) - U(x, t)}{k} = \frac{U(x+h, t+k) - 2U(x, t+k) + U(x-h, t+k)}{h^2}$$

$$(13.4)$$

is obtained. This equation cannot be solved in the explicit stepwise manner used for (12.1), and it is unsuitable for problems in infinite x-regions. But problems in a finite x-interval like that in (13.1) *can* be handled by means of (13.4). To that end, we write (13.4) in the form

$$\lambda U(x+h, t+k) - (1+2\lambda) U(x, t+k) + \lambda U(x-h, t+k) = -U(x, t),$$

$$(13.5)$$

and interpret (13.5) as a system of $(b - a)/h - 1$ simultaneous linear algebraic equations for the $(b - a)/h - 1$ unknown values of U at the grid points $x = a + h, a + 2h, \cdots, b - h$ for the level $t + k$. If the values of U at the grid points of the level t are already known, the values for $t + k$ can be found by solving this algebraic system, provided its determinant does not vanish. That it does not vanish will be shown shortly, but for the moment we shall take it for granted.

This method is stable for all values of λ. For the proof one could employ the usual Fourier analysis of the solution, but we shall establish it here by means of a maximum principle for the solution $U(x, t)$ of (13.4). Let $(x_0, t + k)$ be a grid point in the interval $a \leq x \leq b$ at the level $t + k$, such that

$$U(x_0, t + k) \geq U(x, t + k), \qquad x = a, a + h, \cdots, b,$$

and rewrite (13.4) in the form

$$U(x, t + k) = U(x, t) - \lambda[2U(x, t + k)$$

$$- U(x + h, t + k) - U(x - h, t + k)]. \quad (13.6)$$

If x_0 is an interior point of the interval $a \leq x \leq b$, then (13.6) must be satisfied for $x = x_0$ and, since the expression in brackets is nonnegative, it follows that

$$U(x_0, t + k) \leq U(x_0, t).$$

Similarly, if x_1 is a point for which

$$U(x_1, t + k) \leq U(x, t + k), \qquad x = a, a + h, \cdots, b,$$

and x_1 is an interior point of $a \leq x \leq b$, we have

$$U(x_1, t + k) \geq U(x_1, t).$$

Hence, if

$$M = \max \left[U(a, t + k), \max_{a<x<b} U(x, t), U(b, t + k) \right],$$

$$m = \min \left[U(a, t + k), \min_{a<x<b} U(x, t), U(b, t + k) \right],$$

it follows that

$$m \leq U(x, t + k) \leq M, \qquad x = a, a + h, \cdots, b.$$

By recursion with respect to t we conclude that *in the rectangle $a \leq x \leq b$, $0 \leq t < T$, the solution $U(x, t)$ of (13.4) is bounded from above and from below by the maximum and minimum respectively of its boundary and initial values.* (The line $t = T$ is not considered part of the boundary in this statement.)

As on previous occasions, such a result implies the stability of the difference equation since the departure caused by a line of errors is itself a solution of the difference equation.

The maximum principle just proved also guarantees that the linear system to be solved at every line $t = $ const. possesses a unique solution. For, if the values of $U(x, t)$, $x = a + h, a + 2h, \cdots, b - h$, as well as $U(a, t + k)$, $U(b, t + k)$ are zero, the values of $U(x, t + k)$ must be zero at all net points. This means that in the homogeneous case there is no solution other than the trivial one, and this proves that there always exists exactly one solution.

13.4. The Solution of the Implicit Difference Equation

The numerical solution of systems of linear algebraic equations is a large and widely studied subject. Fortunately the system represented by (13.5) is of such a simple nature that a very elementary procedure, i.e., Gauss' elimination method, can be conveniently applied. The matrix of the system has zeros everywhere except on the main diagonal and on the two diagonals parallel to it on either side. Such a matrix is sometimes called tridiagonal. To prepare for later applications, we explain the numerical solution of such systems in greater generality than is necessary for the discussion of (13.5).

Let there be given the system of equations

$$
\begin{aligned}
b_1 x_1 + c_1 x_2 &= d_1 \\
a_2 x_1 + b_2 x_2 + c_2 x_3 &= d_2 \\
a_3 x_2 + b_3 x_3 + c_3 x_4 &= d_3
\end{aligned}
$$

$$(13.7)$$

$$
\begin{aligned}
a_{n-1} x_{n-2} + b_{n-1} x_{n-1} + c_{n-1} x_n &= d_{n-1} \\
a_n x_{n-1} + b_n x_n &= d_n.
\end{aligned}
$$

By successive subtraction of a suitable multiple of each equation from the succeeding one, the system can be changed into a simpler one of the same type characterized by coefficients a_j^*, b_j^*, c_j^*, d_j^* instead of a_j, b_j, c_j, d_j, and where, in particular,

$$
\begin{aligned}
a_r^* &= 0, \qquad r = 2, \cdots, n \\
b_r^* &= 1, \qquad r = 1, \cdots, n.
\end{aligned}
$$

$$(13.8)$$

The coefficients c_r^*, d_r^* can be calculated successively from the recursion formulas

$$
c_1^* = \frac{c_1}{b_1}, \qquad d_1^* = \frac{d_1}{b_1},
$$

$$(13.9)$$

$$
c_{r+1}^* = \frac{c_{r+1}}{b_{r+1} - a_{r+1} c_r^*}, \qquad d_{r+1}^* = \frac{d_{r+1} - a_{r+1} d_r^*}{b_{r+1} - a_{r+1} c_r^*}, \qquad r = 1, \cdots, n-1 \quad (13.10)
$$

(We set $c_n = 0$, by definition.)

Equations (13.9) are obviously obtained by division of the first equation with b_1. To prove (13.10) by induction, assume that the rth equation has already been transformed into

$$
x_r + c_r^* x_{r+1} = d_r^*.
$$

Subtraction of a_{r+1} times this equation from the $(r + 1)$th equation

$$
a_{r+1} x_r + b_{r+1} x_{r+1} + c_{r+1} x_{r+2} = d_{r+1}
$$

yields

$$
(b_{r+1} - a_{r+1} c_r^*) x_{r+1} + c_{r+1} x_{r+2} = d_{r+1} - a_{r+1} d_r^*. \qquad (13.11)
$$

Formulas (13.10) are the result of division of this equation by $b_{r+1} - a_{r+1} c_r^*$.

The solution of the transformed system is now immediate: Starting with x_n, the x_r are given successively by

$$
\begin{aligned}
x_n &= d_n^* \\
x_r &= d_r^* - c_r^* x_{r+1}, \qquad r = n-1, n-2, \cdots, 1.
\end{aligned}
$$

In the foregoing argument we have tacitly assumed that $b_1 \neq 0$ and that $b_{r+1} - a_{r+1}c_r^* \neq 0$. Should the latter quantity vanish for some r, then the corresponding equation (13.11) can be solved for x_{r+2} and the problem is reduced to a similar one in one unknown less. The only serious exception would occur if for some r one had simultaneously $b_{r+1} - a_{r+1}c_r^* = 0$, but $d_{r+1} - a_{r+1}d_r^* \neq 0$, for then the equations would be inconsistent. But the system corresponding to (13.5) has already been proved to be consistent, so that this exception cannot arise. However, small values of $|b_{r+1} - a_{r+1}c_r^*|$ can cause serious round-off errors in solving (13.7), which can be avoided by a small but important modification of Gaussian elimination called "pivoting." For a thorough treatment of this matter, see Wilkinson [1958], [1959], and a forthcoming book on matrix computations.

The comparison of the computational effort required by two methods of solving the same problem depends to a large extent on the type of computing machine to be used. On most machines the calculation of the values of U at all the grid points in $a \leq x \leq b$ for a fixed t should not take more than four times as long by the implicit method as by the explicit procedure. Under this hypothesis the implicit method with $\lambda > 2$ is preferable to the explicit one with $\lambda = \frac{1}{2}$.

This estimate is based on the assumption that the discretization errors for the two methods are not decisively different and do not depend in too sensitive a manner on λ. These questions will be discussed in the next section.

The system (13.7) can also be solved by iterative techniques, e.g., by means of overrelaxation (Young [1954]). See Sec. 22 for a treatment of overrelaxation.

13.5. The Convergence of the Implicit Method

The convergence of the solution $U(x, t)$ of the implicit difference equation to the solution $u(x, t)$ of the corresponding differential problem can be studied, under reasonably weak hypotheses, by the Fourier series method. Rather than enter into the necessary lengthy arguments, we shall assume that $u(x, t)$ satisfies the strong regularity assumptions required for an application of the general technique of Sec. 7.2.

Let $u(x, t)$ be the solution of problem (13.1), and $U(x, t)$, the solution of

$$\frac{U(x, t + k) - U(x, t)}{k} = \frac{U(x + h, t + k) - 2U(x, t + k) + U(x - h, t + k)}{h^2},$$

(13.12)

$$U(x, 0) = f(x), \qquad U(a, t) = g(t), \qquad U(b, t) = h(t).$$

As usual, we apply the difference operator to $u(x, t)$ and find, by means of

Taylor's formula and by the relation $u_t = u_{xx}$, that

$$\frac{u(x, t + k) - u(x, t)}{k}$$

$$- \frac{u(x + h, t + k) - 2u(x, t + k) + u(x - h, t + k)}{h^2} = \omega(x, t),$$

where

$$\omega(x, t) = \frac{k}{2} \tilde{u}_{tt} - \frac{h^2}{12} \tilde{u}_{xxxx}. \tag{13.13}$$

The tilde again indicates that the derivatives are to be taken at certain intermediate points, which are, however, slightly different from those occurring in formula (12.15). For the discretization error $v(x, t)$ we obtain the difference equation problem

$$\frac{v(x, t + k) - v(x, t)}{k}$$

$$= \frac{v(x + h, t + k) - 2v(x, t + k) + v(x - h, t + k)}{h^2} + \omega(x, t),$$

$$\tag{13.14}$$

$$v(x, 0) = 0, \qquad v(a, t) = 0, \qquad v(b, t) = 0.$$

For the appraisal of $v(x, t)$ we need a simple extension of the maximum principle derived in Sec. 13.3. In analogy with (13.6), we write (13.14) in the form

$$v(x, t + k) = v(x, t) - \lambda[2v(x, t + k) - v(x + h, t + k)$$

$$- v(x - h, t + k)] + k \omega(x, t).$$

By an exact repetition of the previous argument, we find for $v(x, t + k)$ an inequality of the form

$$m' \le v(x, t + k) \le M',$$

where

$$M' = \max \left[0, \max_{a \le x \le b} (v(x, t) + k \omega(x, t)) \right],$$

and m' is defined analogously. Here the fact that the boundary values of v are zero has been used.

We conclude that $v(x, t)$ satisfies *a fortiori* the inequality

$$|v(x, t + k)| \le \max_{a \le x \le b} (|v(x, t)| + k|\omega(x, t)|), \tag{13.15}$$

from which again follows the appraisal (12.16).

The right member of (12.16) increases with k if h is kept fixed, and it is plausible that the discretization error itself becomes larger if a larger time step is used. This dependence can be expected to be particularly pronounced when u_{tt} is large. In this connection we add the remark that it is permissible to vary k from step to step in the computation. In a problem where u_{tt} varies considerably, while u_{xxxx} possesses a moderate bound, this may save computing time. We denote the varying time steps by k_j, $j = 1, 2, \cdots$, set $t_0 = 0$, $t_j = \Sigma_{\nu=1}^{j} k_\nu$, $m_j = \max_{a \leq x \leq b}|v(x, t_j)|$, $j = 1, \cdots, n$, and observe that by virtue of (13.13)

$$|\omega(x, t_j)| \leq \omega_j = \frac{k_{j+1}}{2} \max_{\substack{a \leq x \leq b \\ t_j \leq t \leq t_{j+1}}} |u_{tt}| + \frac{h^2}{12} \max_{\substack{a \leq x \leq b \\ 0 \leq t \leq t_{j+1}}} |u_{xxxx}|.$$

From (13.15) we have

$$m_{j+1} \leq m_j + k_{j+1}\omega_j$$

and hence, since $m_0 = 0$,

$$m_{j+1} \leq \sum_{\nu=0}^{j} k_{\nu+1}\omega_\nu \leq \frac{1}{2}\sum_{\nu=0}^{j} k_{\nu+1}^2 \max_{\substack{a \leq x \leq b \\ t_\nu \leq t \leq t_{\nu+1}}} |u_{tt}| + \frac{h^2}{12} t_{j+1} \max_{\substack{a \leq x \leq b \\ 0 \leq t \leq t_{j+1}}} |u_{xxxx}|.$$

The derivatives of u are unknown, of course, but at every step of the computation one can calculate an approximation μ_j to the maximum of $|u_{tt}|$ by using suitable combinations of the values of U already found. If we then determine k_{j+1} in such a way that $k_{j+1}\mu_j$ is independent of j, there is hope that the accuracy of the computation will be improved.

SECTION 14. MORE GENERAL LINEAR PARABOLIC PROBLEMS IN TWO VARIABLES: EXPLICIT METHODS

14.1. Formal Explicit Difference Approximations

In this section we are concerned with differential equations of the form

$$u_t = a_0(x, t)u_{xx} + a_1(x, t)u_x + a_2(x, t)u + d(x, t). \tag{14.1}$$

A simple finite-difference equation formally analogous to (14.1) can be obtained by replacing u_t, u_x by the respective forward finite-difference quotients, and u_{xx} by the second central-difference quotient. There results then the equation

$$U(x, t + k) = \sum_{r=-1}^{+1} c_r(x, t)\, U(x + rh, t) + k\, d(x, t), \tag{14.2}$$

where

$$c_{-1}(x, t) = \lambda \, a_0(x, t),$$
$$c_0(x, t) = 1 - 2\lambda \, a_0(x, t) - \lambda h \, a_1(x, t) + \lambda h^2 \, a_2(x, t), \qquad (14.3)$$
$$c_1(x, t) = \lambda \, a_0(x, t) + \lambda h \, a_1(x, t).$$

This is, of course, only one of many difference equations that can be legitimately called finite-difference analogs of (14.1). Even if we limit ourselves to *explicit* formulas involving only net points at *two* consecutive *t* levels, there are still an infinity of possibilities since there are infinitely many difference approximations to u_x and u_{xx}. More generally, *an expression of the form*

$$L_h(U) \equiv U(x, t + k) - \sum_r c_r(x, t) \, U(x + rh, t), \qquad (14.4)$$

where the summation extends over some finite set of grid points, may be called a formal approximation to the differential expression

$$L(u) \equiv u_t - a_0(x, t)u_{xx} - a_1(x, t)u_x - a_2(x, t)u, \qquad (14.5)$$

if every function $\phi(x, t)$ *for which* ϕ_t *and* ϕ_{xx} *are continuous satisfies the limit relation*

$$\lim_{h \to 0} \frac{1}{k} L_h(\phi) = L(\phi) \qquad \text{for} \qquad \lambda = \frac{k}{h^2} = \text{const.} \qquad (14.6)$$

If $\phi(x + rh, t)$ and $\phi(x, t + k)$ are expanded by Taylor's formula in powers of rh and k respectively, relation (14.6) is seen to be equivalent to the following conditions on the $c_r(x, t)$:

$$\lim_{h \to 0} \frac{1}{k} \left(\sum_r c_r - 1 \right) = a_2, \qquad \lim_{h \to 0} \frac{h}{k} \sum_r r c_r = a_1, \qquad \lim_{h \to 0} \frac{1}{2} \frac{h^2}{k} \sum_r r^2 c_r = a_0. \qquad (14.7)$$

We shall limit the discussion to difference expressions *whose coefficients c_r are twice continuously differentiable with respect to h at h = 0.*

A particularly important class of finite-difference approximations are those for which *all c_r are nonnegative for $h \le h_1$ (h_1 a positive constant), in the domain R of the (x, t)-plane under consideration. They will be called approximations of positive type.*

We see from formulas (14.3) that the special difference approximation (14.2) is of positive type if the inequalities

$$a_0(x, t) > 0, \qquad \lambda < \frac{1}{2a_0(x, t)} \qquad (14.8)$$

are satisfied in R. The second inequality in (14.8) implies our previous stability condition $\lambda \le \frac{1}{2}$ when $a_0(x, t) \ge 1$. We shall show that *all difference approximations of positive type are stable.*

Actually, our definition of stability refers to difference problems with subsidiary boundary conditions or initial conditions rather than to difference equations alone. We shall give the proof here for a problem in a finite x-interval. The modifications for the simpler problem in $-\infty < x < \infty$ are obvious.

At this stage it becomes desirable to insert a more precise formulation of the superposition principle and its use for the construction of solutions of nonhomogeneous linear difference problems.

14.2. Solution of Nonhomogeneous Linear Difference Problems by Superposition

Let

$$\mathscr{L}(W) = G \tag{14.9}$$

be a difference equation in the independent variables x, t. The variable x may be thought of as a vector since the beginning of what follows is valid in any number of space dimensions. In view of the linearity of the operator $\mathscr{L}$, the equations

$$\mathscr{L}(W^*) = G^*, \qquad \mathscr{L}(W^{**}) = G^{**}$$

imply that $W = W^* + W^{**}$ solves

$$\mathscr{L}(W) = G^* + G^{**}.$$

Hence, if $G_r(x, t)$ is defined in the grid by

$$G_r(x, nk) = \begin{cases} G(x, rk), & n = r \\ 0, & n \neq r \end{cases}$$

and if

$$\mathscr{L}(W_r) = G_r,$$

then

$$W = \sum_{r=0}^{N} W_r \tag{14.10}$$

solves

$$\mathscr{L}(W) = G \qquad \text{for} \qquad t = 0, k, \cdots, Nk,$$

because

$$G = \sum_{r=0}^{N} G_r \qquad \text{for} \qquad t = 0, k, \cdots, Nk.$$

In this manner the construction of a particular solution of (14.9) is reduced to the solution of a special type of nonhomogeneous difference equation whose right member vanishes outside one t level. If we wish to go beyond this point, we must specify in more detail the type of difference equation we are dealing with. Let us assume that $\mathscr{L}(W)$ involves, for $t = rk$, the values of W at the two levels $t = rk$, $t = (r + 1)k$ only, and that, if W_r is prescribed on $t = rk$, it can be calculated successively at all higher levels. If the value on $t = rk$ is taken as *zero*, then the equation $\mathscr{L}(W_r) = G_r$ is satisfied for all $t < rk$ by setting these $W_r = 0$ there. For this particular choice of initial values for W_r, (14.10) can also be written

$$W(x, t) = \sum_{r=0}^{t/k} W_r(x, t), \qquad 0 \leq t \leq Nk, \qquad (14.11)$$

since $W_r(x, t) = 0$ for $rk \geq t$, i.e., for $r \geq t/k$. We see from (14.11) that the particular solution (14.11) possesses the initial values

$$W(x, 0) = W_0(x, 0) = 0. \qquad (14.12)$$

Once W_r has been calculated at the level $t = (r + 1)k$, which is easy to do since $W_r = 0$ for $t = rk$, the subsequent calculation of W_r on higher t levels proceeds precisely as for the homogeneous equation since G_r is zero there. Thus for $t > rk$ W_r can be regarded as that solution of the homogeneous equation which for $t = (r + 1)k$ assumes the initial values obtained by requiring $\mathscr{L}(W_r) = G$ on $t = rk$ and setting $W_r = 0$ there.

As an illustration we apply the foregoing remarks to the problem

$$L_h(U) = k\, d(x, t), \qquad 0 < t \leq T, \qquad a < x < b,$$

$$U(x, 0) = f(x), \qquad U(a, t) = \phi(t), \qquad U(b, t) = \psi(t),$$

where L_h is the operator defined in (14.4). If r in (14.4) ranges over values other than $r = -1, 0, +1$, there arises a new difficulty here which is not present in problems without lateral boundary conditions: There may be grid points in the interval $a < x < b$ such that the application of the operator L_h introduces values of U outside $a \leq x \leq b$. This difficulty can be overcome either by extending the definition of $\phi(t)$ and $\psi(t)$ into strips outside the domain $0 < t \leq T$, $a \leq x \leq b$, or by limiting the consideration to operators L_h for which the values of $c_r(x, t)$ vanish whenever $x + rh$ is a point outside $a \leq x \leq b$. In computational practice, operators L_h, where $c_r \neq 0$ for $|r| > 1$, do not seem to have been used much. However, there is no theoretical reason for excluding them from the discussion; on the contrary, the possibility of using grid points outside the boundary increases the flexibility of our reasoning.

We therefore reformulate the problem in a slightly more general form. We denote by R the domain $0 < t \leq T$, $a < x < b$; by R' the domain $0 < t \leq T$, $-\infty < x \leq a$; and by R'' the domain $0 < t < T$, $b \leq x < \infty$.

The problem consists in finding for $0 \leq t \leq T$ a function $U(x, t)$ defined in the grid such that

$$
\begin{aligned}
L_h(U) &= k\, d(x, t) && \text{in } R, \\
U &= \phi(x, t) && \text{in } R', \\
U &= \psi(x, t) && \text{in } R'', \\
U &= f(x) && \text{for } t = 0.
\end{aligned}
\tag{14.13}
$$

Here $\phi(x, t)$, $\psi(x, t)$, $f(x)$ are given functions defined in R', R'', and on $t = 0$ respectively.

In accordance with the general superposition principle, let the functions $W_r(x, t)$ be defined by the conditions

$$
L_h(W_r) = 0, \qquad \text{for } a < x < b, \quad t > (r + 1)k
$$

$$
W_r(x, t) = \begin{cases} k\, d(x, t), & \text{for } a < x < b, \quad t = (r + 1)k \\ 0, & \text{for } t \leq rk \\ 0, & \text{in } R' \text{ and } R''. \end{cases}
\tag{14.14}
$$

Then

$$
W = \sum_{r=0}^{t/k} W_r
\tag{14.15}
$$

is a solution of the difference equation in (14.13) which vanishes for $t = 0$ and in $R' \cup R''$. Hence, the solution of problem (14.13) is

$$
U = U_c + W,
\tag{14.16}
$$

where U_c is the "complementary" solution of the homogeneous difference equation, i.e.,

$$
L_h(U_c) = 0 \quad \text{in} \quad R,
$$

$$
U_c = \phi(x, t) \quad \text{in} \quad R', \qquad U_c = \psi(x, t) \quad \text{in} \quad R'',
$$

$$
U_c = f(x) \quad \text{for} \quad t = 0. \tag{14.17}
$$

An analogous superposition principle in the theory of linear parabolic differential equations reduces the solution of nonhomogeneous problems to an integration over a family of solutions of the corresponding homogeneous problem (Carslaw and Jaeger [1947], p. 19). It is sometimes referred to as Duhamel's method.

14.3. Boundedness and Stability Properties of Difference Expressions of Positive Type

THEOREM 14.1.   *Let the expression $L_h(U)$ in problem (14.13) be of positive type and assume that it is a formal approximation to the differential* *expression $L(u)$ of formula (14.5). Denote by $\bar{d}$, $\bar{\phi}$, $\bar{\psi}$, $\bar{f}$ the least upper bounds for the numerical values of the functions $d(x, t)$, $\phi(x, t)$, $\psi(x, t)$, $f(x)$ introduced in (14.13), in their respective domains of definition. Let $|h| \leq h_1$. Then there exists a constant M depending on λ, T, and h_1 but not on x, t, h such that the solution $U(x, t)$ of problem (14.13) satisfies the inequality*

$$|U(x, t)| \leq M[\max(\bar{f}, \bar{\phi}, \bar{\psi}) + t\bar{d}]. \tag{14.18}$$

Proof. By means of the superposition principle $U(x, t)$ can be represented as the sum of $t/k + 2$ solutions of the homogeneous difference equation. One of these is the function U_c defined in (14.17), and the others assume the value $k\,d(x, t)$ on one line $t = \text{const.}$ and vanish below the line. Consider the function U_c first. On the line $t = k$ either we have $U_c(x, k) \leq \max(\bar{\phi}, \bar{\psi})$ or there is a grid point (x_0, k), with $a < x_0 < b$, where $U_c(x, k)$ assumes its maximum for the line $t = k$. In the latter case it follows from the difference equation, because of $c_r(x, t) \geq 0$ and the first of equations (14.7), that

$$U_c(x, k) \leq \bar{f} \sum_r c_r(x_0, k) = \bar{f}[1 + a_2(x_0, k)k + o(k)].$$

In the same way one sees that either $U_c(x, k) \geq -\max(\bar{\phi}, \bar{\psi})$ or $U_c(x, k) \geq -\bar{f}[1 + a_2(x_1, k)k + o(k)]$, where x_1 is a certain point in $a < x < b$. Therefore, if $|a_2(x, t)k + o(k)| \leq \bar{a}k$ in R, we have

$$|U_c(x, k)| \leq \max(\bar{\phi}, \bar{\psi}, \bar{f})(1 + \bar{a}k).$$

The argument can now be repeated for the step from $t = k$ to $t = 2k$, etc. We obtain, in general

$$|U_c(x, t)| \leq \max(\bar{\phi}, \bar{\psi}, \bar{f})(1 + \bar{a}k)^{t/k}.$$

The functions W_r of (14.14) can be appraised by the same method, which shows that

$$|W_r(x, t)| \leq (1 + \bar{a}k)^{t/k}k\bar{d}.$$

Hence, if we take $M \geq (1 + \bar{a}k)^{T/k}$, for $0 < k \leq \lambda h_1^2$, the conclusion of the theorem follows from the representation $U = U_c + \Sigma_{r=0}^{t/k} W_r$.

An analogous, somewhat simpler theorem holds for the problem on the infinite interval $-\infty < x < \infty$. Rather than treat both cases here we refer to John [1952] for the discussion of the latter problem.

From Theorem 14.1 it follows immediately that the *difference problem* (14.13) *is stable if $L_h(U)$ is of positive type.* In fact, the departure $\epsilon(x, t)$ caused by errors less than or equal to δ at every grid point is itself a solution of a problem like (14.13) with functions $d(x, t)$, $\phi(x, t)$, $\psi(x, t)$, $f(x)$ whose upper bounds satisfy the inequalities $\bar{d} \leq \delta/k$, $\bar{\phi} \leq \delta$, $\bar{\psi} \leq \delta$, $\bar{f} \leq \delta$. Application of (14.18) yields $\epsilon(x, t) = O(\delta/k)$.

On the basis of the inequality (14.18) the discretization error can be easily appraised, provided the solution of the continuous problem is sufficiently smooth in the closure of R. This is the content of the next theorem.

THEOREM 14.2. *Let $u(x, t)$ be a solution of the differential equation $L(u) = d(x, t)$ in R, and assume that u_t and u_{xx} are continuous in the closure of R. Let $U(x, t)$ be the solution of a difference equation problem* (14.13) *such that the difference equation approximates $L(u) = d(x, t)$ formally and such that $\phi(x, t) = u(d, t)$ in R', $\psi(x, t) = u(b, t)$ in R'', $f(x) = u(x, 0)$, and $\phi = \psi = 0$ elsewhere. If $U(x, t)$ satisfies the inequality* (14.18), *then*

$$\lim_{h \to 0} U(x, t) = u(x, t).$$

If, in addition, u_{tt} and u_{xxxx} are bounded for $0 \leq t \leq T$, $-\infty < x < \infty$, then $U(x, t) - u(x, t) = O(h^2)$.

Proof. Extend the definition of u for x outside $a \leq x \leq b$ by setting $u \equiv 0$ in R' and R''. From (14.4) and (14.6) we obtain $L_h(u) = o(k) + k\, d(x, t)$ in R, and therefore

$$L_h(v) = o(k) \qquad \text{uniformly in } R,$$

where $v = U - u$. Hence, v solves a problem of type (14.13) with the $d(x, t)$ of that formula given by $d(x, t) = o(k)/k, \bar{f} = \bar{\phi} = \bar{\psi} = 0$, and the first part of the theorem follows immediately from inequality (14.18). If u_{tt} and u_{xxxx} exist and are bounded, the expression $o(k)$ above is $O(kh^2)$, as can be seen by expanding $L_h(u)$ up to terms of fourth degree. This leads to a correspondingly stronger statement concerning the smallness of v.

The theorem just proved is open to the criticism formulated on previous occasions: the smoothness requirements on u are too strong to be realistic. The convergence and the discretization error for initial-value problems in finite domains under realistic assumptions on the regularity of u have not yet been sufficiently studied, except for differential equations with constant coefficients.

14.4. The Boundedness Condition of John

The preceding section might give rise to the erroneous impression that it is essential for a difference equation to be of positive type if it is to be computationally useful. Actually, the stability and convergence properties of the difference equation are direct consequences of the boundedness property expressed in inequality (14.18). Such boundedness properties exist for a wider class of difference equations than those of positive type. A sufficient condition was formulated and proved by John [1952] for the initial-value problem on the infinite x-axis. For certain problems in a finite interval, the condition carries over without serious complications. John's condition is essentially expressed by the inequality

$$\left| \lim_{h \to 0} \sum_r c_r(x, t) e^{ir\theta} \right| \le e^{-\alpha \theta^2} \qquad \text{for } |\theta| \le \pi. \tag{14.19}$$

If an $\alpha > 0$ exists such that (14.19) is true and if certain minor regularity requirements are satisfied, then an inequality of type (14.18) is valid. More precise formulations are found in the following.

The proof is rather long and will therefore be given here only under the simplifying hypothesis that the $c_r(x, t)$ are independent of x, t, and h. The extension to the case that c_r depends on t only offers no difficulties, but if the c_r depend on x or h, new techniques have to be introduced.

Before we proceed to explain the proof, we illustrate the meaning of the theorem by two simple examples.

1. The approximation (12.1) to $u_t = u_{xx}$ corresponds to the coefficients $c_{-1} = \lambda$, $c_0 = 1 - 2\lambda$, $c_1 = \lambda$. Condition (14.19) becomes

$$\left| 1 - 4\lambda \sin^2 \frac{\theta}{2} \right| \le e^{-\alpha \theta^2}, \qquad |\theta| \le \pi.$$

This condition is not satisfied for $\lambda \ge \frac{1}{2}$, $\theta = \pi$. Its failure for $\lambda = \frac{1}{2}$ indicates that (14.19) is truly a sufficient and not also a necessary condition for $L_h(U)$ to satisfy an inequality like (14.18). For small $|\theta|$ we conclude from the expansions $1 - 4\lambda \sin^2(\theta/2) = 1 - \lambda\theta^2 + \cdots$ and $e^{-\alpha\theta^2} = 1 - \alpha\theta^2 + \cdots$ that condition (14.19) is satisfied if $\alpha < \lambda$. Since $\lim_{\alpha \to 0} e^{-\alpha\theta^2} = 1$ uniformly for $|\theta| \le \pi$, α can be chosen so small that the inequality remains satisfied throughout that interval, provided the left member is bounded away from unity in every interval $0 < \theta_0 \le \theta \le \pi$. For $\lambda < \frac{1}{2}$ this is obviously the case.

2. The coefficients

$$c_{-2} = c_2 = -\frac{\epsilon\lambda}{1 - 3\epsilon}, \qquad c_{-1} = c_1 = \frac{(1 + \epsilon)\lambda}{1 - 3\epsilon}, \qquad c_0 = 1 - \frac{2\lambda}{1 - 3\epsilon},$$

where ϵ is a parameter, define a formal approximation to $u_t = u_{xx}$. For positive ϵ it is not of positive type. Condition (14.19) becomes

$$\left| 1 - \frac{2}{1 - 3\epsilon}\lambda + 2\frac{1 + \epsilon}{1 - 3\epsilon}\lambda \cos\theta - 2\frac{\epsilon}{1 - 3\epsilon}\lambda \cos 2\theta \right| \le e^{-\alpha\theta^2}, \qquad |\theta| \le \pi.$$

If λ and ϵ are sufficiently small, the same argument as in example 1 shows that an $\alpha > 0$ can be found for which the inequality is true.

We now turn to the proof of the sufficiency of condition (14.19) for the initial-value problem in the infinite interval, assuming that $L_h(U)$ has constant coefficients c_r and is a formal approximation to a differential expression of the form (14.5) with constant coefficients. Because of the superposition principle, the theorem will be essentially proved if it is shown to be true for homogeneous differential equations. The solution $U(x, t)$ of $L_h(U) = 0$ is a linear combination of the values of the initial function $f(x)$ at the grid points, i.e.,

$$U(sh, nk) = \sum_\rho g_{\rho s n} f(\rho h). \tag{14.20}$$

Since the c_r are all zero for sufficiently large r, say for $|r| > N$, the coefficients $g_{\rho s n}$ vanish for $|\rho| > nN$.

The $g_{\rho s n}$ are the same for all functions $f(x)$. By means of a suitable choice of $f(x)$ for which $U(x, t)$ can be calculated explicitly, we can derive an explicit expression for the $g_{\rho s n}$. The particular initial function $f(x) = e^{ix}$ is very convenient for this purpose. We then find that

$$U(sh, nk) = \sum_\rho g_{\rho s n} e^{i\rho h},$$

and, by means of the orthogonality relation

$$\frac{1}{2\pi} \int_{-\pi}^{\pi} e^{i(\rho - \sigma)\theta} \, d\theta = \begin{cases} 1, & \rho = \sigma \\ 0, & \rho \neq \sigma, \end{cases}$$

it follows that

$$g_{\rho s n} = \frac{1}{2\pi} \int_{-\pi}^{\pi} U(s\theta, nk) e^{-i\rho\theta} \, d\theta. \tag{14.21}$$

On the other hand, this particular solution $U(x, t)$ can be calculated stepwise from $L_h(U) = 0$. We have, from (14.4),

$$U(sh, k) = e^{ish} \sum_r c_r e^{irh}$$

and, generally,

$$U(sh, nk) = e^{ish} \left(\sum_r c_r e^{irh} \right)^n.$$

Insertion into (14.21) yields

$$g_{\rho s n} = \frac{1}{2\pi} \int_{-\pi}^{\pi} \left(\sum_r c_r e^{ir\theta} \right)^n e^{i(s - \rho)\theta} \, d\theta. \tag{14.22}$$

This representation of $g_{\rho s n}$ will now enable us to derive an inequality for $g_{\rho s n}$ which, when inserted into (14.20), proves the boundedness of $U(sh, nk)$.

Lemma 14.3. *Assume that the quantities c_r are constants independent of h and satisfy the conditions $\Sigma_r\, c_r = 1$, $\Sigma_r\, r c_r = 0$ [see (14.7)], and (14.19). Then*

$$g_{\rho s n} = O\left[\frac{n}{(|s - \rho| + \sqrt{n})^3}\right]. \tag{14.23}$$

Proof. We simplify the notation by setting $s - \rho = \tau$ and

$$\sum_r c_r e^{i r \theta} = \phi(\theta)$$

in (14.22). From condition (14.19) and from (14.22) we obtain immediately the appraisal

$$|g_{\rho s n}| = \left|\frac{1}{2\pi}\int_{-\pi}^{\pi}\phi^n(\theta)e^{i\tau\theta}\, d\theta\right| \le \frac{1}{2\pi}\int_{-\pi}^{\pi}e^{-\alpha n\theta^2}\, d\theta = O\left(\frac{1}{\sqrt{n}}\right). \tag{14.24}$$

As there may be $O(n)$ terms in the right member of (14.20), this estimate alone is not sufficiently precise for our purpose.

A second inequality can be obtained by repeated integration by parts in (14.22). To this end we must first investigate the derivatives of $\phi^n(\theta)$. We have

$$\phi'(0) = i\sum_r r c_r = 0,$$

and, therefore,

$$\phi'(\theta) = O(\theta), \qquad \text{as } \theta \to 0. \tag{14.25}$$

Furthermore we find, using (14.19) and (14.25), that

$$\frac{d^3}{d\theta^3}\,\phi^n = n(n-1)(n-2)\phi^{n-3}\phi'^3 + 3n(n-1)\phi^{n-2}\phi'\phi'' + n\phi^{n-1}\phi'''$$

$$= O(n^3|\theta|^3 + n^2\theta + n)e^{-\alpha(n-3)\theta^2}. \tag{14.26}$$

Now we perform three successive integrations by parts in (14.22) and find, making use of the periodicity of $\phi(\theta)$, that

$$g_{\rho s n} = -\frac{i}{2\pi(s - \rho)^3}\int_{-\pi}^{\pi}\left[\frac{d^3}{d\theta^3}\,\phi^n(\theta)\right]e^{i(s-\rho)\theta}\, d\theta.$$

Inserting (14.26) into the integral, after a short calculation we obtain the appraisal

$$g_{\rho s n} = O((\rho - s)^{-3}n), \tag{14.27}$$

which together with (14.24) implies (14.23). To see this last point, it suffices to write (14.24) and (14.27) respectively in the forms

$$|g_{\rho s n}|^{1/3} n^{1/2} \le C n^{1/3},$$

$$|g_{\rho s n}|^{1/3} |\tau| \le C n^{1/3},$$

with a suitably large constant C, and to add these inequalities.

With the help of this lemma, the right member of (14.20) can now easily be appraised. We find

$$|U(sh, nk)| \le K\bar{f} \sum_{\rho = -nN}^{nN} \frac{n}{(|s - \rho| + \sqrt{n})^3},$$

where K is a constant and $\bar{f}$ is an upper bound for $|f(x)|$ in $-\infty < x < \infty$. Assume first that $s \le nN$. Setting $s - \rho = \tau = -\tau'$, we see then that

$$\sum_{\rho = -nN}^{nN} \frac{n}{(|s - \rho| + \sqrt{n})^3} \le \int_0^{nN - s} \frac{n}{(\tau' + \sqrt{n})^3} \, d\tau'$$

$$+ \frac{1}{\sqrt{n}} + \int_0^{nN + s} \frac{n}{(\tau + \sqrt{n})^3} \, d\tau = O(1). \quad (14.28)$$

If $s > nN$ the argument is similar, except that the first integral in the middle member of (14.28) is absent.

From the resulting inequality,

$$|U(x, t)| \le M\bar{f}, \qquad -\infty < x < \infty, \qquad 0 \le t \le T,$$

for the solution of the homogeneous difference equation, the inequality

$$|U(x, t)| \le M(\bar{f} + t\bar{d})$$

for the solution of the equation with nonhomogeneous term $k \, d(x, t)$ can be derived in the usual way by the superposition principle.

We refer to John [1952] for the extension of this result to difference equations with nonconstant coefficients. The following theorem is formulated for the general case.

THEOREM 14.4.   *Let the expression* $L_h(U)$ *of* (14.4) *be a formal approximation to* $L(u)$ *of* (14.5). *Assume that the coefficients* $c_r(x, t) = c_r(x, t, h)$ *of* (14.4) *are for* $-\infty < x < \infty, 0 \le t \le T, 0 \le h \le h_1$ *uniformly continuous and bounded, together with their first and second derivatives with respect to* x *and* h. *If*

$$\left| \sum_r c_r(x, t, 0)e^{ir\theta} \right| \le e^{-\alpha\theta^2}, \qquad |\theta| \le \pi,$$

for some positive constant α, *then the solution* $U(x, t)$ *of the difference equation* $L_h(U) = k\,d(x, t)$ *with the initial values* $U(x, 0) = f(x)$ *satisfies the inequality*

$$|U(x, t)| \leq M(\bar{f} + t\bar{d}), \quad -\infty < x < \infty, \quad 0 \leq t \leq T, \quad 0 < h \leq h_1,$$

where $\bar{f}$ *and* $\bar{d}$ *are upper bounds for* $|f(x)|$ *and* $|d(x, t)|$, *and* M *is a constant independent of* x, t, *and* h.

Some information concerning certain problems in finite intervals can be immediately obtained from Theorem 14.4:

A differential problem

$$L(u) = d(x, t), \quad 0 < t \leq T, \quad a < x < b,$$

$$u(x, 0) = f(x), \quad a < x < b, \tag{14.29}$$

$$u(a, t) = \phi(t), \quad u(b, t) = \psi(t), \quad 0 < t \leq T,$$

can be reduced to a similar problem with $\phi(t) \equiv \psi(t) = 0$, provided $\phi(t)$ and $\psi(t)$ are differentiable. To this end we need only set

$$u = u^* + \frac{(b - x)\,\phi(t) + (x - a)\,\psi(t)}{b - a}$$

and obtain a new problem of the same kind,

$$L(u^*) = d^*(x, t), \quad 0 < t \leq T, \quad a < x < b,$$

$$u^*(x, 0) = f^*(x), \quad a < x < b, \tag{14.30}$$

$$u^*(a, t) = u^*(b, t) = 0, \quad 0 < t < T.$$

It is moreover convenient to perform the transformation

$$x^* = \frac{x - a}{b - a},$$

which changes the end points a and b into 0 and 1 respectively. In view of these facts, a discussion of the special finite-difference problem

$$L_h(U) = k\,d(x, t), \quad 0 < t \leq T, \quad 0 < x < 1,$$

$$U(x, 0) = f(x), \quad 0 < x < 1, \tag{14.31}$$

$$U(0, t) = U(1, t) = 0, \quad 0 < t \leq T,$$

serves for a wide class of numerical problems.

The definition of the functions occurring in (14.31) can be extended into the whole strip $-\infty < x < \infty$, $0 \leq t \leq T$ in such a way as to obtain a pure initial-value problem whose solution vanishes on the lines $x = 0$, $x = 1$. This is done by setting

$$f(-x) = -f(x), \qquad d(-x, t) = -d(x, t),$$

$$c_{-r}(-x, t) = c_r(x, t) \qquad \text{in } -1 < x < 0,$$

and by continuing these functions as periodic functions of x with period 2. These functions will, in general, have jump discontinuities at integral values of x. We define their values at these points as the average of their two limits there.

The stepwise construction of $U(x, t)$ shows that the solution of this initial-value problem is itself an odd periodic function in the grid. But the definition $c_{-r}(-x, t) = c_r(x, t)$ limits the scope of this method to a narrow class of difference equations since $c_r(x, t)$ must possess a considerable degree of smoothness at $x = 0$ and $x = 1$. (John's conditions on the c_r are slightly weaker but a little more involved to enunciate than those of Theorem 14.4.) Example 2 at the beginning of this section is a case to which the present argument can be applied.

SECTION 15. FURTHER EXPLICIT AND IMPLICIT METHODS FOR LINEAR PROBLEMS

15.1. A More General Approach to Implicit Methods

Much of the content of Sec. 14 can be extended to implicit difference equations of the form

$$L_h(U) = \sum_r b_r \, U(x + rh, t + k) - \sum_r c_r \, U(x + rh, t) = 0, \quad (15.1)$$

where b_r and c_r are functions of x, t, and h. No theory that can compare with the generality of John [1952] has been developed for such approximations, but some of the arguments carry over without difficulty.

The following is an example of somewhat greater generality than the difference equation (13.4). Let the heat equation $u_t - u_{xx} = 0$ be approximated by

$$\frac{1}{k} L_h(U) \equiv \frac{U(x, t + k) - U(x, t)}{k}$$

$$- \sigma \frac{U(x + h, t + k) - 2U(x, t + k) + U(x - h, t + k)}{h^2}$$

$$- (1 - \sigma) \frac{U(x + h, t) - 2U(x, t) + U(x - h, t)}{h^2} = 0, \quad (15.2)$$

where σ is a parameter. For $\sigma = 0$ this equation reduces to the ordinary explicit scheme, and for $\sigma = 1$ it yields equation (13.4). For any σ, equation (15.2) is clearly a formal approximation to the heat equation, and its numerical solution by the method of Sec. 13.4 offers no new difficulties. It was used, with $\sigma = \frac{1}{2}$, by Crank and Nicolson [1947] (see Sec. 17.2).

The conditions on the coefficients of (15.1) which make the operator $L_h(U)$ there a formal approximation to the $L(u)$ of (14.5) in the sense of formula (14.6) can be readily derived by expanding (15.1) formally into a Taylor series. They turn out to be

$$\lim_{h \to 0} \sum_r b_r = 1, \qquad \lim_{h \to 0} h^{-2}\Big(\sum_r c_r - 1\Big) = \lambda a_2,$$

$$\lim_{h \to 0} h^{-1} \sum_r (c_r - b_r) r = \lambda a_1, \qquad \lim_{h \to 0} \sum_r (c_r - b_r) r^2 = 2\lambda a_0. \quad (15.3)$$

For the difference equation (15.2) the coefficients are

$$b_{-1} = b_1 = -\lambda\sigma, \qquad b_0 = (1 + 2\sigma\lambda);$$
$$c_{-1} = c_1 = (1 - \sigma)\lambda, \qquad c_0 = [1 - 2(1 - \sigma)\lambda]. \quad (15.4)$$

Incidentally, if we wish to approximate the heat equation $u_t = u_{xx}$ by a difference expression of the form (15.1) by using only the six points $(x + rh, t + nk)$ $(r = -1, 0, 1; n = 0, 1)$, and if we require that the coefficients of $L_h(U)$ depend only on the combination $\lambda = k/h^2$ of k and h, then (15.2) is the only such approximation for which $(1/k)L_h(\phi) - \phi_t - \phi_{xx} = O(h^2)$ with any sufficiently smooth function ϕ. One may ask whether the parameter σ can be chosen so as to obtain a still better approximation. This is not possible for arbitrary ϕ. But if $\phi = u$—and this is the only function ϕ for which $L_h(\phi)$ is needed in the appraisal of the discretization error—the value $\sigma = (6\lambda - 1)/(12\lambda)$ produces the formula $(1/k) L_h(u) - u_t - u_{xx} = O(h^4)$. For the proof of this fact one expands (15.2) up to terms of order $O(h^4)$ and makes use of the relation $u_{xxxx} = u_{xxt} = u_{tt}$. If, in addition, one takes $\lambda = 1/\sqrt{20}$, even the terms of next higher order cancel and the error term is $O(h^6)$. But these facts cannot be simply extended to more general differential equations.

One can generalize the concept of a difference equation of positive type so as to apply to (15.1). A natural extension of the definition is to require that

$$c_r \geq 0 \text{ and } b_r \begin{cases} \geq 0, & r = 0, \\ \\ \leq 0, & r \neq 0, \end{cases} \quad (15.5)$$

for then the simple argument based on the maximum value of $U(x, t)$ that was used in Sec. 12.1, 12.2, and 13.3 can be applied again. We shall not discuss the details of this approach since the difference approximations of positive type fail to include some computationally useful formulas such as (15.2) for $(1 - \sigma)\lambda > \frac{1}{2}$.

Instead, we shall treat the particular difference equation (15.2) by the method of Fourier series, i.e., by the technique introduced in Sec. 4 in connection with the differential equation of wave propagation. Incidentally, it can easily be shown—but it will not be done here—that every differential expression $L(u)$ of the form (14.5) can be approximated by a difference expression $L_h(U)$ of the form (15.1) with $b_r = c_r = 0$ for $|r| > 1$, and such that, *for fixed x, t*, and for $h = 0$, the b_r, c_r are of the form (15.4) with some value of σ. It is likely that the results to be discussed here remain valid for implicit difference equations of this type that approximate differential equations with *variable* coefficients. A study of this question would be desirable since implicit methods are now very widely used.

The Fourier-series method will at the same time establish that the difference equation problem possesses a solution for arbitrary initial values. If there exists a solution, it must be the only one since (15.2) constitutes a system of linear algebraic equations for the values of U at the level $t + k$ in terms of its values at t, with coefficients that are independent of t. If such a system possesses a solution for arbitrary initial values $U(\rho h, 0) = f(\rho h)$, then its determinant is not zero, and the solution is unique.

Let $U(x, t)$ be the solution of the difference equation (15.2) which satisfies the subsidiary conditions

$$U(x, 0) = f(x), \qquad 0 < x < \pi;$$
$$U(0, t) = U(\pi, t), \qquad 0 < t \leq T. \tag{15.6}$$

We have seen at the end of Sec. 14.4 that the limitation to a particular interval and to homogeneous boundary conditions does not entail an essential loss of generality.

For the study of the convergence of $U(x, t)$ to $u(x, t)$, we assume that $f(x)$ possesses a Fourier series of the form

$$f(x) = \sum_{r=1}^{\infty} a_r \sin rx$$

such that

$$\sum_{r=1}^{\infty} |a_r| < \infty. \tag{15.7}$$

This is the case, for instance, if the periodic function $f(x)$ is continuous and has a derivative that is continuous except for a finite number of jump discontinuities.

We now attempt to solve the difference equation by a uniformly convergent series of the form $\Sigma_{r=1}^{\infty} a_r \, \psi_r(t) \sin rx$. The condition $\psi_r(0) = 1$ will guarantee that this series satisfies the initial condition. The lateral boundary conditions are automatically fulfilled. If $\psi_r(t) \sin rx$ is inserted into (15.2), a simple calculation shows that the difference equation is satisfied, provided $\psi_r(t)$ is a solution of the difference equation

$$\psi_r(t + k)\left(1 + 4\sigma\lambda \sin^2 \frac{rh}{2}\right) = \psi_r(t)\left(1 - 4(1 - \sigma)\lambda \sin^2 \frac{rh}{2}\right).$$

Its solution with the inital value $\psi_r(0) = 1$ is

$$\psi_r(t) = \phi_r^{t/k},$$

where

$$\phi_r = \frac{1 - 4(1 - \sigma)\lambda \sin^2 (rh/2)}{1 + 4\sigma\lambda \sin^2 (rh/2)}. \tag{15.8}$$

Thus

$$U(x, t) = \sum_{r=1}^{\infty} a_r \phi_r^{t/k} \sin rx \tag{15.9}$$

is the desired solution of (15.2), (15.6), whenever this series converges. Because of (15.7), a sufficient condition for its convergence—even for uniform convergence—is

$$|\phi_r| \leq 1, \qquad r = 1, 2, \cdots \tag{15.10}$$

for all r and h. This is the case if and only if

$$2\lambda(1 - 2\sigma) \leq 1. \tag{15.11}$$

For $\sigma < \frac{1}{2}$, the condition (15.11) is equivalent with $\lambda \leq 1/[2(1 - 2\sigma)]$. If $\sigma \geq \frac{1}{2}$, it is true for all h and k.

To prove that $U(x, t)$ tends to the solution $u(x, t)$ of the differential problem, as h and k tend to zero, we must investigate the behavior of $\phi_r^{t/k}$ for fixed r in this passage to the limit. From (15.8) we have, since $\sin^2 (rh/2) = r^2h^2/4 + O(h^4)$,

$$\phi_r^{t/k} = \left[\frac{1 - (1 - \sigma)r^2k + o(k)}{1 + \sigma r^2k + o(k)}\right]^{t/k} = [1 - r^2k + o(k)]^{t/k},$$

i.e.,

$$\lim_{h \to 0} \phi_r^{t/k} = e^{-r^2 t}. \tag{15.12}$$

This shows that, as $h \to 0$, every term of (15.9) tends to the corresponding term of (13.2), which was the Fourier-series representation of the solution $u(x, t)$ of the corresponding differential equation problem. If (15.10) is satisfied, the convergence of the series (15.9) is uniform with respect to

h, so that the termwise passage to the limit $h \to 0$ is legitimate. Hence, we have then indeed $\lim_{h \to 0} U(x, t) = u(x, t)$.

For the study of the stability, it is more convenient to represent the values of $U(x, t)$ in the grid by a finite Fourier series instead of by the infinite series (15.9). For the round-off errors cannot be regarded as the values which a smooth function independent of h assumes at the grid points. Therefore let $N = \pi/h$ be the number of grid points on a line $t = $ const., and consider an arbitrary line of errors ϵ_ρ, $\rho = 1, 2, \cdots$, $N - 1$, at $t = 0$. These errors can be represented by the finite Fourier series

$$\epsilon_s = \sum_{r=1}^{N-1} A_r \sin srh, \qquad s = 1, 2, \cdots, N - 1,$$

with

$$A_r = \frac{2}{N} \sum_{\rho=1}^{N-1} \epsilon_\rho \sin \rho rh, \qquad r = 1, 2, \cdots, N - 1 \qquad (15.13)$$

(see Sec. 5). By the same argument as for the infinite Fourier series we conclude that

$$U^*(sh, nk) = \sum_{r=1}^{N-1} A_r \phi_r^{t/k} \sin srh \qquad (15.14)$$

is, in the points of the grid, the solution of the difference equation problem with the initial values ϵ_s or, in other words, it is the departure due to the errors ϵ_s on the initial line. To appraise the order of magnitude of $U^*(sh, nk)$, we insert (15.13) into (15.14) and find, after an interchange of summations,

$$U^*(sh, nk) = \sum_{\rho=1}^{N-1} g_{\rho s n} \epsilon_\rho, \qquad (15.15)$$

with

$$g_{\rho s n} = \frac{2}{N} \sum_{r=1}^{N-1} \phi_r^{t/k} \sin srh \sin \rho rh. \qquad (15.16)$$

If (15.11) is satisfied, which will be assumed, the inequality (15.10) holds, and (15.16) implies that

$$|g_{\rho s n}| \leq 2. \qquad (15.17)$$

Let $|\epsilon_r| \leq \delta$, $r = 1, 2, \cdots, N - 1$; then we can conclude from (15.15) that

$$|U^*(sh, nk)| \leq 2N\delta = 2\pi\delta/h. \qquad (15.18)$$

The cumulative departure due to round-off errors at all grid points is then of the order of magnitude $O(\delta h^{-1} k^{-1}) = O(\delta h^{-3})$, a fact which establishes stability according to the definition in Sec. 5.

The preceding arguments are elementary and simpler than those of Sec.

14, but the results fall short of what one would like to achieve. If we could prove a boundedness relation of the form

$$|U(x, t)| \leq M \max_{0 \leq x \leq \pi} |f(x)| \qquad (M = \text{const.})$$

instead of (15.18), as we did for the explicit methods, we should be able to deduce satisfactory appraisals of the discretization error and the cumulative round-off departure. The former would be $O(h^2)$ and the latter $O(\delta h^{-2})$, for fixed λ, if $u(x, t)$ satisfies the stringent smoothness conditions that are usually imposed in this context. However, the extension of John's method to the implicit scheme (15.2) encounters some serious difficulties, and it appears as yet to be unknown whether the boundedness relation above is true.

The inequality (15.18) is certainly very crude and wasteful. Since ϕ_r is a decreasing function of r, by performing a summation by parts on (15.16) one can show that $g_{\rho s n} = O((|\rho - s| + 1)^{-1})$. Inserting this into (15.15) shows that

$$|U^*(sh, nk)| \leq M\delta|\log h|, \qquad (15.19)$$

if $2\lambda(1 - 2\sigma) \leq 1$. The constant M is independent of h, k, and λ. The inequality (15.19) is better than (15.18) and might be used to derive improved appraisals of the discretization and round-off errors. But (15.19) still falls short of the boundedness relation valid for the explicit methods discussed earlier. We therefore dispense with a detailed proof of (15.19). (See Wasow [1958].)

The statement that a finite-difference method is stable or convergent for all values of $\lambda = k/h^2$ has to be interpreted with care. It does not necessarily imply that the solution of the difference problem is close to that of the differential problem whenever h and k are sufficiently small. For the assumption that λ is constant, even if arbitrarily large, may conceivably have been used in the proof. For instance, in the next section we are going to discuss a finite-difference problem whose solution tends to that of the heat equation for all λ, as $h \to 0$, but not if h and k tend to zero in such a way that k/h remains constant. An inspection of the arguments of this section shows, however, that for $\sigma \geq \frac{1}{2}$ the value of λ did not enter the reasoning, so that our present method is then convergent and stable no matter how h and k tend to zero. This is a genuine advantage over the method to be discussed in the next section. In concrete language it means, for instance, that we may perform a sequence of calculations, each time using a grid that has been refined by halving the preceding mesh lengths. The sequence of answers so obtained will converge to the solution of the differential problem.

The size of the discretization error has been studied, for $\sigma = \frac{1}{2}$, by

Juncosa and Young [1957] and, for $\sigma \geq \frac{1}{2}$, by Wasow [1958]. It turns out that the discretization error is $O(k + h^2)$ if $\sigma > \frac{1}{2}$, and $O(k^2 + h^2)$ if $\sigma = \frac{1}{2}$, provided k/h is bounded and the initial function possesses bounded fourth derivatives.

15.2. Explicit Methods Using More than Two Grid Lines

About the first finite-difference approximation proposed for the numerical solution of parabolic problems was the equation

$$\frac{U(x, t + k) - U(x, t - k)}{2k} = \frac{U(x - h, t) - 2U(x, t) + U(x + h, t)}{h^2},$$

$$(15.20)$$

which occurs in Richardson's fundamental paper [1910]. The use of the central time difference in the left member eliminates the term of order $O(k)$ in the Taylor expansion, If (15.20) is to be solved numerically, the value of U for $t = k$ must first be calculated independently by some other method. However, formula (15.20) is now only of historical interest as a reminder of the need for mathematical analysis of formally plausible procedures, because it is unstable for all values of $\lambda = k/h^2$. The instability has a somewhat more subtle character than in previous examples. Richardson failed to notice it, because its influence was not yet completely destructive over the small t range of his calculations (see O'Brien, Hyman, and Kaplan [1951]). The claim that (15.20) is unstable is usually justified by exhibiting a particular solution that grows exponentially with the number of t steps *in a fixed grid*. Since this does not by itself establish instability according to our definition, we give a more complete argument here.

The solution of (15.20) with the initial values

$$U(x, 0) = f(x), \qquad U(x, k) = g(x), \qquad -\infty < x < \infty \quad (15.21)$$

is of the form

$$U(sh, nk) = \sum_{\rho} g_{\rho s n} f(\rho h) + \sum_{\sigma} h_{\sigma s n} g(\sigma h), \qquad (15.22)$$

where $g_{\rho s n}$ and $h_{\sigma s n}$ are certain constants, and the summations extend over a finite number of terms. To find $g_{\rho s n}$, we take, in particular,

$$f(x) = e^{ix}, \qquad g(x) = 0.$$

From the resulting equality

$$U(sh, nk) = \sum_{\rho} g_{\rho s n} e^{i\rho h}$$

it follows, as before, that

$$g_{\rho s n} = \frac{1}{2\pi} \int_{-\pi}^{\pi} U(s\theta, nk) e^{-i\rho \theta} \, d\theta. \qquad (15.23)$$

On the other hand, we find directly from (15.20) that

$$U(x, 2k) = e^{ix}, \qquad U(x, nk) = e^{ix}\psi_{n-1},$$

where ψ_n is the solution of the difference equation problem

$$\psi_{n+1} = \psi_{n-1} - 8\lambda\psi_n \sin^2\frac{h}{2}, \qquad \psi_0 = 0, \qquad \psi_1 = 1. \qquad (15.24)$$

If we set, for abbreviation,

$$p(h) = 4\lambda \sin^2\frac{h}{2},$$

$$r_1(h) = \sqrt{1 + p^2(h)} + p(h), \qquad r_2(h) = \sqrt{1 + p^2(h)} - p(h),$$

the solution of (15.24) can be written

$$\psi_n = \frac{r_1{}^n(h) - r_2{}^n(h)}{2\sqrt{1 + p^2(h)}},$$

and we find the expression

$$U(sh, nk) = e^{ish}\frac{r_1^{n-1}(h) - r_2^{n-1}(h)}{2\sqrt{1 + p^2(h)}} \qquad (15.25)$$

for this particular solution of (15.20). For our purpose it is sufficient to study the value of g_{00n}, which, by insertion of (15.25) into (15.23) turns out to be

$$g_{00n} = \frac{1}{4\pi} \int_{-\pi}^{\pi} \frac{r_1^{n-1}(\theta) - r_2^{n-1}(\theta)}{\sqrt{1 + p^2(\theta)}} d\theta$$

$$= \frac{1}{4\pi} \int_{-\pi}^{\pi} \frac{r_1^{n-1}(\theta)}{\sqrt{1 + p^2(\theta)}} d\theta - \frac{1}{4\pi} \int_{-\pi}^{\pi} \frac{r_2^{n-1}(\theta)}{\sqrt{1 + p^2(\theta)}} d\theta.$$

Since $|r_2(\theta)| \leq 1$, the second integral in the last expression is uniformly bounded in n. To estimate the first integral, we observe that

$$\frac{4}{\pi^2}\lambda\theta^2 \leq p(\theta) \leq \lambda\theta^2, \qquad |\theta| \leq \pi,$$

so that

$$\left| \frac{1}{4\pi} \int_{-\pi}^{\pi} \frac{r_1^{n-1}(\theta)}{\sqrt{1 + p^2(\theta)}} d\theta \right| \geq \frac{1}{4\pi\sqrt{1 + \lambda^2\pi^4}} \int_{\pi/2}^{\pi} \left(\frac{16}{\pi^4}\lambda^2\theta^4 + 1 \right)^{(n-1)/2} d\theta$$

$$\geq \frac{1}{4\pi\sqrt{1 + \lambda^2\pi^4}} (1 + \lambda^2)^{(n-1)/2}.$$

Hence there exist two constants c, γ, independent of h and n for constant λ, such that $c > 1$ and

$$|g_{00n}| \geq \gamma c^n \tag{15.26}$$

for all sufficiently large n. Now g_{00n} is the value at $x = 0$, $t = nk$ of the solution $U(x, t)$ of (15.20) with the initial values

$$U(x, 0) = \begin{cases} 0, & x \neq 0, \\ 1, & x = 0, \end{cases} \qquad U(x, k) = 0.$$

Since $n = t/(\lambda h^2)$, inequality (15.26) proves the *instability of the* difference equation (15.20) according to the definition given in Sec. 5.1.

Equation (15.20) is an example of a difference approximation for parabolic equations that uses more than two grid lines. Several other such schemes have been proposed (see Collatz [1955], p. 267 ff.), some of them stable. We single out for a more detailed discussion an interesting method proposed in an article by DuFort and Frankel [1953]. These authors follow Richardson in the approximation of u_t by $(2k)^{-1}[U(x, t + k) - U(x, t - k)]$. But for the second derivative with respect to x they use the approximate expression

$$h^{-2}[U(x + h, t) - U(x, t + k) - U(x, t - k) + U(x - h, t)].$$

In other words, the term $2U(x, t)$ occurring in the simplest approximation to u_{xx} has been replaced by the average of its values in the grid points above and below the point (x, t). The resulting difference equation for the approximation of the simple heat equation is then

$$\frac{U(x, t + k) - U(x, t - k)}{2k}$$
$$= \frac{U(x + h, t) - U(x, t + k) - U(x, t - k) + U(x - h, t)}{h^2}. \tag{15.27}$$

This equation uses only every other point of the grid. It may be considered as pertaining to a diagonal grid whose meshes are rhombi with sides of length $\sqrt{h^2 + k^2}$. If the parabolic equation is of the more general type (14.1), the first derivatives, too, should be approximated by difference quotients in this coarser grid. As in Richardson's method, the values on the line $t = k$ must be calculated by some independent procedure before the calculation by (15.27) can be started.

In carrying out the computation by means of (15.27), there is some freedom in the order in which new points are added. One may, for example, first calculate the values at all the alternate points on a line $t = nk$, and then the values at the remaining half of the points on this line, and next proceed to the line $t = (n + 1)k$. Or one may push the calculation forward in triangular fashion, following successively one or the other of the two diagonal directions of the oblique net mentioned before. The authors call these the "leap-frog" and "pyramid" methods respectively.

The advantage of the method of DuFort and Frankel is that it is an explicit scheme which is *convergent and stable for all* λ. (Actually, these facts have not yet been completely proved for all equations of the form (14.1), but the arguments can doubtless be extended to the general case by the method used in John [1952].) It is very remarkable that the simple operation of replacing $U(x, t)$ by $\frac{1}{2}[U(x, t + k) + U(x, t - k)]$ changes Richardson's completely unstable scheme into a completely stable one! The proof will be given by an adaptation of the method of John explained in Sec. 14.4.

The solution $U(x, t)$ of (15.27) in the grid, with given initial functions $U(x, 0) = f(x)$, $U(x, k) = g(x)$, for $-\infty < x < \infty$, again admits a representation of the form

$$U(sh, nk) = \sum_{\rho} g_{\rho sn} f(\rho h) + \sum_{\rho} h_{\rho sn} g(\rho h), \qquad (15.28)$$

whose coefficients $g_{\rho sn}$, $h_{\rho sn}$ are, of course, not the same as for Richardson's method. They are zero whenever $|\rho - s| > n$. As before, the particular solution $U(x, t)$ corresponding to the initial functions $f(x) = e^{ix}$, $g(x) = 0$ on the whole x-axis can be used to express the coefficients $g_{\rho sn}$ in the form

$$g_{\rho sn} = \frac{1}{2\pi} \int_{-\pi}^{\pi} U(s\theta, nk) e^{-i\rho\theta} \, d\theta.$$

On the other hand, this particular solution $U(s\theta, nk)$ of (15.27) can be found explicitly by the technique of separation of variables. Setting

$$U(s\theta, nk) = \psi_n e^{is\theta}, \qquad \psi_0 = 1, \qquad \psi_1 = 0,$$

and inserting this into (15.27) with h replaced by θ, there results the linear difference-equation problem

$$(2\lambda + 1)\psi_{n+1} - 4\lambda(\cos\theta)\psi_n + (2\lambda - 1)\psi_{n-1} = 0,$$
$$\psi_0 = 1, \qquad \psi_1 = 0$$

for ψ_n, which can be solved by the standard method. The solution turns out to be

$$\psi_n = \psi_n(\theta) = -r_1 r_2 \frac{r_1^{n-1} - r_2^{n-1}}{r_1 - r_2}, \qquad (15.29)$$

where $r_j = r_j(\theta)$, $j = 1, 2$, are the roots of the quadratic equation

$$Q(r, \theta) \equiv (2\lambda + 1)r^2 - 4\lambda r \cos\theta + 2\lambda - 1 = 0. \qquad (15.30)$$

The problem of finding a sufficiently strong appraisal for $g_{\rho s n}$ from its integral representation, which may be written

$$g_{\rho s n} = \frac{1}{2\pi} \int_{-\pi}^{\pi} \psi_n e^{i(s-\rho)\theta} \, d\theta, \tag{15.31}$$

is a little more involved than the analogous argument in Sec. 14.4, because the function ψ_n is somewhat more complicated than the function $(\Sigma_r c_r e^{ir\theta})^n$ in (14.22), but the technique is basically the same.

We begin with the observation that $|\psi_n|$ is an even function of $\cos \theta$. Therefore we have from (15.31) that

$$|g_{\rho s n}| \le \frac{1}{2\pi} \int_{-\pi}^{\pi} |\psi_n| \, d\theta = \frac{2}{\pi} \int_{0}^{\pi/2} |\psi_n| \, d\theta. \tag{15.32}$$

If $\theta_0 > 0$ is sufficiently small, then it is seen from (15.30) that r_1 and r_2 are real and distinct in $0 \le \theta \le \theta_0$, and there admit power series whose beginnings are

$$r_1 = 1 - \lambda\theta^2 + O(\theta^4), \qquad r_2 = \frac{2\lambda - 1}{2\lambda + 1} + O(\theta^2), \qquad 0 \le \theta \le \theta_0.$$

Hence there exists an $\alpha > 0$ such that

$$|r_j| \le e^{-\alpha\theta^2}, \qquad j = 1, 2, \qquad 0 \le \theta \le \theta_0. \tag{15.33}$$

If $\theta_0 \le \theta \le \pi/2$ there exists a number $p < 1$ depending on θ_0 such that

$$|r_j| \le p < 1, \qquad \text{in } \theta_0 \le \theta \le \pi/2,$$

as a simple analysis of (15.30) will show. Using Cauchy's integral formula and the fact that $r_1 r_2 = (2\lambda - 1)/(2\lambda + 1)$, it can easily be verified that the function ψ_n in (15.29) permits the integral representation

$$\psi_n = \frac{1 - 2\lambda}{2\pi i} \oint_C \frac{r^{n-1}}{Q(r, \theta)} \, dr, \qquad \text{for } \theta_0 \le \theta \le \pi/2, \tag{15.34}$$

where C is the circle $|r| = p_0$ with $p < p_0 < 1$. Hence there exists a constant c such that

$$|\psi_n| \le c p_0^{n-1}, \qquad \text{for } \theta_0 \le \theta \le \pi/2.$$

Also, (15.29) and (15.33), together with the fact that $r_1 \ne r_2$ in $\theta \le \theta \le \theta_0$, imply that for c sufficiently large

$$|\psi_n| \le c e^{-n\alpha\theta^2}, \qquad \text{for } 0 \le \theta \le \theta_0. \tag{15.35}$$

Insertion of the last two inequalities into (15.32) leads to the first appraisal

$$g_{\rho s n} = O\left(\frac{1}{\sqrt{n}}\right), \tag{15.36}$$

analogous to (14.24).

To prove that the second appraisal of John's method, i.e., formula (14.27), is also true in the present case, (15.31) must be integrated by parts three times, which yields

$$|g_{\rho s n}| = \left| \frac{1}{2\pi(s-\rho)^3} \int_{-\pi}^{\pi} \frac{d^3\psi_n}{d\theta^3} e^{i(s-\rho)\theta} \, d\theta \right| \leq \frac{\text{const.}}{|s-\rho|^3} \int_0^{\pi} \left| \frac{d^3\psi_n}{d\theta^3} \right| d\theta. \tag{15.37}$$

In the interval $\theta_0 \leq \theta \leq \pi/2$, the derivative $d^3\psi_n/d\theta^3$ can be appraised by differentiating in (15.34) inside the integral sign. This shows that $|d^3\psi_n/d\theta^3| \leq c_1 p_0^{n-1}$, for $\theta_0 \leq \theta \leq \pi/2$, $c_1 = \text{const.}$ In $0 \leq \theta \leq \theta_0$ the denominator $r_1 - r_2$ of (15.29) is bounded away from zero. Furthermore, since r_1 and r_2 are even functions of θ,

$$\frac{dr_j}{d\theta} = O(\theta), \qquad \frac{d^2 r_j}{d\theta^2} = O(1), \qquad \frac{d^3 r_j}{d\theta^3} = O(\theta),$$

$$0 \leq \theta \leq \theta_0, \qquad j = 1, 2. \tag{15.38}$$

Differentiating (15.29), we find, after a short calculation based on these relations and on (15.33), that

$$\frac{d^3\psi_n}{d\theta^3} = O(n^3|\theta^3| + n^2|\theta|)e^{-\alpha(n-3)\theta^2}, \qquad \text{for } 0 \leq \theta \leq \theta_0. \tag{15.39}$$

Now we insert these appraisals of $|d^3\psi_n/d\theta^3|$ into (15.37) and, after some manipulations, we obtain the same result as (14.27), namely,

$$g_{\rho s n} = O(n(\rho - s)^{-3}).$$

From here on the argument is literally the same as in Sec. 14.4, and leads to the inequality

$$\left| \sum_{\rho} g_{\rho s n} f(\rho h) \right| \leq M\bar{f}, \qquad t \geq 0, \qquad -\infty < x < \infty, \tag{15.40}$$

where M denotes, as previously, a constant independent of h, k, x, and t (but not of λ), and $\bar{f}$ is an upper bound for $|f|$ in $-\infty < x < \infty$.

There is no need to reproduce here the very similar proof of the inequality

$$\left| \sum_{\sigma} h_{\sigma s n} g(\sigma h) \right| \leq M\bar{g}, \qquad t \geq 0, \qquad -\infty < x < \infty.$$

If the last two inequalities are added, a reference to (15.28) finally yields the appraisal

$$|U(x, t)| \leq M(\bar{f} + \bar{g}), \qquad t \geq 0, \qquad -\infty < x < \infty. \quad (15.41)$$

Equation (15.41) not only establishes the stability of the method but also leads, in the usual way, to a convergence theorem for the initial-value problem on the infinite x-axis. We shall not carry out this calculation, but we observe that the size of the discretization error depends on the goodness of the approximation on the line $t = k$. The formal Taylor expansion of (15.27) is

$$U_t = U_{xx} - \frac{k^2}{h^2} U_{tt} + \frac{h^2}{12} U_{x^4} - \frac{k^2}{6} U_{tt} + \cdots. \quad (15.42)$$

This implies that the discretization error v is of order $O(h^2)$ for any fixed λ, provided $v(x, k)$ is of this order.

As in the section on always stable implicit methods, Sec. 13.3, it is natural to ask whether stability and convergence are preserved even if λ tends to infinity, as $h \to 0$. Equation (15.42) shows that, when k/h remains constant in the passage to the limit, the difference equation (15.27) is a formal approximation to a differential equation of hyperbolic type, not to $u_t = u_{xx}$. Hence $k = o(h)$ is a necessary condition if (15.27) is to be used for the approximation of the latter equation.

15.3. Problems of Higher Order

The main effort in the numerical analysis of the future will probably be concentrated on problems more complicated than those discussed so far in this chapter. At the present time, few general results are available to a worker in this field. He has to rely on his own ingenuity, on fragmentary plausibility considerations consisting mostly in formal extensions of facts known to be true for simpler equations, and on numerical experimentation.

As an illustration of the treatment of linear problems of higher order, we mention the equation

$$L(u) \equiv u_{x^4} + u_{t^2} = 0, \quad (15.43)$$

with the initial conditions

$$u, u_t \text{ prescribed on } 0 < x < 1, t = 0,$$
$$u, u_x \text{ prescribed on } x = 0, t > 0, \text{ and on } x = 1, t > 0. \quad (15.44)$$

This problem occurs in the study of the vibrations of a clamped beam.

We have not given a general definition of what is to be understood by parabolic differential equations, and this is not the place to discuss this point systematically. A general treatment can be found, for example, in

Courant and Hilbert [1937], Chap. 3. We content ourselves with an argument similar to that given in Sec. 11.1 for the heat equation. The problem (15.43), (15.44) is equivalent to the system

$$u_x = w, \qquad v_x = z, \qquad w_x = v_t, \qquad z_x = -u_t, \qquad (15.45)$$

combined with certain boundary conditions. The system (15.45) is not hyperbolic, because equation (6.9), which determines the characteristic directions, here becomes

$$\begin{vmatrix} 1 & 0 & 0 & 0 \\ 0 & 1 & 0 & 0 \\ 0 & -\lambda & 1 & 0 \\ \lambda & 0 & 0 & 1 \end{vmatrix} = 0,$$

and this has no solution. On the other hand, the system

$$u_x = w - \epsilon^2 z_t, \qquad v_x = z + 4\epsilon^2 w_t, \qquad w_x = v_t, \qquad z_x = -u_t,$$

whose characteristic directions are determined from the equation

$$\begin{vmatrix} 1 & 0 & 0 & \epsilon^2\lambda \\ 0 & 1 & -4\epsilon^2\lambda & 0 \\ 0 & -\lambda & 1 & 0 \\ \lambda & 0 & 0 & 1 \end{vmatrix} \equiv (1 - \epsilon^2\lambda^2)(1 - 4\epsilon^2\lambda^2) = 0,$$

is readily seen to be hyperbolic. As $\epsilon \to 0$, the system tends to (15.45), and the characteristic directions become parallel to the x-axis.

The simplest formal approximation is obtained by replacing the derivatives with central-difference quotients. In this manner one finds the difference expression

$$L_h(U) = h^{-4}[U(x - 2h, t) - 4U(x - h, t) + 6U(x, t) - 4U(x + h, t)$$
$$+ U(x + 2h, t)] + k^{-2}[U(x, t - k) - 2U(x, t) + U(x, t + k)], \quad (15.46)$$

which is connected with $L(u)$ by the formula

$$L_h(\phi) = L(\phi) + \frac{h^2}{6}\,\tilde{\phi}_{x^6} + \frac{k^2}{12}\,\tilde{\phi}_{t^4},$$

valid for any sufficiently smooth function ϕ. The tilde indicates that the function is to be taken at some intermediate point.

From the formula

$$L_h(U) = 0,$$

$U(x, t)$ can be successively calculated in $h < x < 1 - h$, $k < t$, provided the values on the boundary and at the grid points nearest to the boundary are given. These can be determined approximately from the boundary conditions by replacing u_x, u_t there by the difference quotients in the direction towards the interior of the domain.

Collatz [1951] has shown that the solutions of (15.46) of the form

$$U(x, t) = \sin \omega x e^{\alpha t} \tag{15.47}$$

decrease with increasing t if and only if $\lambda \leq \frac{1}{2}$. It is plausible—and probably provable by the method of John—that this is the exact condition for stability and bounded behavior of the solutions.

Crandall [1954] has suggested that one should use the analog of (15.2) with $\sigma = \frac{1}{2}$ in this case; i.e., the first bracketed expression in the right member of (15.46) should be replaced by the average of its values on the lines t and $t + k$. The hope that this implicit method might be stable for *all* values of λ is strengthened by showing that now the solutions of the form (15.47) shrink with increasing t, no matter what the value of λ. The matrix of the system of linear equations that has to be solved at every step is no longer tridiagonal, but may have up to five nonzero elements in every row. It would therefore be interesting to find out if the explicit method of DuFort and Frankel can be extended to such problems.

SECTION 16. OTHER DEFINITIONS OF CONVERGENCE. THE THEORY OF LAX AND RICHTMYER

16.1. Remarks on Functional Analysis

A central topic of this book is the question as to how well a solution $U(x, t)$ of a difference equation approximates the solution $u(x, t)$ of a related differential equation problem. This question has naturally led us to search for upper bounds for the quantity $|U - u|$. The appraisals obtained have usually been either valid uniformly for all values of x and t in the domain under consideration or at least uniformly with respect to x, when t is given. From the point of view of functional analysis, this way of measuring the discrepancy between two functions is only one among infinitely many, and often by no means the simplest. For instance, the quantity

$$\left\{ \int_a^b [\phi(x) - \psi(x)]^2 \, dx \right\}^{1/2} \tag{16.1}$$

is frequently taken as a measure of the extent to which two functions $\phi(x)$ and $\psi(x)$ differ in the interval $a \leq x \leq b$.

In an important article Lax and Richtmyer [1956] have developed a theory of the stability and convergence of linear difference equations which is based on the concepts and methods of functional analysis. Only a very brief description of the ideas and results of that paper will be given here since a full account would require too much space. (See also Sec. 29.)

The terminology of functional analysis takes its inspiration from the analogy with ordinary geometry. A set of functions is called a *space*, each function being one point of the space. Such a space is *linear* if it contains all linear combinations with constant coefficients of any two of its elements. It is a *normed* linear space if a nonnegative number $\|\phi\|$ is associated with each function $\phi(x)$, called the *norm* of $\phi(x)$, which is analogous to distance from the origin in ordinary geometry. It would lead us much too far if we tried to give even an abbreviated account of these ideas here. We mention only one of the important requirements a norm must satisfy, i.e., the *triangle inequality*

$$\|\phi + \psi\| \leq \|\phi\| + \|\psi\|.$$

If the functions of the space are defined in the interval $a \leq x \leq b$, the most frequently employed norms are

$$\sup_{a \leq x \leq b} |\phi(x)| \qquad (16.2)$$

and

$$\left[\int_a^b \phi^2(x)\, dx \right]^{1/2}. \qquad (16.3)$$

The *distance* between two functions $\phi(x)$ and $\psi(x)$ is, of course, defined as the norm of their difference, i.e., as $\|\phi - \psi\|$. Observe that (16.2) is the norm that has been the tacit basis of most of our investigations so far. The distance corresponding to the norm (16.3) is defined by (16.1).

A sequence of functions $\phi_n(x)$ is said to *converge* to $\phi(x)$, with respect to a given norm, if $\lim_{n \to \infty} \|\phi_n - \phi\| = 0$. It is essential to realize that a sequence of functions may converge with respect to one norm without converging with respect to another. Thus, the sequence $|x|^n$ tends to zero in $-1 \leq x \leq 1$ with respect to the norm of (16.3) but not with respect to that of (16.2).

The work of Lax and Richtmyer [1956] is based on the theory of Banach spaces. This is a type of normed linear space that enjoys a number of additional restrictive properties, the most important one of which is *completeness*. To explain this concept, we recall Cauchy's theorem that a sequence of real numbers a_n, $n = 1, 2, \cdots$, converges to a limit number a

if and only if $\lim_{n,m \to \infty} |a_n - a_m| = 0$. A normed linear space is called *complete* if it has the analogous property, i.e., if to every sequence $\phi_n(x)$ for which $\lim_{n,m \to \infty} \|\phi_n - \phi_m\| = 0$ there corresponds a function $\phi(x)$ in the same space such that $\lim_{n \to \infty} \|\phi_n - \phi\| = 0$.

The space of all continuous functions in the interval $a \leq x \leq b$ is complete with respect to the norm (16.2). This is nothing but a rewording of a well-known theorem on uniform convergence. If this space is extended to the set of all functions for which $\int_a^b \phi^2(x)\, dx$ exists (in the sense of Lebesgue), a complete space with respect to the norm in (16.3) is obtained. Both these spaces are Banach spaces.

16.2. Convergence and Stability in the Sense of Lax and Richtmyer

Let us assume that the initial function of the linear differential equation problem to be solved belongs to some Banach space $\mathscr{B}$ of functions of x alone. The particular norm used need not be specified as yet. It cannot be expected that a solution of the differential equation problem will exist for every initial function in $\mathscr{B}$. To arrive at a well-rounded theory, some fairly mild conditions must be imposed on the initial-value problem and the space $\mathscr{B}$. These conditions will not be discussed here in detail. They amount essentially to requiring that the initial-value problem be well posed, in the sense of the Introduction, and that every function of $\mathscr{B}$ can be approximated by initial functions for which a genuine solution exists. These assumptions make it possible to associate with *every* initial function in $\mathscr{B}$ a solution in a somewhat generalized sense. For any fixed value of t such a solution is a function of x alone. This function will be an element of $\mathscr{B}$, and it is a limit (in the norm of $\mathscr{B}$) of genuine solutions of the differential equation.

The solutions $U(x, t)$ of the *difference* equations to be studied are defined only at the points of a grid. If $U(x, t)$ is to be an element of $\mathscr{B}$ for fixed t, its definition must be extended over the whole x interval under consideration. Let us assume that this has been done in some reasonable manner, say, by linear interpolation.

In the framework of these ideas, the solution $U(x, t)$ of a difference problem will be said to converge to a solution $u(x, t)$ of a differential problem if $\lim_{h \to 0} \|U(x, t) - u(x, t)\| = 0$. A finite-difference problem is called *convergent* if its solution converges to that of the formally corresponding differential equation problem *for all initial functions in $\mathscr{B}$*. This is a more stringent requirement than those imposed in our treatment so far. We have usually been satisfied with establishing convergence [in the sense of the norm of (16.2)] for the functions in some incomplete subset of the underlying Banach space.

A finite-difference equation is called *stable* by Lax and Richtmyer if the solution $U(x, t)$ corresponding to an initial function $f(x)$ satisfies a boundedness relation of the form

$$\|U(x, t)\| \leq M(t)\|f(x)\|, \qquad \text{for } 0 \leq t \leq T, \tag{16.4}$$

where $M(t)$ is independent of h. (Here k is assumed to be a given function of h such that $\lim_{h \to 0} k = 0$.) This is to be true for all $f(x)$ in $\mathscr{B}$. Again, this condition is much more restrictive than the one adapted in Chap. 1, since we permit $M(t)$ to grow like a power of h^{-1}.

If the terms "convergence" and "stability" are understood in the way just explained, it can be proved that, for a difference equation approximating a differential equation in the formal sense, *convergence and stability are equivalent.*

With the norm we have used so far, we could have availed ourselves of this beautiful theorem wherever we had succeeded in proving a relation of the form (16.4), i.e., for all the explicit methods for parabolic problems. Equation (15.2) is stable, in the sense of equation (16.4) for the norm (16.2), if $(1 - \sigma)\lambda \leq \frac{1}{2}$, since it is then of positive type, but we have not succeeded in proving (16.4) generally for that equation.

Lax and Richtmyer avoid the difficulties that seem to be inherent in the use of the norm (16.2) by basing the second, more specialized part of their paper on the norm (16.3) instead. They prove a number of general theorems concerning the stability of linear difference equations with constant coefficients, which imply the stability and, hence, the convergence of all the methods for linear problems discussed here, provided h and k are subject to the necessary restrictions. These results are not restricted to problems in one space dimension, and they include certain problems of hyperbolic type as well.

In spite of the beauty and generality of these results, the norm (16.2) has a greater appeal to a computer. The statement that $\int_a^b [U(x, t) - u(x, t)]^2 \, dx$ tends to zero, as $h \to 0$, contains less information regarding the closeness of $U(x, t)$ to $u(x, t)$ at a grid point than the analogous statement for $\sup_{a \leq x \leq b} |U(x, t) - u(x, t)|$. An appraisal of the discretization error based on the former norm will give us only a bound on the mean square error on a line. At a single point $U(x, t)$ might conceivably even fail to be bounded. Furthermore, the extension of the definition of $U(x, t)$ to points not in the grid is somewhat artificial and would make the computational use of explicit appraisals awkward.

It is generally true that norms defined in terms of integrals, and particularly the mean square norm, are easier to handle than the maximum modulus norm. It is therefore a very important fact that, if a sequence of functions of n variables converges in the mean square norm, *and if the same is true of its partial derivatives up to some even order $m > n/2$, then the sequence converges uniformly.* This result is frequently referred to as *Sobolev's lemma.* With its help many of the modern techniques in the theory of partial differential equations can be brought to bear on practically important questions of convergence and error analysis for difference equations. However, an adequate account of these developments transcends the scope of this book.

SECTION 17. NONLINEAR PROBLEMS

17.1. Semilinear Equations

The simplest fairly general type of nonlinear parabolic differential equations, and the only one for which an approximating difference equation has been studied systematically, is

$$u_t = a_0(x, t)u_{xx} + a_1(x, t)u_x + d(x, t, u). \tag{17.1}$$

By analogy with the usage in the theory of hyperbolic equations, (17.1) should be called *semilinear.* It is a special type of quasilinear equation, since the latter term is used to denote any differential equation that is linear in the highest derivatives of u.

John [1952] investigates difference approximations of the form

$$U(x, t + k) = \sum_r c_r(x, t) \, U(x + rh, t) + k \, d(x, t, U(x, t)). \tag{17.2}$$

Among more general results, he proves the following theorem:

THEOREM 17.1. *Let the equations* (17.1) *and* (17.2) *satisfy the following hypotheses. In the domain R defined by $-\infty < x < \infty$, $0 \le t \le T$, the coefficient a_0 possesses uniformly continuous second derivatives, and is positive and bounded away from zero; a_1 has in R uniformly continuous first derivatives; d has uniformly continuous derivatives with respect to x and u, for all u, and is bounded and uniformly continuous as a function of its three arguments for (x, t) in R and any bounded u interval. Furthermore, the $c_r(x, t)$ satisfy the conditions* (14.7), *are twice continuously differentiable with respect to x and h, and satisfy the inequality* (14.19). *Then the solution $U(x, t)$ of* (17.2) *with initial values $U(x, 0) = f(x)$ that are bounded and Riemann integrable tends in R to the corresponding solution of* (17.1).

In this form the theorem is rather difficult to prove without the apparatus developed by John, even if we do not aim, as John does, to prove at the same time the existence of a solution u of the continuous problem. However, if we *include the existence, boundedness, and uniform continuity in R of* u_t *and* u_{xx} *among our hypotheses, as well as the boundedness of* $|d_u(x, t, u)|$ *for all u and all* (x, t) *in R*, then the convergence proof becomes a routine application of the general scheme of Sec. 7.2.

To show this, let $L_h(U)$ and $L(u)$ have the meaning defined in (14.4) and (14.5) respectively (with $a_2 \equiv 0$). Then we have to compare the equations

$$L_h(U) = k \, d(x, t, U) \tag{17.3}$$

and

$$L(u) = d(x, t, u) \tag{17.4}$$

under the assumption that $U(x, 0) - u(x, 0) = 0$. By virtue of (14.6) and our hypotheses concerning u, we have

$$L_h(u) = kL(u) + o(k) = k \, d(x, t, u) + o(k)$$

uniformly in R, and therefore, subtracting the last equation from (17.3),

$$L_h(v) = k[d(x, t, U) - d(x, t, u)] + o(k).$$

As usual, v stands for $U - u$. Since $d(x, t, u)$ has a uniformly bounded derivative with respect to u for *all* values of u (this is actually an unnecessarily strong assumption), the last equality can be written

$$L_h(v) = \mu(x, t, u, v, h), \tag{17.5}$$

where

$$|\mu| \leq \beta k(|v| + \omega), \qquad \beta = \text{const.}, \tag{17.6}$$

where ω is a positive function of x, t, and h such that

$$\lim_{h \to 0} \omega = 0, \qquad \text{uniformly in } R.$$

Let $\bar{v}$ and $\bar{\omega}$ denote the least upper bounds of $|v|$ and ω in R. That $\bar{v}$ exists is clear from the construction of $U(x, t)$ by means of equation (17.2), but it might conceivably diverge, as $h \to 0$. To see that it does not, we apply Theorem 14.4 to equation (17.5) and obtain the relation

$$\bar{v} \leq M\beta \, T(\bar{v} + \bar{\omega}).$$

This inequality shows that $\lim_{h \to 0} \bar{v} = 0$, provided $T < 1/(M\beta)$, since then $\bar{v} \leq M\beta T\bar{\omega}/(1 - M\beta T)$. To extend the result beyond this possibly rather narrow strip, assume that $0 < T_1 < 1/(M\beta) < T$, and consider $t = T_1$ as a new starting line for our problem. By another application of Theorem 14.4, we have for the maximum $\bar{v}_2$ of $|v|$ in $T_1 \leq t \leq T_2$ the inequality

$$\bar{v}_2 \leq M[\beta(T_2 - T_1)(\bar{v}_2 + \omega) + \bar{v}_1],$$

where $\bar{v}_1 = \text{l.u.b.}_{0 \leq t \leq T_1} |v|$. This extends the validity of the statement $\lim_{h \to 0} v = 0$ to the strip $T_1 < t \leq T_2$, where T_2 must be chosen so that $M \beta(T_2 - T_1) < 1$. Repeating the procedure, the convergence of U to u can be proved in the whole region R.

It is probably not very difficult to extend this result to boundary-value problems in finite intervals and to some of the other explicit and implicit methods we have met.

17.2. Examples of Other Parabolic Problems

Under this heading fall most of the parabolic problems which are actually solved by finite-difference methods in applications to physics and technology. The state of the theory in this field is still very fragmentary. We shall content ourselves with the discussion of a few examples. In addition we mention papers by Rose [1956], Douglas [1956, 1958], Lees [1957] that contain interesting results in this direction.

There is one point, however, which deserves a remark of more general character. The difference quotient $k^{-1}[u(x, t + k) - u(x, t)]$ approximates the derivative $u_t(x, t)$ to within an error term of order $O(k)$. If $u(x, t + k)$ is expanded about $(x, t + \frac{1}{2}k)$ instead of about (x, t), it is seen that the difference quotient differs from $u_t(x, t + \frac{1}{2}k)$ by a term of order $O(k^2)$ only. More generally, in choosing a finite-difference equation which approximates a given parabolic differential equation much effort is frequently spent on achieving a high symmetry about the points $(x, t + \frac{1}{2}k)$. For instance, if the differential equation contains a term of the form $F(u)$, where $u = u(x, t)$ is the unknown function, this is often replaced by $F(\frac{1}{2}[U(x, t + k) + U(x, t)])$ in the approximating difference equation. If $F(u)$ is a complicated function, the numerical task of finding $U(x, t + k)$ is then much greater than for a difference equation containing the term $F(U(x, t))$ as an approximation for $F(u)$.

Similarly, the choice $\sigma = \frac{1}{2}$ is often recommended as the best value in equation (15.2), because the formal error when U is replaced by any sufficiently smooth function $\phi(x, t)$ in the difference equation is then $O(k^2 + h^2)$ at the point $(x, t + \frac{1}{2}k)$, rather than $O(k + h^2)$, the order of the formal error at (x, t).

Given our incomplete theoretical knowledge of these matters, only numerical experimentation can ultimately decide what is the best finite-difference scheme for a parabolic problem. However, there are a few observations of a theoretical character that should be made in this connection. If the reason for choosing a more complicated difference equation is that it changes the order of magnitude of the formal error in the equation from $O(k + h^2)$ to $O(k^2 + h^2)$, it is implicitly assumed that $\lim_{h \to 0} h^2/k = 0$ in the passage to the limit. Hence no improvement can be expected unless

h^2 is small with respect to k. On the other hand, there is the second implicit hypothesis that the discretization error is of the order of magnitude of the formal error in the difference equation. This has so far been proved for a very few simple problems only. Therefore the computational advantages of a complicated symmetric formula over a simpler unsymmetric one should not be taken for granted.

Another objection could be raised concerning the advantages of symmetric formulas, but this one is more easily dispelled: If (x, t) is a net point, the formal error term $O(k^2 + h^2)$ was obtained by expanding the terms of the difference equation formally about the point $(x, t + \frac{1}{2}k)$. Since the difference equation contains the values at the net points and not halfway between them, it is not obvious that improving the order of the formal error at the halfway points will also improve it at the net points. In fact, a shift from $t + \frac{1}{2}k$ to t might be expected to introduce another error of order $O(k)$. To answer this objection, we recall that, in the usual appraisal of the discretization error on the basis of the formal error in the difference operator, the latter operator has to be applied only to the particular function $u(x, t)$ that solves the given differential problem (see Sec. 7.2). It can be shown that for this special function u the change from $(x, t + \frac{1}{2}k)$ to (x, t) as the point around which Taylor's expansion takes place does *not* introduce error terms of order $O(k)$.

We illustrate this last point with the difference equation

$$\frac{1}{k}[U(x, t + k) - U(x, t)]$$

$$-\frac{1}{2h^2}[U(x + h, t + k) - 2U(x, t + k) + U(x - h, t + k)]$$

$$-\frac{1}{2h^2}[U(x + h, t) - 2U(x, t) + U(x - h, t)]$$

$$-F\left(\frac{U(x, t + k) + U(x, t)}{2}\right) = 0,$$

which is a formal approximation to the differential equation

$$u_t - u_{xx} - F(u) = 0.$$

If an arbitrary, sufficiently smooth function $\phi(x, t)$ is inserted for $U(x, t)$ in the difference equation, expansion about the point (x, t) yields

$$\phi_t - \phi_{xx} - F(\phi) + \frac{k}{2}[\phi_{tt} - \phi_{xxt} - F'(\phi)\phi_t] + O(k^2 + h^2)$$

for the left member. Thus, the formal error is $O(k + h^2)$. However, if ϕ happens to solve the differential equation and is sufficiently smooth, the expression in brackets in the last formula vanishes and the formal error at (x, t) is $O(k^2 + h^2)$.

Examples

1. Let c be a given positive constant and let $d(x, t)$ and $f(x)$ be given functions with period 2π in x. Find a function u such that

$$u_t = cu_{xx} - \tfrac{1}{2}u_x{}^2 + d(x, t) \qquad \text{for } -\infty < x < \infty, \qquad t > 0,$$

and

$$u(x, 0) = f(x), \qquad u(x + 2\pi, t) = u(x, t).$$

This problem has to do with the burning of gas in a rocket.

It is not difficult to set up various explicit and implicit difference schemes for this equation. The resulting equations for $U(x, t + k)$ are nonlinear in the values of $U(x, t)$. If implicit methods are to be used, this is a serious inconvenience. One way to overcome it is to "linearize" the difference problem by replacing the *first* factor u_x in the term $-\tfrac{1}{2}u_x{}^2 = -\tfrac{1}{2}u_x u_x$ by a difference quotient at the level $t + k$, and the *second* by one at the level t. Nothing definite is known yet concerning the convergence and stability of this method.

2. The main problem considered in the paper by Crank and Nicolson [1947] is the solution of the following system of two simultaneous differential equations:

$$\left. \begin{array}{l} u_t = u_{xx} - qw_t \\[2mm] w_t = -cwe^{-A/u} \end{array} \right\} \quad \text{for } t > 0, \qquad 0 < x < 1 \tag{17.7, 17.8}$$

$(q, c, A$ are positive constants), subject to the nonlinear boundary conditions

$$u(x, 0) = f_1(x), \qquad w(x, 0) = f_2(x), \tag{17.9}$$

$$u_x(0, t) = h_1(u), \qquad u_x(1, t) = h_2(u). \tag{17.10}$$

Problems of this sort arise in the study of the flow of heat generated by a chemical reaction in a medium where the rate of the reaction depends on the local temperature.

Various techniques are discussed in Crank and Nicolson [1947]. Since no error analysis is feasible for such a complicated problem, the authors judge the size of the discretization error to be expected by the order of magnitude of the error terms that arise when the difference expressions are developed by Taylor's series.

In the method most recommended by Crank and Nicolson [1947] the differential equation (17.7) is approximated by the difference equation

$$\frac{U(x, t + k) - U(x, t)}{k}$$

$$= \frac{1}{2h^2} [U(x + h, t + k) - 2U(x, t + k) + U(x - h, t + k)]$$

$$+ \frac{1}{2h^2} [U(x + h, t) - 2U(x, t) + U(x - h, t)]$$

$$- q \frac{W(x, t + k) - W(x, t)}{k}. \tag{17.11}$$

The formal error term for this equation at the point $(x, t + \frac{1}{2}k)$ is $O(k^2 + h^2)$.

To obtain an equally accurate approximation for (17.8), the latter equation is integrated from t to $t + k$, and the resulting equation,

$$\log \frac{w(x, t + k)}{w(x, t)} = -c \int_t^{t+k} e^{-A/u(\sigma)} \, d\sigma,$$

is approximated by

$$\log \frac{W(x, t + k)}{W(x, t)} = -kce^{-2A/[U(x,t+k) + U(x,t)]},$$

i.e., by

$$W(x, t + k) = W(x, t)e^{2E}, \tag{17.12}$$

with

$$E = -\tfrac{1}{2}kce^{-2A/[U(x,t+k) + U(x,t)]}. \tag{17.13}$$

The formal error involved in this approximation is $O(k^2)$.

The basis for the approximation formula for the first of the boundary conditions (17.10) is the difference relation

$$\frac{U(h, t) - U(-h, t)}{2h} = h_1 \left[\frac{U(0, t + k) + U(0, t)}{2} \right], \tag{17.14}$$

whose formal error at the level $t + \frac{1}{2}k$ is $O(h^2 + k^2)$. Since (17.14) involves the value of $U(-h, t)$, another equation is needed to make a fully determined problem. It is obtained by requiring the validity of (17.11) for $x = 0$ and not only for $x \geq h$. The other end point, $x = 1$, is treated similarly.

The determination of the values of $U(x, t_1 + k)$, when $U(x, t_1)$, $W(x, t_1)$ are known on the segment $t = t_1$, requires the solution of a fairly complicated system of nonlinear equations. It is achieved in Crank and Nicolson [1947] by an iterative method.

It would be interesting to investigate whether this complicated method is really warranted by the ensuing gain in accuracy. Formula (17.11) probably has the advantage of being stable for all mesh ratios since this is so for linear equations (see Sec. 15.1). The order of magnitude of the discretization error depends on the relative order of magnitude of h and k. If $k = O(h^2)$, we expect a discretization error that is $O(k)$, since the formal error in equation (17.11) is $O(k^2 + h^2)$. Then one might be satisfied with the simpler formula

$$W(x, t + k) - W(x, t) = -kcW(x, t)e^{-A/U(x,t)}$$

instead of (17.12). This would facilitate the calculation of $U(x, t + k)$ since now $W(x, t + k)$ can be calculated explicitly from $U(x, t)$ and $W(x, t)$. The implicit system of equations for the values of $U(sh, t + k)$, $s = -1, 0, 1, \cdots, 1/h, 1/h + 1$, is of course still nonlinear because of the occurrence of the functions h_1 and h_2, and therefore this system will have to be solved by some process of iteration. Crank and Nicolson [1947] take $h = \frac{1}{8}$, $k = \frac{1}{64}$, i.e., $k = h^2$, so that in the absence of better information one feels justified in relying on the theoretical considerations valid, in the linear case, when $k = O(h^2)$.

3. The flow of heat in the shell of projectiles is governed by nonlinear parabolic differential equations because the thermal properties of steel vary appreciably over the range of temperatures encountered. One problem of this sort was solved numerically by Eddy [1952], with the help of a scheme suggested by von Neumann.

The differential equation considered was

$$A(u)u_t = (B(u)u_x)_x, \qquad B(u) > 0,$$

with the initial condition

$$u(x, 0) = c = \text{const.}$$

and the boundary conditions

$$B(u)u_x = \begin{cases} H(u, t), & x = 0 \\ \\ 0, & x = l. \end{cases}$$

We refer to Eddy's paper for the physical meaning of the functions $A(u)$, $B(u)$, $H(u, t)$.

The method used by Eddy resembles in many ways that of the preceding example, but there are a few new features. First, a more consistent use is made of the idea of replacing the value of U at every point by its average value at two other points. Second, in order not to have to solve a complicated system of nonlinear equations for $U(x, t + k)$ in terms of $U(x, t)$, the function u in $A(u)$ and $B(u)$ is replaced, not by an average of values of U at t and $t + k$ but by the *extrapolated mean* μU defined by

$$\mu U = \tfrac{3}{4}[U(x,t) + U(x + h, t)] - \tfrac{1}{4}[U(x, t - k) + U(x + h, t - k)]. \quad (17.15)$$

It involves a formal error of order $O(h^2 + k^2)$ at the point $(x + \tfrac{1}{2}h, t + \tfrac{1}{2}k)$. The derivative u_x is approximated by

$$\delta U = \frac{1}{h}\left[\frac{U(x + h, t + k) + U(x + h, t)}{2} - \frac{U(x, t + k) + U(x, t)}{2}\right]. \quad (17.16)$$

If in the expressions $B(u)u_x$ the quantities u and u_x are replaced by the respective approximations (17.15) and (17.16), the finite-difference expression $B(\mu U)\,\delta U$ is obtained, which involves the six points indicated in Fig. 17.1. The small circle at $(x + \tfrac{1}{2}h, t + \tfrac{1}{2}k)$ marks the point at which

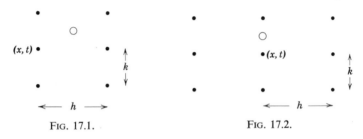

FIG. 17.1.   FIG. 17.2.

the difference expression is "centered" in the sense that formal expansion about this point yields the closest approximation to $B(u)u_x$, the error term being of the order $O(h^2 + k^2)$. The differential expression $(B(u)u_x)_x$ is then approximated by the backward-difference quotient of $B(\mu U)\,\delta U$, which yields a difference expression "centered" at $(x, t + \tfrac{1}{2}k)$ and involving an error of $O(h^2 + k^2)$. Figure 17.2 shows the stencil for this approximation.

To approximate the boundary conditions without having to introduce net points outside the interval $0 \leq x \leq l$, the lines $x = 0$, $x = l$ are placed halfway between the grid points, so that these grid points have the coordinates $x = (s + \tfrac{1}{2})h$, $t = nk$ $(s, n = 0, 1, \cdots)$. The expression $B(\mu U)\,\delta U$ formed at $x = h/2, t = nk$ is a formal approximation to the order $O(h^2 + k^2)$ of $B(u)u_x$ at the point $x = h$, $t = (n + \tfrac{1}{2})k$. Since $B(u)u_x = H(u, t)$ at $x = 0$, the differential expression $(B(u)u_x)_x$ can be approximated at $(\tfrac{1}{2}h, nk + \tfrac{1}{2}k)$ by subtracting from $B(\mu U)\,\delta U$, taken at $(\tfrac{1}{2}h, nk)$, an approximation to $H(u, t)$ at $(0, nk + \tfrac{1}{2}k)$ and dividing by k. A convenient approximation to $H(u, t)$ at that point is obtained by replacing u and t by $\tfrac{3}{2}U(0, nk) - \tfrac{1}{2}U(0, (n - 1)k)$ and $(n + \tfrac{1}{2})k$ respectively.

With this setup the values of U at $t = k$ must be calculated independently by some different method. From then on the determination of U on successive t levels proceeds by solving a system of linear equations, as in Sec. 13.4.

For linear differential equations the method just described reduces again to (15.2) with $\sigma = \frac{1}{2}$. The doubts raised at the beginning of this section concerning the advantages of the complicated averaging procedures are also pertinent here.

3

ELLIPTIC EQUATIONS

SECTION 18. SOME NUMERICAL PROBLEMS INVOLVING ELLIPTIC PARTIAL DIFFERENTIAL EQUATIONS

To introduce this chapter, we shall list a few elliptic problems for which engineers and others really want numerical answers. (See Sec. 1 for a definition of the term *elliptic*.) There are difficulties in solving these problems that one does not yet know how to overcome.

Let R denote an open region of n dimensional space ($n = 2$ or 3), with a boundary C made up of one or more differentiable curves or surfaces. For $n = 2$, suppose that any one of the finite number of simple closed curves comprising C may be given the parametric representation $x(s)$, $y(s)$, where $0 \leq s \leq s_m$ and s represents arc length. We shall ordinarily suppose that $x(s)$ and $y(s)$ are real analytic functions of s (i.e., have Taylor series expansions about every point s) in each of a finite number m of closed intervals

$$0 = s_0 \leq s \leq s_1, \qquad s_1 \leq s \leq s_2, \cdots, \qquad s_{m-1} \leq s \leq s_m.$$

Such a C is said to be *piecewise analytic*. An analogous definition can be given for boundary surfaces in three dimensions.

In practice the periodic functions $x(s)$, $y(s)$ defining each boundary curve of R ($n = 2$) are often not only piecewise analytic, but are even piecewise polynomial functions of low degree. On the other hand, a restriction to functions $x(s)$, $y(s)$ periodic and analytic on the entire boundary C is not sufficient in practice, for very often engineering drawings show several corners where two lines meet, or where such corners are "faired" with an arc of a circle. Piecewise analyticity seems general enough to cover most practical cases for $n = 2$ or 3, and restrictive enough to permit powerful mathematical tools to be used (especially for $n = 2$).

18.1. General Laplacian Boundary-Value Problem

Let u be a function of $n = 2$ or 3 space variables x, y, and perhaps z. Define the *Laplacian* operator

$$\Delta u = u_{xx} + u_{yy} \qquad (+\, u_{zz}, \text{ if } n = 3).$$

Let u_n denote the *inward normal derivative* of u on C. Let $f(P)$ be a sufficiently smooth function defined for P in R. Let $\alpha(P)$, $\beta(P)$, $\gamma(P)$, piecewise sufficiently smooth, be defined for P on C.

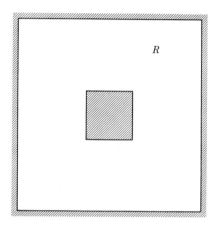

FIG. 18.1. Hollow square.

A fairly common class of problems is included in the following general *boundary-value problem*: Solve Poisson's partial differential equation

$$\Delta u(P) = f(P), \qquad P \text{ in } R \tag{18.1}$$

subject to the boundary condition

$$\alpha(P)\, u(P) + \beta(P)\, u_n(P) + \gamma(P) = 0, \qquad P \text{ on } C. \tag{18.2}$$

For $n = 2$ we find among others the following regions R in Southwell [1946]: the interior of a triangle or rectangle, a hollow square (Fig. 18.1), and a pierced triangle (Fig. 18.2), as well as more complicated ones.

As a particular case of the problems (18.1), (18.2), there is a *torsion problem* of elasticity (Sokolnikoff [1956], p. 116), in which $n = 2$, $\alpha(P) = 1$, $\beta(P) = \gamma(P) = 0$, and $f(P) = -2$. Thus one is to solve the equation $\Delta u(P) = -2$ in a plane region with $u(P) = 0$ on the boundary C.

Perhaps the most famous boundary-value problem in mathematics is the *plane Dirichlet problem*, in which $n = 2$, $f(P) = 0$, $\alpha(P) = 1$, $\beta(P) = 0$, and $\gamma(P)$ is arbitrary. Thus $u(P)$ is prescribed on C, and one seeks $u(P)$ in R so that $\Delta u(P) = 0$ in R.

Certain more complicated physical problems have discontinuities which lead to *interface conditions*. For example, R may be divided into two regions R_1, R_2 by an interface C_1, where the solution must satisfy the condition

$$u_n|_1 = ku_n|_2, \tag{18.3}$$

where k is a nonzero constant.

It is typical of physical problems involving partial differential equations that the boundary and interface conditions usually cause more numerical

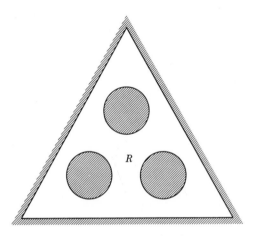

Fig. 18.2.   Pierced triangle.

difficulties than the differential equation itself. This is, incidentally, often also true for ordinary differential equations.

18.2. A Water Drainage Problem

Mr. David Isherwood of the U.C.L.A. College of Engineering has studied a water drainage problem with the help of SWAC, an automatic digital computer. A major part of the calculation involves a special case of the general boundary-value problem described above. Figure 18.3 shows a vertical cross section of soil being drained of water by parallel drainage pipes laid perpendicular to the plane of the paper. One wants to know the proper size, depth, and spacing of the pipe, as functions of the soil's permeability and other parameters, in order that a field be drained of water sufficiently rapidly. It is assumed that the problem is independent of the dimension perpendicular to the paper.

By symmetry the soil can be reduced to the two-dimensional region R of Figs. 18.3 and 18.4, in which x, y coordinates have been introduced

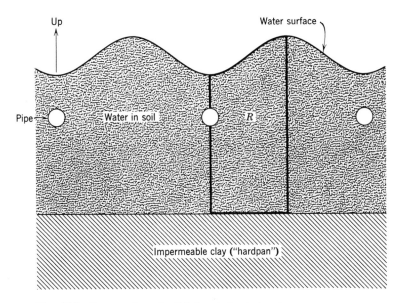

FIG. 18.3. Cross section of soil being drained, showing pipes and region R of Fig. 18.4.

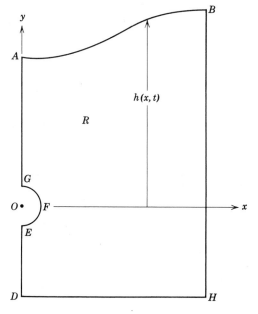

FIG. 18.4. Typical region R of Fig. 18.3.

with origin at the pipe's center. Let t denote time. Let $h(x, t)$ denote the y distance of the water surface above the line $y = 0$. For a given fixed t, a velocity potential function $\phi = \phi(P, t)$ can be defined by the boundary-value problem:

$$\Delta\phi(P, t) = 0, \qquad P \text{ in } R, \tag{18.4}$$

with mixed boundary conditions

$$\phi(P, t) = 0, \qquad P \text{ on } EFG, \tag{18.5}$$

$$\phi(P, t) = h(x, t), \qquad P \text{ on } AB, \tag{18.6}$$

and

$$\phi_n(P, t) = 0, \qquad P \text{ on } GA \text{ and } BHDE. \tag{18.7}$$

Thus problem (18.4)–(18.7) is a special case of (18.1), (18.2). (For a reference on soil drainage, see Kirkham and Gaskell [1951].)

The complete problem really involves the independent variables x, y, and t. The rate $\partial h(x, t)/\partial t$ of dropping of the water surface at time t is defined by

$$\frac{\partial h(x, t)}{\partial t} = c\left(\frac{\partial \phi}{\partial y} - \frac{\partial \phi}{\partial x}\frac{\partial h}{\partial x}\right). \tag{18.8}$$

Here c is a permeability constant, while ϕ is to be found by solving the problem (18.4)–(18.7). (One may interpret the right side of (18.8) as $c\,d\phi/dy$, where the total derivative with respect to y is taken along the interior normal to the curve AB.)

Isherwood's complete problem is to solve the system (18.4)–(18.8), where $h(x, 0)$ is a prescribed constant. As a problem of mixed type, it belongs in Chap. 4, but the subproblem (18.4)–(18.7) belongs here. As one might suspect, equation (18.8) seems to cause more practical difficulty than the system (18.4)–(18.7).

Typical dimensions are as follows: $DH = 40$, and pipe radius $= \frac{1}{2}$; at $t = 0$, $OA = 16$ and $BH = 24$. This makes the pipe quite small in relation to other dimensions.

18.3. An Oil-Flow Problem

The oil industry provides many problems involving potential flow. We are indebted to Dr. W. J. Karplus ([1954] and [1956]) of the U.C.L.A. College of Engineering for the following problem dealing with "water coning."

Most commercial oil reservoirs consist of an oil-saturated sand, bounded above by an impermeable stratum and below by a water-saturated sand. Since oil is less dense than water, there is a horizontal oil-water interface. When an oil well is drilled so that it partially penetrates the oil zone, and oil is removed at a constant rate v, the oil-water interface will assume a new steady-state shape as a result of the pressure gradients in the oil zone. The shape of this interface will depend upon the depth d of penetration, the thickness l of the oil zone, the production rate v, the permeability k of the sand, the viscosity μ of the oil, and the densities of oil and water, ρ_o and ρ_w. The problem is to determine this dependence by numerical calculation.

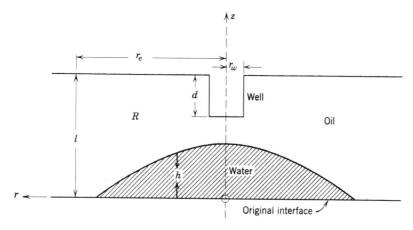

FIG. 18.5. Geometry of an oil-flow problem. R is a three-dimensional region with cylindrical symmetry.

In Karplus' problem we assume cylindrical symmetry, and take the r, z coordinates shown in Fig. 18.5. Let $\phi(r, z)$ be a velocity potential in the oil, and let $p(r, z)$ denote the pressure. According to Darcy's law (see Muskat [1946]):

$$\phi = k\mu^{-1}(p + g\rho_o z); \qquad (18.9)$$

here the vector velocity $\mathbf{v} = -(\phi_r, \phi_z) = -\nabla\phi$, and g is the force of gravity per unit mass. Since the flow is divergence-free, Laplace's equation is satisfied in the oil region R:

$$-\nabla \cdot \mathbf{v} = \Delta\phi = 0 \qquad \text{in } R. \qquad (18.10)$$

At the well (whose radius is a constant r_w), we take the boundary condition

$$\phi = \phi_w, \qquad r = r_w, \qquad l - d \leq z \leq l, \qquad (18.11)$$

where ϕ_w is a prescribed constant. At some large radius r_e one postulates the boundary condition

$$\phi = \phi_e, \qquad r = r_e, \qquad l - d \leq z \leq l. \qquad (18.12)$$

At the top of the oil layer there is horizontal flow, with the boundary condition

$$\partial\phi/\partial z = 0, \qquad r_w < r < r_e, \qquad z = l. \tag{18.13}$$

Another boundary condition comes at the free oil-water interface, whose height $h(r)$ must be determined as part of the problem. There is tangential flow at the interface, so that

$$\partial\phi/\partial n = 0, \qquad 0 \leq r < r_e, \qquad z = h(r). \tag{18.14}$$

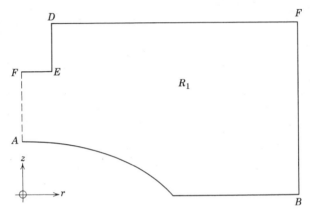

FIG. 18.6. Region R_1 for oil-flow problem. R_1 is a two-dimensional radial cross section of the R of Fig. 18.5.

Now the pressure at the interface must just balance the static head of the water cone:

$$p(r, h) = p_0 - \rho_w g\, h(r). \tag{18.15}$$

Combining (18.9) and (18.15), we have a second condition for the oil-water interface:

$$\phi(r, h) = c_1\, h(r) + c_2, \tag{18.16}$$

where

$$c_1 = -gk\mu^{-1}(\rho_w - \rho_o) \qquad \text{and} \qquad c_2 = k\mu^{-1}p_0. \tag{18.17}$$

Thus Karplus' problem consists of Laplace's differential equation (18.10) in R, with boundary conditions (18.11)–(18.13) on fixed boundaries, and the boundary condition (18.14) on a free oil-water surface determined by (18.16), (18.17).

If we denote by R_1 the two-dimensional meridional section of R pictured in Fig. 18.6, then, for $r > 0$, equation (18.10) takes the form

$$\phi_{rr} + \frac{1}{r}\phi_r + \phi_{zz} = 0 \qquad \text{for } 0 < r \text{ in } R_1. \tag{18.18}$$

Since symmetry requires that $\phi_r \to 0$ as $r \to 0$, we may supplement (18.18) with the boundary condition

$$\phi_r = 0, \qquad r = 0. \tag{18.19}$$

Then any solution of the above problem in R also satisfies the problem (18.18), (18.11)–(18.14), (18.16), (18.17), (18.19) in R_1. Conversely, as is shown by Huber [1954],* any solution of the latter problem in R_1 also generates a solution of the former problem in R.

Problems with such a free surface AB are found to be much more difficult to solve numerically than those like (18.1), (18.2) in a fixed region. A contribution to their solution will be found in Garabedian [1956]. In practice one often first solves the problem tentatively with an assumed position for AB. It is hoped that this tentative solution will tell one approximately how to correct the position of AB. One then solves the problem again with the corrected position of AB, etc.

18.4. A Stress Problem

Quite important in the theory of elasticity are boundary-value problems for the *biharmonic* operator Δ^2 in two dimensions:

$$\Delta^2 u = \Delta(\Delta u) = u_{xxxx} + 2u_{xxyy} + u_{yyyy}. \tag{18.20}$$

Let $g(P)$, $h(P)$ be sufficiently smooth functions defined on the boundary C, while $f(P)$, also sufficiently smooth, is defined in R. A representative biharmonic problem is to solve

$$\Delta^2 u(P) = f(P), \qquad P \text{ in } R, \tag{18.21}$$

subject to the boundary conditions

$$u(P) = g(P), \qquad P \text{ on } C, \tag{18.22}$$

and

$$u_n(P) = h(P), \qquad P \text{ on } C. \tag{18.23}$$

It appears that solving problem (18.21)–(18.23) is of more practical importance than solving problem (18.1), (18.2), at least to the airframe industry.

A typical problem of the class (18.21)–(18.23), shown to us by Dr. B. H. Colvin of the Boeing Airplane Co., deals with finding the stress distribution in a cut block in tension. Figure 18.7 shows a cross section of this block, which is homogeneous in the dimension perpendicular to the paper. The block is intended to simulate the behavior of a flanged joint in sheet metal, in which the legs of the joint are pulled by the sheet metal attached to its underside. The cross section of the block is symmetric in the line $y = 0$. The cut FO is considered to have no thickness.

* The authors are indebted to Professor P. Henrici for this reference.

In this problem we take for R the right half ($x > 0$) of Fig. 18.7. The body equation is (18.21). The boundary conditions (18.22), (18.23) take the following forms:

On FO, $u = u_x = 0$.

On CD, $u = \frac{1}{2}(y - \frac{1}{4})$ and $u_x = 0$.

On OA, $u = u_y = 0$.

On DE, $u = \frac{15}{8}$ and $u_y = \frac{1}{2}$.

On AB, $u = \frac{1}{2}y^2$ and $u_x = 0$.

On EF, $u_x = 0$.

On BC, $u = \frac{1}{8}$ and $u_y = \frac{1}{2}$.

The above problem was characterized by Colvin as being of moderate difficulty in this field.

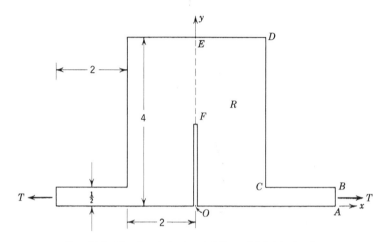

Fig. 18.7. Simulated sheet-metal flanged joint in tension.

18.5. A Boundary-Layer Problem

Janssen [1956] has considered a two-dimensional incompressible steady-state flow with constant viscosity. He wants to find the flow in the infinite part of the (x, y)-plane exterior to a simple obstacle.

Let C be a simple closed curve in the (x, y)-plane, and take for R the open region exterior to C. Let $\psi(x, y)$ be a stream function for the flow, with $(-\psi_y, \psi_x)$ as the velocity vector. Then the scalar vorticity of the flow is given by the formula

$$\zeta(x, y) = \Delta \, \psi(x, y) \qquad \text{in } R. \tag{18.24}$$

The motion in R is governed by the Navier-Stokes equation

$$\Delta\zeta = v^{-1}(\psi_x\zeta_y - \zeta_x\psi_y) \qquad \text{in } R, \tag{18.25}$$

where v is a nondimensional viscosity coefficient. (See Milne-Thomson [1950], p. 509.)

Since R is an unbounded region, there turn out to be boundary conditions both on C and at ∞. For the latter, Janssen gives:

$$\psi(x, y) = -y + o(r), \qquad \text{as } r = (x^2 + y^2)^{1/2} \to \infty, \qquad (18.26)$$

$$\zeta(x, y) = o(r), \qquad \text{as } r \to \infty. \qquad (18.27)$$

Thus the flow is asymptotically uniform at ∞. At the surface of the obstacle, the boundary conditions are that

$$\psi(x, y) = 0 \qquad \text{on } C \qquad (18.28)$$

and

$$\psi_n(x, y) = 0 \qquad \text{on } C. \qquad (18.29)$$

In summary, we have to solve equations (18.24), (18.25) for ψ and ζ, with boundary conditions (18.26)–(18.29). In contrast to the earlier problems of this section, this is a *nonlinear* boundary-value problem. Its approximate solution is very difficult, even for simple curves C. Although Janssen used an analog computer to approximate the solution, it would seem challenging to try it on a digital computer.

18.6. A Membrane Eigenvalue Problem

Heretofore the problems have been of the boundary-value type. There are also a number of eigenvalue problems for elliptic operators, of which perhaps the simplest is the vibrating membrane problem. It is simple enough to be of considerable mathematical interest, and there are important applications, e.g., in the theory of wave guides.

The region R and boundary C are as before. We seek a function $u(P)$ not identically zero in R and a number $\lambda > 0$ such that

$$-\Delta u(P) = \lambda u(P), \qquad P \text{ in } R. \qquad (18.30)$$

The simplest boundary condition is that

$$u(P) = 0, \qquad P \text{ on } C. \qquad (18.31)$$

It is known (see Courant and Hilbert [1953], Chap. 6) that there is a sequence of eigenvalues λ_k for which the problem (18.30), (18.31) is solvable:

$$0 < \lambda_1 \leq \lambda_2 \leq \lambda_3 \leq \cdots,$$

and $\lim \lambda_k = \infty$. One ordinarily seeks to know $\lambda_1, \cdots, \lambda_p$ for p up to 5 or 10, and the corresponding eigenfunctions $u_k(P)$:

$$-\Delta u_k(P) = \lambda_k u_k(P), \qquad P \text{ in } R.$$

Physically, the $\lambda_k^{1/2}$ are proportional to the pure frequencies of stationary vibration of an ideal drumhead with shape R.

In Sec. 24 will be found some discussion of the membrane eigenvalue problem for an L-shaped region which is the union of three unit squares; see Fig. 18.8.

A good many relations between λ_1 and the shape and size of R have been given by Pólya and Szegö [1951].

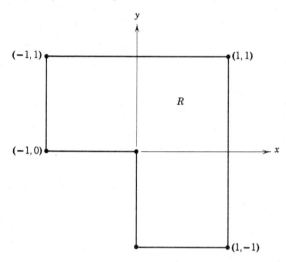

FIG. 18.8. L-shaped region for the membrane eigenvalue problem.

18.7. A Simple Reactor Problem

Eigenvalue problems concerned with the Laplace operator have a much more compelling application in the design of nuclear reactors, whether stable (for power production) or unstable (atom bombs). The physical principles behind the equations are described by Glasstone and Edlund [1952].

A type of problem of considerable interest is the following. A region R of three-dimensional space is divided into two regions R_1 and R_2; see the schematic drawing of Fig. 18.9. Region R_2 has excluded interiors, shaded in the figure, with surfaces A. There are two unknown functions to be determined, $u(P)$ and $v(P)$, and one unknown eigenvalue λ. The differential equations are

$$\Delta\, u(P) - a\, u(P) + \lambda b\, v(P) = 0, \qquad P \text{ in } R_1,$$

$$\Delta\, u(P) - a\, u(P) = 0, \qquad P \text{ in } R_2,$$

$$\Delta\, v(P) + d\, u(P) - c\, v(P) = 0, \qquad P \text{ in } R_1 \text{ or } R_2.$$

Here a, b, c, d are given constants. There are several types of boundary and interface conditions:

On the surfaces A one has

$$u(P) = q\, u_n(P), \quad P \text{ on } A,$$

$$v(P) = p\, u_n(P), \quad P \text{ on } A,$$

where p and q are given constants.

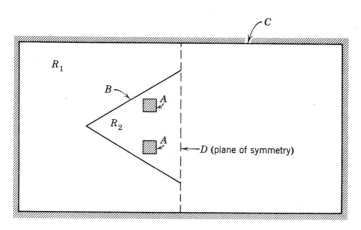

FIG. 18.9. Schematic drawing of nuclear reactor.

On the interface B between regions R_1 and R_2

$$u \text{ and } v \text{ are continuous,}$$

$$u_n(P)|_1 = \rho\, u_n(P)|_2, \quad P \text{ on } B,$$

$$v_n(P)|_1 = \sigma\, v_n(P)|_2, \quad P \text{ on } B.$$

Here ρ, σ are given negative constants if the normal derivatives are always taken toward the interiors of the respective regions.

On the outside surface C,

$$u(P) = 0, \quad P \text{ on } C,$$

$$v(P) = 0, \quad P \text{ on } C.$$

On the plane of symmetry D,

$$u_n(P) = 0, \quad P \text{ on } D,$$

$$v_n(P) = 0, \quad P \text{ on } D.$$

It is the least λ that one wants to compute in this problem.

18.8. A Biharmonic Eigenvalue Problem

Eigenvalue problems are of considerable interest also for the biharmonic operator. Even for the square no analytic solution is known.

For example, one may seek $u(P)$ and a constant λ such that

$$\Delta^2 u(P) = \lambda u(P), \qquad P \text{ in } R,$$

with boundary conditions

$$u(P) = 0, \qquad P \text{ on } C,$$

$$u_n(P) = 0, \qquad P \text{ on } C.$$

This λ is simply related to a frequency of vibration of an ideal elastic plate clamped at the edges. There is a sequence of eigenvalues with $0 < \lambda_1 \leq \lambda_2 \leq \lambda_3 \leq \cdots$.

18.9. Plateau's Problem

One of the most interesting and stimulating to research of all mathematical problems is *Plateau's problem*, here presented in its *restricted form*.

Let $f(x, y)$, defined on the boundary C of a simply connected plane region R, represent the height of a given space curve Γ above the point (x, y) on C. The problem is to construct a surface S of least area (minimal surface) through Γ. Let $u = u(x, y)$ represent the height of S above (x, y), for (x, y) in R. Then the surface area of S is equal to

$$A = \int\!\!\int_R (1 + u_x^2 + u_y^2)^{1/2} \, dx \, dy. \tag{18.32}$$

The Euler equation (19.16) associated with minimizing A is

$$(1 + u_y^2)u_{xx} - 2u_x u_y u_{xy} + (1 + u_x^2)u_{yy} = 0. \tag{18.33}$$

The partial differential equation problem, then, is to find a function $u = u(x, y)$ which with its derivatives up to second order is continuous in R, and which satisfies (18.33) and the boundary condition

$$u(x, y) = f(x, y) \qquad \text{for } (x, y) \text{ on } C. \tag{18.34}$$

The restricted nature of this problem refers to the assumption that the minimal surface S spanning Γ can be represented by a single-valued function $u = u(x, y)$. In general, S might be multiple-valued in such a representation, although a minimal surface might still span Γ.

The Plateau problem is difficult to solve, theoretically and practically. A fundamental approach in both theory and practice is to vary the surface until the integral in (18.32) is minimized. Analogous approaches will prove useful in many of the problems formulated in this section.

18.10. Eigenvalue Problem for the Wave Equation

One of the main uses of Laplace's operator is in quantum wave mechanics. When Schrödinger's equation is separated, one has the following eigenvalue problem in three dimensions: To find λ and $\psi(x, y, z)$ such that

$$\Delta \psi(x, y, z) + [\lambda - V(x, y, z)] \psi(x, y, z) = 0, \qquad (18.35)$$

where $V(x, y, z)$ is a potential function that depends on the molecule being studied. It is required that ψ remain finite, as $x^2 + y^2 + z^2 \to \infty$.

The equation for an ionized hydrogen molecule provides an interesting example of Schrödinger's equation. Assume that two protons are at a fixed distance ρ from each other. Let $r_i = r_i(x, y, z)$ be the distance from the ith proton to the point (x, y, z), for $i = 1, 2$. Then we have the potential

$$V(x, y, z) = \frac{2}{\rho} - \frac{2}{r_1} - \frac{2}{r_2}. \qquad (18.36)$$

With this potential V, each eigenvalue λ of (18.35) is proportional to an admissible energy level of the system.

SECTION 19. SELECTED RESULTS FROM THE THEORY OF ELLIPTIC PARTIAL DIFFERENTIAL EQUATIONS

In this section are given selected results from the theory of elliptic partial differential equations which bear on the solution of such equations by difference methods. For a discussion of Green's function, which would be appropriate to this section, see Sec. 23.6.

19.1. Variational Formulations

Many—perhaps most—elliptic partial differential equation problems are related to the minimization or maximization of an integral, which often represents an energy of a physical system. These matters are well developed in Courant and Hilbert [1953] and in Kantorovič and Krylov [1952], and we will mainly specialize them to integrals with quadratic integrands. We make no attempt to state the differentiability conditions completely.

For simplicity, we deal with two dimensions ($n = 2$). Let R and C be as in Sec. 18, and let u_s denote $\partial u/\partial s$ along the positive direction of C, where s is arc length. Let

$$I(u) = \iint_R (\tfrac{1}{2}au_x{}^2 + bu_xu_y + \tfrac{1}{2}cu_y{}^2 - \tfrac{1}{2}fu_2 + gu)\, dx\, dy$$

$$+ \int_C (\tfrac{1}{2}\alpha u^2 + \gamma u)\, ds, \quad (19.1)$$

where a, b, c, f, g are continuously differentiable functions of x, y, and α, γ are continuously differentiable functions of s on C. Assume that the function $v(x, y)$ minimizes $I(u)$ with respect to all functions of some class K including all sufficiently differentiable functions on $\bar{R}\ (= R \cup C)$ that may be required to satisfy certain boundary conditions on C. This means that, for any function $w(x, y)$ which is the difference of two functions in K, we demand that

$$I(v + w) \geq I(v). \quad (19.2)$$

To see what requirement (19.2) imposes on v, we shall transform $I(v + w) - I(v)$, following similar arguments given, e.g., by Courant and Hilbert [1953], pp. 184 and 191. By direct substitution of $v + w$ into (19.1), we find that

$$I(v + w) - I(v) = T_1 + T_2 + T_3 + T_4,$$

$$T_1 = \iint_R (av_xw_x + bv_xw_y + bv_yw_x + cv_yw_y - fvw + gw)\, dx\, dy,$$

$$T_2 = \int_C (\alpha v + \gamma)w\, ds, \quad (19.3)$$

$$T_3 = \tfrac{1}{2}\iint_R (aw_x{}^2 + 2bw_xw_y + cw_y{}^2 - fw^2)\, dx\, dy,$$

$$T_4 = \tfrac{1}{2}\int_C \alpha w^2\, ds.$$

We now eliminate the factors w_x, w_y from T_1 by application of the divergence theorem, stated in equation (24.47). Let $p = (av_x + bv_y)w$, $q = (bv_x + cv_y)w$. Then

$$\iint_R [(av_x + bv_y)w_x + (bv_x + cv_y)w_y]\, dx\, dy$$

$$= -\iint_R [(av_x + bv_y)_x + (bv_x + cv_y)_y]w\, dx\, dy$$

$$+ \int_C \left[(av_x + bv_y)\frac{dy}{ds} - (bv_x + cv_y)\frac{dx}{ds}\right]w\, ds. \quad (19.4)$$

Substituting (19.4) into (19.3) yields the relations

$$I(v + w) - I(v) = T_1^* + T_2^* + T_3 + T_4, \qquad (19.5)$$

where T_3, T_4 are given in (19.3), and where

$$T_1^* = \int\int_R [-L(v) + g]w \, dx \, dy,$$

$$T_2^* = \int_C \left[\alpha v + (av_x + bv_y)\frac{dy}{ds} - (bv_x + cv_y)\frac{dx}{ds} + \gamma \right] w \, ds, \qquad (19.6)$$

with

$$L(u) = (au_x + bu_y)_x + (bu_x + cu_y)_y + fu$$
$$= au_{xx} + 2bu_{xy} + cu_{yy} + (a_x + b_y)u_x + (b_x + c_y)u_y + fu. \qquad (19.7)$$

We shall now transform T_2^* to introduce the inner normal derivative v_n and the positive tangential derivative v_s. Let a prime denote $\partial/\partial s$ on C. On C

$$v_n = -v_x y' + v_y x', \qquad v_s = v_x x' + v_y y',$$

whence

$$v_x = v_s x' - v_n y', \qquad v_y = v_s y' + v_n x'. \qquad (19.8)$$

Substituting from (19.8) into T_2^*, we find that

$$T_2^* = \int_C [\alpha v + \gamma + \beta v_n + \delta v_s]w \, ds, \qquad (19.9)$$

where α, γ are as in (19.1), and

$$\beta = -ay'^2 + 2bx'y' - cx'^2,$$
$$\delta = (a - c)x'y' + b(y'^2 - x'^2). \qquad (19.10)$$

Putting (19.9) into (19.5), we finally have

$$I(v + w) - I(v) = \int\int_R [-L(v) + g]w \, dx \, dy + \int_C [\alpha v + \beta v_n + \gamma + \delta v_s]w \, ds$$

$$+ \tfrac{1}{2}\int\int_R (aw_x^2 + 2bw_x w_y + cw_y^2 - fw^2) \, dx \, dy + \tfrac{1}{2}\int_C \alpha w^2 \, ds. \qquad (19.11)$$

Note that there has been no linearization in deriving (19.11); it is identically correct.

One now asserts that, if (19.2) holds, then one must have

$$L(v) = g \qquad \text{in } R. \qquad (19.12)$$

The argument is a familiar one in the calculus of variations, although our carrying quadratic terms in (19.11) necessitates a little more argument, which we summarize. Suppose there were a point P of R where (19.12) failed to hold; for definiteness, suppose $L(v) - g > 0$ at P. We claim that we can construct a smooth function $w(x, y)$, vanishing on C and on R except near P, such that (19.2) fails to hold. We first construct a smooth function $v_1(x, y)$, which is greater than $q > 0$ in a small neighborhood of P in which $L(v) - g > 0$, and zero elsewhere. Now let $w(x, y) = \epsilon\, v_1(x, y)$. For a sufficiently small ϵ, the third term of (19.11) can be neglected against the first term, and we will have $I(v + w) - I(v) < 0$, as we indicated, proving (19.12). Equation (19.12) is called the *Euler equation* for the minimization of (19.1).

Further conclusions from (19.11) depend upon the boundary conditions satisfied by functions of the class K. If the functions u of K are unrestricted on C, then it follows from (19.2) that

$$\alpha v + \gamma + \beta v_n + \delta v_s = 0 \qquad \text{on } C. \tag{19.13}$$

For, if (19.13) were false at any point P of C, it would again be possible to create a smooth function w such that (19.2) fails. Being a consequence of the minimization of $I(u)$ without any boundary restriction on the functions u of K, (19.13) is called the *natural boundary condition* for the minimization of (19.1) or for the solution of (19.12). It is natural because it is satisfied automatically by the function v minimizing $I(u)$, without being imposed. However, it is important to realize that (19.13) is not a natural property of a solution of (19.12).

Often the functions u of K are constrained by the physical system to satisfy the *Dirichlet boundary condition*

$$u(P) = \psi(P) \qquad \text{for } P \text{ in } C_1, \tag{19.14}$$

where C_1 is part (or all) of the boundary C. But (19.14) implies that in (19.3) $w = 0$ on C_1. In this case, the natural boundary condition (19.13) holds only on that part of C (if any) that is not in C_1. Because of (19.14) all contributions to boundary integrals in (19.11) vanish on C_1.

It is possible to conclude (19.12) and (19.13) not only from the condition that $I(u)$ is a minimum for v but also from the weaker hypothesis that $I(u)$ is *stationary* at v, i.e., that $(d/d\epsilon)\, I(v + \epsilon w) = 0$ for $\epsilon = 0$ and all admissible w. For this derivative is actually equal to the sum of the first and second right-hand terms of (19.11).

In summary, *if a particular function $v(x, y)$ renders $I(u)$ in (19.1) stationary with respect to all functions such that (19.14) holds, then $v(x, y)$ satisfies the differential equation (19.12) in R, with boundary conditions (19.13) for P on $C - C_1$, and (19.14) for P on C_1.* The converse is also true: A solution of the boundary-value problem (19.12)–(19.14) also renders $I(u)$ stationary.

For the more general variational problem with

$$I(u) = \int\int_R F(x, y, u, u_x, u_y) \, dx \, dy + \int_C G(s, u, u_s) \, ds, \quad (19.15)$$

the corresponding Euler equation is

$$F_{u_x u_x} u_{xx} + 2F_{u_x u_y} u_{xy} + F_{u_y u_y} u_{yy} + F_{u_x u} u_x$$
$$+ F_{u_y u} u_y + F_{x u_x} + F_{y u_y} - F_u = 0 \quad \text{in } R, \quad (19.16)$$

and the natural boundary condition is

$$G_{u_s u_s} u_{ss} + G_{u_s u} u_s + G_{s u_s} - G_u - F_{u_x} \frac{dy}{ds} + F_{u_y} \frac{dx}{ds} = 0 \quad \text{on } C. \quad (19.17)$$

In Sec. 19.3 we shall consider general boundary conditions on the functions u of K which enable us to conclude that the second integral of (19.11) vanishes.

As we noted, the Euler equation (19.12) is a consequence merely of the stationary character of $I(u)$. But the computational usefulness of the variational approach seems to be limited to those cases where $I(u)$ is rendered a local minimum or maximum by the function $v(x, y)$ solving the Euler equations.

Knowing that v satisfies (19.12) and (19.13), how can we tell whether $I(v)$ is actually a minimum, a maximum, or merely stationary? Unfortunately, the part of the calculus of variations dealing with this question is comparatively deep, and we shall indicate only one relevant idea. When (19.12) and (19.13) hold, we see from (19.11) that

$$I(v + w) - I(v) = \tfrac{1}{2} \int\int_R (a w_x{}^2 + 2b w_x w_y + c w_y{}^2 - f w^2) \, dx \, dy$$
$$+ \tfrac{1}{2} \int_C \alpha w^2 \, ds. \quad (19.18)$$

Suppose the function v minimizes $I(u)$ uniquely, i.e., that $I(v + w) - I(v) > 0$ for all nonzero admissible w. Then from (19.18) one can prove that

$$Q(\xi_1, \xi_2) = a\xi_1{}^2 + 2b\xi_1\xi_2 + c\xi_2{}^2 \geq 0 \quad (19.19)$$

for all x, y and for all real numbers ξ_1, ξ_2 not both zero, i.e., that the quadratic form Q is positive semidefinite. Moreover, under certain conditions, the form Q can be shown to be positive definite in R. We omit the arguments.

Similarly, for $I(v)$ to be a maximum Q must be negative semidefinite. But the semidefiniteness of Q, whether positive or negative, implies that $b^2 - ac \leq 0$, i.e., that (19.12) is elliptic or parabolic. Thus the unique minimization of $I(u)$ is not possible for hyperbolic equations.

The importance of the variational formulation lies in several directions. First, in theoretical work on boundary-value problems it permits broader existence theorems since less differentiability is required in (19.1) than in (19.12). Second, frequently the stationary value of $I(v)$ is actually a minimum. This permits one to solve (19.1) in principle or practice by a *method of descent*, in which u is varied in such a way that $I(u)$ approaches its minimum (see Tompkins [1956]). Finally, as indicated above, the variational formulation gives us insight into the nature of the boundary conditions.

For numerical analysis the ideas of the descent method and of the natural boundary conditions have direct applications. It is in principle easy to create classes K with only a finite number of parameters, and then to minimize $I(u)$ over these finite-dimensional spaces. We shall do this in Sec. 24.2.

The above variational approach has a complete analog with respect to difference methods also, although so far it has been only partly developed in the literature. As will be seen in Sec. 20, there is considerable uncertainty in the choice of difference equations to approximate partial differential equations and their boundary conditions, particularly at boundaries or interfaces. The variational method helps us in at least two ways. First, it eliminates certain boundary conditions from special consideration by showing them to be natural. Second, it permits us to concentrate on the fairly clear problem of accurately approximating the integral (19.1) by a sum Σ of ordinates of a net function defined over a grid of points in $\bar{R}$. For, once we have found the sum Σ, the methods of differential calculus will tell us automatically the corresponding difference equations that define the net function minimizing Σ. This is sometimes a more satisfactory way to derive the difference equations than the more obvious approach of replacing partial derivatives by finite differences.

Although we have left many things unsaid, it is the above considerations that make variational approaches computationally significant for elliptic problems, but probably not for hyperbolic problems. Their usefulness in parabolic problems is left open here.

A common variational problem arises when (19.1) takes the special from

$$I(u) = \int\int_R (\tfrac{1}{2}|\nabla u|^2 - \tfrac{1}{2}fu^2 + gu)\, dx\, dy + \int_C (\tfrac{1}{2}\sigma u^2 + \phi u)\, ds. \quad (19.20)$$

Here $f = f(x, y)$, $\phi = \phi(s)$, and $\sigma = \sigma(s)$ are sufficiently smooth functions of their arguments. For these choices the Euler equation (19.12) takes the form

$$\Delta u + fu = g \qquad \text{in } R, \tag{19.21}$$

while the natural boundary condition (19.13) becomes

$$u_n = \phi + \sigma u \qquad \text{on } C, \tag{19.22}$$

where u_n denotes the inward normal derivative.

Thus the *boundary-value problem* (19.21, 19.22) *is solved by those* $v(P)$ *for which the* $I(u)$ *of* (19.20) *is rendered stationary*. The stationary value can be shown to be a minimum if $f \leq 0$ and $\sigma \geq 0$.

If we put $f = 0$, $\phi = -\gamma/\beta$, and $\sigma = -\alpha/\beta$, we see that the two-dimensional boundary-value problem (18.1), (18.2) can be given a variational formulation in terms of (19.20) whenever $\beta(P) \neq 0$ in (18.2).

If $\beta(P) = 0$ on some part C_1 of the boundary, the corresponding boundary condition (18.2) takes the Dirichlet form

$$\alpha(P)\, u(P) + \gamma(P) = 0 \qquad \text{on } C_1,$$

which must be imposed on the class K of functions from which one seeks the function u minimizing (19.20). We thus see how the variational formulation enables us to distinguish between boundary conditions which must be "forced" and those which are satisfied automatically.

The stress problem (18.21)–(18.23) can be shown to be solved by the function v which minimizes the integral

$$I(u) = \int\!\!\int_R \{[\Delta\, u(P)]^2 + f(P)u(P)\}\, dx\, dy$$

among the class of sufficiently differentiable functions u satisfying the boundary conditions (18.22), (18.23). Since in this case F depends on u_{xx} and u_{yy}, this result is not a special case of (19.15), but it can be derived in a similar way.

19.2. Variational Formulation of Certain Eigenvalue Problems

In Sec. 19.1 we studied the functions which render $I(u)$ in (19.1) stationary with respect to all functions u in a certain class K. Class K consisted of those sufficiently smooth functions defined on $\bar{R}$ which might in addition be required to satisfy the Dirichlet boundary condition (19.14) on C_1, which is part or all of C.

We now shall consider the homogeneous case of (19.1) with $g = \alpha = \gamma = 0$ and $b^2 - ac < 0$:

$$I(u) = \int\!\!\int_R (\tfrac{1}{2}au_x^2 + bu_xu_y + \tfrac{1}{2}cu_y^2 - \tfrac{1}{2}fu^2)\, dx\, dy. \tag{19.23}$$

Suppose that the functions u of K are subjected to the further constraint

$$J(u) = \tfrac{1}{2} \int\!\!\int_R u^2 \, dx \, dy = \text{const.} \tag{19.24}$$

We shall then consider the following problem, which arises in the mechanics of continua:

PROBLEM 1. *To find the nonzero functions u in K which satisfy* (19.24), *and which make $I(u)$ stationary.*

As with the analogous problem of the differential calculus, problem 1 can be solved with the aid of a Lagrange multiplier λ. In fact, it can be shown that problem 1 is solved by the same functions u which solve:

PROBLEM 2. *To find the nonzero functions u in K for which there exists a constant λ such that $I(u) - \lambda J(u)$ is stationary.*

Because both $I(u)$ and $J(u)$ are homogeneous of second order, the value of $I(u)/J(u)$ does not change when u is multiplied by a nonzero constant factor. It can then be shown that problems 1 and 2 are solved by the same functions u which solve:

PROBLEM 3. *To find the functions u in K for which $\rho(u) = I(u)/J(u)$ is stationary.*

It turns out that the stationary values of $\rho(u)$ in problem 3 are precisely the values of λ associated with stationary values in problem 2. The function $\rho(u)$ is called the *Rayleigh quotient* of the problems. The reader is referred to Courant and Hilbert [1953, 1937] for a discussion of the equivalence of these problems.

Now the results we cited in Sec. 19.1 can be used to show that problem 2 is equivalent to a certain problem for a partial differential equation. We may write

$$I(u) - \lambda \ J(u) = \int\!\!\int_R (\tfrac{1}{2}au_x^2 + bu_xu_y + \tfrac{1}{2}cu_y^2 - \tfrac{1}{2}fu^2 - \tfrac{1}{2}\lambda u^2) \, dx \, dy. \tag{19.25}$$

By (19.12) and (19.13), it follows that a function in K which renders (19.25) stationary must satisfy the condition

$$-L(u) = \lambda u \qquad \text{in } R, \tag{19.26}$$

and the natural boundary condition

$$\beta u_n + \delta u_s = 0 \qquad \text{on } C - C_1, \tag{19.27}$$

where C_1 is the part of C (if any) where u is required to satisfy a Dirichlet boundary condition of type

$$u(P) = \psi(P) \qquad \text{for } P \text{ on } C_1. \tag{19.14}$$

The β and δ are given by (19.10), and $L(u)$ is as in (19.7).

We may thus formulate a fourth problem equivalent to the others:

Problem 4. To find functions u and corresponding constants λ satisfying (19.26) *in R, such that u satisfies* (19.27) *on $C - C_1$ and* (19.14) *on C_1.*

Problem 4 is called an *eigenvalue problem* for the operator $-L(u)$, and such problems arise very often in physical investigations. There is an extensive mathematical theory of such problems, expounded in Courant and Hilbert [1953], in Gould [1957], and elsewhere. We will discuss the computational aspects of one such problem in Sec. 24.

19.3. Self-Adjointness

It should be noted that the Euler equation (19.12) that arose from our variational approach is not the most general second-order linear partial differential equation. In fact, the operator L of (19.7) is a *self-adjoint operator*. Self-adjointness of L means that, for any two sufficiently smooth functions v, w,

$$\int\int_R [wL(v) - vL(w)]\, dx\, dy \tag{19.28}$$

is a function of the values of v, w and their derivatives *on C alone*.

If one uses the divergence theorem (24.47) to evaluate (19.28), when $L(u)$ is defined in (19.29), one finds that self-adjointness simply means that $d = a_x + b_y$ and $e = b_x + c_y$. Self-adjointness is analogous to the symmetry of a matrix operator.

Somewhat more important is the concept of the self-adjointness of a boundary-value *problem*. For a general operator

$$L(u) = au_{xx} + 2bu_{xy} + cu_{yy} + du_x + eu_y + fu, \tag{19.29}$$

the boundary-value problem

$$L(u) = g \qquad \text{in } R, \tag{19.30}$$

with the general boundary condition

$$\alpha_1 u + \gamma_1 + \beta_1 u_n + \delta_1 u_s = 0 \qquad \text{on } C, \tag{19.31}$$

is called a *self-adjoint problem* if the operator L is self-adjoint, and if the value of the integral (19.28) necessarily vanishes for any two sufficiently smooth functions v, w which satisfy the corresponding homogeneous boundary conditions

$$\alpha_1 v + \beta_1 v_n + \delta_1 v_s = 0 \qquad \text{on } C,$$

$$\alpha_1 w + \beta_1 w_n + \delta_1 w_s = 0 \qquad \text{on } C. \tag{19.32}$$

(Actually the last requirement about the integral implies the self-adjointness of the operator L.)

The concept of a self-adjoint problem evolved partly in order to characterize those problems for which the variational approach is valid. To make the connection, we transform (19.28) into a boundary integral by applying the divergence theorem. Omitting the details, which parallel those of (19.4), we find that

$$\iint_R [wL(v) - vL(w)] \, dx \, dy = \int_C w[(av_x + bv_y) \, dy - (bv_x + cv_y) \, dx]$$

$$- \int_C v[(aw_x + bw_y) \, dy - (bw_x + cw_y) \, dx]$$

$$= \int_C [(\beta v_n + \delta v_s)w - (\beta w_n + \delta w_s)v] \, ds, \tag{19.33}$$

where β and δ are the expressions given in (19.10).

For (19.33) to vanish whenever v, w satisfy (19.32), it is essential that the last line integral vanish. We shall now show that the vanishing of (19.33) implies that

$$\beta \delta_1 - \delta \beta_1 = 0 \qquad \text{for all } s. \tag{19.34}$$

First, in the set C_1 of points s where $\beta_1 = 0$ it follows from (19.32) that $vw_s - wv_s = 0$, and this, in turn, implies that the last integrand in (19.33) is equal to

$$\beta(v_n w - w_n v), \qquad s \text{ in } C_1. \tag{19.35}$$

If β were not identically zero in C_1 (i.e., if $\beta \delta_1 - \delta \beta_1 \not\equiv 0$ in C_1), β would be nonzero at some point P_1 and, hence, of one sign in an interval J around P_1. But one could easily construct smooth functions v, w such that $v_n w - w_n v$ vanishes on C outside J and is of one sign in J. This would mean that the last line integrand in (19.33) could not vanish. Hence $\beta \equiv 0$ in C_1.

In the set $C - C_1$ where $\beta_1 \neq 0$, we can use (19.32) to replace v_n and w_n by

$$-\beta_1^{-1}(\alpha_1 v + \delta_1 v_s) \qquad \text{and} \qquad -\beta_1^{-1}(\alpha_1 w + \delta_1 w_s),$$

respectively, and then rewrite the last integrand of (19.33) as

$$\frac{1}{\beta_1} (\beta_1 \delta - \beta \delta_1)(w v_s - v w_s), \qquad s \text{ in } C - C_1. \tag{19.36}$$

Just as before, unless $\beta_1\delta - \beta\delta_1 \equiv 0$ in $C - C_1$, we could construct such functions v, w that (19.33) would not vanish. This concludes our proof that $\beta\delta_1 - \delta\beta_1 = 0$ on C.

It follows from (19.34) that β_1, δ_1 are proportional to β, δ, so that in (19.31) one can insist without loss of generality that $\beta_1 = \beta$, $\delta_1 = \delta$; i.e., in a self-adjoint problem, the boundary conditions (19.31) are of the special form (19.13). Conversely, if the boundary conditions take the special form (19.13), and if the operator L is self-adjoint, the problem is also self-adjoint.

Hence the Euler equations for a minimization problem always lead to problems of the form (19.12), (19.13), i.e., to self-adjoint problems. Thus no problem which is not self-adjoint can be treated by minimizing an expression of type (19.1).

The three principal forms that the boundary conditions (19.31) can take are:

$$u = \psi \qquad \text{on } C,$$

$$\beta u_n + \delta u_s = \psi \qquad \text{on } C,$$

$$\alpha u + \beta u_n + \delta u_s = \psi \qquad \text{on } C.$$

These are, respectively, the *Dirichlet*, the *Neumann*, and the *third* boundary conditions. When different ones of these conditions hold on different arcs of C, the boundary conditions are said to be *mixed*.

When $L(u)$ is the Laplacian Δu, we see from (19.10) that $\beta = -1$ and $\delta = 0$. Then $\beta u_n + \delta u_s = -u_n$, and the Neumann boundary condition takes the familiar form

$$u_n = \psi \qquad \text{on } C,$$

while the third boundary-value problem becomes

$$\alpha u + \beta u_n = \psi \qquad \text{on } C. \tag{19.37}$$

It is for this reason that we had no term in u_s in the boundary condition (18.2).

We have proved for the Laplace operator Δ that any boundary-value problem $\Delta u = g$ with boundary conditions of type (19.37) is a self-adjoint problem. The reader may well wonder what boundary-value problems for a self-adjoint operator L are not self-adjoint. We shall therefore give a simple one-dimensional example. Let the problem be to solve

$$L(u) = u''(x) = 0, \qquad a \le x \le b, \tag{19.38}$$

with boundary condition

$$u(a) = u_a, \qquad u'(a) = u_a'. \tag{19.39}$$

Then

$$\int_a^b [v\,L(u) - u\,L(v)]\,dx = \int_a^b (vu'' - uv'')\,dx$$

$$= v(a)\,u'(a) - u(a)\,v'(a) - v(b)\,u'(b) + u(b)\,v'(b).$$
$$(19.40)$$

Now, if u and v are two smooth functions, we see that the integral

$$\int_a^b [v\,L(u) - u\,L(v)]\,dx \qquad (19.41)$$

indeed depends only on the boundary values of u and v, so that L is a self-adjoint *operator*. However, the fact that u and v both satisfy the homogeneous version of (19.39), i.e.,

$$u(a) = u'(a) = 0, \qquad (19.42)$$

does not imply that (19.40) is zero. Hence the *problem* (19.38), (19.39) is not self-adjoint.

The so-called *adjoint problem* to (19.38), (19.39) is the problem with boundary conditions which, together with (19.39), are sufficient to insure the vanishing of (19.40) when made homogeneous, i.e.,

$$L(v) = 0, \qquad a \le x \le b,$$
$$v(b) = v_b, \qquad v'(b) = v_b'.$$

19.4. Interface Conditions

The question of self-adjointness is very important for problems like the reactor problem of Sec. 18, in which there are interior points (1 dim.), curves (2 dim.), or interfaces (3 dim.) on which the differential equation is not satisfied, but on which there are boundary conditions. The following discussion is limited to one dimension for simplicity; comparable material for two dimensions is found in Hildebrandt [1955].

Consider the self-adjoint operator

$$L(u) = u''(x) + f(x)\,u(x), \qquad -1 \le x \le 1. \qquad (19.43)$$

Suppose we want to solve a boundary-value problem for $L(u)$ on the interval $[-1, 1]$, with the exception of the "interface" $x = 0$:

$$L(u) = g(x), \qquad -1 \le x < 0 \quad \text{and} \quad 0 < x \le 1. \qquad (19.44)$$

Appropriate boundary conditions must deal with $u(x)$ for $x = -1, -0,$ $+0,$ and 1. Let us suppose they take the following form, analogous to those in Sec. 18.7:

$$u(-1) = u_{-1}, \qquad u(1) = u_1, \tag{19.45a}$$

$$u(-0) = u(+0), \qquad k\,u'(-0) = u'(+0), \tag{19.45b}$$

where u_{-1}, u_1, k are prescribed constants.

To test the self-adjointness of the problem (19.44), (19.45), we perform the partial integration analogous to (19.40):

$$\int_{-1}^{1} [v\,L(u) - u\,L(v)]\,dx$$

$$= \int_{-1}^{1} (vu'' + fvu - uv'' - fuv)\,dx = \Big[vu' - uv'\Big]_{+0}^{1} + \Big[vu' - uv'\Big]_{-1}^{-0}$$

$$= v(1)\,u'(1) - u(1)\,v'(1) - v(-1)\,u'(-1) + u(-1)\,v'(-1)$$

$$+ v(-0)\,u'(-0) - u(-0)\,v'(-0) - v(+0)\,u'(+0) + u(+0)\,v'(+0). \tag{19.46}$$

Now we want to know whether the boundary terms in (19.46) vanish when u and v both satisfy the homogeneous form of (19.45):

$$u(-1) = u(1) = 0, \qquad u(-0) = u(+0), \qquad k\,u'(-0) = u'(+0); \tag{19.47}$$

$$v(-1) = v(1) = 0, \qquad v(-0) = v(+0), \qquad k\,v'(-0) = v'(+0). \tag{19.48}$$

We see at once from (19.47) and (19.48) that the first four terms on the right-hand side of (19.46) do vanish. The issue therefore hangs on the last four terms. We use the conditions (19.47) on u alone to write the last four terms of (19.46) in the form

$$v(-0)\,u'(-0) - u(-0)\,v'(-0) - v(+0)k\,u'(-0) + u(-0)\,v'(+0)$$

$$= u'(-0)[v(-0) - k\,v(+0)] - u(-0)[v'(-0) - v'(+0)]. \tag{19.49}$$

But from (19.48) it is clear that (19.49) does not necessarily vanish unless $k = 1$. This means that *the problem (19.44), (19.45) is self-adjoint only when $k = 1$, i.e., when there is continuity of u and u' at $x = 0$, so that there is really no interface at all.*

For $k \ne 1$, (19.49) cannot vanish for all u satisfying (19.47) unless v satisfies the following conditions:

$$v(-1) = v(1) = 0, \qquad v(-0) = k\,v(+0), \qquad v'(-0) = v'(+0). \tag{19.50}$$

The corresponding nonhomogeneous conditions on v are

$$v(-1) = v_{-1}, \qquad v(1) = v_1, \qquad v(-0) = k\,v(+0), \qquad v'(-0) = v'(+0).$$
$$(19.51)$$

The problem

$$L(v) = g(x) \qquad (19.52)$$

with boundary conditions (19.51) is called the *adjoint problem* to (19.44), (19.45). Unless $k = 1$, (19.51), (19.52) and (19.44), (19.45) are different problems.

Let us consider the possibility of a variational approach to the solution of the problem (19.44), (19.45) for $k \neq 1$. One naturally thinks of setting up the one-dimensional analog of (19.1), viz.,

$$I(u) = \tfrac{1}{2} \int_{-1}^{1} (u'^2 - fu^2 + 2gu)\, dx, \qquad (19.53)$$

and trying to minimize it over a suitable class K of admissible functions u. Clearly the class K must include only functions satisfying the end point conditions (19.45a) and also the interface conditions (19.45b), because neither is natural [i.e., an automatic consequence of the minimization of $I(u)$].

However, as in Sec. 19.3, the fact that (19.44), (19.45) is not a self-adjoint problem can be shown to prevent its solution from being found as the minimum of (19.53). In fact, the $I(u)$ of (19.53) ordinarily has no minimum for $k \neq 1$, but has only a lower bound. For low values of $I(u)$, the functions u look like the solution of (19.44), (19.45a) on the interval $[-1, 1]$, with small adjustments near $x = 0$ needed to satisfy (19.45b). These facts can be shown by a study of (19.56) below.

On the other hand, it is possible to define the solution v of (19.44), (19.45) as the function minimizing an integral $I(u)$ with a discontinuous weight function. In effect we are saying that the non-self-adjoint problem (19.44), (19.45) can be made self-adjoint with a weight function or integrating factor. It will turn out that the second half of condition (19.45b) is automatically satisfied, and we might call it a *natural interface condition* for our example.

Let us set

$$I(u) = \tfrac{1}{2}p \int_{-1}^{-0} (u'^2 - fu^2 + 2gu)\, dx + \tfrac{1}{2} \int_{+0}^{1} (u'^2 - fu^2 + 2gu)\, dx. \quad (19.54)$$

Here p is a weight factor yet to be determined. Let class K consist of functions u sufficiently smooth in $[-1, 0]$ and $[0, 1]$, continuous at 0, and satisfying (19.45a). Let w be the difference of any two functions in K. We shall let $u = v + w$, where v is a possible minimizing function for $I(u)$. Then

$$I(v + \epsilon w) - I(v) = p\epsilon \int_{-1}^{-0} (v'w' - fvw + gw)\, dx$$

$$+ \epsilon \int_{+0}^{1} (v'w' - fvw + gw)\, dx + \tfrac{1}{2}p\epsilon^2 \int_{-1}^{-0} (w'^2 - fw^2)\, dx$$

$$+ \tfrac{1}{2}\epsilon^2 \int_{+0}^{1} (w'^2 - fw^2)\, dx. \tag{19.55}$$

By our hypothesis on K, $w(-0) = w(+0) = w(0)$. Hence, integrating (19.55) by parts, we find that

$$I(v + \epsilon w) - I(v) = \epsilon w(0)[pv'(-0) - v'(+0)]$$

$$- p\epsilon \int_{-1}^{-0} (v'' + fv - g)w\, dx - \epsilon \int_{+0}^{1} (v'' + fv - g)w\, dx$$

$$+ \frac{p\epsilon^2}{2} \int_{-1}^{-0} (w'^2 - fw^2)\, dx + \frac{1}{2}\epsilon^2 \int_{+0}^{1} (w'^2 - fw^2)\, dx. \tag{19.56}$$

Now, if v is to render $I(u)$ stationary for the given value of p, all the terms multiplying ϵ in (19.56) must vanish. Hence (19.44) must be satisfied by v and, moreover, one must have

$$pv'(-0) = v'(+0). \tag{19.57}$$

Thus (19.57) is a natural interface condition. Since we are interested in satisfying (19.45b), *we must take $p = k$*. When we do take $p = k$, a function in K which makes (19.54) stationary certainly solves the problem (19.44), (19.45). We have therefore produced a variational formulation of (19.44), (19.45).

To see whether $I(u)$ is actually minimized by v when $p = k$, we must look at the ϵ^2 terms in (19.56). It is sufficient that $f \le 0$ and $k \ge 0$. It is necessary that $k \ge 0$ since otherwise the two terms in ϵ^2 have opposite signs.

For two-dimensional problems, Hildebrandt [1955] found essentially the same condition $k \ge 0$ to be sufficient for a variational approach to an eigenvalue problem related to (19.44), (19.45). The sign $k \ge 0$ corresponds to the sign actually found in the diffusion equations of Sec. 18. We therefore conclude that the ideas of the calculus of variations may have important applications to reactor problems. We do not claim to have a theory in this direction, but only this one example to illustrate how a simple interface condition can be dealt with variationally.

Considerations analogous to those just given may tell us how to modify the Rayleigh quotient $\rho(u)$ when dealing with eigenvalue problems with interfaces. This is important, because a correctly stated Rayleigh quotient can give a very accurate eigenvalue from an eigenfunction of only moderate accuracy. Another of the important advantages of self-adjointness in an eigenvalue problem is that it guarantees that the eigenvalues λ are real numbers. See Friedman [1956], p. 201.

19.5. Maximum Principle

Perhaps the most useful analytical tool in the study of elliptic partial differential equations is the *maximum principle*. We shall state it for the equation

$$L(u) = \Delta u + du_x + eu_y + fu = 0, \tag{19.58}$$

which is the canonical form of elliptic equations of second order.

THEOREM 19.1. *If* $f \leq 0$, *a nonconstant solution* u *of* $L(u) = 0$ *cannot assume a positive maximum or a negative minimum inside R.*

Proof. We give the proof for $f < 0$. If u has a positive maximum at P in R, then $u_x(P) = u_y(P) = 0$, while $u_{xx}(P) \leq 0$, $u_{yy}(P) \leq 0$. Hence

$$L(u) = \Delta\, u(P) + f(P)\, u(P) \leq f(P)\, u(P) < 0,$$

so that we cannot have $L(u) = 0$.

The proof when $f = 0$ is slightly more difficult, and may be found, for example, in Tamarkin and Feller [1941].

THEOREM 19.2. *A nonconstant solution of* $\Delta u = 0$ *cannot assume its minimum or maximum value inside R.*

Proof. Although it does not furnish the most direct proof, one may recall that any harmonic function $u(x, y)$ is the real part of an analytic function w of $z = x + iy$. Then, by Cauchy's integral theorem,

$$w(z) = \frac{1}{2\pi i} \int_{\Gamma} \frac{w(\zeta)\, d\zeta}{\zeta - z}, \tag{19.59}$$

where Γ is a circle of radius r and center z located, with its interior, inside R. Since $\zeta = z + re^{i\theta}$, we can write (19.59) in the form

$$w(z) = \frac{1}{2\pi} \int_{0}^{2\pi} w(z + re^{i\theta})\, d\theta. \tag{19.60}$$

Taking the real part of (19.60).

$$u(x, y) = \frac{1}{2\pi} \int_0^{2\pi} u(x + r \cos \theta, y + r \sin \theta) \, d\theta; \qquad (19.61)$$

i.e., $u(x, y)$ *is the average of its values on any circle* Γ.

The theorem follows by applying (19.61) to any point (x, y) where u assumes a maximum or minimum without being locally constant. Formula (19.61) has an independent importance.

The importance of the maximum principle, which is the content of Theorems 19.1 and 19.2, will come out in Sec. 23. An immediate corollary of Theorem 19.1 is that a solution u of $L(u) = 0$ must certainly be bounded in R by its extreme values on C. In particular, if $u = 0$ on C, then $u = 0$ throughout R. From this immediately follows the fact that there cannot be two solutions of a boundary-value problem $L(u) = 0$ with the same continuous boundary values on C.

SECTION 20.   FORMULATING ELLIPTIC DIFFERENCE EQUATION PROBLEMS

There are many methods of solving numerical problems involving elliptic partial differential equations. Probably the most frequently used in practice is the one that solves a related problem in finite differences, and this is the only method treated in this book. For other tested methods, see Collatz [1955]. Interesting theoretical methods described by Bergman and Schiffer [1953] also appear promising for elliptic problems, although they have been little exploited for numerical calculations.

20.1. Discretization and Problems Raised by It

Because of the discrete structure of computation with digital computers, it is essential before solving a continuous problem with them to reduce the problem to a form involving a finite set of variables. For simplicity we formulate our discussion for two dimensions, but many of the ideas will go over to three or more dimensions.

In the methods of the finite-difference type, the connected open domain R of the independent variable (x, y) is replaced by a finite set S, the number N of whose members is relatively large. Each dependent function $u(x, y)$ is replaced by a function $U(P)$ defined on S. The partial differential equation problem determining $u(x, y)$ is thus replaced by a finite system of simultaneous equations determining the function $U(P)$. This process we call *discretization*, and in its general form it assumes nothing about whether the members of the set S are points, arcs, areas, or other entities. And nothing is said about how the function $U(P)$ is to be computed from the system of equations determining it—not even whether the computing methods are to be deterministic or of the Monte Carlo type (discussed in Sec. 23, where even infinite sets S are considered).

Conventionally each P is a *point* (x_P, y_P) in or near the set $\bar{R} = R \cup C$, where C is the boundary of R. The simultaneous equations determining $U(P)$ are *finite-difference equations*, and this is the origin of the term *finite-difference methods*. In the traditional literature on these methods the value of U at (x_P, y_P) is regarded as an isolated value, to be compared only with $u(x_P, y_P)$ when one discusses the difference between u and U. However, there is now an increasing tendency to regard (x_P, y_P) as merely a *representative point* of a *two-dimensional* region of nearby points (x, y), and to regard $U(x_P, y_P)$ as a representative value of a function $U(x, y)$ defined for all (x, y) in $\bar{R}$. Thus in both Secs. 23 and 24 we shall be discussing finite-difference methods in connection with functions $U(x, y)$ defined on the whole closed region $\bar{R}$.

The point of view that $U(x_P, y_P)$ is merely a representative of the values of a function $U(x, y)$ defined on all of $\bar{R}$ has two practical advantages: First, it helps us to set up better difference equations for the $U(x_P, y_P)$ in difficult geometrical situations, e.g., near interfaces. Second, it assists analysis very much by permitting U and u to have the same domain of arguments (x, y), so that U and u can be thought of as belonging to the same function space. The first advantage will be illustrated in Sec. 20.8; the second, in our treatment of discretization error in Sec. 23 and in our discussion of the difference methods for eigenvalue problems in Sec. 24.3.

In a new development of this idea of representative P, Hersch [1955], and Hersch, Pfluger, and Schopf [1956] have defined the members P of S as open squares of a square network, called *meshes* or *cells*. In this way $U(P)$ is a function defined on the cells, and is thus immediately interpretable also as a (discontinuous) function of the continuous variable (x, y). Although the use of cell functions looks very promising, it is yet too new to have much literature for us to summarize.

In keeping with existing practice, let us take the members P of S to be points of the plane. The points P are usually arranged in a regular pattern, e.g., at the nodes of a square lattice in the plane, and we shall later see good reasons for preferring such regular nets. But sometimes the P are situated quite irregularly—to conform to an irregular boundary curve C, for example—and we shall discuss irregular nets first.

The discretization of an elliptic partial differential equation problem raises a great number of problems, both practical and mathematical, and we list some of these here. The answers to these problems are generally unknown, and their tentative answers already fill a considerable literature which records some of the current state of the art. Most of this book is devoted to a discussion of these problems, as they concern hyperbolic and parabolic problems as much as elliptic problems.

1. What is the best way of selecting the points P, as regards regularity, orientation, refinement, possible use of square, rectangular, triangular, hexagonal, or other special nets?

2. What is the best way to define a net analog of the boundary C, and to deal with the boundary conditions at C?

3. What are the best finite-difference expressions to use as analogs of Δ in the net, and particularly near the boundary? Same question for other differential operators, and especially for the normal derivative u_n at the boundary.

4. Having made decisions answering 1, 2, and 3, how can one practically proceed from a blueprint of R and C to setting up the difference equations for U? In particular, how can one get the difference equations suitably represented inside the automatic digital computer with which one intends to solve them?

5. What is the best way to solve the resulting system of equations for the values of $U(P)$, particularly with an automatic computer?

6. Does $U(P) \to u(x, y)$, as $P \to (x, y)$, and as the net is suitably refined?

7. If we do not know that the solution u of the continuous problem exists, can we prove its existence by showing the convergence of $U(P)$ to such a solution, as the net is refined? (This question lies outside of numerical analysis, but has motivated considerable mathematical work with difference equations, e.g., Courant, Friedrichs, and Lewy [1928] and Ladyženskaya [1957].)

8. How can one bound the discretization error $|u(P) - U(P)|$ for a given net? Can one also bound the error in estimating such derivatives as $u_x(P)$ by difference quotients on the net?

In the present state of the art, questions 1, 2, 3, and particularly 4 and 5, seem to be the most vital ones for practical computing. Although question 4 is not primarily a mathematical problem, it must be answered before elliptic partial differential equations can be solved with any facility on automatic computers. Its solution is not particularly simple (see Sec. 25). In the present early stages of automatic computation, the vital questions are usually cruder than with desk computing, which has had a much longer history of development. Since these cruder questions appear less "mathematical," they tend to be overlooked by mathematical analysts.

20.2. The Method of Lines

In one class of method for solving elliptic (and other) partial differential equations, one of the variables, say x, is discretized, while the other variable y is left continuous. When suitable finite-difference expressions are substituted for the x derivatives, the partial differential equation is converted into a coupled system of ordinary differential equations in the independent variable y, i.e., a *difference-differential equation*. The method is usually called the *method of lines* in the Soviet Union, where it has been used a good deal. See Kantorovič and Krylov [1952] and Faddeeva [1949].

When one actually uses the method of lines on an automatic digital computer, it is usual to discretize the problem also in the y-direction, by means of one or another of the finite-difference methods for solving systems of ordinary differential equations (Runge-Kutta, Milne, etc.). Thus, in principle, the method of lines is included in the methods described in Sec. 20.1. However, as ordinarily used, the number of subdivisions in the y-direction far exceeds the number in the x-direction, and so one is dealing with a rectangular net with very long rectangles. For this reason the method of lines is quite different in character from ordinary network methods.

Although the method is apparently a very useful one, we shall not treat it further in this book.

20.3. Types of Problems to be Discretized

In its full application, the method of finite differences deals with the discretization of an arbitrary problem involving partial differential equations and, in particular, with any of the problems outlined in Sec. 18. To narrow the field, however, we shall confine ourselves to problems of the following type. Define a two-dimensional region R and its boundary C as in Sec. 18. Let $\bar{R}$ be the closed region $R \cup C$. Let a, b, c, d, e, f, and g be sufficiently differentiable functions of x and y, for (x, y) in $\bar{R}$. Assume $b^2 - ac \leq -\epsilon < 0$ in $\bar{R}$ (uniform ellipticity condition). Let α, β, γ, and δ be functions of arc length s on C. We deal with the following general problem, or particular cases of it:

To find $u(x, y)$ such that

$$L(u) \equiv au_{xx} + 2bu_{xy} + cu_{yy} + du_x + eu_y + fu = g \quad \text{in } R, \quad (20.1)$$

with boundary condition

$$\alpha u + \beta u_n + \gamma + \delta u_s = 0 \quad \text{on } C. \quad (20.2)$$

Frequently the problem (20.1, 20.2) will be *self-adjoint*, a term defined in Sec. 19.3.

We shall consider related eigenvalue problems in Sec. 24.

20.4. Irregular Nets

In problems where the region R has a curved boundary C, and especially where R has a long and narrow protusion, it is sometimes convenient to take the points P of the net in an irregular pattern. This is the case, for example, in studying the stresses in turbine blades. For such problems an irregular net may be more manageable than a square net. For one thing, without excessive refinement a square net can easily become disconnected across a narrow neck of R. For another thing, to fit a curved boundary with a square net ordinarily requires adding to the net region certain points of C which are not lattice points of the net (see Secs. 20.9 and 20.10). This usually causes some points of the net region to be very close to neighboring points, which may, in turn, cause some awkwardness in solving the resulting equations. But, with an irregular net, one can choose the points P to have such a gradual irregularity that there are no near-together points. Finally, with irregularly positioned nodes, one can always place a node on the normal to C through a given node P on C. This makes easy a difference representation of the normal derivative u_n at P, in considerable contrast to regular nets.

Having fixed on a net of points P in $\bar{R}$, regular or irregular, how shall one determine the system of equations which replaces the differential equation (20.1)? A reasonable procedure, proposed by H. Reichenbach [unpublished], is the following. First, for each point P, one determines a group of points Q_i ($i = 1, 2, \cdots, r_P$) called *neighbors* of P. For Laplace's equation one thinks of r_P as being approximately 5 or 6. Now, for simplicity, let P have coordinates $(0, 0)$, while Q_i has coordinates (x_i, y_i). Let $P = Q_0$. One seeks a linear algebraic expression of the type

$$L_h(u) = \sum_{i=0}^{r_P} \sigma(P, Q_i)\, u(Q_i) \tag{20.3}$$

to represent the differential operator $L(u)$ at P. The following is a technique for obtaining (20.3). One makes a formal Taylor expansion of $u(x, y)$ about $(0, 0)$, up to terms of second degree:

$$u(Q_i) = u(x_i, y_i) = u(P) + x_i\, u_x(P) + y_i\, u_y(P) + \tfrac{1}{2}x_i^2\, u_{xx}(P)$$
$$+ x_i y_i\, u_{xy}(P) + \tfrac{1}{2}y_i^2 u_{yy}(P) + \cdots. \tag{20.4}$$

Substituting (20.4) in (20.3), we have

$$L_h(u) = F_P\, u(P) + D_P\, u_x(P) + E_P\, u_y(P) + A_P\, u_{xx}(P)$$
$$+ 2B_P\, u_{xy}(P) + C_P\, u_{yy}(P) + \cdots,$$

where

$$F_P = \sum_{i=0}^{r_P} \sigma(P, Q_i), \qquad\qquad D_P = \sum_{i=0}^{r_P} x_i\, \sigma(P, Q_i),$$

$$E_P = \sum_{i=0}^{r_P} y_i\, \sigma(P, Q_i), \qquad\qquad A_P = \tfrac{1}{2}\sum_{i=0}^{r_P} x_i^2\, \sigma(P, Q_i), \qquad (20.5)$$

$$B_P = \tfrac{1}{2}\sum_{i=0}^{r_P} x_i y_i\, \sigma(P, Q_i), \qquad C_P = \tfrac{1}{2}\sum_{i=0}^{r_P} y_i^2\, \sigma(P, Q_i).$$

Now, for $L_h(u)$ to be a formal approximation to the $L(u)$ of (20.1), it is sufficient that

$$A_P = a(P), \qquad B_P = b(P), \qquad C_P = c(P),$$
$$D_P = d(P), \qquad E_P = e(P), \qquad F_P = f(P). \qquad (20.6)$$

The system (20.5), (20.6) is six equations in the unknowns $\sigma(P, Q_i)$, and one would ordinarily expect to need at least six unknowns $\sigma(P, Q_i)$ to satisfy them; i.e., each P must have at least five neighbors.

To study the relation between $L_h(u)$ and $L(u)$ for small values of the x_i, y_i, let us suppose that each $x_i = \xi_i h$, $y_i = \eta_i h$ $(i = 1, \cdots, r_P)$, i.e., that the points Q_i are fixed in their relative location from P as the scale is changed by varying h. Then the equations (20.5), (20.6) take the form

$$\sum \sigma_i = f, \qquad \frac{1}{2}\sum \xi_i^2 \sigma_i = \frac{a}{h^2},$$

$$\sum \xi_i \sigma_i = \frac{d}{h}, \qquad \frac{1}{2}\sum \xi_i \eta_i \sigma_i = \frac{b}{h^2}, \qquad (20.7)$$

$$\sum \eta_i \sigma_i = \frac{e}{h}, \qquad \frac{1}{2}\sum \eta_i^2 \sigma_i = \frac{c}{h^2};$$

we have written $\sigma_i = \sigma(P, Q_i)$ for brevity. If the system (20.7) has a unique solution $\{\sigma_i\}$ for any value of h, then this solution is unique for all values of h, by the fundamental properties of a linear system. Clearly, as $h \to 0$, the σ_i are $O(h^{-2})$.

Now if equations (20.7) are satisfied, then $L_h(u)$ and $L(u)$ differ only by terms of degree three or higher in the x_i, y_i. Consequently, when (20.7) holds, one can be sure that

$$L_h(u) - L(u) = O(h^{-2})\, O(h^3) = O(h), \qquad \text{as } h \to 0. \qquad (20.8)$$

One could improve the last term of (20.8) to $O(h^2)$ by introducing enough more points Q_i, or enough symmetry in their location, that the terms of $L_h(u) - L(u)$ of degree three in the x_i, y_i all vanish. This is usually done with regular nets (see Sec. 20.6).

A number of proposals for setting up difference equations contemplate the solution of the system (20.5), (20.6) for each node P, generally on an automatic digital computer. Let us examine some of the properties of such an $L_h(u)$. In the first place, it is essential in most methods of Secs. 21 and 22 for solving $L_h(u) = g$ that the coefficient $\sigma(P, Q_0) = \sigma(P, P)$ be nonzero for each P. Some other properties turn out to be desirable. For example, that the coefficient matrix corresponding to $L_h(u)$ be *symmetric*, which means that $\sigma(P, Q) = \sigma(Q, P)$ for each P, Q in the network. Another useful property is that L_h be of *positive type* (Motzkin and Wasow [1953]), i.e., that for each P

$$\frac{\sigma(P, Q_i)}{\sigma(P, P)} < 0, \qquad i = 1, \cdots, r_P, \tag{20.9}$$

or, at least, of *nonnegative type*:

$$\frac{\sigma(P, Q_i)}{\sigma(P, P)} \le 0, \qquad i = 1, \cdots, r_P. \tag{20.10}$$

The names "positive" and "nonnegative" come from the nature of the coefficients when the equation $L_h(u) = 0$ is solved for $u(P)$ in the form frequently used in iterative processes:

$$u(P) = \sum_{i=1}^{r_P} \left[\frac{-\sigma(P, Q_i)}{\sigma(P, P)} \right] u(Q_i). \tag{20.11}$$

It is the coefficients in (20.11) which are positive or nonnegative. It should be noted that "positivity of type" is a property of both the operator L_h and the neighbor system (since the addition of one extra neighbor Q with $\sigma(P, Q) = 0$ will destroy positivity), whereas nonnegativity depends only on L_h. For that reason nonnegativity seems to us to be the more important concept.

Another important condition is that of *diagonal dominance* [of the matrix representing the linear system]:

$$\left. \begin{array}{ll} \displaystyle\sum_{i=1}^{r_P} |\sigma(P, Q_i)| \le |\sigma(P, P)| & \text{for all } P, \\[2ex] \text{with strict inequality for at least one } P. \end{array} \right\} \tag{20.12}$$

We shall occasionally use the terms "positive type" and "diagonal dominance" also for L_h at one point P. For one point P, diagonal dominance means that (20.12) holds, with equality permitted.

Conditions (20.10) and (20.12) are hypotheses sufficient to prove the useful maximum principle for solutions of $L_h(U) = 0$ (see Sec. 23). They also make possible the convergence of certain methods of solving systems (see Secs. 21.4 and 22).

Now the system (20.5), (20.6) can, in principle, ordinarily be solved uniquely for each point P. For this it is necessary to assume some things about the number and location of the neighbors Q_i of P, e.g., that they are not collinear. However, it is difficult in the general case to say whether the resulting system will be of positive or nonnegative type, or whether it will have diagonal dominance. Motzkin and Wasow [1953] have even proved a certain negative theorem in this connection. Namely, at a given point P, even for the widest possible neighbor system in which all nodes of a fixed net are neighbors of P, there exists an elliptic operator L for which the corresponding difference operator L_h of (20.3) is not of nonnegative type. (Their theorem was actually stated only for regular nets.) For practical applications to operators which are strongly elliptic (i.e., $b^2 - ac \ll 0$), the force of the Motzkin-Wasow theorem is weakened by the fact that, for a net with a large number of points, the elliptic operator of the theorem will generally be close to parabolic.

Ordinarily the operator L_h will not have a symmetric matrix, as the nature of equations (20.5), (20.6) makes symmetry most unlikely. A further study of the above properties of L_h will be deferred to Sec. 20.7, where, in dealing with a square net, it will be possible to prove definite results.

20.5. Variational Method of Setting up Difference Equations

At this point we shall indicate a method which will lead to a *symmetric* operator L_h whenever we have a right to expect it, i.e., when L is self-adjoint. This is the *variational method* of setting up the difference operator (20.3), based on Sec. 19.1. Some of the following ideas have been implicitly used by MacNeal [1953] in connection with using network analyzers for solving Laplace's equation.

Suppose first that we have a self-adjoint elliptic boundary-value problem $L(u) = g$ with natural boundary conditions (19.13). We recall from Sec. 19.1 that the solution u minimizes the integral $I(u)$ of (19.1):

$$I(u) = \iint\limits_{R} (\tfrac{1}{2}au_x^2 + bu_xu_y + \tfrac{1}{2}cu_y^2 - \tfrac{1}{2}fu^2 + gu)\,dx\,dy$$

$$+ \int\limits_{C} (\tfrac{1}{2}\alpha u^2 + \gamma u)\,ds. \quad (20.13)$$

Suppose that for each P in the net, one follows the ideas leading to (20.3) to get a formal approximation for $u_x(P)$ and $u_y(P)$ in terms of linear combinations of $u(Q_i)$ for certain neighbors Q_i of P. By substituting these and the value of u into (20.13) at the point P, one arrives at formal approximations to the integrands of (20.13) which are quadratic functions of the $u(Q_i)$.

Suppose, moreover, that one has two quadrature formulas of the types

$$\iint_R F(x, y)\, dx\, dy \doteq \sum_P w(P)\, F(P), \qquad \int_C G(s)\, ds \doteq \sum_P \omega(P)\, G(P), \quad (20.14)$$

where $\omega(P)$ and $w(P)$ are appropriate positive weight functions—perhaps the length of the part of C (for ω) or the area of the part of R (for w) which appropriately belongs to P in the sense of Sec. 20.1.

Setting $F(P)$ to be the result of substituting the linear approximations to $u_x(P)$, $u_y(P)$ into the integrand of the double integral of (20.13), and setting $G(P)$ to be the corresponding point function for the line integral, we can use (20.14) to approximate $I(u)$ by a nonhomogeneous quadratic function of the unknown values $U(P)$ of a net function U:

$$I_h(U) = \tfrac{1}{2} \sum_{P,Q} A(P, Q)\, U(P)\, U(Q) + \sum_P B(P)\, U(P). \qquad (20.15)$$

If the matrix of coefficients $A(P, Q)$ in (20.15) is not symmetric, we can make it so by replacing both $A(P, Q)$ and $A(Q, P)$ by their average value $\tfrac{1}{2}[A(P, Q) + A(Q, P)]$. We therefore assume symmetry in the coefficients $A(P, Q)$ of (20.15).

Now the solution $u(x, y)$ of the boundary-value problem $L(u) = g$ renders the function $I(u)$ stationary. We agree to determine a net function $U(P)$ by the analogous requirement that it render the function $I_h(U)$ stationary. Since $I_h(U)$ is a quadratic function of the N variables $U(P)$, we can differentiate (20.15) with respect to each of the variables, and obtain the following system of N linear algebraic equations in the N unknown node values $U(P)$:

$$\sum_Q A(P, Q)\, U(Q) + B(P) = 0 \qquad \text{for all } P. \qquad (20.16)$$

The N equations (20.16) are the symmetric difference equations derived by the variational method for natural boundary conditions. If we had not assumed that $A(P, Q) = A(Q, P)$ in (20.15), the symmetry would have arisen automatically in deriving (20.16) from (20.15).

If the boundary conditions for the given self-adjoint boundary-value problem are not natural, we still get a symmetric matrix (20.16). For, by our analysis in Sec. 19.3, we see that the nonnatural boundary conditions for a self-adjoint problem must take the form $u = \psi(s)$ on some subset C_1 of C. In our approximation (20.15) to $I(u)$, we set the corresponding values of $U(P)$, P in C_1, equal to $\psi(P)$. This has the effect of replacing some variables $U(P)$ in U by constant values, but does not alter the fact that $I_h(U)$ is a quadratic function of the remaining variables $U(P)$. Hence (20.16) is still a symmetric set of linear equations.

Now, in practice, solving the system (20.16) is far easier when the quadratic function (20.15) is actually *minimized* or *maximized* by the solution. This will occur whenever the symmetric coefficients $A(P, Q)$ in (20.15) form a *semidefinite* matrix. Moreover, if the matrix $[A(P, Q)]$ is semidefinite, the solution $U(P)$ of (20.15) is unique if and only if $[A(P, Q)]$ is actually definite. Hence, there is some interest in knowing conditions sufficient to make $[A(P, Q)]$ semidefinite or definite.

THEOREM 20.1.   *Suppose that in* (20.13) $a \geq 0$, $\alpha \geq 0$, *and* $f \leq 0$. *Then the matrix* $[A(P, Q)]$ *of* (20.16) *is positive semidefinite*.

Proof. If the conclusion were false, then the quadratic function (20.15) would have to assume all real values as U varies. But, since the problem is elliptic, $b^2 - ac < 0$ for all P. Hence

$$au_x{}^2 + 2bu_xu_y + cu_y{}^2 \geq 0$$

for all u_x, u_y. Hence the same form remains nonnegative when one substitutes linear combinations of the $U(P)$ for u_x, u_y. Similarly, αu^2 and $-fu^2$ are nonnegative. Because these forms are nonnegative, and because the weights $w(P)$ and $\omega(P)$ of (20.14) are positive, the sum of the quadratic terms in (20.15) is nonnegative. Hence $[A(P, Q)]$ is semidefinite, as claimed.

Under the hypotheses of Theorem 20.1, the matrix $[A(P, Q)]$ will usually be definite and not only semidefinite. But this will not always be the case, and it is difficult to think of hypotheses which would insure definiteness. Moreover, as we shall see in Secs. 21 and 22, semidefiniteness will win most of the advantages of definiteness.

Although having a symmetric semidefinite or definite matrix of coefficients has some advantages, it probably should not be the primary consideration in selecting difference equations.

If one simulates the solution of a Dirichlet problem by a finite electric network of resistances, the resulting system of linear equations for the node voltages will necessarily have a symmetric and definite matrix. This is because a passive electric circuit automatically assumes an equilibrium position of minimum energy. Thus the difference equations solved by a network analyzer are of the type described in this section.

We shall give an example of the variational method in connection with a square net in Sec. 20.8.

20.6. Square Nets: Approximating the Derivatives

Two considerations favor a regular spacing of the nodes P in digital computing. First, for irregular nets the determination of the appropriate difference equation to replace the partial differential equation requires an amount of computation which is prohibitive in desk computation and which can be a considerable bother in automatic computation. Second, for maximum speed, automatic computers demand simplicity of structure in a problem, and regular networks are much simpler than irregular. For these reasons we deal mainly with regular networks of points P in this book. For simplicity of exposition we continue to confine the treatment to two dimensions ($n = 2$).

The only regular polygons which can fill the plane are triangles, squares, and hexagons, and thus there are only three finite-difference networks of corresponding regularity. Because the hexagons have a rather complicated cell shape to fit into the boundaries, the only regular networks in common use are those composed of squares (*square nets*) or of equilateral triangles (*triangular nets*). A third network in common use is composed of rectangles, chosen frequently to match some lack of isotropy of the x- and y-directions. We shall mainly discuss square nets in this section.

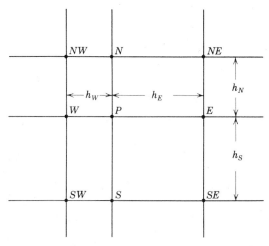

Fig. 20.1. Node abbreviations for an irregular net composed of vertical and horizontal lines.

Suppose the infinite plane of the two-dimensional region R (with closure $\bar{R}$) of Sec. 18 is subdivided by two families of parallel lines into a square *net*. Let the *lines* of the net be $x = \mu h$ and $y = \nu h$ ($\mu, \nu = 0, \pm 1, \pm 2, \cdots$.). The points ($\mu h, \nu h$) are called the *lattice points* of the net. The lattice points in $\bar{R}$ are called *nodes* of the net, but we shall also define other nodes in connection with the treatment of the boundary C in Sec. 20.9. The smallest squares bounded by four lines of the net are called *meshes* or *cells* of the net. Each mesh is bounded by four line segments called *links*.

To discuss the approximation of partial derivatives by finite differences in a square net, we shall give some remainder formulas taken from Kantorovič and Krylov [1952]. For later use near boundaries, we shall give them in more generality than necessary for a square net.

For any point $P = (x_P, y_P)$ we consider eight neighboring nodes of a net made up of horizontal and vertical lines, not necessarily equally spaced. The six relevant lines are $x = x_P - h_W$, $x = x_P$, $x = x_P + h_E$, and $y = y_P - h_S$, $y = y_P$, $y = y_P + h_N$. The eight neighboring nodes are given compass abbreviations, as in Fig. 20.1. Thus NE stands for the point $(x_P + h_E, y_P + h_N)$, etc. Let $u(NE)$, $u(P)$, etc., denote values of $u(x, y)$ at NE, P, etc. Let $h = \max(h_W, h_E, h_N, h_S)$.

DEFINITION. Given an interval or region I. By $M_k(I)$ $(k = 1, 2, \cdots)$ we denote the supremum of absolute values of all the partial derivatives of $u(x, y)$ of order k in the interval or region. For example,

$$M_2(R) = \max\left(\sup_R |u_{xx}|, \sup_R |u_{xy}|, \sup_R |u_{yy}|\right).$$

THEOREM 20.2. *Let I be the open x interval from W to E. Suppose that u is continuous, together with u_x, u_{xx}, on the closed interval $\bar{I}$, and that u_{xxx} is continuous on I. Then*

$$u_x(P) = \frac{h_W h_E^{-1}[u(E) - u(P)] + h_E h_W^{-1}[u(P) - u(W)]}{h_W + h_E} + R_x'(P)$$

$$= \frac{h_W}{h_E(h_E + h_W)} u(E) + \frac{h_E - h_W}{h_E h_W} u(P) \tag{20.17}$$

$$- \frac{h_E}{h_W(h_E + h_W)} u(W) + R_x'(P),$$

where

$$R_x'(P) = \frac{-h_E h_W}{6} u_{xxx}(\xi, y_P), \qquad x_P - h_W < \xi < x_P + h_E. \tag{20.18}$$

Moreover, if $h \geq \max(h_W, h_E)$,

$$|R_x'(P)| \leq \tfrac{1}{6} h^2 M_3(I). \tag{20.19}$$

Proof. By Taylor's theorem with a remainder,

$$u(E) = u(P) + u_x(P)h_E + \tfrac{1}{2} u_{xx}(P)h_E^2 + \tfrac{1}{6} u_{xxx}(\xi_E)h_E^3,$$

$$x_P < \xi_E < x_P + h_E; \tag{20.20}$$

$$u(W) = u(P) - u_x(P)h_W + \tfrac{1}{2} u_{xx}(P)h_W^2 - \tfrac{1}{6} u_{xxx}(\xi_W)h_W^3,$$

$$x_P - h_W < \xi_W < x_P. \tag{20.21}$$

Solving (20.20) for $u_x(P)$ gives

$$u_x(P) = \frac{u(E) - u(P)}{h_E} - \frac{1}{2} u_{xx}(P)h_E - \frac{1}{6} u_{xxx}(\xi_E)h_E{}^2. \quad (20.22)$$

Solving (20.21) for $u_x(P)$ gives

$$u_x(P) = \frac{u(P) - u(W)}{h_W} + \frac{1}{2} u_{xx}(P)h_W - \frac{1}{6} u_{xxx}(\xi_W)h_W{}^2. \quad (20.23)$$

To eliminate $u_{xx}(P)$ between (20.22) and (20.23), we add $h_W(h_E + h_W)^{-1}$ times (20.22) to $h_E(h_E + h_W)^{-1}$ times (20.23). The result is (20.17), except that we have

$$R_x{}'(P) = \frac{-h_E h_W}{6} \left[\frac{h_E\, u_{xxx}(\xi_E) + h_W u_{xxx}(\xi_W)}{h_E + h_W} \right]. \quad (20.24)$$

Since u_{xxx} is continuous, and since the expression within brackets in (20.24) is a weighted average (with positive weights) of two values of u_{xxx}, we can rewrite (20.24) in the form (20.18), proving the theorem. (Actually the continuity of u_{xxx} need not be assumed, but only its existence.)

The analogous theorem for $u_y(P)$ is too obvious to state.

The following theorem follows immediately from Theorem 20.2 and its analog for $u_y(P)$.

THEOREM 20.3. *Under the hypotheses of Theorem 20.2, if $h_W = h_E = h$,*

$$u_x(P) = \frac{u(E) - u(W)}{2h} + R_x{}'(P), \quad (20.25)$$

where

$$R_x{}'(P) = -\tfrac{1}{6}h^2\, u_{xxx}(\xi, y_P), \qquad x_P - h < \xi < x_P + h. \quad (20.26)$$

Also,

$$u_y(P) = \frac{u(N) - u(S)}{2h} + R_y{}'(P), \quad (20.27)$$

where

$$R_y{}'(P) = -\tfrac{1}{6}h^2\, u_{yyy}(x_P, \eta), \qquad y_P - h < \eta < y_P + h. \quad (20.28)$$

Moreover, we have

$$|R_y{}'(P)| \le \tfrac{1}{6}h^2\, M_3(I_1), \quad (20.29)$$

where I_1 is the open y interval from S to N.

Note that in (20.25) we employed a *centered difference quotient* to approximate $u_x(P)$, with an error $O(h^2)$, as $h \to 0$. Had we used instead a *one-sided difference* like $h^{-1}[u(E) - u(P)]$, the error would have been $O(h)$, as $h \to 0$. The centered differences are far better in this respect.

For the second derivative there is an analogous theorem:

THEOREM 20.4. *Let I be the open x interval from W to E. Suppose $u, u_x, u_{xx},$ and u_{xxx} are continuous on $\bar{I}$ and that u_{xxxx} is continuous on I. Then*

$$u_{xx}(P) = \frac{[u(E) - u(P)]/h_E - [u(P) - u(W)]/h_W}{(h_W + h_E)/2} + R_x''(P)$$

$$= 2\left[\frac{u(E)}{h_E(h_E + h_W)} - \frac{u(P)}{h_W h_E} + \frac{u(W)}{h_W(h_W + h_E)}\right] + R_x''(P),$$

$$(20.30)$$

where

$$R_x''(P) = \frac{h_W - h_E}{3} u_{xxx}(P) - \frac{h_W{}^2 - h_W h_E + h_E{}^2}{12} u_{xxxx}(\xi, y_P),$$

$$x_P - h_W < \xi < x_P + h_E. \quad (20.31)$$

Moreover, if $h \geq \max(h_W, h_E)$,

$$|R_x''(P)| \leq \tfrac{1}{3} h M_3(I) + \tfrac{1}{12} h^2 M_4(I). \quad (20.32)$$

Proof. Theorem 20.4 is proved much like Theorem 20.2. Taylor expansions analogous to (20.20) and (20.21) are carried one term further. One solves for $u_{xx}(P)$ and eliminates $u_x(P)$, obtaining formula (20.30) with an error term

$$R_x''(P) = \frac{h_W - h_E}{3} u_{xxx}(P) - \frac{1}{12(h_W + h_E)} [h_E{}^3 u_{xxxx}(\xi_E)$$

$$+ h_W{}^3 u_{xxxx}(\xi_W)].$$

Again, one can consolidate the fourth derivative to obtain (20.31). A simple estimate yields (20.32) from (20.31), proving the theorem.

Under the weaker hypotheses of Theorem 20.2, using (20.20) and (20.21), one can derive formula (20.30) with the error term

$$R_x''(P) = \frac{1}{3} \frac{h_E{}^2 u_{xxx}(\xi_E) - h_W{}^2 u_{xxx}(\xi_W)}{h_E + h_W},$$

so that

$$|R_x''(P)| \leq \tfrac{2}{3} M_3(I) h. \quad (20.33)$$

There are obvious analogs for $u_{yy}(P)$. For equally spaced nets, one has:

THEOREM 20.5. *Under the hypotheses of Theorem 20.4, if $h_W = h_E = h$,*

$$u_{xx}(P) = \frac{u(W) - 2u(P) + u(E)}{h^2} + R_x''(P), \quad (20.34)$$

where

$$R_x''(P) = - \frac{h^2}{12} u_{xxxx}(\xi), \qquad x_P - h < \xi < x_P + h. \qquad (20.35)$$

We have

$$|R_x''(P)| \le \tfrac{1}{12}h^2 M_4(I). \qquad (20.36)$$

Theorems 20.3 and 20.5 show the great advantage of equally spaced nets, in that the error term in the difference expressions drops from $O(h)$ to $O(h^2)$, as $h \to 0$, when $h_E = h_W$.

A difference formula for $u_{xy}(P)$ is more awkward in apparently requiring use of the diagonal neighbors NE, NW, etc., of Fig. 20.1. For simplicity, we confine ourselves to a square net for the following result:

THEOREM 20.6. *Suppose that u together with all its partial derivatives of orders up to 3 is continuous in the closed square Σ, where $|x - x_P| \le h$, $|y - y_P| \le h$; and suppose that the partial derivatives of order 4 are continuous in the corresponding open square. Then*

$$u_{xy}(P) = \frac{u(NE) - u(NW) + u(SW) - u(SE)}{4h^2} + R_{xy}(P), \qquad (20.37)$$

where

$$R_{xy}(P) = \tfrac{1}{6}h^2[u_{xxxy}(\xi_1, \eta_1) + u_{xyyy}(\xi_2, \eta_2)],$$

$$x_P - h < \xi_i < x_P + h, \qquad y_P - h < \eta_i < y_P + h, \qquad i = 1, 2.$$

We have

$$|R_{xy}(P)| \le \tfrac{1}{3}h^2 M_4(\Sigma). \qquad (20.38)$$

The proof proceeds from the Taylor expansion for $u(NE)$, $u(NW)$, etc., and will be omitted.

There are approximations of higher order to the various derivatives. For example, if the 6th derivatives of u are continuous on the closed interval from $(x_P - 2h, y_P)$ to $(x_P + 2h, y_P)$, then one can show that

$$u_{xx}(P) = \frac{u(W) - 2u(P) + u(E)}{h^2}$$

$$- \frac{h^2}{12}\left[\frac{u(WW) - 4u(W) + 6u(P) - 4u(E) + u(EE)}{h^4}\right] + R_x'''(P)$$

$$= \frac{1}{12h^2}[-u(WW) + 16u(W) - 30u(P) + 16u(E) - u(EE)]$$

$$+ R_x'''(P), \qquad (20.39)$$

where $R_x'''(P) = O(h^4)$ as $h \to 0$.

In (20.39) the point WW is $(x_P - 2h, y_P)$, etc. (See Fig. 20.2.) Such approximations give great accuracy in the interior of a region R, but it is very difficult to be comparably accurate near C. For this reason they are not used very much. Note also that (20.39) is not of positive type [see (20.9)].

20.7. Square Nets: Approximating $L(u)$ and Δu

Directly from the above formulas, in a square net one can set up a formal difference approximation to the differential operator $L(u)$ of (20.1). Ignoring the "edge effects" of the boundary conditions, one simply replaces u_x, u_{xx}, u_{xy}, u_{yy}, etc., in (20.1) by the appropriate formulas (20.25), (20.34), (20.37), and their y analogs, each of which has an error bound of form CM_4h^2. Following the notation of Fig. 20.1, we make the following replacements, expressed in terms of a function U defined on the net:

replace u_{xx} by $h^{-2}[U(W) - 2U(P) + U(E)]$;

replace u_{yy} by $h^{-2}[U(S) - 2U(P) + U(N)]$;

replace u_{xy} by $(2h)^{-2}[U(NE) - U(NW) + U(SW) - U(SE)]$; (20.40)

replace u_x by $(2h)^{-1}[U(E) - U(W)]$;

replace u_y by $(2h)^{-1}[U(N) - U(S)]$.

Let

$$L(u) = au_{xx} + 2bu_{xy} + cu_{yy} + du_x + eu_y + fu.$$

If the expressions (20.40) are combined, one gets the following corresponding finite difference operator $L_h(U)$:

$$L_h U(P) = h^{-2} \sum_Q A(P, Q) U(Q), \quad Q = P, N, E, NE, \text{etc.,} \quad (20.41)$$

where

$$
\begin{aligned}
A(P, P) &= -2a - 2c + fh^2; & A(P, NE) &= \tfrac{1}{2}b; \\
A(P, E) &= a + \tfrac{1}{2}hd; & A(P, NW) &= -\tfrac{1}{2}b; \\
A(P, W) &= a - \tfrac{1}{2}hd; & A(P, SW) &= \tfrac{1}{2}b; \quad (20.42) \\
A(P, N) &= c + \tfrac{1}{2}he; & A(P, SE) &= -\tfrac{1}{2}b. \\
A(P, S) &= c - \tfrac{1}{2}he;
\end{aligned}
$$

All the functions a, b, c, d, e, f in (20.42) are evaluated at $P = (x_P, y_P)$.

If one applies the operator L_h to any four-times continuously differentiable function $u(x, y)$ in the square Σ of Theorem 20.6, one finds the following result:

THEOREM 20.7. *Let $u(x, y)$ satisfy the hypotheses of Theorem* 20.6 *in the* *square Σ of that theorem. Then, with the above notation, we have*

$$L_h u(P) - L u(P) = \frac{1}{12} a_P h^2 u_{xxxx}(Q_1) - \frac{2b_P}{6} h^2 [u_{xxxy}(Q_2) + u_{xyyy}(Q_3)]$$

$$+ \frac{1}{12} c_P h^2 u_{yyyy}(Q_4) + \frac{1}{6} h^2 d_P u_{xxx}(Q_5) + \frac{1}{6} h^2 e_P u_{yyy}(Q_6), \quad (20.43)$$

where each Q_i is in Σ. Moreover,

$$|L_h u(P) - L u(P)| \le h^2 M_4(\Sigma) \left[\frac{1}{12} |a(P)| + \frac{2}{3} |b(P)| + \frac{1}{12} |c(P)| \right]$$

$$+ \frac{h^2}{6} M_3(\Sigma) [|d(P)| + |e(P)|] = O(h^2), \quad \text{as } h \to 0. \quad (20.44)$$

The proof consists merely in assembling the bounds from (20.19), (20.29), (20.36), and (20.38).

Theorem 20.7 shows that the replacement of $L(u)$ by $L_h(U)$ causes a formal discretization error of $O(h^2)$ in the operator at an interior point of a square net. This will be used in Sec. 23 in assessing $|u - U|$.

The method we have just finished is reasonably well suited to approximating general elliptic operators $L(u)$. Let us consider what kind of a matrix is formed by the $A(P, Q)$ of (20.42), still ignoring the effects of the boundary conditions. Since L is elliptic, a and c have the same sign and thus

$$A(P, P) \text{ *differs from 0 for all sufficiently small h.*} \quad (20.45)$$

We noted the importance of (20.45) in Sec. 20.4.

We see from (20.42) that, if h is small enough, but regardless of the sign of f,

$$\frac{A(P, E)}{A(P, P)} < 0, \qquad \frac{A(P, N)}{A(P, P)} < 0, \text{ etc.}$$

That is,

> *if $b = 0$, the operator L_h is of positive type at
> P for all sufficiently small h, with respect to the* (20.46)
> *four neighbors E, N, W, S.*

Note from (20.42) that, if h is small enough, then, since a and c have the same sign,

$$|A(P, E)| + |A(P, N)| + |A(P, W)| + |A(P, S)|$$

$$= |A(P, E) + A(P, N) + A(P, W) + A(P, S)| = |2a + 2c|.$$

Hence,

if $f/a \leq 0$, if $b = 0$, and if h is small enough,

$$\sum_i |A(P, Q_i)| = |A(P, E)| + |A(P, N)| + |A(P, W)|$$
$$+ |A(P, S)| \leq |A(P, P)|. \quad (20.47)$$

But (20.47) states that, at each point P, L_h has *diagonal dominance*. If the coefficients corresponding to the boundary conditions also have diagonal dominance, and if inequality occurs in (20.47) for at least one P, then the whole matrix also has diagonal dominance.

When $b \neq 0$, or if $f/a > 0$, we see that (20.47) will fail for all sufficiently small h. Diagonal dominance seems incompatible with the presence of a term in u_{xy}, for the neighbor system of Fig. 20.1. When $b \neq 0$ we also lose (20.46), and the operator L_h is no longer of positive type at P.

Symmetry of the matrix of coefficients of (20.41) means that $A(P, Q) = A(Q, P)$, for each P, Q. From (20.42),

$$A(P, E) = a(P) + \tfrac{1}{2}h\, d(P). \quad (20.48)$$

If one constructs $L_h U(E)$, the point P becomes the "western" neighbor of E. Thus, from (20.42) again

$$A(E, P) = a(E) - \tfrac{1}{2}h\, d(E). \quad (20.49)$$

Hence ordinarily $A(P, E) \neq A(E, P)$, and thus our above L_h is not ordinarily symmetric. We have symmetry only if a, b, c are constant and d, e are 0. Even when L is self-adjoint (meaning that $d = a_x + b_y$; see Sec. 19.1), when we have a right to expect L_h to be symmetric, we do not ordinarily find symmetry. For then

$$A(P, E) = a(P) + \tfrac{1}{2}h\, a_x(P) + \tfrac{1}{2}h\, b_y(P),$$
$$A(E, P) = a(E) - \tfrac{1}{2}h\, a_x(E) - \tfrac{1}{2}h\, b_y(E). \quad (20.50)$$

If a is sufficiently smooth, one might expect that both $a(P) + \tfrac{1}{2}h\, a_x(P)$ and $a(E) - \tfrac{1}{2}h\, a_x(E)$ are almost equal to $a(x_P + \tfrac{1}{2}h)$, and hence to each other. But the terms of (20.50) in b_y seem to prevent even approximate symmetry.

In summary, in a square grid the above process of directly replacing derivatives by difference quotients gives an $L_h(U)$ with an error term (20.44) of order $O(h^2)$. But L_h is not usually symmetric, even when L is self-adjoint.

As a special case of (20.41) we have the so-called *five-point Laplace difference operator* defined by

$$\Delta_h U = h^{-2}[U(E) + U(N) + U(W) + U(S) - 4U(P)] \quad (20.51)$$

A *stencil* or *molecule* or *star* is the pattern of points involved in a difference operator, together with the numerical coefficients, often written symbolically. Thus (20.51) might be represented by

$$\frac{1}{h^2} \begin{bmatrix} 0 & 1 & 0 \\ 1 & -4 & 1 \\ 0 & 1 & 0 \end{bmatrix} U \quad \text{or} \quad \text{①—(-4)—① } \frac{U}{h^2}.$$

The following error expression results from Theorem 20.5:

THEOREM 20.8. *Suppose u has continuous derivatives* u_x, u_{xx}, u_{xxx} *in the closed interval from W to E, and that* u_{xxxx} *is continuous in the open interval from W to E. Suppose* u_y, u_{yy}, u_{yyy}, *and* u_{yyyy} *have analogous continuity properties in the interval from S to N. Then*

$$\Delta_h u(P) - \Delta u(P) = \frac{h^2}{12}\left[u_{xxxx}(\xi, y_P) + u_{yyyy}(x_P, \eta)\right], \quad (20.52)$$

where

$$x_P - h < \xi < x_P + h \quad \text{and} \quad y_P - h < \eta < y_P + h.$$

Analogous to (20.51) is a formula obtained by rotating the network through 45°:

$$\Delta_h{}^\times U = (\sqrt{2}h)^{-2}[U(NE) + U(NW) + U(SW) + U(SE) - 4U(P)]. \quad (20.53)$$

The error in (20.53) is also $O(h^2)$, as $h \to 0$. In fact, one can show that

$$\Delta_h{}^\times u - \Delta u = \frac{h^2}{12}\left[u_{xxxx}(Q_1) + 6u_{xxyy}(Q_2) + u_{yyyy}(Q_3)\right],$$

where Q_1, Q_2, Q_3 are in Σ.

Similar formulas can be derived for a regular triangular network, including the expression

$$\Delta u(P) = \frac{2[\Sigma\, u(Q) - 6u(P)]}{3h^2} + O(h^2), \quad (20.54)$$

where the summation is over the six neighbors of P. A triangular net was used, for example, for a problem of elasticity by Hochstrasser [1954], together with the variational method for erecting difference equations.

Returning to a square net, and using the more accurate formulas of type (20.39), one can build approximations for the Laplacian of greater local accuracy. For example, using (20.39) directly, we can write

$$\begin{aligned}
\Delta u = \frac{1}{12h^2}\{&-[u(EE) + u(NN) + u(SS) + u(WW)] \\
&+ 16[u(E) + u(N) + u(S) + u(W)] \\
&- 60u(P)\} + O(h^4).
\end{aligned} \quad (20.55)$$

(See Fig. 20.2 for the location of *EE*, *NN*, etc.) Formula (20.55) suffers
from the difficulty that its accuracy is difficult to match near *C*. Moreover,
its use of points at a distance $2h$ from *P* is a mild disadvantage in the
solution of the linear equations associated with $L(u) = g$. It is a more
serious disadvantage for nodes near the boundary, because the greater size
of the molecule causes many more interior points of the net to become
irregular. The meaning of "irregular" will be brought out in Sec. 20.9.
Note that (20.55) is not of positive type.

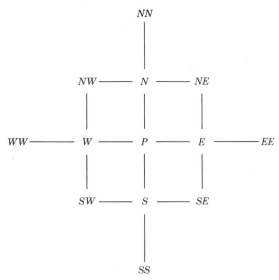

FIG. 20.2. Node abbreviations for a regular square net.

There is another well-known approximation to Δu which is very accurate
for approximating harmonic functions *u*. This is the so-called *nine-point
approximation* to Laplace's equation:

$$\Delta_h^{(9)} U = (6h^2)^{-1}\{U(NE) + U(NW) + U(SW) + U(SE)$$
$$+ 4[U(E) + U(N) + U(W) + U(S)] - 20U(P)\}. \quad (20.56)$$

Actually $\Delta_h^{(9)} = \tfrac{2}{3}\Delta_h + \tfrac{1}{3}\Delta_h^\times$.

If *u* has sufficiently many continuous derivatives, then, according to
Kantorovič and Krylov [1952], p. 201:

$$\Delta_h^{(9)} u(P) - \Delta u(P) = \frac{1}{2} h^2 \Delta^2 u(P) + \frac{2}{6!} h^4[\Delta^3 u(P) + 2(\Delta u)_{xxyy}(P)]$$

$$+ \frac{2}{3}\frac{h^6}{8!}[3\Delta^4 u(P) + 16(\Delta^2 u)_{xxyy}(P) + 20u_{xxxxyyyy}(P)] + \cdots. \quad (20.57)$$

Here $\Delta^2 u$ means $\Delta(\Delta u)$, and $\Delta^3 u = \Delta(\Delta^2 u)$.

If u is a harmonic function, then $\Delta u \equiv \Delta^2 u \equiv \Delta^3 u \equiv 0$, and every term on the right-hand side of (20.57) disappears except $(2h^6/3 \cdot 8\,!)\, 20u_{xxxxyyyy}(P)$, so that $\Delta_h^{(9)} u - \Delta u = O(h^6)$, as $h \to 0$. Hence (20.56) is an extremely accurate approximation to use *when solving Laplace's equation* by finite-difference methods. Since (20.56) is also of positive type and diagonally dominant, it is a very strong formula. The same considerations hold if one solves the Poisson equation $\Delta u = g$ when g is harmonic (i.e., $\Delta g = 0$).

However, if one is solving a more general problem in which the Laplacian Δu is only one term in the equation (e.g., the Poisson equation $\Delta u = x^2 + y^2$), then $\Delta^2 u \neq 0$ and $\Delta_h^{(9)} u - \Delta u = O(h^2)$. Then $\Delta_h^{(9)} U$ seems to be no better than the operator $\Delta_h U$ of (20.51).

To get approximations of higher order to a general differential operator L over a square net, one could proceed systematically as we did in Sec. 20.4, getting a series of equations like (20.7).

For a discussion of the use of a fine net and a coarse square net in the same region R, see Sec. 25.4.

For a treatment of various finite-difference formulas for a square net, see Bickley [1948] and Collatz [1955].

20.8. Application of the Variational Method to a Reactor Diffusion Equation

Suppose a network of horizontal and vertical lines is introduced on the plane; we do not assume equal spacing for these lines. Suppose a region R is the union of rectangular meshes of the net. Suppose that R is divided into subregions R_i. We shall permit interfaces between regions R_i to occur on any link of the net, but not elsewhere. Thus each subregion is also a union of meshes of the net. Without loss of generality we may take each R_i to be one mesh of the net.

The diffusion equation for each neutron group in a two-dimensional reactor has the form

$$D_i \Delta u - \sigma_i u + \psi = 0 \qquad \text{in } R_i, \tag{20.58}$$

where D_i, σ_i are positive constants in R_i. We wish to derive some difference equations corresponding to (20.58) by the variational method of Sec. 20.5. The principal question in practice is how to choose the equations at points P belonging to interfaces.

It can be shown by the methods of Sec. 19.4 that the solution u of (20.58) maximizes the following integral

$$I(u) = \sum_i \int\!\!\int_{R_i} \left[-\frac{D_i}{2}(u_x^2 + u_y^2) - \frac{\sigma_i}{2} u^2 + \psi u \right] dx\,dy. \tag{20.59}$$

Let $I_i(u)$ be the contribution to $I(u)$ from the subregion R_i. For $i = 1$, for example,

$$I_1(u) = \iint\limits_{R_1} \left[-\frac{D_1}{2}(u_x{}^2 + u_y{}^2) - \frac{\sigma_1}{2}u^2 + \psi u \right] dx \, dy. \quad (20.60)$$

Following the variational method, we replace $I_1(u)$ by a quadratic function of the values of a net function defined at the four nodes P, N, NW, W of

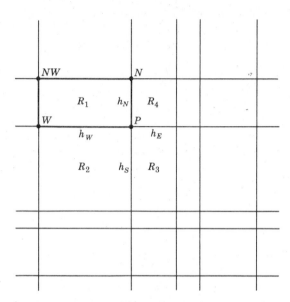

FIG. 20.3. Designation of regions and nodes for the variational determination of difference equations.

R_1 (see Fig. 20.3). There is a great deal of freedom in our choice of quadratic functions. We elect to represent $\iint_{R_1} u^2 \, dx \, dy$ by the formula

$$\iint\limits_{R_1} u^2 \, dx \, dy \doteq \frac{h_N h_W}{4}(U_P{}^2 + U_N{}^2 + U_{NW}{}^2 + U_W{}^2), \quad (20.61)$$

and use the analogous formula for

$$\iint\limits_{R_1} \psi u \, dx \, dy.$$

For the integral of $u_x{}^2 + u_y{}^2$ we proceed as follows. Assume that u_x has the constant value $h_W^{-1}(U_P - U_W)$ on the segment from W to P, and the constant value $h_W^{-1}(U_N - U_{NW})$ on the segment from NW to N. We then apply the trapezoidal rule to integrate with respect to y. We get

$$\iint_R u_x^2 \, dx \, dy \doteq \frac{1}{2} h_W h_N \left[\left(\frac{U_P - U_W}{h_W} \right)^2 + \left(\frac{U_N - U_{NW}}{h_W} \right)^2 \right]. \quad (20.62)$$

Applying a similar formula for u_y^2, we finally get the representation

$$\frac{1}{2} \iint_{R_1} D_1(u_x^2 + u_y^2) \, dx \, dy \doteq \frac{D_1 h_N}{4 h_W} [(U_P - U_W)^2 + (U_N - U_{NW})^2]$$

$$+ \frac{D_1 h_W}{4 h_N} [(U_{NW} - U_W)^2 + (U_N - U_P)^2]. \quad (20.63)$$

When we sum (20.63), (20.61), and the analogous formula for ψu, we get a quadratic function $I_{1h}(U)$ of the U_i which corresponds to $I_1(u)$. We have

$$I_{1h}(U) = - \frac{D_1 h_N}{4 h_W} [(U_P - U_W)^2 + (U_N - U_{NW})^2]$$

$$- \frac{D_1 h_W}{4 h_N} [(U_{NW} - U_W)^2 + (U_N - U_P)^2]$$

$$- \frac{\sigma_1 h_N h_W}{8} (U_P^2 + U_N^2 + U_{NW}^2 + U_W^2)$$

$$+ \frac{h_N h_W}{4} (\psi_P U_P + \psi_N U_N + \psi_{NW} U_{NW} + \psi_W U_W). \quad (20.64)$$

When we sum $I_{ih}(U)$ over all i, we get the nonhomogeneous quadratic function $I_h(U)$ corresponding to $I(u)$. This is the special case of (20.15). Our numerical problem is to find a U which maximizes $I_h(U)$.

To find the difference equations at P corresponding to (20.16), we first take the partial derivative of $I_{1h}(U)$ with respect to U_P. We have

$$\frac{\partial I_{1h}(U)}{\partial U_P} = - \frac{D_1 h_N}{2 h_W} (U_P - U_W) - \frac{D_1 h_W}{2 h_N} (U_P - U_N)$$

$$- \frac{\sigma_1 h_N h_W}{4} U_P + \frac{h_N h_W \psi_P}{4}. \quad (20.65)$$

Now, by summing expressions like (20.65) for $i = 1, 2, 3, 4$, and equating the total to zero, we find that

$$
\frac{\partial I_h(U)}{\partial U_P} = \frac{D_1 h_W + D_4 h_E}{2h_N} U_N + \frac{D_1 h_N + D_2 h_S}{2h_W} U_W
$$

$$
+ \frac{D_2 h_W + D_3 h_E}{2h_S} U_S + \frac{D_3 h_S + D_4 h_N}{2h_E} U_E
$$

$$
- \left[\frac{D_1 h_W + D_4 h_E}{2h_N} + \frac{D_1 h_N + D_2 h_S}{2h_W} + \frac{D_2 h_W + D_3 h_E}{2h_S} \right.
$$

$$
+ \frac{D_3 h_S + D_4 h_N}{2h_E} + \frac{1}{4}(\sigma_1 h_N h_W + \sigma_2 h_W h_S
$$

$$
+ \left. \sigma_3 h_S h_E + \sigma_4 h_E h_N) \right] U_P
$$

$$
+ \frac{1}{4}\, \psi_P(h_N h_W + h_W h_S + h_S h_E + h_E h_N) = 0. \tag{20.66}
$$

The linear system of which (20.66) is one equation is seen to be symmetric. It is also of positive type with diagonal dominance. It is hence an excellent system from the standpoint of numerical solution.

The same expression (20.66) was obtained by Varga [1957b] by approximating the divergence theorem for the diffusion.

When each $D_i = 1$, and $\sigma_i = \psi = 0$, (20.58) reduces to Laplace's equation, while the difference operator in (20.66) becomes the Shortley-Weller expression (20.69), with the multiplicative factor

$$
\frac{(h_E + h_W)(h_S + h_N)}{4}.
$$

When, moreover, the h_i all equal h, the expression reduces to (20.51).

20.9. Treatment of Dirichlet Boundary Conditions

Let us first suppose that we have a Dirichlet problem for a differential equation $Lu = g$, i.e., that u is prescribed at the boundary C of R. We continue to deal with a regular square net.

If C is composed of vertical and horizontal links of the net, so that R is actually a union of meshes of the net, then there is no problem with using any five-point or nine-point formula for $L_h(U)$. One simply gives U its prescribed boundary values at each node on C. This means that for some nodes P, some of the neighbors N, NW, etc., are on C, and the corresponding values $U(N)$, $U(NW)$, etc., are prescribed constants.

When selecting boundary values $U(Q)$, Q on C, it is not necessarily best to take $U(Q) = u(Q)$, because that is giving undue weight to one point Q. Rather, it is a good idea to let $U(Q)$ be an average of the values of $u(Q')$, for points Q' of C in the appropriate vicinity of Q. It can be shown in certain cases that this trick can decrease the value of $|U(P) - u(P)|$ in R by a whole order of magnitude. The essential tools for such a demonstration are found in Walsh and Young [1954], Theorem 4.1.

If C includes diagonals of some meshes of the net, the five-point formulas still apply without difficulty because no interior point P has a neighbor

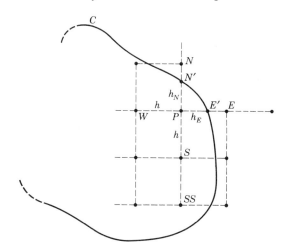

FIG. 20.4. Methods of interpolating Dirichlet boundary conditions.

outside R. However, for nine-point formulas, certain points P will have a neighbor NW, NE, SE, or SW outside R. The reader is referred to Milne [1953], pp. 147 ff., for a method of altering the molecule in such cases.

Still more serious is the case when C is composed of irregular curves. These hardly ever contain a node of the net, and something quite different must be done. There are three general methods in practice.

1. *Interpolation of degree zero.* One proposal is to select a net boundary C_h which is composed of links of the net, and perhaps also diagonals of meshes if one deals with a five-point formula. Then the boundary conditions on C are replaced by boundary conditions on C_h. That is, for each node Q of C_h, one selects a boundary value $U(Q)$ that is equal to $u(Q')$ for some closest point Q' of C. Or, better yet, one averages a set of nearby boundary values $u(Q')$ for Q' on C.

For example, given the curve C in Fig. 20.4, one might select C_h to pass through P. Then, in this zeroth degree interpolation, one might take

$U(P)$ to be $u(N')$, or $u(E')$, or (best) the average of $u(Q)$ for Q on C approximately between N' and E'.

The replacement of $u(P)$ by $u(N')$ can be considered as interpolation at P by a polynomial of degree 0 with the value $u(N')$ at N'. Hence the term, *interpolation of degree zero*. For a smooth function u, the local error of such interpolation is $O(h)$, as $h \to 0$, as we see from the mean-value theorem of the differential calculus.

2. *Interpolation of degree one.* A more precise treatment has been recommended by Collatz [1933, 1955], who does not fix the value of $U(P)$ *a priori*. Instead, he selects some nearest point along a grid line (N' in Fig. 20.4) of C and adjusts $U(P)$ so that it linearly interpolates the prescribed constant $u(N')$ and the variable $U(S)$. (We use Fig. 20.4 just for a concrete example of the general practice.) Thus $U(P)$ is not determined by a "body equation" of type (20.66), but, instead, by the interpolation formula

$$U(P) = \frac{hu(N') + h_N \, U(S)}{h + h_N} \qquad (20.67)$$

Note that we still have the same number of linear equations as unknown values $U(P)$. Note also that (20.67) is of positive type, with diagonal dominance. Finally, observe that (20.67) is independent of the operator L_h.

We are interpolating by means of a polynomial of degree one. If u were sufficiently differentiable, the local error in an interpolation like (20.67) would be $O(h^2)$.

However, one might have introduced $U(N)$ as a variable to be determined by the interpolation formula

$$\frac{(h - h_N) \, U(P) + h_N U(N)}{h} = u(N'). \qquad (20.68)$$

In this case, the interpolation formula (20.68) would no longer be of positive type for the variable $U(N)$.

3. *Interpolation of degree two.* Clearly we may continue to increase the degree of the interpolation. For example, we might specify $U(P)$ in Fig. 20.4 to be on the parabola passing through $(N', u(N'))$, $(S, U(S))$, and $(SS, U(SS))$. We would formally expect this to yield an error of order $O(h^3)$, as $h \to 0$, when applied to a sufficiently smooth function. The formula could not be expected to be of positive type, however. Moreover, for a finite h, in using points N', S, and SS to determine $U(P)$, we have the intuitive feeling that we have gone too far afield. Shortley and Weller [1938] and Mikeladze [1941] have proposed a different method of obtaining the same asymptotic order of accuracy, probably with greater accuracy for finite h. Moreover, their approach leads to a formula of positive type. It is limited, however, to equations with no term in u_{xy}.

We consider a five-point operator. With respect to this operator, an interior node P of R_h is called *regular* if the four links joining P to its four neighbors E, N, W, and S all lie within the closed region $\bar{R}$. At regular interior nodes we can apply the five-point operator. Otherwise, P is called an *irregular interior node*. In our interpretation of the Shortley-Weller method, the points of C_h consist of lattice points of the net which are already on C plus new points connected with irregular interior nodes, as follows. For each irregular interior node, there are one or more of the four cardinal directions in which the closed link from P does not lie entirely within $\bar{R}$. In each such direction, select the point of C on the link which lies closest to P, and add this to C_h. Thus in Fig. 20.4, the points N' and E' are added to C_h. Next, boundary values $U(Q)$ are defined for every point of C_h, according to the principles mentioned above.

Finally, we define a modified form of the body equation for each irregular interior point. These are derived as appropriate linear combinations of the difference quotients for unequally spaced nodes defined in Theorems 20.2 and 20.4 of Sec. 20.6. Corresponding to the Laplace operator Δu, for example, Shortley and Weller define a five-point formula consisting of adding the expression (20.30) and its analog for u_{yy}. One obtains what we shall call $\Delta^{(h)} U$. Suppose that h_E, h_W, h_N, and h_S are the distances from P to E, W, N S, respectively. Then

$$
\Delta^{(h)} U(P) = \frac{[U(E) - U(P)]/h_E - [U(P) - U(W)]/h_W}{(h_E + h_W)/2}
$$
$$
+ \frac{[U(N) - U(P)]/h_N - [U(P) - U(S)]/h_S}{(h_S + h_N)/2}
$$
$$
= \frac{2U(E)}{h_E(h_E + h_W)} + \frac{2U(N)}{h_N(h_N + h_S)} + \frac{2U(W)}{h_W(h_E + h_W)}
$$
$$
+ \frac{2U(S)}{h_S(h_N + h_S)} - \left(\frac{2}{h_N h_S} + \frac{2}{h_E h_W}\right) U(P). \quad (20.69)
$$

From Theorem 20.4 one proves that, if u is continuous, together with its partial derivatives of orders up to and including 4, then

$$
\Delta^{(h)} u - \Delta u = \frac{h_E - h_W}{3} u_{xxx}(P) + \frac{h_N - h_S}{3} u_{yyy}(P)
$$
$$
+ \frac{h_W{}^2 - h_W h_E + h_E{}^2}{12} u_{xxxx}(Q_H) + \frac{h_S{}^2 - h_S h_N + h_N{}^2}{12} u_{yyyy}(Q_V).
$$
$$
(20.70)
$$

Here Q_H is on the interval from W to E, while Q_V is on the interval from N to S. As a result, for a sufficiently smooth function u, the error in the approximation to Δu at P is of the order $O(h)$. It will be shown in Sec. 23, for the Dirichlet problem, that, under suitable hypotheses, the resulting contribution to the error $U - u$ is of the order $O(h^3)$.

20.10. Normal Derivative Boundary Conditions

Boundary conditions of Dirichlet type offer comparatively little difficulty in making the transition to difference equations, even when the boundary C is a curved one. The situation is much more complicated for boundary conditions involving the normal derivative u_n, and it is far from clear how

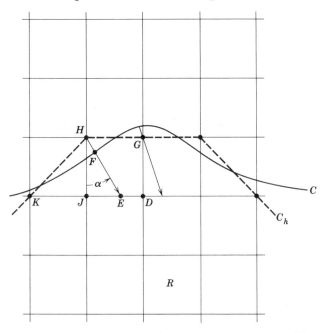

FIG. 20.5. Method of interpolating Neumann boundary conditions.

best to deal with curved boundaries. Methods of dealing with normal derivative conditions are given by Shaw [1950], Allen [1954], Batschelet [1952], and Viswanathan [1957]. In all of them it is assumed that C has a continuously turning tangent; i.e., corners are excluded.

As an example of what can be done, consider the section of a curved boundary in Fig. 20.5. Suppose we wish to solve the equation

$$\Delta u = 0 \quad \text{in } R, \tag{20.71}$$

and suppose the boundary condition is that

$$u_n = g(P), \quad P \text{ on } C. \tag{20.72}$$

First, a net boundary C_h is chosen, shown by a dashed line in Fig. 20.5. At each node of C_h, a perpendicular is dropped onto C, and continued until it crosses another link or node of the net inside R. (This must happen, if h is small enough.) For example, the perpendicular from H meets C at F, and meets the link from J to D at E. The angle α is shown in Fig. 20.5. A value for $U(E)$ is determined by linear interpolation between $U(J)$ and $U(D)$. A "normal derivative" for the net function U is defined by the divided difference of $U(H)$ and $U(E)$; in Fig. 20.5 this is

$$\frac{U(E) - U(H)}{h/\cos \alpha}. \tag{20.73}$$

If one equates expression (20.73) to the prescribed normal derivative $g(F)$ at F, one obtains an equation for $U(H)$. If it is desired, one can eliminate $U(E)$ by expressing it in terms of $U(J)$ and $U(D)$. For example, in Fig. 20.5 one has $JE = h \tan \alpha$, $ED = h(1 - \tan \alpha)$, so that $U(E) = U(J)(1 - \tan \alpha) + U(D) \tan \alpha$, and finally that

$$U(J)(\cos \alpha - \sin \alpha) + U(D) \sin \alpha - U(H) \cos \alpha = h \, g(F). \tag{20.74}$$

An equation like (20.74) can be obtained corresponding to each point of C_h. An equation $\Delta_h U = 0$, where Δ_h is as in (20.51), is defined for each interior node of the net.

Since $\alpha \leq \pi/4$ in Fig. 20.5, one sees that (20.74), as an equation for $U(H)$, is an equation of nonnegative type with diagonal dominance. This will be true for all boundary points. Moreover, the equations for interior points like J and D are also of nonnegative type with diagonal dominance. The whole matrix of equations $AU = B$ is of nonnegative type, where U is defined over the set $C_h \cup R_h$, and has diagonal dominance in an extended sense in which there may be inequality in (20.12) at no point P.

We have indicated above how difference equations can be set up to model the Neumann problem for (20.71, 20.72). We have not discussed the existence of a solution, which will depend on the values $g(P)$. If it exists, the solution will be unique up to an additive constant, as can be shown from the nature of the matrix. The computation of a solution will be discussed slightly in Secs. 21, 22, and 25.9.

It is clear from the foregoing that setting up the difference equations for the problem (20.71), (20.72) is complicated when C is curved, and there has been little study of general procedures for it. It is probable that the third boundary problem, in which the boundary conditions take the form

$$\alpha u + \beta u_n = \gamma, \tag{20.75}$$

can be treated in a similar manner.

Fortunately, in many applications, normal derivative conditions occur only along straight lines, e.g., lines of symmetry, and often these lines can be taken parallel to a coordinate axis. For example, for Laplace's equation the boundary condition $u_n = 0$ might occur on the boundary $x = 0$ of a region R with $x > 0$. For such a problem it is advisable to modify the above procedure and introduce nodes for $x = -h$ as well as for $x = 0$, $x = h$, $x = 2h$, etc. The boundary condition $u_n = 0$ can then be simulated by the condition $U(-h, y) = U(h, y)$ for each relevant y. In addition, on the line $x = 0$, one introduces the net "body equation"

$$U(h, y) + U(0, y + h) + U(-h, y) + U(0, y - h) - 4U(0, y) = 0.$$

$$(20.76)$$

This treatment corresponds to a difference treatment of the analytic extension of the solution $u(x, y)$ to negative x by the convention $u(x, y) = u(-x, y)$. The numerical advantage lies in the representation of u_n by *centered differences*

$$\frac{U(h, y) - U(-h, y)}{2h},$$

instead of by *one-sided differences*

$$\frac{U(h, y) - U(0, y)}{h}.$$

For a simple boundary-value problem in a square, the use of centered differences has been shown by Giese [1958] to result in a smaller discretization error than would result from one-sided differences.

20.11. Singularities and Free Boundaries

We have said nothing about an important class of problems in which one of the coefficients of the partial differential equation (20.1) becomes singular at one or more points Q of R. In such problems the solution $u(P)$ will ordinarily also have a singularity at Q, and the finite-difference method will hardly be applicable in its direct form. The accepted technique in such problems is to "subtract out the singularity"; i.e., one finds a function $w(P)$ such that $u - w$ is regular at Q. For examples, see Motz [1946] and Woods [1953].

In another class of difficult problems, the position of the boundary C is not given, but must be determined as part of the problem. These are the so-called *free-boundary* problems, of which the oil-flow problem of Sec. 18 is an example. For a recent discussion of one problem in three dimensions, see Garabedian [1956].

SECTION 21. CLASSICAL THEORY OF SOLVING ELLIPTIC DIFFERENCE EQUATIONS

In this section and in Sec. 22 we shall consider several of the methods by which the difference equations set up in Sec. 20 can be solved. For the most part we shall postpone to Sec. 25 detailed consideration of how such methods are actually put on digital computers. We shall assume that the reader has the background in matrix theory referred to on p. 206.

21.1. The Difference Equations as a Matrix Equation

Suppose an elliptic homogeneous second-order linear partial differential operator L is discretized according to the methods of the last section. For any given problem, let $\bar{R}_h$ denote the union of R_h and any of the points of C_h for which values $U(P)$ are to be determined. We shall call $\bar{R}_h$ the *working domain*. For any point P of $\bar{R}_h$, the corresponding difference operator L_h can be written in the form

$$L_h U(P) = \sum_{Q \in \bar{R}_h} A(P, Q)\, U(Q), \tag{21.1}$$

where the $A(P, Q)$ are numbers which, like $\bar{R}_h$, depend on the choice of the net and the parameter h. Let N denote the number of points P in $\bar{R}_h$. It is often convenient to consider the ordered set of values $U(P)$ as a vector U of N components. The linear operator L_h is then represented as a square matrix A of order N, and $L_h(U) = AU$.

A boundary-value problem $L(u) = g$ for the continuous operator L, when discretized, takes the form

$$A U = B, \tag{21.2}$$

where B is a vector of constants determined by g and by the boundary conditions. Similarly, an eigenvalue problem $L(u) = \lambda u$ for the continuous operator becomes an algebraic eigenvalue problem for the matrix A:

$$A U = \lambda_h U. \tag{21.3}$$

In Secs. 21 through 25 we use capital letters like U, X for vectors to contrast them with u, which represents a function of the continuous variables x, y. We always denote the dimension of the vector U by N.

We shall use the symbol $\|U\|$ to denote a general norm of U, and $\|U\|_2$ to denote the *Euclidean length*:

$$\|U\|_2 = \left(\sum_{i=1}^{N} U_i^2 \right)^{1/2}$$

For treatments of norms see Ostrowski [1955] or Householder [1954].

The discretized problems (21.2) and (21.3) are special cases of the two classical computation problems of linear algebra. About these problems there is a vast literature which is growing rapidly. For surveys of methods see Bodewig [1956], Dwyer [1951], and Householder [1953]. This literature is mostly expressed in matrix notation, and for background the reader must have some familiarity with matrix algebra, with the analytic geometry of lines, planes, and quadric surfaces in N-dimensional space, with quadratic forms, with matrices as linear transformations, with the Jordan normal form of a matrix and its geometric significance, and with norms of vectors and matrices. Such a background is well presented from the computing point of view in the first chapter of Faddeeva [1950], translated by Benster, and in the first chapter of Courant and Hilbert [1953].

The origin of the matrix A in the difference operator (21.1) gives A a quite special nature, and most success in solving (21.2) or (21.3) comes from using methods adapted to this special nature. Let us list some of the special properties:

The matrix A is of *large order N*, ranging from perhaps fifty to many thousands in current machine work.

A is a *sparse* matrix, meaning that the proportion of nonzero elements $A(P, Q)$ is very small. For an element $A(P, Q)$ differs from zero only when nodes P and Q are coupled in a single difference expression representing a derivative or boundary condition of the problem. For Laplace's equation, for example, the difference expression (21.4) will yield at most five nonzero elements in any row of A. The opposite of sparse is *dense*. The *density* of A is the fraction of nonzero elements.

Another special property that A may have is that the nonzero elements $A(P, Q)$ are often easy to generate from the problem whenever they are needed, and hence may not have to occupy valuable storage space in the computer. Whenever the coefficients of the partial differential equation are simple functions of the space coordinates, the techniques for obtaining $A(P, Q)$ can be coded and used to generate $A(P, Q)$ whenever it is needed. Such a matrix is called a *generated* matrix, as opposed to a *stored* matrix.

If the original continuous problem is real and self-adjoint, we saw in Sec. 20 that it is possible to form the difference equations so that $A(P, Q) = A(Q, P)$, and so A is equal to its transpose A^T and is hence *symmetric*. Many practical and theoretical aspects of solving a linear system, and especially of computing matrix eigenvalues, are substantially simplified when A is symmetric. This is one of the great advantages of the variational point of view, and it applies whether or not the problem is elliptic.

As we saw in Sec. 19, for certain self-adjoint elliptic boundary-value problems the solution u is the unique function minimizing a certain quadratic functional $I(w)$ over a certain class of functions w. In the variational approach in Sec. 20, we set up a corresponding quadratic form $I_h(W)$, where W is a vector, and then the solution U of the discretized problem is the unique vector minimizing $I_h(W)$ among vectors W satisfying the appropriate boundary conditions. This means that the matrix A is not only symmetric; it is also *semidefinite* (proved in Sec. 20.5) and usually also *definite*.

Definiteness is thus another special property frequently observed in symmetric matrices associated with elliptic difference equations. $I(w)$ is often interpreted physically as an energy associated with w in the continuous problem. Thus most linear boundary-value problems which amount to minimizing an energy can be discretized as matrix problems (21.2) with a definite symmetric matrix A. Definiteness of A greatly aids in the solution of (21.2) by almost any method. It should be remarked, however, that definiteness of A is quite irrelevant to solving the eigenvalue problem (21.3).

Our emphasis on symmetry and definiteness should not lead the reader to believe that in practice the matrix A is taken to be symmetric and definite whenever it could be so chosen. Actual practice is quite the opposite, even for such a classical problem as Dirichlet's—to solve $\Delta u = 0$ in R with u prescribed on C. If R is the union of squares of a square net, and if C_h is selected from nodes of the net alone, so that there are no irregular interior points of R_h, then the usual discretization

$$\Delta_h(U) = h^{-2}[U(x + h, y) + \cdots + U(x, y - h) - 4U(x, y)] \quad (21.4)$$

leads to a symmetric and definite matrix A. But selections of C_h outside the nodes will introduce irregular interior points and will usually upset the symmetry, as we shall see in Sec. 24.

Also, refining the net in parts of R will usually upset the symmetry, unless one follows a variational approach. For example, consider point 2 at the edge of a refined net in Fig. 21.1. To solve Laplace's equation, one would ordinarily set up the difference equation, based on (21.4),

$$U_4 + U_6 + U_0 + U_7 - 4U_2 = 0 \quad (21.5a)$$

at point 2, and the equation

$$U_2 + U_3 + U_0 + U_5 - 4U_1 = 0 \quad (21.5b)$$

at point 1. Now, since point 2 enters in (21.5b), whereas point 1 does not occur in (21.5a), the system of equations is not symmetric. Moreover, the system cannot even be made symmetric by multiplying various equations through by appropriate factors. See Sec. 25.4 for further treatment of refined nets.

We remind the reader that a *permutation matrix* Π is a square matrix whose elements are either 0 or 1, with exactly one element 1 in each row and each column. Since Π is orthogonal, $\Pi\Pi^T = I$, so that $\Pi^{-1} = \Pi^T$.

We now write A in the form $[a_{ij}]$. We say that A is *reducible* if the set of integers $\{1, \cdots, N\}$ is the union of two nonempty sets S and T such that $a_{ij} = 0$ for all i in S and all j in T. That is, A is reducible if there is a

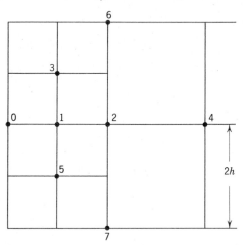

Fig. 21.1. Square network refined or graded in a subregion.

permutation matrix Π such that we have the partitioned representation

$$\Pi A \Pi^T = \begin{bmatrix} A_1 & 0 \\ A_2 & A_3 \end{bmatrix}. \tag{21.6}$$

If the matrix A of a system $AU = B$ is reducible, it means that some $N_1(<N)$ components of U are uniquely determined by some N_1 components of B. In a boundary-value problem this means that the same N_1 values of the net function U are independent of part of the boundary conditions. This can occur, for example, if R_h consists of two sets unconnected by links of the net within R. But then we would have two isolated boundary-value problems. For a reasonably posed elliptic difference-equation problem, A should not be reducible.

21.2. Elimination Methods

Undoubtedly the most popular method for solving systems of linear equations with dense matrices is Gaussian elimination, with its numerous variants (see Dwyer [1951]). A dense system of N equations in N unknowns can be solved with the order of $N^3/3$ multiplications, plus other arithmetic operations which are ordinarily ignored in making rough time estimates.

A complete error analysis by von Neumann and Goldstine [1947, 1951] gives rigorous error bounds for the accumulated round-off error in fixed-point solution of a linear system with a digital computer. A far simpler and more practical treatment of round-off is given by Wilkinson [1959] and in his forthcoming book on solving matrix problems.

Elimination methods are rarely applied to the solution of elliptic difference equations, for the following reason. Elimination is ordinarily coded by actually storing the matrix A, and gradually transforming it by elementary operations into a triangular form. But for partial difference equations, N is usually chosen so large that we can store N or $2N$ or $8N$ elements, but not anything like N^2 or $N^2/2$ elements. Even though Laplace's equation in two dimensions, for example, has only approximately $5N$ nonzero elements which we need to store, the elimination serves to introduce many more, and therefore looks hopeless.

Let us take a closer look at just how many nonzero elements are introduced by elimination. A matrix $B = [b_{ij}]$ is called *lower triangular* if $b_{ij} = 0$ whenever $i < j$. *Upper triangular* is defined analogously. Suppose A is symmetric and positive definite. Then the triangular decomposition theorem of Banachiewicz [1938] states that *there is a lower triangular matrix M such that $MM^T = A$* (see Faddeeva [1950]). Up to the signs of its columns, M is unique. A constructive proof of the theorem can be given like the proof of (21.8) below.

Now one of the variants of Gaussian elimination (the so-called *square root* method to solve $AX = B$) can be phrased as follows: Find a lower triangular matrix M such that $MM^T = A$; then solve $MY = B$ for Y; then solve $M^T X = Y$ for X; this X solves the system $AX = B$. Such direct methods are very desirable for two sorts of reasons. First, they may be expected to be faster than iterative methods, since there is no waiting for convergence to take place. Second, they permit one to solve systems $AU = B_i$ with several different right-hand sides without having to repeat all the work of solution for each new B_i. (That is, M is formed once and for all.) The key question is: can we somehow find and store M in a reasonable number of cells? The hoped for answer is that M itself may turn out to be a sparse matrix, and preferably one which can itself be generated rather than stored. Limited conversations with Mr. L. R. Turner of the Cleveland Laboratories of the National Aeronautics and Space Administration suggest that he has used such direct methods to some extent, at least with punched-card computing machinery on problems of moderate size. For Poisson's difference equation over a square net in a rectangle, Dr. J. H. Wilkinson of the National Physical Laboratories (England) reports very satisfactory results with such a direct method.

The following is the authors' analysis of the situation. For simplicity, suppose that the working domain $\bar{R}_h$ is a square array of $N = n^2$ points, and that the difference problem yields a five-point formula coupling $U(x, y)$ with the four neighbor values $U(x \pm h, y)$, $U(x, y \pm h)$. Suppose the points of $\bar{R}_h$ are numbered by successive rows, in the order of reading a page, so that the first row includes points $1, 2, \cdots, n$, and the second row has points $n + 1, \cdots, 2n$, etc. Then the matrix A (assumed to be positive definite) can be partitioned into n-by-n blocks, and has the structure of (21.7):

$$A = \begin{bmatrix} T_1 & D_1^T & 0 & 0 & \cdots & 0 & 0 \\ D_1 & T_2 & D_2^T & 0 & \cdots & 0 & 0 \\ 0 & D_2 & T_3 & D_3^T & \cdots & 0 & 0 \\ \multicolumn{7}{c}{\dotfill} \\ 0 & 0 & 0 & 0 & \cdots & T_{n-1} & D_{n-1}^T \\ 0 & 0 & 0 & 0 & \cdots & D_{n-1} & T_n \end{bmatrix}. \tag{21.7}$$

Here each T_i is a positive definite n-by-n square matrix which is itself of *tridiagonal* form, meaning that its nonzero elements are all on its main diagonal and the two adjacent diagonals, and each D_i is a diagonal matrix. We say that A is *block tridiagonal*. Such matrices will be discussed further in Sec. 22.

Applying the Banachiewicz theorem, we decompose the above A into MM^T, where the lower triangular matrix M has the partitioned form:

$$M = \begin{bmatrix} M_{11} & 0 & 0 & \cdots & 0 \\ M_{21} & M_{22} & 0 & \cdots & 0 \\ \multicolumn{5}{c}{\dotfill} \\ M_{n1} & M_{n2} & M_{n3} & \cdots & M_{nn} \end{bmatrix}.$$

It will be shown that

> Each M_{ii} is a nonsingular lower triangular matrix, each $M_{i+1,i}$ is an upper triangular matrix, and M_{ij} $= 0$ for $i > j + 1$. (21.8)

We prove (21.8) by induction on the number of blocks in each column. For $n = 1$, the theorem is clearly true. Suppose that, for $n = k$, we have proved that A has the decomposition $A = M_k M_k^T$, where

$$M_k = \begin{bmatrix} P_1 & 0 & 0 & \cdots & 0 & 0 \\ Q_1 & P_2 & 0 & \cdots & 0 & 0 \\ 0 & Q_2 & P_3 & \cdots & 0 & 0 \\ \multicolumn{6}{c}{\dotfill} \\ 0 & 0 & 0 & \cdots & Q_{k-1} & P_k \end{bmatrix}. \tag{21.9}$$

Here each P_i is a nonsingular lower triangular matrix and each Q_i is an upper triangular matrix. Now take any A which is blockwise $(k + 1)$-by-$(k + 1)$, and partition it as

$$A = \begin{bmatrix} A_k & C^T \\ C & T_{k+1} \end{bmatrix},$$

where $C = [0 \quad 0 \quad \cdots \quad 0 \quad D_k]$. Let $A = M_{k+1}M_{k+1}^T$, by the Banachiewicz theorem. From the inductive hypothesis it follows that M_{k+1} must take the form

$$M_{k+1} = \begin{bmatrix} M_k & 0 \\ Q & P_{k+1} \end{bmatrix}.$$

But, since

$$\begin{bmatrix} A_k & C^T \\ C & T_{k+1} \end{bmatrix} = \begin{bmatrix} M_k & 0 \\ Q & P_{k+1} \end{bmatrix} \begin{bmatrix} M_k^T & Q^T \\ 0 & P_{k+1}^T \end{bmatrix}, \tag{21.10}$$

it follows that $QM_k^T = C$. Hence Q has the form $Q = [0 \quad 0 \quad \cdots \quad Q_k]$, and $Q_k P_k^T = D_k$. Then $Q_k = D_k(P_k^T)^{-1}$, an upper triangular matrix. It further follows from (21.10) that

$$T_{k+1} = QQ^T + P_{k+1}P_{k+1}^T = Q_k Q_k^T + P_{k+1}P_{k+1}^T.$$

Hence P_{k+1} is a lower triangular matrix with $P_{k+1}P_{k+1}^T = T_{k+1} - Q_k Q_k^T$. That P_{k+1} is nonsingular follows by taking the determinant of (21.10):

$$0 \neq \det A = (\det M_k)^2(\det P_{k+1})^2,$$

since A is definite. We have thus proved (21.8). Note that in the proof we made no use of the fact that the number n^2 of elements in a block equalled the number of blocks in the matrix A.

We thus see that the nonzero elements of M in (21.9) lie in $n + 1$ diagonals, so that M has fewer than $(n + 1)n^2 \doteq n^3$ nonzero elements out of a full triangle of $(n^2/2)(n^2 + 1) \doteq n^4/2$ elements. Thus the density of M is about $2/n$. To store M would require nN memory cells—far fewer than $N^2/2$ but far more than the approximately $5N$ elements of A. Hence the usefulness of the square-root method to solve (21.2) seems to depend on whether one can afford to store M or, possibly, generate it as needed.

For the Laplacian difference operator (21.4) it might be possible to find a formula for M, not only for a square array $\bar{R}_h$ (which may be a degenerate case) but also for a general net region $\bar{R}_h$ in the plane. If so, the square-root method might be a useful numerical method. The matter needs investigation. Generating M for a general elliptic operator seems quite unlikely. (See Markowitz [1957] for another method for inverting a sparse matrix.)

There is one very useful by-product of our proof of (21.8) (the special case where each block is a scalar, but where A is not):

If A is a tridiagonal positive definite matrix, then A can be written in the form $A = MM^T$, where M is a bidiagonal matrix whose only nonzero elements are on the main diagonal and the adjacent diagonal below.

Now two-point boundary-value problems for an ordinary linear second-order differential operator lead to tridiagonal matrices when certain difference methods are applied, and are frequently solved by this method. Block tridiagonal matrices ($n > 1$) are useful for certain *implicit methods* for partial difference equations, which we have discussed for parabolic equations in Sec. 13.4, and will consider again in Sec. 22.3.

The solution of a large-matrix problem $AU = B$ by elimination by blocks is made easier if the positive definite matrix A, unlike A in (21.7), has the following structure:

$$A = \begin{bmatrix} P_1 & 0 & 0 & \cdots & 0 & Q_1^T \\ 0 & P_2 & 0 & \cdots & 0 & Q_2^T \\ \multicolumn{6}{c}{\cdots\cdots\cdots\cdots\cdots\cdots\cdots\cdots\cdots} \\ 0 & 0 & 0 & \cdots & P_{k-1} & Q_{k-1}^T \\ Q_1 & Q_2 & Q_3 & \cdots & Q_{k-1} & P_k \end{bmatrix}. \tag{21.11}$$

Of (21.11) one says that the blocks P_i are *uncoupled* ($i = 1, \cdots, k-1$). Now $A = MM^T$, where

$$M = \begin{bmatrix} M_1 & 0 & 0 & \cdots & 0 & 0 \\ 0 & M_2 & 0 & \cdots & 0 & 0 \\ \multicolumn{6}{c}{\cdots\cdots\cdots\cdots\cdots\cdots\cdots\cdots\cdots} \\ 0 & 0 & 0 & \cdots & M_{k-1} & 0 \\ N_1 & N_2 & N_3 & \cdots & N_{k-1} & M_k \end{bmatrix}.$$

Here each $M_i M_i^T = P_i$, and each M_i can be calculated independently of the others ($i = 1, \cdots, k-1$). The situation is especially favorable if all the P_i are identical, because then only one M need be computed.

With Laplace's difference equation over a large network $\bar{R}_h$, it is possible to write A in approximately the form (21.11) by reordering the points of $\bar{R}_h$ into $k-1$ *uncoupled groups* (i.e., into groups whose members have no neighbors in other groups). This may be done as follows, for example, for a five-point formula over a square network of n^2 points (i,j) ($i,j = 1, 2, \cdots, n$). Suppose n has the factorization $n = rm$, where r and m are integers.

In group 1 put all (i,j) with $i = 1, \cdots, m-1$ and $j = 1, \cdots, m-1$.

In group 2 put all (i, j) with $i = 1, \cdots, m - 1$ and $j = m + 1, \cdots, 2m - 1$, etc. In group $k - 1 = r^2$, put all (i, j) with $i = (r - 1)m + 1, \cdots, rm$, and $j = (r - 1)m + 1, \cdots, rm$. Finally, group k includes all (i, j) not heretofore assigned.

Thus we have divided $\bar{R}_h$ into $r^2 = k - 1$ groups (blocks) which do not abut, and have put all the other points of $\bar{R}_h$ (the "mortar" joining these blocks) into the last group. The only coupling between the first $k - 1$ groups is through the kth group. In this example, the first $k - 1$ groups are alike and, if the equation, like (21.4), is invariant under translation, $k - 1$ of the k matrices P_i are identical ($i \leq k - 1$). Then one can reduce the solution of $AU = B$ to the calculation and storage of M_1 such that $P_1 = M_1 M_1^T$, followed by calculation and storage of $N_1, N_2, \cdots, N_{k-1}$, M_k. Such an arrangement might make it possible to store M and use the square-root method under certain conditions, even for very large matrices.

Somewhat related proposals for uncoupling A for more complicated network problems have been made by Kron [1955], with his method of "tearing." See also Roth [1956] and Householder [1957] for expositions of Kron's methods.

In the present example, it takes about $m^4/2$ cells to store M_1. The last group has approximately $2(r - 1)n$ members, and storage of $N_1, \cdots,$ N_{k-1}, M_k would therefore require up to $2(r - 1)n^3$ cells. We might ask how to select r with $mr = n$ so as to minimize $f(r) = 2(r - 1)n^3 + m^4/2$. A little calculus yields the result that $r \doteq n^{1/5}$, and $f(r) \doteq \frac{5}{2} n^{16/5}$. Thus the storage requirement for this M is slightly higher than for M in (21.9). However, the advantage of having all or almost all P_i identical, with the resultant possibility of precomputing M_i, may make uncoupling occasionally a profitable method. Moreover, a more detailed study of the N_i might reveal many zero elements or elements which could be generated.

We surmise that our considerations for definite matrices A and the square-root method apply approximately as well to general matrices and other forms of elimination.

In summary, although elimination methods are seldom used for solving elliptic difference equations, we have examined two possible ways in which one direct method might be adapted to such problems. While our examination does not make it likely that direct methods will be useful for general elliptic problems, there appears to be some hope for special problems like Dirichlet's, particularly for special regions. More work needs to be done.

For the use of the discrete Green's function (defined in Sec. 23.6) for an elimination solution of Poisson's difference equation, see Bahvalov [1957] and Saltzer [1958].

21.3. Iterative Methods

Methods for solving a given computational problem are ordinarily divided into *direct* and *iterative*. Direct methods, of which the solution of $AU = B$ by elimination is typical, are those which would yield the exact answer in a finite number of steps if there were no round-off error. Ordinarily the algorithm of a direct method is rather complicated and nonrepetitious. Iterative methods, on the other hand, consist of the repeated application of a simple algorithm, but ordinarily yield the exact answer only as a limit of a sequence, even in the absence of round-off error. Treatments of these classes of methods for matrix problems can be found in Householder [1953] and Bodewig [1956].

As we indicated above, iterative methods are preferred for solving large sparse systems $AU = B$ because they can usually take full advantage of the numerous zeros in A, both in storage and in operation. Moreover, they tend to be self-correcting, in contrast to direct methods, and hence minimize round-off error trouble. (However, Wilkinson [unpublished] reports very little difficulty with round-off in elimination methods.)

The method of *conjugate gradients* of Hestenes and Stiefel [1952] is one of a class of *finite iterations*, being repetitive in structure and yet terminating in a finite number of steps. It has not been widely adopted for partial difference equations because of the relatively high storage requirements and the relatively complex structure of each iterative step. Lanczos [1952] has proposed a similar method.

In any iterative method to solve the nonsingular system $AU = B$ (whose solution is $A^{-1}B$), a sequence U_k is defined with the hope that $U_k \to A^{-1}B$, as $k \to \infty$. In an iteration of *degree* r, U_k is a function of A, B, U_{k-1}, $U_{k-2}, \cdots, U_{k-r}$. Because of storage requirements in a computer, there is a demand for keeping r very low, and usually $r = 1$, so that $U_k = F_k(A, B, U_{k-1})$. If F_k is independent of k, the iteration is called *stationary*. If F_k is a linear function of U_{k-1}, the iteration is called *linear*. Certainly the linear iterations are the most clearly understood, and will be discussed first.

By definition, the most general linear function $F_k(A, B, U_{k-1})$ is $H_k U_{k-1} + V_k$, where $H_k = H_k(A, B)$ is a matrix and V_k is a column vector. If the iteration is to be useful, it should leave the solution invariant, i.e.,

$$A^{-1}B = H_k A^{-1}B + V_k.$$

From this it follows that $V_k = (I - H_k)A^{-1}B$ or, if we define M_k to be $(I - H_k)A^{-1}$, we find that the linear iteration takes the standard form

$$U_k = H_k U_{k-1} + M_k B, \tag{21.12}$$

where H_k, M_k depend on A, B and satisfy the relation

$$H_k + M_k A = I; \tag{21.13}$$

see Forsythe [1953].

To study the convergence, note that

$$A^{-1}B = H_k A^{-1}B + M_k B. \tag{21.14}$$

Subtracting (21.14) from (21.12), and defining the error $E_k = U_k - A^{-1}B$, we see that

$$E_k = H_k E_{k-1}. \tag{21.15}$$

That is, *the error E_k satisfies the fundamental iteration* (21.12) *with B set equal to zero.* (This is a fundamental property of all linear iterations in any vector space.)

It follows from (21.15) that

$$E_k = K_k E_0, \qquad K_k = H_k H_{k-1} \cdots H_1. \tag{21.16}$$

Thus the convergence of the iteration for a given initial error E_0 depends on whether $K_k E_0 \to 0$, as $k \to \infty$.

In pure analysis, where one considers exact arithmetic with real numbers, it is possible that $K_k E_0 \not\to 0$ for certain relatively rare special choices of E_0, while $K_k E_0 \to 0$ for the usual choices of E_0. For example, suppose $K_k = H^k$ (see below), where H has some eigenvalues $|\lambda_i| > 1$ and the other $|\lambda_i| < 1$. Then $H^k E_0 \not\to 0$ if and only if E_0 has no component in the subspace spanned by the "dominant" eigenvectors (i.e. those belonging to the $|\lambda_i| > 1$). Such E_0 form a linear subspace of lower dimension than N. However, in machine computation, one almost always has to round numbers, and this ordinarily will introduce into HE_0 a small component of some of the dominant eigenvectors. If so, the $H^k E_0$ will fail to converge to zero. As a result of this discussion, we may make the following practical rule:

The iteration (21.12) *will ordinarily be convergent for a given initial error E_0 if and only if $K_k X \to 0$ for arbitrary X in the space.*

For stationary linear iterations $H_k \equiv H$ and $K_k = H^k$, and then the matter of convergence hangs on whether $H^k X \to 0$ for arbitrary X. Moreover, the rapidity with which $E_k \to 0$ depends on how large $H^k E_0$ is for fairly large k. It is therefore important to review the behavior of $H^k X$.

Let the eigenvalues of H be denoted by $\lambda_1, \lambda_2, \cdots, \lambda_N$. Recall from the theory of the Jordan canonical form J of H that there exists a nonsingular matrix S such that $S^{-1}HS$ is a blockwise diagonal matrix, each of whose diagonal blocks has the form

$$J_i = \begin{bmatrix} \lambda_i & 1 & & & & \\ & \lambda_i & 1 & & & \\ & & \lambda_i & 1 & & \\ \cdot & \cdot & \cdot & \cdot & \cdot & \cdot & \cdot & \cdot & \cdot & \cdot \\ & & & & \lambda_i & 1 \\ & & & & & \lambda_i \end{bmatrix} \text{(order } N_i\text{)}.$$

(Note that the same eigenvalue λ may appear in several blocks J_i, with different names λ_i.) In other words, in a certain oblique column coordinate system (the columns of S), H takes the relatively simple form of a direct sum of, say, m transformations J_i. We can decompose X in the same coordinate system, writing $X = X_1 + \cdots + X_m$, where the term X_i of the sum corresponds to the Jordan block J_i. We may assume $X_i \neq 0$.

Now $J_i = \lambda_i I + C$, where C is of order N_i and consists of ones on the superdiagonal and zeros elsewhere. It is easily seen that C^r has ones on the rth superdiagonal and zeros elsewhere $(r = 1, 2, \cdots, N_i - 1)$, while $C^{N_i} = 0$, where N_i is the order of J_i. Hence

$$J_i^k = (\lambda_i I + C)^k = \lambda_i^k I + \binom{k}{1}\lambda_i^{k-1}C + \cdots + \binom{k}{N_i - 1}\lambda_i^{k-N_i+1}C^{N_i-1},$$
$$k \geq N_i - 1$$

and

$$J_i^k X_i = \lambda_i^k X_i + \binom{k}{1}\lambda_i^{k-1}CX_i + \cdots + \binom{k}{N_i - 1}\lambda_i^{k-N_i+1}C^{N_i-1}X_i.$$
$$(21.17)$$

Asymptotically, as $k \to \infty$, it is the last term of (21.17) which dominates. Thus

$$J_i^k X_i \sim \binom{k}{N_i - 1}\lambda_i^{k-N_i+1}C^{N_i-1}X_i, \qquad \text{as } k \to \infty. \qquad (21.18)$$

The symbol $\sim$, widely used to denote asymptotic equality of real-valued functions, is used for vectors in (21.18) as follows: By "$U_k \sim V_k$ (as $k \to \infty$)" where U_k and V_k are vectors, we mean that for any norm:

    (i) $\|U_k\| > 0$ and $\|V_k\| > 0$ for all sufficiently large k; and
    (ii) $\|U_k - V_k\|/\|V_k\| \to 0$, as $k \to \infty$.
[If (i) and (ii) are true in one norm, they are true in any norm.]

Any eigenvector W_i of the block J_i must satisfy the equation $(J_i - \lambda_i I)W_i = 0$, i.e., $CW_i = 0$. Hence $W_i = (k, 0, \cdots, 0)^T = ke_1$, and e_1 is (up to scalar multiples) the only eigenvector of the block J_i.

Now C^{N_i-1} is a matrix whose only nonzero element is a 1 in the upper right-hand corner. Hence, for all X_i with nonvanishing last component, the vector $V_i = C^{N_i-1}X_i$ is a multiple of e_1, and is an eigenvector of J_i. From (21.18), we have

$$J_i^k X_i \sim \binom{k}{N_i - 1} \lambda_i^{k-N_i+1} V_i, \qquad \text{as } k \to \infty. \tag{21.19}$$

Clearly $J_i^k X_i \to 0$, as $k \to \infty$, for arbitrary X_i if and only if $|\lambda_i| < 1$. Since each block of J behaves like (21.19), we see that:

$H^k X \to 0$ *for an arbitrary vector X if and only if each eigenvalue λ_i of H is less than one in absolute value.* (21.20)

Condition (21.20) is sometimes wrongly cited as saying that $H^k X$ converges to a limit vector if and only if each $|\lambda_i| < 1$. But from (21.19) we see that $J_i^k X_i$ will converge to V_i if $\lambda_i = 1$ and $N_i = 1$. Thus (Oldenburger [1940]):

$H^k X$ *converges to some limit vector if and only if all $|\lambda_i| < 1$ or $\lambda_i = 1$, with $N_i = 1$ for each block J_i* (21.21) *with an eigenvalue $\lambda_i = 1$.*

Actually, $\lambda_i = 1$ means that $I - H$ is singular, and this is associated with the stationary iterative solution of a consistent system $AU = B$ with singular A. But singular systems $AU = B$ are frequently solved, especially for $B = 0$ in connection with the eigenvalue problem (21.3). We defer further discussion of this to Sec. 21.6.

The asymptotic behavior of E_k, as $k \to \infty$, can be analyzed for stationary linear processes. From (21.16) we see that

$$E_k = H^k E_0. \tag{21.22}$$

Since $S^{-1}HS = J$, we have $HS = SJ$, from which it follows that, corresponding to each block J_i of J, there is exactly one column S_i of S which is an eigenvector of H. Now E_0 has a unique decomposition in the directions of the columns of S:

$$E_0 = E_{0,1} + \cdots + E_{0,N}.$$

Of the vectors $E_{0,1}, \cdots, E_{0,N}$, let W_i denote the one in the direction of the column S_i. Thus W_i is an eigenvector of H belonging to λ_i. From (21.19) we see that what is important is the behavior of those among the canonical blocks J_i with a maximal value of $|\lambda_i|$, here called $\bar{\lambda}$, which have the largest value of N_i, here called $\bar{N}$. In fact, it follows from (21.19) that

$$E_k \sim \binom{k}{\bar{N} - 1} \sum_i \lambda_i^{k-\bar{N}+1} W_i, \qquad \text{as } k \to \infty. \tag{21.23}$$

The sum in (21.23) is taken over all blocks with both $|\lambda_i| = \bar{\lambda}$ and $N_i = \bar{N}$.

Following Householder [1958], the number $\bar{\lambda} = \max |\lambda_i|$ is here called the *spectral radius* of H. Young [1954a] calls it the "spectral norm." However, $\bar{\lambda}$ is not a norm in the usual sense of the word, as F. L. Bauer has pointed out (oral communication). (To see this, note that $\bar{\lambda} = 0$ for the matrices

$$A = \begin{bmatrix} 0 & 1 \\ 0 & 0 \end{bmatrix} \quad \text{and} \quad B = \begin{bmatrix} 0 & 0 \\ 1 & 0 \end{bmatrix},$$

but $\bar{\lambda} = 1$ for $A + B$. Thus the norm triangle inequality $\|A + B\| \leq \|A\| + \|B\|$ is not satisfied for the $\bar{\lambda}$ "norm.") In the present connection $\bar{\lambda}(H)$ is sometimes called the *convergence factor* of the iteration.

From (21.23) we can show that, for any norm, $\|E_k\|$ behaves roughly like $ck^{\bar{N}-1}\bar{\lambda}^k$, as $k \to \infty$, where c is a constant. Moreover, for large values of k, $\|E_{k+1}\|/\|E_k\|$ averages to $\bar{\lambda}$. (It is difficult to be more precise in this quick survey. But see the example below.) Hence, on the average, the error decreases by the factor $\bar{\lambda}$ at each iterative step. Moreover, the error vector ultimately tends to the subspace spanned by the W_i entering into the sum (21.23).

If $\|E_{k+1}\|/\|E_k\|$ were exactly $\bar{\lambda}$ for all k, then $-\log_{10} \bar{\lambda}$ would be (for $\bar{\lambda} < 1$) the number of decimal digits of accuracy gained in each iterative step. If $\|E_{k+1}\|/\|E_k\| \to \bar{\lambda}$, as $k \to \infty$, then $-\log_{10} \bar{\lambda}$ would be the asymptotic number of decimal digits gained in each iterative step. Since $\|E_{k+1}\|/\|E_k\|$ actually averages to $\bar{\lambda}$, the number $-\log_{10} \bar{\lambda}$ is very important in describing iterations. Young [1954a] has therefore introduced the number $r = -\log \bar{\lambda} \doteq 2.30259(-\log_{10} \bar{\lambda})$ as the *rate of convergence* of the linear iteration (21.12). In a manner of speaking, we could call r the asymptotic average number of "base e digits" by which the error is decreased per iterative step.

It is normal for iterative processes in substantial problems to converge slowly, corresponding to an eigenvalue $\bar{\lambda}(H)$ only slightly less than 1, and a rate of convergence nearly 0. The success of most iterations depends on the use of special tricks called *accelerations* to hasten the progress of E_k to 0. The design of accelerations requires precise information about the asymptotic behavior of E_k.

For the simplest transformations, only one $|\lambda_i| = \bar{\lambda}$ and the corresponding $\bar{N}$ is 1. In that case, $E_k \sim \lambda_i^k W_i$ and

$$E_{k+1} \sim \lambda_i E_k, \qquad \text{as } k \to \infty. \tag{21.24}$$

Even though $\bar{\lambda}$ is close to 1, we can use (21.24) to make a substantial reduction in the error E_{k+1}. For, if $A^{-1}B = U_k + E_k$, and if

$$A^{-1}B = U_{k+1} + \lambda_i E_k + \epsilon_k, \quad \|\epsilon_k\| \text{ small,}$$

then by elimination of E_k we find that

$$A^{-1}B = \frac{U_{k+1} - \lambda_i U_k}{1 - \lambda_i} + \frac{\epsilon_k}{1 - \lambda_i}.$$

Hence the vector

$$U' = \frac{U_{k+1} - \lambda_i U_k}{1 - \lambda_i} \tag{21.25}$$

is very close to $A^{-1}B$, provided only that $\|\epsilon_k\|$ is small compared to $1 - \lambda_i$. Formula (21.25), stated by Lyusternik [1947], is perhaps the most basic of the acceleration formulas.

As an example of typically complicated behavior of E_k, suppose the real matrix H has two pairs of complex eigenvalues $\rho e^{\pm i\phi}$, $\rho e^{\pm i\psi}$, all of dominant modulus $\rho = \bar{\lambda} < 1$, and $\bar{N} = 1$. If E_0 is real, then the sum (21.23) takes the form

$$E_k = \rho^k(e^{ik\phi}W_1 + e^{-ik\phi}\bar{W}_1 + e^{ik\psi}W_2 + e^{-ik\psi}\bar{W}_2)$$

$$= 2\rho^k[\mathrm{Re}\,(W_1 e^{ik\phi}) + \mathrm{Re}\,(W_2 e^{ik\psi})],$$

where the bar denotes complex conjugate. Suppose, for example, that $W_1 = (1, i, 0, 0)$ and $W_2 = (1, i, 1, i)$. Then

$$E_k = 2\rho^k(\cos k\phi + \cos k\psi, -\sin k\phi - \sin k\psi, \cos k\psi, -\sin k\psi)^T,$$

so that

$$\|E_k\|_2 = 2\rho^k[3 + 2\cos k(\phi - \psi)]^{1/2}.$$

While $\|E_k\|_2 \leq 2\sqrt{5}\rho^k \to 0$, we see that $\|E_k\|_2$ varies regularly between $2\rho^k$ and $2\sqrt{5}\rho^k$. Although $\|E_k\|_2^{1/k} \to \rho$, the quotient $\|E_{k+1}\|_2/\|E_k\|_2$ does not converge.

With more than two pairs of complex eigenvalues of dominant modulus, the progress of E_k to 0 can be still more complicated, being subject to more angles of resonant phase. This effect turns out to be very important in trying to find $\bar{\lambda}$ in the method of successive overrelaxation (see Sec. 25).

In studying the convergence of an actual iterative process for solving $AU = B$, it is usually easier to examine the *residuals*

$$R_k = B - AU_k$$

than to examine the errors E_k. (For, in contrast to the E_k, the vectors R_k can be computed without knowing the solution $A^{-1}B$.) Since $R_k = -AE_k$, the relations (21.15), (21.16), (21.22), and (21.23) immediately yield the following relations for the R_k:

$$R_k = (AH_kA^{-1})R_{k-1};$$

$$R_k = (AK_kA^{-1})R_0, \quad \text{where } K_k = H_kH_{k-1}\cdots H_1;$$

$$R_k = (AH^kA^{-1})R_0 = (AHA^{-1})^kR_0, \quad \text{when } H_k \equiv H; \quad (21.26)$$

$$R_k \sim -\left(\frac{k}{N-1}\right)\sum_i \lambda_i^{k-\bar{N}+1}AW_i, \quad \text{as } k \to \infty.$$

Since AHA^{-1} has the same Jordan canonical form as H, we see that the convergence criteria for R_k are the same as those for E_k.

21.4. Method of Simultaneous Displacements; Gradient Method

In several of the best-known iterative methods for solving a nonsingular system $AU = B$, one partitions the matrix A as follows:

$$A = E + D + F,$$

where E contains the below-diagonal elements a_{ij} $(i > j)$ and zeros elsewhere, where D contains the diagonal elements a_{ii} and zeros elsewhere, and where F contains the above-diagonal elements a_{ij} $(i < j)$ and zeros elsewhere. Assume that

$$a_{ii} \neq 0, \quad i = 1, 2, \cdots, N.$$

In the method of *simultaneous displacements*, Jacobi [1845] starts with a trial solution U_0 and proceeds as follows: Suppose that U_{k-1} has been found $(k = 1, 2, \cdots)$. Let $U_{l,r}$ denote the rth component of U_l. For $r = 1, 2, \cdots, N$ one finds $U_{k,r}$ by solving the rth of the equations $AU = B$ for $U_{k,r}$, using the $U_{k-1,s}$ $(s \neq r)$ as the values of the other unknowns. That is, one solves

$$a_{r1}U_{k-1,1} + \cdots + a_{r,r-1}U_{k-1,r-1} + a_{rr}U_{k,r} + a_{r,r+1}U_{k-1,r+1}$$

$$+ \cdots + a_{rN}U_{k-1,N} = b_r, \quad r = 1, \cdots, N \quad (21.27)$$

for $U_{k,r}$.

In (21.27) we have implicitly set up a one-to-one correspondence between the N unknowns U_r and the N equations of the system, so that each equation is solved for the corresponding unknown. For partial difference equations one ordinarily uses the natural correspondence between the value of the unknown function U at a node of the net and the difference expression for that node. For convenience we have written A so that the rth equation corresponds to the rth unknown component.

Clearly the r equations (21.27) are independent and may be solved in any order.

In matrix notation, in the method of simultaneous displacements one finds U_k by solving the equation

$$EU_{k-1} + DU_k + FU_{k-1} = B,$$

or

$$U_k = -D^{-1}(E + F)U_{k-1} + D^{-1}B. \tag{21.28}$$

Comparing (21.28) with (21.12), we see that $H = -D^{-1}(E + F)$, and $M = D^{-1}$. Note that (21.13) is satisfied.

For convergence it is necessary and sufficient that all eigenvalues λ_i of $H = -D^{-1}(E + F)$ be less than 1 in modulus. Equivalently, these λ_i are seen to be zeros of

$$\det(E + \lambda D + F) = 0. \tag{21.29}$$

Ordinarily it is difficult to test the roots of (21.29). If D is a scalar matrix δI, then $E + \lambda D + F = E + D + F + (\lambda - 1)D = A - (1 - \lambda)\delta I$, and each eigenvalue λ_i of H corresponds to an eigenvalue $(1 - \lambda_i)\delta$ of A. This helps locate the λ_i in some cases.

It should be noted that symmetry and positive definiteness of A are not sufficient to assure convergence of the method of simultaneous displacements, even when $D = \delta I$. For, by means of the theorem that a matrix is positive definite if its principal minors are positive, it is readily verified that the matrix

$$A = \begin{bmatrix} 1 & a & a \\ a & 1 & a \\ a & a & 1 \end{bmatrix} \tag{21.30}$$

is positive definite when $-\frac{1}{2} < a < 1$, whereas the present iteration is convergent only for $-\frac{1}{2} < a < \frac{1}{2}$. Let us therefore consider conditions which are sufficient for the iteration to converge.

The most common of these conditions has been stated in a theorem by Collatz [1950] (see Secs. 20.4 and 21.1 for definitions):

> *If A has diagonal dominance and is not reducible, then the method of simultaneous displacements converges.* $\tag{21.31}$

To see the reason for (21.31), let $A = E + D + F$ and consider any λ with $|\lambda| \geq 1$. Let $Q = E + \lambda D + F$; clearly Q has diagonal dominance and is not reducible. Hence, by a classical theorem (see Taussky [1949]), $\det Q \neq 0$. Hence, for all roots λ_i of (21.29), one must have $|\lambda_i| < 1$, and this proves (21.31).

Where the diagonal fails to dominate, the method of simultaneous displacements may fail to converge. For the one-dimensional net illustrated in Fig. 21.2, consider the Dirichlet problem

$$u(x + h) - 2u(x) + u(x - h) = 0, \qquad \text{for } x = N, \cdots, P, Q,$$

$$u(M) = a,$$

$$\frac{\sigma}{h} u(T) + \frac{h - \sigma}{h} u(Q) = u(S) = b.$$

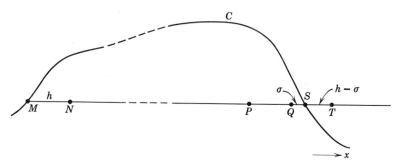

FIG. 21.2. One-dimensional network with one irregular interior point Q.

The matrix A for this problem is

$$A = \begin{bmatrix} -2 & 1 & 0 & 0 & \cdots & 0 & 0 & 0 \\ 1 & -2 & 1 & 0 & \cdots & 0 & 0 & 0 \\ 0 & 1 & -2 & 1 & \cdots & 0 & 0 & 0 \\ \multicolumn{8}{c}{\cdots\cdots\cdots\cdots\cdots\cdots\cdots\cdots} \\ 0 & 0 & 0 & 0 & \cdots & 1 & -2 & 1 \\ 0 & 0 & 0 & 0 & \cdots & 0 & 1-p & p \end{bmatrix}$$

where $p = \sigma/h$.

Now it is easily shown that

$$F(\lambda) = \det (E + \lambda D + F) = p\lambda P_{n-1}(\lambda) + (1 - p) P_{n-2}(\lambda),$$

where $P_\alpha(\lambda)$ is a polynomial of degree α ($\alpha = n - 2, n - 1$), and where n is the number of unknown values $U(N), \cdots, U(P), U(Q), U(T)$. From the last equation one sees that, as $p \to 0$, at least one root of $F(\lambda) = 0$ goes to ∞, since the limiting equation has only $n - 2$ roots. Hence the method of simultaneous displacements will diverge for all sufficiently small values of p.

The method of simultaneous displacements for the Dirichlet problem for the Laplace difference equation (21.4) goes like this: A trial solution $U_0(x, y)$ is chosen. Then, at the kth stage, suppose one has the solution $U_{k-1}(x, y)$. For each (x, y) the value of the new solution $U_k(x, y)$ is obtained by averaging the values of the old solution at the four neighbors of (x, y):

$$U_k(x, y) = \tfrac{1}{4}[U_{k-1}(x + h, y) + U_{k-1}(x - h, y)$$
$$+ U_{k-1}(x, y + h) + U_{k-1}(x, y - h)]. \quad (21.32)$$

The process (21.32) is well adapted to a machine without an extensive internal memory. If the values of U_{k-1} are kept on cards or tape, for example, the values of U_k can easily be generated independently of each other, and it is not necessary to have available the new values of U_k until the function U_k has been computed over the whole net R_h. At the end, one can discard the old values U_{k-1} and repeat the iteration with U_k. The method has been used on the IBM C.P.C. (see Sec. 3 and Yowell [1951]). It might be useful with magnetic tapes on which one cannot read and write simultaneously.

One can interpret k in (21.32) as a timelike variable t, rewriting $U_k(x, y)$ as $U(x, y, t)$. Then (21.32) can be written

$$U(x, y, t + 1) - U(x, y, t) = \tfrac{1}{4}[U(x + h, y, t) + U(x - h, y, t)$$
$$+ U(x, y + h, t) + U(x, y - h, t) - 4U(x, y, t)]$$

or

$$U(x, y, t + 1) - U(x, y, t) = \frac{h^2}{4} \Delta_h U(x, y, t). \quad (21.33)$$

Thus (21.33) can be interpreted as a difference method for solving the initial-value boundary-value problem for the heat equation

$$\frac{\partial u}{\partial t} = c \, \Delta u \quad (21.34)$$

with $c = h^2/4$, time increment 1, and space increments h.

The point here is that the Dirichlet problem for the elliptic difference equation is being solved as the asymptotic solution (as time $t \to \infty$) of the time-dependent problem (21.33). This makes it possible to interpret the iteration physically, and so get an intuitive feeling for its behavior.

The method of simultaneous displacements is more like methods used with analog equipment than is the method of successive displacements (Sec. 21.6). For with analog equipment one usually solves the system $\Delta_h U = 0$ by setting up a circuit to model the solution of an equation like

$$\frac{\partial U}{\partial t} = \Delta_h U, \quad (21.35)$$

and (21.35) is close in its behavior to (21.33). Also, the flow of electricity used in the typical device naturally occurs simultaneously all over the network, rather than successively in different parts of the circuit.

When a matrix A is symmetric and definite, one of the important and interesting methods of solving a system $AU = B$ is the *gradient method*, and this method is also applicable to certain functional equations. We shall now develop the background of one form of the gradient method, and then relate it to the method of simultaneous displacements. We shall phrase the formulas to bring out the natural relation of these methods with Richardson's method developed in Sec. 21.5.

Let us write the system of linear equations in the form $AU = B$, and adjust the sign so that A is a positive definite matrix. Consider the real-valued quadratic function

$$E(U) = U^T A U - 2B^T U, \tag{21.36}$$

which is identical with the function $I_h(U)$ of (20.15), except for a slight difference of notation. Since

$$E(U) = (U - A^{-1}B)^T A(U - A^{-1}B) - B^T A^{-1}B,$$

one sees that $E(U)$ attains its minimum value $-B^T A^{-1}B$ precisely when $U = A^{-1}B$, the solution. For all other values of U, $E(U) > -B^T A^{-1}B$. Thus solving the system $AU = B$ is equivalent to finding a U to minimize the quadratic function $E(U)$.

Now let U_0 be picked arbitrarily, and consider the following iteration for computing a sequence $\{U_k\}$. Given U_{k-1}, compute the (downhill) *gradient* direction (i.e., direction of *steepest descent*) of $E(U)$ at U_{k-1}. This is the direction

$$-\nabla E(U)|_{U = U_{k-1}} = -2(AU_{k-1} - B) = 2R_{k-1},$$

where $R_{k-1} = B - AU_{k-1}$ is the *residual* of the system $AU = B$ at $U = U_{k-1}$.

Since $E(U)$ decreases in the direction of R_{k-1}, it is reasonable to choose

$$U_k = U_{k-1} + \alpha_{k-1}R_{k-1}, \tag{21.37}$$

where the positive number α_{k-1} is yet to be determined. One idea is to choose α_{k-1} so that it makes $E(U_{k-1} + \alpha R_{k-1})$ a minimum among all choices of real α. In this manner one appears to be making the fastest progress toward minimizing $E(U)$. The reader can show that, for any α and any vectors U, Z,

$$E(U) - E(U + \alpha Z) = 2\alpha Z^T R - \alpha^2 Z^T AZ, \tag{21.38}$$

where $R = B - AU$. Hence $E(U_{k-1} + \alpha R_{k-1})$ is minimized when α is given the *optimum* value $R_{k-1}^T R_{k-1}/R_{k-1}^T A R_{k-1}$, and this choice is sometimes made. Its use requires the storage of an R as well as a U, and the computation of AR, with a resulting doubling of the magnitude of the computation. For this reason the optimization of α is not recommended. Moreover, as Stiefel [1955] points out, choosing the optimum α is usually a short-sighted strategy anyway! For a further discussion of this optimum gradient method, see Forsythe [1953] and references cited there.

Suppose, however, that all α_k are to take the same value α. Then by (21.37) one has

$$U_k = U_{k-1} + \alpha(B - AU_{k-1}),$$

so that the error $E_k = U_k - A^{-1}B$ satisfies the recurrence

$$E_k = E_{k-1} + \alpha(-AE_{k-1}) = (I - \alpha A)E_{k-1}. \tag{21.39}$$

Thus we have a stationary linear iteration with $H = I - \alpha A$. Let μ_i be the eigenvalues of A, and λ_i those of H. We have $\lambda_i = 1 - \alpha\mu_i$ ($i = 1, 2, \cdots, N$). Since A is positive definite, all $\mu_i > 0$. The criterion $|\lambda_i| < 1$ for convergence then takes the form

$$0 < \alpha < \frac{2}{\max_i \mu_i}. \tag{21.40}$$

In order to minimize $\max |\lambda_i|$, and thus get the fastest possible convergence, we must choose α so that

$$\max_i |1 - \alpha\mu_i| = \min. \tag{21.41}$$

Suppose all we know about the μ_i is that they lie in an interval $[a, b]$ ($0 < a < b < \infty$). For every α the function $|1 - \alpha\mu|$ assumes its maximum at one of the end points $\mu = a$ or $\mu = b$. The best choice of α, i.e., the one for which $\max (|1 - \alpha a|, |1 - \alpha b|)$ is smallest, is the one for which $1 - \alpha a = -(1 - \alpha b)$, i.e., $\alpha^{-1} = (a + b)/2$. With this choice of α we have, for all i,

$$|1 - \alpha\mu_i| \leq \frac{b - a}{b + a} = \frac{b/a - 1}{b/a + 1} < 1. \tag{21.42}$$

Thus the convergence factor for the gradient method with a properly chosen constant α is bounded by a certain function of b/a.

As an illustration we consider the system of linear equations resulting from Dirichlet's problem for Laplace's equation when the difference operator Δ_h is taken instead of Δ. Let A be the positive definite matrix corresponding to the operator $-h^2\Delta_h$ in two dimensions. It will be shown in Sec. 21.5 that the eigenvalues of A occur in pairs μ_i, $8 - \mu_i$, except for possible extra values $\mu_i = 4$. Hence for that A the best single value of α

is $\frac{1}{4}$, in the sense of minimizing $\max |\lambda_i|$. If we now set $\alpha \equiv \frac{1}{4}$ in (21.37), we have

$$U_k = U_{k-1} + \tfrac{1}{4}(B - AU_{k-1}) = U_{k-1} + \tfrac{1}{4}(B + h^2 \Delta_h U_{k-1}).$$

Since the terms in B are simply the boundary values of $U(x, y)$, the above equation is equivalent to

$$U_k(x, y) = U_{k-1}(x, y) + \tfrac{1}{4}[U_{k-1}(x + h, y) + \cdots$$
$$+ U_{k-1}(x, y - h) - 4U_{k-1}(x, y)],$$

or

$$U_k(x, y) = \tfrac{1}{4}[U_{k-1}(x + h, y) + \cdots + U_{k-1}(x, y - h)]. \quad (21.43)$$

Taken together with (21.32), relation (21.43) proves that the *gradient method* $\alpha \equiv \frac{1}{4}$ *is identical with the method of simultaneous displacements for the Dirichlet problem with the operator* Δ_h.

The considerations stated above for the Laplacian operator Δ_h have a wider application. As shown in Sec. 20, diagonal dominance of the matrix A can occur for the difference equations corresponding to the first boundary-value problem for any elliptic operator with no term in u_{xy}. If, moreover, the problem is self-adjoint, it can be shown that the matrix A can be taken symmetric and definite, and the gradient method (21.37) is applicable; condition (21.40) indicates the range of α for which convergence is assured. The gradient method is identical with the method of simultaneous displacements whenever A is symmetric and definite, with a scalar matrix as its diagonal (i.e., $D = cI$).

21.5. Richardson's Method

When A is a positive definite matrix, formula (21.37) suggests that the relaxation parameter α may depend on the iteration number k, so that $\alpha = \alpha_k$. In Sec. 21.4 we referred to choosing α_{k-1} to minimize $E(U_k)$. In this section we shall develop what is called *Richardson's method*. The idea of the method is applicable to the solution of any system $AU = B$ with positive definite A, whether or not it arises from difference equations.

By (21.39) we see that $E_k = (I - \alpha_{k-1}A)E_{k-1}$, so that

$$E_k = (I - \alpha_0 A)(I - \alpha_1 A) \cdots (I - \alpha_{k-1}A)E_0. \quad (21.44)$$

We may write (21.44) in the form

$$E_k = P_k(A)E_0, \quad (21.45)$$

where

$$P_k(x) = \prod_{i=0}^{k-1} (1 - \alpha_i x)$$

is a polynomial in x with the special property that

$$P_k(0) = 1. \quad (21.46)$$

The numbers $1/\alpha_i$ of (21.44) are the zeros of the polynomial P_k. Hence selecting the $\alpha_0, \cdots, \alpha_{k-1}$ in (21.44) is equivalent to choosing a polynomial P_k of degree k with the constraint (21.46).

If the eigenvalues of A are μ_i, those of $P_k(A)$ are $P_k(\mu_i)$. Let us again make the reasonable supposition that all we know about the μ_i is that they lie in a certain real interval $[a, b]$, where a, b $(0 < a < b < \infty)$ are known constants. (In practice a reasonable b is easily found from Gerschgorin's theorem (Milne [1953], p. 169), while a number a such that $0 < a < \min \mu_i$ may be hard to find.) Let us represent E_0 in the basis of eigenvectors X_i of A (diagonalizable because symmetric):

$$E_0 = \sum_{i=1}^{N} \gamma_i X_i.$$

Then, from (21.45),

$$E_k = \sum_{i=1}^{N} \gamma_i P_k(\mu_i) X_i. \tag{21.47}$$

If we want to make E_k small, it is important to make the $P_k(\mu_i)$ small $(i = 1, \cdots, N)$. In view of our ignorance of the μ_i, all we can do is make $|P_k(x)|$ small for x throughout the interval $a \leq x \leq b$.

In an early paper Richardson [1910] suggested sprinkling the k zeros α_i^{-1} of $P_k(x)$ fairly uniformly over the interval $[a, b]$. If k is not too large, this process may be effective. A more sophisticated idea is to find the $P_k(x)$ whose values for $a \leq x \leq b$ are numerically as small as possible in some sense. While Stiefel [1958] has considered an integral measure of smallness of P_k, many writers have preferred to consider making max $|P_k(x)|$ the measure of smallness of P_k. The precise problem is then to find P_k with $P_k(0) = 1$ such that

$$\max_{a \leq x \leq b} |P_k(x)| \text{ is a minimum.} \tag{21.48}$$

The polynomial minimizing (21.48) was given in 1892 by W. Markoff [1916], namely,

$$P_k(x) = \frac{T_k\left(\dfrac{b + a - 2x}{b - a}\right)}{T_k(y_0)}, \qquad y_0 = \frac{b + a}{b - a} > 1, \tag{21.49}$$

where $T_k(y) = \cos(k \arccos y)$ is the ordinary Čebyšev polynomial adjusted to the interval $[-1, 1]$. We shall not prove this. The polynomial $P_k(x)$ is simply the Čebyšev polynomial adjusted to the interval $[a, b]$, and scaled to satisfy (21.46). The number y_0 is the image of 0 under the linear transformation taking a to 1, and b to -1. Markoff's result is continually being rediscovered by enterprising numerical analysts!

To derive an expression for $T_k(y)$ for $|y| > 1$, let $y = \cos \alpha$, where α is some complex number. Then

$$2T_k(y) = 2 \cos k\alpha = e^{ik\alpha} + e^{-ik\alpha}$$

$$= (\cos \alpha + i \sin \alpha)^k + (\cos \alpha - i \sin \alpha)^k$$

$$= (y + \sqrt{y^2 - 1})^k + (y - \sqrt{y^2 - 1})^k.$$

Then from (21.49) we find that, as $k \to \infty$,

$$\max_{a \leq x \leq b} |P_k(x)| = [T_k(y_0)]^{-1} = \frac{2}{(y_0 + \sqrt{y_0^2 - 1})^k + (y_0 - \sqrt{y_0^2 - 1})^k},$$

$$\leq \frac{2}{(y_0 + \sqrt{y_0^2 - 1})^k} = 2(y_0 - \sqrt{y_0^2 - 1})^k.$$

(The above inequality is also an asymptotic equality. Thus, as $k \to \infty$, the eigenvalues $|P_k(\mu_i)|$ are uniformly bounded by $2(y_0 - \sqrt{y_0^2 - 1})^k$. Hence, for the first k steps of the iteration (21.37), a finite analog of the rate of convergence of Sec. 21.3, namely,

$$-\log \left(\frac{\|E_k\|}{\|E_0\|} \right)^{1/k}, \tag{21.50}$$

is bounded by

$$-\frac{1}{k} \log 2 + \log (y_0 + \sqrt{y_0^2 - 1}),$$

whose asymptotic value (as $k \to \infty$)—the rate of convergence of Sec. 21.3 —is equal to $\log (y_0 + \sqrt{y_0^2 - 1})$. Also, $y_0 - \sqrt{y_0^2 - 1}$ is an asymptotic bound for the corresponding convergence factor. We call the quantity $(\|E_k\|/\|E_0\|)^{1/k}$ the *average convergence factor* for the first k steps, and the quantity in (21.50) the *average rate of convergence* for these steps.

Todd [1949] has defined the *P-condition number* of any positive definite matrix A with eigenvalues μ_i by

$$P = \frac{\max_i \mu_i}{\min_i \mu_i}.$$

In our application, the quantity P is thus less than or equal to b/a, since the interval $[a, b]$ contains all the μ_i. Since the number

$$y_0 = \frac{b/a + 1}{b/a - 1} \leq (P + 1)(P - 1)^{-1}$$

is a function only of this bound b/a, and since our bound for the average rate of convergence of Richardson's process is a function only of y_0, we see that the possible speed of convergence of the process for most matrices A and vectors U_0 is limited by the value of P. Even if one chose a, b optimally, the convergence factor could never have a smaller value than the value obtained by setting $y_0 = (P + 1)(P - 1)^{-1}$:

$$y_0 - \sqrt{y_0{}^2 - 1} \geq (P + 1)(P - 1)^{-1} - \sqrt{(P + 1)^2(P - 1)^{-2} - 1}.$$

For most substantial problems, $P \gg 1$, so that $y_0 \doteq 1 + 2a/b$. Hence, approximating the square root,

$$y_0 - \sqrt{y_0{}^2 - 1} \doteq 1 + \frac{2a}{b} - \sqrt{\frac{1 + 4a}{b - 1}} \doteq 1 - 2\sqrt{\frac{a}{b}} \geq 1 - \frac{2}{\sqrt{P}}, \quad (21.51)$$

since $P \leq b/a$. The corresponding relation for the rate of convergence is

$$\log(y_0 + \sqrt{y_0{}^2 - 1}) \doteq 2\sqrt{\frac{a}{b}} \leq \frac{2}{\sqrt{P}}. \quad (21.52)$$

From (21.42) we see that the rate of convergence of the method of simultaneous displacements is

$$\log y_0 \doteq \frac{2a}{b} \leq \frac{2}{P}.$$

A comparison with (21.52) shows how much one gains in convergence by use of Richardson's method.

However, if one is using iteration processes of degree 1 (Sec. 21.3), one cannot let $k \to \infty$ in Richardson's process. As long as one actually uses (21.37) for each computation step, the α_i must be known at the start of the computation. Since the α_i^{-1} are the zeros of the polynomial $P_k(x)$, one must have some fixed k in mind from the start. Usually k is fixed at K, an integer near 20, perhaps. One then determines the α_i from the tabulated roots of Čebyšev polynomials, and computes $U_1, \cdots, U_K$ from (21.37). If E_K is not small enough, one uses the same values of α_i to make another cycle of K steps, etc.

In such a process, called *semi-iterative* by Varga [1957a], the average convergence factor is $[T_K(y_0)]^{-1/K}$. While

$$\lim_{K \to \infty} [T_K(y_0)]^{-1/K} = y_0 - \sqrt{y_0{}^2 - 1},$$

it takes comparatively large values of K before the limit is practically attained.

In connection with various iterative processes, it will be useful to consider a simple example, the solution of the Dirichlet problem for the five-point Laplace difference operator over a square net. Let R be the square

$0 < x < \pi, 0 < y < \pi$. Let $h = \pi/n$, so that R is divided into n^2 square meshes with $N = (n - 1)^2$ interior nodes comprising R_h. Let

$$\Delta_h U = h^{-2}[U(x + h, y) + U(x, y + h) + U(x - h, y)$$
$$+ U(x, y - h) - 4U(x, y)].$$

It is convenient to denote the $(n - 1)^2$ eigenvectors of $-\Delta_h$ by $X_{pq}(x, y)$, with corresponding positive eigenvalues μ_{pq} $(p, q = 1, 2, \cdots, n - 1)$; thus

$$-\Delta_h X_{pq} = \mu_{pq} X_{pq}.$$

It is easily shown by substitution that one may take

$$X_{pq}(x, y) = \sin px \sin qy, \qquad p, q = 1, \cdots, n - 1,$$

and that

$$\mu_{pq} = 4h^{-2}\left(\sin^2 \frac{ph}{2} + \sin^2 \frac{qh}{2}\right), \qquad p, q = 1, \cdots, n - 1.$$

Moreover,

$$\min \mu_{pq} = \mu_{1,1} = 8h^{-2} \sin^2 \frac{h}{2} \to 2, \qquad \text{as } h \to 0;$$

$$(21.52a)$$

$$\max \mu_{pq} = \mu_{n-1,n-1} = 8h^{-2}\left(1 - \sin^2 \frac{h}{2}\right) \sim 8h^{-2}, \qquad \text{as } h \to 0.$$

The convergence of the method of simultaneous displacements is controlled by the eigenvalues of $-D^{-1}(E + F) = -D^{-1}(A - D) = I - D^{-1}A = I - h^2(-\Delta_h)/4$. But these are

$$\lambda_{pq} = 1 - \sin^2 \frac{ph}{2} - \sin^2 \frac{qh}{2}$$

$$= \frac{\cos ph + \cos qh}{2}, \qquad p, q = 1, \cdots, n - 1.$$

Clearly the convergence factor of the method is

$$\lambda = \max |\lambda_{pq}| = \cos h \sim 1 - \frac{h^2}{2}, \qquad \text{as } h \to 0.$$

The corresponding rate of convergence is approximately $h^2/2$.

As a numerical example we shall sometimes take $n = 45$, corresponding to a Dirichlet problem with 1936 interior nodes. For the solution of this problem by the method of simultaneous displacements we have $\bar{\lambda} = \cos(\pi/45) = \cos 4° = 0.99756$. The corresponding rate of convergence is approximately 0.00244.

One may easily show that the relation $\bar{\lambda} = \cos h$ holds also for the simple Laplace difference operator in three or more dimensions.

Now for Richardson's method, one can take $a = \mu_{11}$ and $b = \mu_{n-1,n-1}$. Then $P = b/a \doteq \sin^{-2}(h/2) \doteq 4h^{-2}$, and $y_0 = (P + 1)(P - 1)^{-1} \doteq 1 + h^2/2$. Then, by (21.51), we find for the asymptotic (as $K \to \infty$) average convergence factor the value

$$y_0 - \sqrt{y_0{}^2 - 1} \sim 1 - 2\sqrt{\frac{h^2}{4}} = 1 - h, \qquad \text{as } h \to 0.$$

The corresponding rate of convergence is h. Note the large factor of gain over the rate of convergence $h^2/2$ of the method of simultaneous displacements.

To see what average rates of convergence may be expected for finite values of K, we take the above square and assume that h is small enough that such approximations as $(1 + h)^{-1} \doteq 1 - h$ are true with sufficient accuracy. Using the expressions for $T_K(y)$ given after (21.49) above, we shall give an expression for the average rate of convergence in K steps. Now

$$[T_K(y_0)]^{-1} = \frac{2}{(y_0 + \sqrt{y_0{}^2 - 1})^K + (y_0 - \sqrt{y_0{}^2 - 1})^K}$$

$$\doteq \frac{2}{(1 + h)^K + (1 - h)^K}$$

$$= \frac{2}{(1 + h)^K\{1 + [(1 - h)/(1 + h)]^K\}}$$

$$\doteq \frac{2}{(1 + h)^K[1 + (1 - 2h)^K]}.$$

Now let $K = mn$, where $h = \pi/n$ as usual. Then $K = \pi m/h$, and

$$(1 - 2h)^K = (1 - 2h)^{2\pi m/2h} \doteq e^{-2\pi m}.$$

Hence the average convergence factor, $[T_K(y_0)]^{-1/K}$, is given by

$$\frac{2^{1/K}}{(1 + h)[1 + (1 - 2h)^K]^{1/K}} \doteq \left(\frac{2}{1 + e^{-2\pi m}}\right)^{1/mn} \frac{1}{1 + h}.$$

Then the average rate of convergence, the negative logarithm of the last expression, is

$$\log(1 + h) + \frac{1}{mn}\log(1 + e^{-2\pi m}) - \frac{1}{mn}\log 2 \doteq h - \frac{\log 2 - e^{-2\pi m}}{mn}$$

$$\doteq h - \frac{0.693 - e^{-2\pi m}}{K}$$

$$\doteq h - \frac{0.693}{K}.$$

Thus the effect of a finite K, when $e^{-2\pi m} \ll 0.693$, is to reduce the average rate of convergence below its asymptotic value $(K \to \infty)$ by approximately the fraction

$$\frac{0.693}{Kh} = \frac{0.693}{\pi m} \doteq \frac{0.221}{m}. \tag{21.53}$$

To hold the reduction down to 22%, it is necessary to make $m \geq 1$, i.e., to use $K \geq n$. The important point to note is that this minimum necessary K depends on $h = \pi/n$. *Thus the finer the network, the higher must be the degree of the Richardson polynomials if the average rate of convergence is to remain approximately h.*

For $n = 45$, the value of y_0 is 1.00244, and the asymptotic value of the average convergence factor is 0.93254. But for $K = 10$, one attains only the factor 0.977, a value requiring about three times as many iterations as the limiting value 0.93254. For $K = 20$, one finds approximately 0.957, a value yielding about two-thirds of the asymptotic rate of convergence. For these values of $m = K/n$, it is not quite correct to neglect $e^{-2\pi m}$ against log 2, but (21.53) shows the order of magnitude of the rate of convergence.

For a general matrix problem Young [1954] considers the effect on the rate of convergence of incorrectly estimating the lower eigenvalue $\mu_1 \doteq a$.

While large values of K are desirable for good convergence, they introduce a new difficulty indicated by Young [1954]: a possible loss of accuracy due to round off within a single cycle of the Richardson process. For a fixed value of K, consider the progress of the error E_k for $k \leq K$. It is convenient to use the coordinate system of the eigenvectors. Write

$$E_k = \sum_{i=1}^{N} \gamma_i^{(k)} X_i,$$

where the X_i are as in (21.47). By (21.44),

$$\gamma_i^{(k)} = \gamma_i \prod_{h=0}^{k-1} (1 - \alpha_h \mu_i). \tag{21.54}$$

Now the numbers $\alpha_0, \cdots, \alpha_{K-1}$ have been selected so that

$$\gamma_i^{(K)} = \gamma_i \, P_K(\mu_i) = \gamma_i \prod_{h=0}^{K-1} (1 - \alpha_h \mu_i)$$

is small for each eigenvalue μ_i of A. But there is no assurance that the intermediate quantities $\gamma_i^{(k)}$ of (21.54) are small. If they grow markedly, then the final small number $\gamma_i^{(K)}$ will have to be the difference of various numbers of large magnitude. Such "catastrophic cancellation" (Prof. D. H. Lehmer's phrase) invariably results in a loss of significant digits, whether one uses a fixed point or a floating point.

It is therefore essential to inhibit the growth of the numbers $\gamma_i^{(k)}$ for $k < K$. We still have at our disposal the order in which the numbers $\alpha_0, \cdots, \alpha_{K-1}$ are selected from among the reciprocals of the zeros of $P_K(x)$. Our desire is roughly that $\max_i |\gamma_i^{(k)}|$ should steadily decrease, as k goes from 0 to K. For this would seem to avoid as much loss of leading digits as possible.

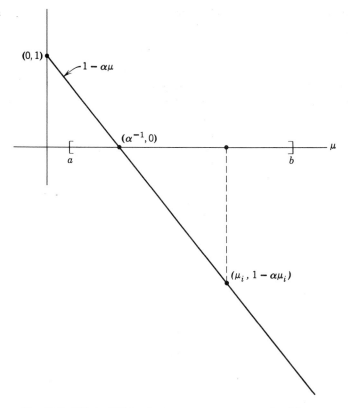

FIG. 21.3. Effect of Richardson process on components of the error.

No detailed study of the optimal ordering of the α_h is known to the authors. Young notes that an ascending order of the α_h is far superior to a descending order. The reason is that, for all $\alpha_h < 2/b$ (approximately half the α's), each factor $1 - \alpha_h \mu_i$ in (21.54) is less than one in absolute value. Hence there is no growth of numbers while one uses these smaller values of α. Meanwhile, one will have greatly decreased the $|\gamma_i^{(k)}|$ corresponding to the larger μ_i, so that they can survive the use of larger α_h later on. But, if one started with the larger α_h, the factors $|1 - \alpha_h \mu_i|$ would be very large for the large μ_i at the outset, and there would be a great growth in the numbers.

Young recommends starting with a middle value of α, and then alternately proceeding from the next lower to the next higher. It would be interesting to look for still better orderings.

The analysis of the Richardson process is aided by concentrating on the reciprocals α_h^{-1} which, as zeros of the Čebyšev polynomial $T_K(x)$, lie in the interval $[a, b]$. The effect of the operation $I - \alpha A$ applied to E_k is to change the components $\gamma_i^{(k)}$ to

$$\gamma_i^{(k+1)} = (1 - \alpha\mu_i)\gamma_i^{(k)}.$$

This is illustrated in Fig. 21.3.

Young and Warlick [1953] have reported experiments with Richardson's method on ORDVAC for the Dirichlet problem for Δ_h over a square net with 361 interior points ($n = 20$). In spite of the growth of the round-off error, they found it possible to get convergence with K up to approximately 40, and give a number of interesting data. For this comparatively low value of n, the value $K = 40$ yields about 90% of the asymptotic rate of convergence, in agreement with (21.53) for $m = 2$.

If one changes to an iteration of degree 2 (Sec. 21.3), it is possible in practice to let $k \to \infty$ in Richardson's process, as was pointed out by Stiefel [1958]. We give a brief outline of the reason. First, from (21.45), we see that

$$\begin{aligned}
E_{k-1} &= P_{k-1}(A)E_0, \\
E_k &= P_k(A)E_0, \\
E_{k+1} &= P_{k+1}(A)E_0, \\
AE_k &= AP_k(A)E_0.
\end{aligned} \tag{21.55}$$

Now the polynomials P_k of (21.49), like all polynomials orthogonal with respect to a measure over the real axis, satisfy a three-term recurrence formula of the type

$$x\,P_k(x) = q_1\,P_{k-1}(x) + q_2\,P_k(x) + q_3\,P_{k+1}(x), \tag{21.56}$$

where q_1, q_2, q_3 depend on k. By (21.46),

$$q_1 + q_2 + q_3 = 0. \tag{21.57}$$

Multiplying the equations (21.55) respectively by $q_1, q_2, q_3, -1$, and adding, we see by (21.56) that

$$q_1E_{k-1} + q_2E_k + q_3E_{k+1} - AE_k = 0. \tag{21.58}$$

Since $E_i = U_i - A^{-1}B$, we have $AE_k = AU_k - B = -R_k$, whence

$$q_1U_{k-1} + q_2U_k + q_3U_{k+1} - (q_1 + q_2 + q_3)A^{-1}B + R_k = 0.$$

Now, using (21.57), we finally learn that

$$U_{k+1} = -q_3^{-1}(R_k + q_2 U_k + q_1 U_{k-1}).$$ (21.59)

Formula (21.59) shows that U_{k+1} can be expressed linearly in terms of U_k and U_{k-1}. When $0 < a < b$, Stiefel [1958] writes (21.59) in the following form (here Δ temporarily denotes a difference, and not the Laplace operator):

$$U_{k+1} = U_k + \Delta U_k,$$

$$\Delta U_k = \frac{1}{\cosh(k+1)\omega} \left\{ \frac{4R_k}{b-a} \cosh k\omega + [\cosh(k-1)\omega] \Delta U_{k-1} \right\},$$ (21.60)

where ω is defined by

$$\cosh \omega = \frac{b+a}{b-a}.$$

For $k = 0$, we replace ΔU_k in (21.60) by the special definition

$$\Delta U_0 = 2(b+a)^{-1} R_0.$$ (21.61)

The iteration (21.60), (21.61) can be carried out on a computer without a preliminary choice of the final value of k, in contrast to the earlier method of this section. The method (21.60), (21.61) has been tested by Mr. Werner Frank [unpublished], who finds it apparently stable.

Related ideas have been exploited for the matrix eigenvalue problem in the *spectroscopic eigenvalue analysis* of Lanczos [1955].

21.6. Method of Successive Displacements

The method of successive displacements for solving $AU = B$ can be considered a variant of the method of simultaneous displacements. Let A be an arbitrary matrix with no $a_{ii} = 0$ and define D, E, F as in Sec. 21.4. The variation consists in using a new component $U_{k,r}$ in equations (21.27) as soon as it has been computed.

In addition to the fixed one-to-one correspondence between the components of U and the equations assumed in the earlier method, we now have to fix on a certain cyclic order σ of the integers $1, 2, \cdots, N$, the order in which the components U_r will be computed. By permuting the rows and columns of A with the same permutation, we can still associate the rth component U_r with the rth equation, and we will always do this. We can also rearrange the components so that they are computed in the order $U_1, U_2, \cdots, U_N$, and shall do this for notational convenience. All the matters now to be discussed depend on the correspondence between equations and unknowns, and on the choice σ of the order of solving the equations.

With the above ordering, the method of successive displacements is defined by changing (21.27) so that it reads

$$a_{r1}U_{k,1} + \cdots + a_{rr}U_{k,r} + a_{r,r+1}U_{k-1,r+1} + \cdots + a_{rN}U_{k-1,N} = b_r,$$

$$r = 1, \cdots, N. \quad (21.62)$$

When solving equation (21.62) for the component $U_{k,r}$, one always employs the latest values of all other components, including (for example) the value $U_{k,r-1}$ computed in the most recent step at the same cycle of computation. From the standpoint of a digital computer, the use of (21.62) means that only a single vector U has to be stored at one time, whereas in the earlier method one generally would have to store a portion of both U_{k-1} and U_k.

The change of $U_{k-1,r}$ to its new value $U_{k,r}$ is sometimes called a *relaxation* step, or a *displacement*.

In matrix notation, the present method determines U_k by solving for U_k the equation

$$EU_k + DU_k + FU_{k-1} = B. \quad (21.63)$$

Hence

$$U_k = -(D + E)^{-1}FU_{k-1} + (D + E)^{-1}B. \quad (21.64)$$

Comparing (21.64) with (21.12), we see that $H = -(D + E)^{-1}F$, while $M = (D + E)^{-1}$. Note that (21.13) holds.

For convergence it is necessary and sufficient that all eigenvalues η_i of $-(D + E)^{-1}F$ be less than 1 in modulus. Equivalently, these η_i are the zeros of the determinantal equation:

$$\det (\eta E + \eta D + F) = 0. \quad (21.65)$$

However, (21.65) is often impractical to solve, and various indirect approaches are used to determine whether the method converges.

The method of successive displacements was mentioned by Seidel [1874], who did not advocate its use. Nevertheless, it is commonly known as the *Seidel* or *Gauss-Seidel* method. In connection with elliptic difference equations it is often named after *Liebmann* [1918]. The method has been the subject of many investigations, and particularly often it has been compared with the method of simultaneous displacements in regard to convergence questions.

It is comparatively easy to prove directly that:

> *If A has diagonal dominance and is not reducible,* (21.66)
> *then the method of successive displacements converges.*

In the proof, which is omitted here, one can get a somewhat better estimate of the convergence factor than in the corresponding proof for the method of simultaneous displacements. For proofs see Collatz [1950] or Faddeeva [1950], and improvements by Sassenfeld [1951].

The proof given in Sec. 21.4, with the one-dimensional example of Fig. 21.2, shows also that the method of successive displacements diverges for all sufficiently small p.

The result (21.66) is parallel to that of (21.31). Since, as shown in Sec. 20, diagonal dominance is characteristic of elliptic operators lacking a u_{xy} term, the Collatz theorem is very useful for such equations. For general elliptic operators, however, diagonal dominance is lacking. For self-adjoint elliptic operators it turns out (see Sec. 20.5) that the corresponding matrix problem $AU = B$ can usually be given a positive definite symmetric matrix. The following result implies convergence where it cannot be concluded for the method of simultaneous displacements—namely, whenever A is positive definite and symmetric.

THEOREM 21.1 (Reich). *If A is symmetric and nonsingular, and if all $a_{ii} > 0$, then the method of successive displacements for solving $AU = B$ converges for all initial vectors U_0 if and only if A is a positive definite matrix.*

The "if" part of the theorem has been stated many times, but the first complete proofs seem to be those of Schmeidler [1949] and Reich [1949]. We shall give the former. The "only if" part of the theorem is due to Reich, but we shall give Ostrowski's very simple proof [1954]. Of course, positive definiteness of A itself implies that all $a_{ii} > 0$.

It follows from our consideration of error in Sec. 21.3 that it is sufficient to prove the theorem for $B = 0$. Let $E(U) = U^T A U$ denote the value of the quadratic form whose matrix is A. It will be desirable to renumber the iterates in the form $U^{(k)}$, where k now increases at each iterative step, N times per cycle. Consider the kth step of the iteration, and let the ith component be the only one that changes between $U^{(k-1)}$ and $U^{(k)}$. Then, before the kth step, one has, for that $i = i(k)$,

$$\sum_{j=1}^{N} a_{ij} U_j^{(k-1)} = -R_i^{(k-1)}, \tag{21.67}$$

where $R^{(k-1)} = -AU^{(k-1)}$, as before. After the kth step, one has for the same i

$$\sum_{j=1}^{N} a_{ij} U_j^{(k)} = 0, \qquad i = i(k). \tag{21.68}$$

Subtracting (21.67) from (21.68), and recalling that $U_j^{(k-1)} = U_j^{(k)}$ for $j \neq i$, we have

$$a_{ii}[U_i^{(k)} - U_i^{(k-1)}] = R_i^{(k-1)}.$$

Now let $Z = e_i$, the ith coordinate unit vector, and let $U^{(k)} = U^{(k-1)} + \alpha_k Z$. Then $\alpha_k = U_i^{(k)} - U_i^{(k-1)}$, the change in the ith component, and also $|\alpha_k| = \|U^{(k)} - U^{(k-1)}\|_2$. Hence

$$a_{ii}\alpha_k = R_i^{(k-1)}. \tag{21.69}$$

By (21.38) and (21.69),

$$
\begin{aligned}
E(U^{(k)}) - E(U^{(k-1)}) &= E(U^{(k-1)} + \alpha_k Z) - E(U^{(k-1)}) \\
&= -2\alpha_k Z^T R^{(k-1)} + \alpha_k^2 Z^T A Z \\
&= -2\alpha_k e_i^T R^{(k-1)} + \alpha_k^2 e_i^T A e_i \\
&= -2\alpha_k R_i^{(k-1)} + \alpha_k^2 a_{ii} = -2a_{ii}\alpha_k^2 + a_{ii}\alpha_k^2 \\
&= -a_{ii}\alpha_k^2 = -a_{ii}\|U^{(k)} - U^{(k-1)}\|_2^2;
\end{aligned}
$$

i.e.,

$$E(U^{(k)}) - E(U^{(k-1)}) = -a_{ii}\|U^{(k)} - U^{(k-1)}\|_2^2. \tag{21.70}$$

From (21.70) we see that $E(U^{(k)}) \le E(U^{(k-1)})$, since $a_{ii} > 0$.

Suppose that A is positive definite. Let $U^{(0)}$ be arbitrary. Certainly $E(U^{(0)}) \ge 0$. From (21.70), it follows that $E(U^{(k)}) \downarrow \epsilon$, as $k \uparrow \infty$, where $\epsilon \ge 0$. Hence $E(U^{(k)}) - E(U^{(k-1)}) \to 0$, as $k \to \infty$. From (21.70) again, $U^{(k)} - U^{(k-1)} \to 0$, as $k \to \infty$, so that the ith component $U_i^{(k)} - U_i^{(k-1)} \to 0$, as $k \to \infty$, for all i. Consequently $U_i^{(k)} - U_i^{(k-\nu)} \to 0$, as $k \to \infty$, for all i and for $\nu = 1, 2, \cdots, N$.

It then follows from (21.68) that

$$\sum_{j=1}^{N} a_{ij} U_j^{(k)} \to 0, \qquad \text{for all } i,$$

as $k \to \infty$; i.e.,

$$A U^{(k)} \to 0, \qquad \text{as } k \to \infty. \tag{21.71}$$

Premultiplying (21.71) by A^{-1}, we see that $U^{(k)} \to 0$, as $k \to \infty$, and we have proved the "if" part of the theorem for $B = 0$. (Some incomplete proofs before 1949 assumed without proof that $\epsilon = 0$.)

If A is not positive definite, it must be indefinite, since it is symmetric and not singular. Hence $E(U^{(0)}) < 0$ for certain $U^{(0)}$. By (21.70), $E(U^{(k)})$ cannot increase, since all $a_{ii} > 0$, so that $E(U^{(k)})$ cannot approach 0. Hence $U^{(k)}$ cannot approach 0. This short argument is sufficient to prove the "only if" part of the theorem.

Instead of the above proofs based on the quadratic form $E(U)$, matrix proofs like Reich's involve bounding the η solving (21.65). Although these are technically more difficult, they can be extended to *almost symmetric* matrices A (see Stein [1951]).

On the other hand, the quadratic-form proof can be extended to a similar theorem for an algorithm with three important modifications:

1. Over- or underrelaxation
2. Variations from a strict cyclic order of relaxation
3. Simultaneous solution for r $(1 < r < N)$ components U_i, provided that the corresponding minor of A is positive definite.

(See Ostrowski [1954] and Schechter [1959] for a thorough treatment.) Similar ideas have been considered by Hestenes and Stein [1951]. Here we wish to consider only extension 1. Assume $A = A^T$ and $a_{ii} > 0$, as before.

From the standpoint of the quadratic form $E(U)$, one can look at the basic relaxation step of solving (21.62) for $U_{k,r}$ quite differently. Change the notation U_k to $U^{(k)}$, as in the proof of Theorem 21.1, and note that $U^{(k)} = U^{(k-1)} + \alpha e_i$, where e_i is one of the unit vectors, and $i = i(k)$. Now, by (21.38), we have that

$$E(U^{(k-1)}) - E(U^{(k-1)} + \alpha e_i) = -2\alpha e_i^T A U^{(k-1)} - \alpha^2 e_i^T A e_i$$
$$= 2\alpha R_i^{(k-1)} - \alpha^2 a_{ii}. \qquad (21.72)$$

Hence $E(U^{(k-1)} + \alpha e_i)$ is a quadratic function of the scalar parameter α. Since $a_{ii} > 0$, we see that $E(U^{(k-1)} + \alpha e_i)$ is minimized when $\alpha = R_i^{(k-1)}/a_{ii}$. Hence the choice

$$U^{(k)} = U^{(k-1)} + a_{ii}^{-1} R_i^{(k-1)} e_i,$$

which is that of the method of successive displacements, is equivalent to minimizing $E(U)$ along the line $U^{(k-1)} + \alpha e_i$.

From (21.72) we see moreover that

$$E(U^{(k-1)}) - E(U^{(k-1)} + a_{ii}^{-1} \omega R_i^{(k-1)} e_i) = \omega(2 - \omega) a_{ii}^{-1} [R_i^{(k-1)}]^2.$$
$$(21.73)$$

Hence $E(U^{(k-1)} + \alpha e_i)$ is decreased for any value

$$\alpha = \omega R_i^{(k-1)}/a_{ii},$$

so long as $0 < \omega < 2$. The value $\omega = 1$ corresponds to the above method; any value with $0 < \omega < 1$ is *underrelaxation*; any value with $1 < \omega < 2$ is *overrelaxation*. The scalar ω is called the *relaxation parameter*.

Formula (21.73) can be used in place of (21.70) to extend Reich's theorem to a modified method of successive displacements in which ω is permitted arbitrary variation in an interval $\omega_1 \leq \omega \leq \omega_2$, where $0 < \omega_1 < \omega_2 < 2$. On the face of it, there seems no reason to use any value of ω other than $\omega = 1$, since other values of ω cause $E(U^{(k)})$ to remain higher than with $\omega = 1$. However, Sec. 22 will show the great value of overrelaxation in connection with certain elliptic difference equations.

In certain problems, especially those involved in computing eigenvalues (see Secs. 20.5 and 24), A is a symmetric positive semidefinite matrix with all $a_{ii} > 0$. Then the equation $AU = 0$ has nonzero solutions, and we define S to be the linear subspace of all such solutions. It is reasonable to ask whether the method of successive displacements can be used to locate points of S. An affirmative answer is given by the following apparently new theorem.

THEOREM 21.2. *If A, a matrix of order N, is symmetric and positive semidefinite, with all $a_{ii} > 0$, then the method of successive displacements for solving $AU = 0$ converges for all initial vectors U_0 to some solution U_∞ of the equation. Moreover, U_∞ is zero only for initial vectors U_0 in a subspace of dimension less than N.*

Proof. The "if" part of the proof of Reich's theorem is valid down to conclusion (21.71): that $AU_k \to 0$, as $k \to \infty$. Now $U_k = H^k U_0$, where $H = -(D + E)^{-1}F$, by (21.64).

Let $D + E = L$. The matrix $H = -L^{-1}F$ has certain canonical blocks J_i, as described in Sec. 21.3. For any vector Y in S, we have $AY = 0$, whence

$$(H - I)Y = (-L^{-1}F - I)Y = -L^{-1}(F + L)Y = -L^{-1}AY = 0, \quad (21.74)$$

so that $HY = Y$. Thus each vector in S is an eigenvector of H belonging to the eigenvalue 1. Conversely, one sees from (21.74) that S contains each eigenvector of H belonging to the eigenvalue 1.

Now $|\lambda_i| < 1$ for all other eigenvalues of H. For otherwise there would be a vector Z, not in S, such that $HZ = \lambda_i Z$, with $|\lambda_i| \geq 1$. If $U_0 = Z$, we would then have $U_k = H^k U_0 = \lambda_i^k U_0$, so that $AU_k = \lambda_i^k AZ \neq 0$, and so AU_k would not go to 0, as $k \to \infty$.

If H had a canonical block J_i of order two or more corresponding to the eigenvalue 1, there would be nonzero vectors V, W such that $(H - I)V = W$, and $(H - I)W = 0$. (Here $W \in S$ is an eigenvector of H, while V would be a principal vector of H.) If we let $U_0 = V$, we would have $HV = V + W$, whence a simple induction would prove that $U_k = H^k V = V + kW$. But then we would have $AU_k = AV \neq 0$, and so again AU_k would not go to 0, as $k \to \infty$. Hence, associated with the eigenvalue 1, H can have only canonical blocks J_i of order 1.

If then follows from (21.23) that $U_k \mapsto U_\infty$, where U_∞ is the vector component of U_0 in the eigenspace S of H associated with $\lambda = 1$. Since $AU_\infty = 0$, the first sentence of the theorem is proved. The second sentence follows from the fact that $U_\infty = 0$ only if U_0 has no component in the eigenspace S.

21.7. Gauss-Southwell Relaxation

Assume A is positive definite and symmetric, and that we wish to solve $AU = B$. As in the method of successive displacements, assume we have fixed on a certain one-to-one correspondence between equations and unknowns. In the earlier method we relaxed (i.e., solved for) the unknowns in a certain fixed cyclic order σ. For hand computation, the early proponents of iteration—Gauss [1823] and Seidel [1874]—recommended that the unknowns be relaxed in a much less regular order. Gauss recommended that one always select a component i for which $|R_j|$ assumes its maximum value. Seidel observed that, by (21.73), $E(U)$ is decreased most when one relaxes a component i for which R_j^2/a_{jj} is a maximum, and recommended that we always select such an i.

Proponents of pencil computation like Southwell [1946] and Fox [1948] have continued to recommend similar, though less rigid, criteria for choosing i. They call the iterative solution of linear equations systems by the term *relaxation*; originally "relaxation" referred only to the process of changing one unknown, and was roughly synonymous with "displacement."

With either Gauss' or Seidel's rule, one must substitute the current solution $U^{(k-1)}$ into each of N equations before starting to compute $U^{(k)}$. On a digital computer such a substitution is likely to be very inefficient since the computation of R_i is likely to take a large part of the time required to go ahead and relax U_i. Suppose, for example, that the a_{ij} are stored on a magnetic drum or other intermediate storage device. To compute R_i, one must form or find $a_{i1}, \cdots, a_{iN}, b_i$, bring them into the arithmetic unit, and form $R_i = b_i - \sum_{j=1}^N a_{ij}U_j$. Having done this, it is a quick matter to compute R_i/a_{ii}, and make an appropriate change in U_i, which may already be in the fast store. Even if U is stored on a magnetic drum and if the a_{ij} are generated, by the time we have computed R_i, we have set all the "red-tape" parameters necessary to change U_i.

Consequently, with automatic computers, there seems to be little advantage in searching for large components $|R_i|$. As a result, the Gauss-Southwell order of relaxing unknowns has pretty much given way to cyclic orders of one kind or another.

Cyclic orders have the advantage, with respect to acceleration, that they represent a *linear* iteration when examined after each full cycle. Hence the general techniques of linear analysis (Sec. 21.3) are applicable, and we have applied them in Sec. 21.6. They can also be applied profitably in the search for acceleration procedures. The key point here is a knowledge of the asymptotic behavior of a linear process.

Gaussian or Seidelian relaxation is really a *piecewise linear* process, when rigidly applied. For the space is divided into N regions; in the ith region $|R_i|$ dominates the $|R_j|$. If U is in the ith region, one takes one step of the ith linear process to change U. Now a piecewise linear iteration is very complicated to analyze, and its asymptotic behavior can only be conjectured. Hence accelerations seem pretty difficult to design. It is not known whether Gaussian or Seidelian relaxations always become ultimately periodic, and hence linear. When they are periodic, it is easily shown that the period may be much greater than N.

The IBM computer type 650 has a command TLU (table-look-up) which permits one to search for the largest entry in a table on the drum fairly quickly. The command has been applied to code Gaussian relaxation. In spite of this, it appears to the authors that cyclic methods are more profitable with computers than methods involving a scanning process first.

SECTION 22. EXPLICIT AND IMPLICIT OVERRELAXATION METHODS

22.1. The Young-Frankel Theory of Successive Overrelaxation

The persons who carried out pencil-and-paper relaxation methods to solve elliptic difference equations learned that it pays to use *overrelaxation* (see Fox [1948]). As shown in Sec. 21.6, to solve a system $AU = B$ with a positive definite matrix A by overrelaxation is to compute $U^{(k)} = U^{(k-1)} + \alpha e_i$ by use of a factor α which is ω times larger (for some real $\omega > 1$) than the α for which $E(U^{(k-1)} + \alpha e_i)$ is minimized. Here e_i denotes a unit coordinate vector. And, similarly, for a general system $AU = B$, overrelaxation is the change of any component of U by ω times the amount necessary to satisfy the ith equation exactly ($\omega > 1$).

Now, as shown in Sec. 21.7, when pencil-and-paper methods are displaced by automatic digital computer programs, the original relaxation methods are less successful than the systematic relaxation of the components in a convenient cyclic order. It is clear from the discussion at the end of Sec. 21.4 that overrelaxation will not be profitable in solving the Dirichlet problem by the method of simultaneous displacements. The question remains whether overrelaxation is profitable with the method of successive displacements. This was the subject of Young's 1950 dissertation, published in [1954a]. Much of the same theory had been given by Frankel [1950] for the special case of Laplace's difference equation over a rectangle, with a special cyclic order of relaxation. We shall review Young's theory in this section. Young's theory has been expounded or enlarged by Friedman [1957], by Householder [1958], by DeVogelaere [unpublished], by Arms, Gates, and Zondek [1956], by Keller [1958], and by others. Our treatment is based on that of Friedman, and seems to be simpler than Young's original one. A similar treatment is given by Young [1958].

In brief, Young's answer is that overrelaxation does pay very well for a class of matrices with what he calls property (A), a property associated with many boundary-value problems for many elliptic difference operators. Analysts and programmers have more recently discovered that overrelaxation is also profitable for some matrices not having property (A); we shall reserve consideration of this for Sec. 22.2.

DEFINITION. For an integer $m \geq 2$, a square matrix A of order N is said to be *m-block tridiagonal* if, without reordering the rows or columns, it can be written in the partitioned form

$$\begin{bmatrix} D_1 & F_1 & 0 & \cdot & 0 & 0 & 0 \\ E_1 & D_2 & F_2 & \cdot & 0 & 0 & 0 \\ \multicolumn{7}{c}{\dotfill} \\ 0 & 0 & 0 & \cdot & E_{m-2} & D_{m-1} & F_{m-1} \\ 0 & 0 & 0 & \cdot & 0 & E_{m-1} & D_m \end{bmatrix}, \tag{22.1}$$

where the D_i are arbitrary square matrices. We shall often omit the m.

We mentioned such matrices at the beginning of Sec. 21. Every matrix is 2-block tridiagonal.

DEFINITION. If A is *m*-block tridiagonal and if, moreover, each D_i is a diagonal matrix, then A will be called *diagonally m-block tridiagonal*. Again we shall often omit the m.

DEFINITION. A square matrix A of order N is said to have *property* (A) if there exists a permutation matrix Π such that $\Pi A \Pi^T$ is diagonally block tridiagonal. When A has property (A), we call such a form (22.1) a *diagonally block-tridiagonal representation of A*. We shall usually condense this term for brevity to *tridiagonal representation of A*.

If A has property (A), there ordinarily exist many different matrices Π and many different tridiagonal representations of A. In particular, it is always possible to reduce m to 2 in (22.1) by the following trick: After achieving the form (22.1), permute the rows and columns of A by blocks once more, so that the rows and columns corresponding to $D_1, D_3, D_5, \cdots$ all precede the rows and columns corresponding to $D_2, D_4, D_6, \cdots$. Then A will have been represented in the special form

$$\Pi A \Pi^T = \begin{bmatrix} D_1' & F' \\ E' & D_2' \end{bmatrix}, \qquad D_i' \text{ diagonal}, \tag{22.2}$$

which can be used to characterize matrices A with property (A). However, the representation (22.1) with $m > 2$ is generally more useful.

DEFINITION. In a system of linear equations $AU = B$, the ith and jth unknown components U_i, U_j are said to be *coupled* if either $a_{ij} \neq 0$ or $a_{ji} \neq 0$.

As with the methods of simultaneous displacements and successive displacements, we assume once and for all that there is a fixed one-to-one correspondence between unknowns and equations, and that the numbering is such that the ith unknown is to be determined from the ith equation $(i = 1, \cdots, N)$. It should be noted that this correspondence is not affected by the transformation of A to $\Pi A \Pi^T$. Like the method of successive displacements, the method now to be discussed depends critically on the *order* σ in which the unknowns are determined. We deal here only with *cyclic orders*, in which the components are relaxed in the order $U_{\sigma(1)}, \cdots,$ $U_{\sigma(N)}$, and repeat, where $\sigma(j)$ is some permutation of the integers $1, 2, \cdots, N$.

Corresponding to the tridiagonal representation (22.1) of A, for $j = 1,$ $2, \cdots, m$, we let S_j denote the set of components U_i corresponding to the block D_j of (22.1).

DEFINITION. Let A have property (A). An order σ of solving the equations $AU = B$ is *consistent with the tridiagonal representation* (22.1) *of A* if, for $j = 2, 3, \cdots, m$, within each cycle of the iteration each component U_i of S_{j-1} is computed before any component of S_j with which U_i is coupled.

The most natural order σ consistent with (22.1) is to solve first for all the components of S_1, then for all those of S_2, etc. Since there is no coupling between distinct components of one S_j, it does not matter in what order one solves for them. Moreover, if a component U_i of S_{j-1} is not coupled with a component U_k of S_j, it is also irrelevant to the consistency of σ which of U_i or U_k is determined first.

DEFINITION. Let A have property (A). An order σ of solving the equations $AU = B$ is *consistent* (per se) if there is a tridiagonal representation (22.1) of A with which σ is consistent.

A motivating example of property (A) is provided by elliptic partial differential equations in any number of dimensions. In two dimensions, which is typical, we associate the component U_i with the point $(\mu h, \nu h)$ of a square network in the plane. Suppose we are dealing with Dirichlet's problem for an elliptic partial differential equation in which the u_{xy} term is missing (an essential restriction). Then, as in Sec. 20, it is possible to set up related difference equations of five-point type, in which coupled with

$U(x, y)$ are the four unknown values $U(x + h, y)$, $U(x, y + h)$, $U(x - h, y)$, and $U(x, y - h)$. Such difference equations turn out to have a matrix with property (A). We shall show this in particular for the rectangular net region with interior nodes $(\mu h, \nu h)$, $0 \le \mu h \le rh, h \le \nu h \le sh$. The main thing is to define the sets S_j, since they induce a tridiagonal representation (22.1). The sets S_j may be defined in many ways. The essential feature is that a node of S_j be coupled by a link (defined in Sec. 20) of the net only with nodes of S_{j+1} or S_{j-1}.

The smallest value of m is 2, and we may achieve this by letting S_1 be the set of points with odd parity (i.e., $\mu + \nu$ is odd), and S_2 be the set of points with even parity ($\mu + \nu$ is even). In this case the representation (22.1) takes the form (22.2). One order consistent with this partition is to solve for all components in S_1, and then for all those in S_2. But it would also be a consistent order to solve for the components in S_2 with $\nu = 2$ at any time in the cycle after one has solved for those in S_1 with $\nu = 1, 2$, and 3. There are many other orders consistent with the partition S_1, S_2.

A second partition inducing a tridiagonal representation of A is to put into S_j the points with $\mu + \nu = j$ ($j = 1, 2, \cdots, r + s$). Thus each S_j consists of a diagonal row of points of the rectangular lattice. One order that is always consistent with this partition, of course, is to solve for all points of S_1, then all of S_2, etc., and last, for all of S_{r+s}. But a second order consistent with this partition is to solve for the points across one row after the next, i.e., in the order $(\mu, \nu) = (0, 1), (1, 1), \cdots, (r, 1), (0, 2), (1, 2), \cdots, (r, 2)$, etc.

There are many other partitions of the lattice which satisfy the requirements. Note, however, that it would not be suitable to let S_j be the set of nodes in the jth line of the net, i.e., those with $\nu = j$. For then, nodes of S_j would be coupled among themselves, making D_j a nondiagonal matrix (tridiagonal, in fact). This would keep (22.1) from being a diagonally block tridiagonal representation of A.

We now state a criterion for testing an order σ for consistency (per se) of five-point formulas. Of each pair P, Q of adjacent nodes of the net, one, say P, precedes the other, say Q, in the order σ. If so, draw an arrow from P to Q. Do this for every pair of adjacent nodes. Then, according to David Young (private communication), *the order σ is consistent if and only if each elementary square mesh of the net is bounded by four arrows with a zero circulation*, i.e., if a directed path enclosing the square travels *with* the arrows on two sides of the square and *against* the arrows on two sides. For example, mesh (a) in Fig. 22.1 has a zero circulation, while mesh (b) does not. We shall not prove Young's statement.

Young's theory deals with successive overrelaxation in a given consistent order σ of the components of a system of equations $AU = B$, where the matrix A has property (A). To a great extent all consistent orderings will turn out to be equivalent. We assume that A has property (A), and, without loss of generality, we assume that A is already in some tridiagonal form (22.1) with which σ is consistent. Much of the theory can be developed without assuming the symmetry of A. As with any relaxation

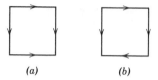

(a)   (b)

Fig. 22.1. Testing the consistency of an ordering of a square net.

process, we assume that no $a_{ii} = 0$. With A in the form of (22.1), let

$$E = \begin{bmatrix} 0 \\ E_1 & 0 \\ & E_2 & \cdot \\ & & \cdot & \cdot \\ & & & \cdot & \cdot \\ & & & & E_{m-1} & 0 \end{bmatrix} ; \quad F = \begin{bmatrix} 0 & F_1 \\ & 0 & F_2 \\ & & \cdot & \cdot \\ & & & \cdot & \cdot \\ & & & & \cdot & F_{m-1} \\ & & & & & 0 \end{bmatrix} ;$$

$$D = \begin{bmatrix} D_1 \\ & \cdot \\ & & \cdot \\ & & & \cdot \\ & & & & D_m \end{bmatrix}.$$

A vector U_0 is selected arbitrarily. At the kth stage of the iteration, one has already determined the vector U_{k-1}, and we now describe how U_k is computed. In the kth sweep ($k = 1, 2, \cdots$), for each fixed $i = 1, 2, \cdots, N$, one first determines a temporary value $U_{k-1/2,\sigma(i)}$ of the $\sigma(i)$th component by an exact displacement ($\omega = 1$), and then immediately computes the final value $U_{k,\sigma(i)}$ by the overrelaxation formula

$$U_{k,\sigma(i)} = U_{k-1,\sigma(i)} + \omega(U_{k-1/2,\sigma(i)} - U_{k-1,\sigma(i)}).$$

It is convenient to give the process a matrix-vector representation. If the reader has doubts about the validity of the matrix formulas below, he should transform them into a component form analogous to (21.62), or see (25.9) for another representation of the method in a special case. One first needs a representation of the vector result $U_{k-1/2}$ of the temporary exact displacement ($\omega = 1$) at each step of the kth sweep. For $i = 1, 2,$ $\cdots$, N, in determining the $\sigma(i)$th component of $U_{k-1/2}$, one uses the newly determined components $U_{k,\sigma(1)}, \cdots, U_{k,\sigma(i-1)}$ of U_k. By the definition of a consistent order, at the time one determines $U_{k-1/2,\sigma(i)}$, one will already have determined all the new components $U_{k,j}$ with $j < \sigma(i)$ with which the component $U_{\sigma(i)}$ is coupled. Consequently, for any of the many different orders σ which are consistent with the tridiagonal representation (22.1) of A, the vector $U_{k-1/2}$ is determined by the equation

$$EU_k + DU_{k-1/2} + FU_{k-1} = B. \tag{22.3}$$

Now each component of U_k is determined in its turn by a displacement of ω times the change from U_{k-1} to $U_{k-1/2}$; i.e.,

$$U_k = U_{k-1} + \omega(U_{k-1/2} - U_{k-1}) = \omega U_{k-1/2} + (1 - \omega)U_{k-1}. \tag{22.4}$$

Eliminating $U_{k-1/2}$ between (22.3) and (22.4), we find that U_k is determined by the equation

$$(E + \omega^{-1}D)U_k + [F + (1 - \omega^{-1})D]U_{k-1} = B, \tag{22.5}$$

provided $\omega \neq 0$, which will be assumed from now on. Comparing (22.5) with (21.63), we see that overrelaxation has the effect of varying the fraction of D which is added to E in multiplying the new components U_k.

Comparing (22.5) with (21.12), we see that $H = H(\omega)$ is given by

$$H(\omega) = -(\omega^{-1}D + E)^{-1}[F + (1 - \omega^{-1})D], \tag{22.6}$$

for all the orders σ consistent with the fixed tridiagonal representation (22.1). When one recalls from the discussion after (21.23) that the convergence of the iteration (22.5) is controlled by the maximum modulus of the eigenvalues of $H(\omega)$, it is natural to ask for what value of the overrelaxation parameter ω the maximum modulus is minimized. This is the technical problem which can be solved beautifully under the hypotheses on A.

We let $\eta_i = \eta_i^{(\omega)}$ denote the eigenvalues of $H(\omega)$. These satisfy the equation det $[H(\omega) - \eta I] = 0$, or, by (22.6),

$$\det [(\omega^{-1}D + E)\eta + (1 - \omega^{-1})D + F] = 0. \tag{22.7}$$

Note that (22.7) reduces to (21.65) for $\omega = 1$; i.e., the eigenvalues of the method of successive displacements equal $\eta_i^{(1)}$, the values of $\eta_i^{(\omega)}$ for $\omega = 1$.

It turns out that the theory of successive overrelaxation is conveniently developed by comparison with the method of simultaneous displacements of Sec. 21.4. We therefore let λ_i denote the eigenvalues of the latter method. As shown in (21.29), these are the roots of the determinantal equation

$$P(\lambda) = \det (E + D\lambda + F) = 0. \tag{22.8}$$

Note that the roots λ_i of (22.8) are independent of the particular tri-diagonal form (22.1) in which we write A, since the transformation $\Pi A \Pi^T$ preserves D as the diagonal of the matrix A. Moreover, $P(\lambda)$ is independent of the order σ. We may write $P(\lambda)$ in the form

$$P(\lambda) = \det \begin{bmatrix} \lambda D_1 & F_1 & & & \\ E_1 & \lambda D_2 & \cdot & & \\ & \cdot & \cdot & \cdot & \\ & & \cdot & \lambda D_{m-1} & F_{m-1} \\ & & & E_{m-1} & \lambda D_m \end{bmatrix}. \tag{22.9}$$

The value of the determinant (22.9) is unchanged if we both premultiply and postmultiply the matrix in (22.9) by the matrix

$$\begin{bmatrix} -I_1 & & & & \\ & I_2 & & & \\ & & -I_3 & & \\ & & & \cdot & \\ & & & & \cdot \\ & & & & & (-1)^m I_m \end{bmatrix},$$

whose determinant is ± 1. Hence

$$P(\lambda) = \det \begin{bmatrix} \lambda D_1 & -F_1 & & & \\ -E_1 & \lambda D_2 & \cdot & & \\ & \cdot & \cdot & \cdot & \\ & & \cdot & \cdot & -F_{m-1} \\ & & & -E_{m-1} & \lambda D_m \end{bmatrix}.$$

Then, by changing the sign of λ wherever found in the last determinant, we see that

$$P(-\lambda) = (-1)^N P(\lambda).$$

This states that P is an odd polynomial if N is odd, and that P is an even polynomial if N is even. But then, for some integer r, $P(\lambda)$ must have the form

$$P(\lambda) = \begin{cases} \lambda^{2r} p_{N/2-r}(\lambda^2), & \text{if } N \text{ is even,} \\ \lambda^{2r+1} p_{(N-1)/2-r}(\lambda^2), & \text{if } N \text{ is odd.} \end{cases} \tag{22.10}$$

In (22.10) $p_\alpha(\rho)$ denotes a polynomial of degree α in ρ, with $p_\alpha(0) \neq 0$.

Hence $p_\alpha(\rho)$ has exactly α nonzero roots ρ_i. This conclusion would be valid even if each D_i were a full matrix, except that, if the D_i were not diagonal, the roots of $P(\lambda) = 0$ in (22.8) would no longer be the eigenvalues of the method of simultaneous displacements. Thus the whole present development depends really on the blockwise tridiagonal nature of A in (22.1), and not on property (A). This fact will be used in our discussion of overrelaxation by lines in Sec. 22.3.

As a consequence of (22.10), the nonzero roots λ_i of (22.8) occur in pairs $\pm\lambda_i$, with one pair corresponding to each root $\rho_i = \lambda_i^2$ of $p_\alpha(\rho)$. In addition, the polynomial $P(\lambda)$ of (22.8) has 0 as a root of multiplicity $2r$ (if N is even) or $2r + 1$ (if N is odd).

Using (22.1), we can write (22.7) in the form

$$
\det
\begin{bmatrix}
\zeta D_1 & F_1 & & & \\
\eta E_1 & \zeta D_2 & & & \\
& & \ddots & & \\
& & & \ddots & \\
& & & \zeta D_{m-1} & F_{m-1} \\
& & & \eta E_{m-1} & \zeta D_m
\end{bmatrix}
= Q(\eta) = 0, \quad (22.11)
$$

where $\zeta = \omega^{-1}(\eta + \omega - 1)$. Following the idea of Friedman [1957], let us transform the matrix in (22.11) by formally multiplying it on the right by the partitioned matrix

$$
M_R =
\begin{bmatrix}
\eta^{-1/2}I_1 & & & & \\
& I_2 & & & \\
& & \eta^{1/2}I_3 & & \\
& & & \ddots & \\
& & & & \eta^{(m-2)/2}I_m
\end{bmatrix},
$$

where, for each i, I_i is the identity matrix of the same order as D_i. We next multiply the resulting matrix on the left by

$$
M_L =
\begin{bmatrix}
I_1 & & & & \\
& \eta^{-1/2}I_2 & & & \\
& & \eta^{-1}I_3 & & \\
& & & \ddots & \\
& & & & \eta^{-(m-1)/2}I_m
\end{bmatrix}.
$$

Now $(\det M_R)(\det M_L) = \det (M_R M_L) = \det (\eta^{-1/2}I) = \eta^{-N/2}$. Hence

$$Q(\eta) = \eta^{N/2} \det \begin{bmatrix} \eta^{-1/2}\zeta D_1 & F_1 & & & & \\ E_1 & \eta^{-1/2}\zeta D_2 & & & & \\ & & \cdot & & & \\ & & & \cdot & & \\ & & & & \cdot & \\ & & & & \eta^{-1/2}\zeta D_{m-1} & F_{m-1} \\ & & & & E_{m-1} & \eta^{-1/2}\zeta D_m \end{bmatrix} \tag{22.12}$$

$$= \eta^{N/2} P(\eta^{-1/2}\zeta)$$
$$= \eta^{N/2} P(\omega^{-1}\eta^{-1/2}(\eta + \omega - 1)).$$

We want to use (22.12) to establish the following relation between the roots $\eta_i^{(\omega)}$ of (22.7) and the roots λ_i of (22.8):

THEOREM 22.1. *Assume $\omega \neq 0$. If λ is any root of (22.8), and if η satisfies the relation*

$$\frac{(\eta + \omega - 1)^2}{\eta} = \omega^2 \lambda^2, \tag{22.13}$$

then η is a root of (22.7). Conversely, if η is a root of (22.7), and if λ satisfies (22.13), then λ is a root of (22.8).

Proof. The roots λ of (22.8) are the zeros of the polynomial $P(\lambda)$ of (22.10). The roots η of (22.7) are the zeros of the polynomial $Q(\eta)$ of (22.12). Directly from (22.12) we see that $Q(\eta) = 0$ if and only if $\omega^{-1}\eta^{-1/2}$ $(\eta + \omega - 1)$ is equal to a λ which makes $P(\lambda) = 0$, i.e., whenever $\omega^{-2}\eta^{-1}$ $(\eta + \omega - 1)^2 = \lambda^2$, or whenever (22.13) holds. This completes the proof.

When $\omega = 1$, the polynomial $Q(\eta)$ takes the form $\eta^{N/2}P(\eta^{1/2})$. Hence, by (22.10),

$$Q(\eta) = \begin{cases} \eta^{N/2+r} \, p_{N/2-r}(\eta), & \text{if } N \text{ is even;} \\ \eta^{(N+1)/2+r} \, p_{(N-1)/2-r}(\eta), & \text{if } N \text{ is odd.} \end{cases}$$

Hence there are $N/2 + r$ [or $(N + 1)/2 + r$] roots $\eta_i^{(1)} = 0$, and the remaining $N/2 - r$ [or $(N - 1)/2 - r$] roots $\eta_i^{(1)}$ are the zeros ρ_i of the corresponding polynomial $p_\alpha(\rho)$. Each such nonzero value of $\eta_i^{(1)}$ is the square of the corresponding root pair $\pm\lambda_i$, in accord with (22.13) for $\omega = 1$:

$$\eta_i^{(1)} = \lambda_i^2. \tag{22.14}$$

In other words, for $\omega = 1$ (method of successive displacements), corresponding to each root $\lambda_i = 0$ of (22.8) is a root $\eta_i^{(1)} = 0$. And corresponding to each nonzero root pair $\pm\lambda_i$ is the root pair $\eta_i^{(1)} = 0, \lambda_i^2$.

When $\omega \neq 1$, one sees from (22.12) that $\eta = 0$ cannot be a zero of $Q(\eta)$. Corresponding to each root $\lambda_i = 0$ of (22.8) is a root $\eta_i^{(\omega)} = -(\omega - 1)$. And corresponding to each nonzero root pair $\pm\lambda_i$ is a pair of nonzero roots obtained from solving the quadratic equation (22.13) with $\lambda^2 = \lambda_i^2$.

We have thus established the fundamental relation between the roots λ_i of the method of simultaneous displacements and the roots $\eta_i^{(\omega)}$ of the method of successive overrelaxation, whenever A has property (A) and whenever the ordering σ is a consistent one. Consistency was used in getting (22.7) and hence (22.11). Property (A) was used to be sure that A can be written in the form (22.1), and that the roots of $P(\lambda)$ in (22.9) are those of the method of simultaneous displacements.

Now property (A) is necessary for (22.13) and for the above theory, as may be shown by the example

$$ A = \begin{bmatrix} 1 & a & a \\ a & 1 & a \\ a & a & 1 \end{bmatrix}. \tag{21.30} $$

For this A, which does not have property (A), the $P(\lambda)$ of (22.8) is $\lambda^3 - 3a^2\lambda + 2a^3$, with roots a, a and $-2a$. But for $\omega = 1$, the polynomial $Q(\eta)$ corresponding to (22.11) is $\eta^3 + (a^3 - 3a^2)\eta^2 + a^3\eta$, whose roots (one of which is 0) are not the squares of the λ_i. Moreover, the nonzero roots λ do not occur in pairs $\pm\lambda_i$.

For the family of matrices (21.30), as a varies, the reader may wish to investigate the relation of $\max_i |\eta_i^{(\omega)}|$ to $\max_i \lambda_i^2$.

Theorem 22.1 shows that the *eigenvalues of $H(\omega)$ are independent of the order σ, so long as σ is consistent with the tridiagonal representation* (22.1). For the eigenvalues of $H(\omega)$ are always expressed in terms of the roots λ of (22.9), and these are independent of σ. But—even more—although $H(\omega)$ changes when one changes the tridiagonal representation of A, *the eigenvalues $\eta_i^{(\omega)}$ of $H(\omega)$ remain the same for any consistent order σ.* This follows because Theorem 22.1 relates the $\eta_i^{(\omega)}$ to the λ_i, and the λ_i as roots of (22.8) are unchanged by any transformation of A to $\Pi A \Pi^T$.

One sees that the matrix $H(\omega)$ is the same matrix for all orders σ consistent with one fixed tridiagonal representation (22.1) of A. However, when the tridiagonal representation is changed, $H(\omega)$ ordinarily changes and may even change its canonical form. This may have an important effect on the nature of $[H(\omega)]^k E_0$, even though all matrices $H(\omega)$ have the same eigenvalues.

The main question in Young's theory is how to choose ω so that convergence will be optimal. In view of the general theory of linear iterations given in Sec. 21, the problem is to choose ω so that

$$\max_i |\eta_i^{(\omega)}| \text{ is a minimum.}$$

The optimal choice of ω can be studied from (22.13), which represents a mapping of the roots λ_i onto roots $\eta_i^{(\omega)}$. In fact, (22.13) shows that the $\eta_i^{(\omega)}$ are the roots η of the equation

$$\eta + \omega - 1 = \omega \lambda_i \eta^{1/2}, \tag{22.15}$$

i.e., of

$$\eta - \omega \lambda_i \eta^{1/2} + \omega - 1 = 0. \tag{22.16}$$

There exists a theory for the case when some λ_i are complex, but it is complicated, and we therefore now *assume that all λ_i are real.* For example, when A is symmetric, with all $a_{ii} > 0$, as often occurs with difference equations, the λ_i are known to be real. For then (22.8) is equivalent to the condition

$$\det\left[-D^{-1/2}(E + F)D^{-1/2} - \lambda I\right] = 0,$$

so that the λ_i are the eigenvalues of the symmetric matrix $-D^{-1/2}(E + F)$ $D^{-1/2}$.

When the λ_i are real, we get two values of $\eta^{1/2}$ by solving the quadratic equation (22.16):

$$\eta^{1/2} = \frac{\omega \lambda_i \pm \sqrt{\omega^2 \lambda_i^2 - 4(\omega - 1)}}{2}. \tag{22.17}$$

[If the negative square root is taken in (22.15), it will lead to two other values of $\eta^{1/2}$, but the same values of η are obtained on squaring (22.17)].

If $\lambda_i = 0$, we have seen that the corresponding root η is $-(\omega - 1)$. Recall that the other zeros of $P(\lambda)$ occur in pairs $\pm \lambda_i$, and agree to take $\lambda_i > 0$. Let us suppose at first that $0 < \lambda_i < 1$, for all i. Now fix attention on one value of λ_i. Then, for real roots $\eta^{1/2}$, the larger in modulus of the $\eta^{1/2}$, by (22.17), is

$$\eta^{1/2} = \tfrac{1}{2}\omega \lambda_i + \tfrac{1}{2}\sqrt{\omega^2 \lambda_i^2 - 4(\omega - 1)}. \tag{22.18}$$

When $\omega = 1$, we have $\eta^{1/2} = \lambda_i$. By differentiating (22.16), we find that

$$\frac{d\eta^{1/2}}{d\omega} = -\frac{1}{2} \frac{1 - \lambda_i \eta^{1/2}}{\eta^{1/2} - \omega \lambda_i / 2}. \tag{22.19}$$

As ω increases from 1, we see from (22.19) that $\eta^{1/2}$ decreases as long as $\eta^{1/2} > \omega \lambda_i / 2$, i.e., by (22.18), as long as $\omega^2 \lambda_i^2 - 4(\omega - 1) > 0$. But, since $\lambda_i < 1$, there will come a value of ω, say ω_i, such that

$$\omega_i^2 \lambda_i^2 - 4(\omega_i - 1) = 0, \qquad \omega_i < 2. \tag{22.20}$$

For $\omega = \omega_i$, equation (22.16) has a double root $\eta^{1/2} = (\omega_i - 1)^{1/2}$. For $\omega > \omega_i$, the product of the two roots $\eta^{1/2}$ is $\omega - 1 > \omega_i - 1$, and hence the modulus of at least one of the two roots $\eta^{1/2}$ is greater than $(\omega_i - 1)^{1/2}$.

In summary, if $0 < \lambda_i < 1$, the minimum modulus (for $1 \leq \omega$) attained by the larger root $\eta^{1/2}$ of (22.16) is found when (22.20) holds, i.e., when

$$\omega = \omega_i = \frac{2(1 - \sqrt{1 - \lambda_i^2})}{\lambda_i^2} = \frac{2}{1 + \sqrt{1 - \lambda_i^2}}. \tag{22.21}$$

The corresponding minimum value of $\eta^{1/2}$ is $(\omega_i - 1)^{1/2}$, and the minimum value of η is

$$\omega_i - 1 = \frac{1 - \sqrt{1 - \lambda_i^2}}{1 + \sqrt{1 - \lambda_i^2}}. \tag{22.22}$$

By a detailed but elementary argument, it can also be shown from (22.19) that the value in (22.22) is the least that can be obtained for all ω $(-\infty < \omega < \infty)$. Hence, with respect to λ_i, the value in (22.21) is the best to take for ω.

Now consider the whole set of eigenvalues λ_i. As stated above, these occur in pairs $\pm \lambda_i$, and we need only consider the positive member of each pair. The largest root η, equal to λ_1^2 when $\omega = 1$, is the critical one. As ω grows from 1, it decreases as long as $\omega < \omega_1$. The best overrelaxation factor then turns out to be

$$\omega = \omega_1 = \omega_{\text{opt}} = \frac{2}{1 + \sqrt{1 - \lambda_1^2}}, \qquad \text{where } \lambda_1^2 = \max_i \lambda_i^2. \tag{22.23}$$

For this value of ω is larger than $\omega_2, \omega_3, \cdots$, so that the roots η_i corresponding to all other root pairs $\pm \lambda_i$ are complex, with modulus $\omega_{\text{opt}} - 1$.

We have thus completely proved a basic result:

THEOREM 22.2. *Assume all λ_i are real, with $|\lambda_i| < 1$. The unique value of ω for which* $\max_i |\eta_i^{(\omega)}|$ *is minimized is the value given by (22.23). And the corresponding modulus of* $\max_i |\eta_i^{(\omega)}|$ *is*

$$\omega_{\text{opt}} - 1 = \frac{1 - \sqrt{1 - \lambda_1^2}}{1 + \sqrt{1 - \lambda_1^2}}. \tag{22.24}$$

It clarifies the situation to examine the roots $\eta_i^{(\omega)}$ a little more closely, for $1 \leq \omega \leq 2$. We recall that the roots $\eta_i^{(1)}$ occur in pairs 0, λ_i^2 corresponding to each $\lambda_i \neq 0$, plus a number of additional 0 roots $\eta_i^{(1)}$. As ω grows from 1 to 2, let us examine the circle $C_\omega = \{\eta : |\eta| = \omega - 1\}$. As the radius increases from 0, the root pairs start toward each other. The ith pair of roots meet at the point $\omega_i - 1$ on C_{ω_i}, and then for $\omega > \omega_i$ go into two complex roots on C_ω (see Fig. 22.2). The optimum value of ω is that for which the pair of roots η_1', η_1 (originally 0, λ_1^2) coalesce at $\omega_{opt} - 1$ (see Fig. 22.3).

Observe that when $\omega = \omega_{opt}$, all eigenvalues of $H(\omega_{opt})$ have modulus $\omega_{opt} - 1$.

On the other hand, if some $\lambda_i > 1$, successive overrelaxation will be

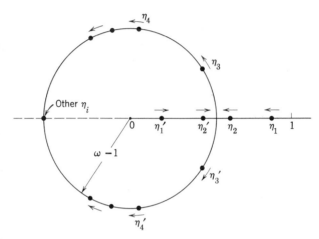

Fig. 22.2. Successive overrelaxation: the motion of the η_i as ω increases from 1 to ω_{opt}.

divergent for all real ω. For (22.17) tells us that for all real ω and for one of the two roots $\eta^{1/2}$,

$$|\eta^{1/2}| > \tfrac{1}{2}|\omega| + \tfrac{1}{2}\sqrt{\omega^2 - 4\omega + 4 + \omega^2(\lambda_i^2 - 1)} > \tfrac{1}{2}|\omega| + \tfrac{1}{2}|\omega - 2| \geq 1.$$
$$(22.25)$$

Hence $\eta > 1$, and the process diverges. Thus successive overrelaxation in a consistent ordering for matrices with property (A) and real λ_i will never be a convergent iteration for real ω unless the process of simultaneous displacements itself converges. The power of Young's method lies in its acceleration of the rate of convergence of an already convergent process, not in any ability to create a convergent algorithm when the method of simultaneous displacements diverges.

We saw in Sec. 21 that the method of successive displacements ($\omega = 1$) always converges for a definite matrix A. Hence definiteness and property (A) are sufficient to imply all of Young's theory, including the convergence of the method of simultaneous displacements.

To see the order of gain possible with successive overrelaxation, consider the Dirichlet difference problem of Sec. 21.5. As we saw before, the roots of the method of simultaneous displacements are

$$\lambda_{p,q} = 1 - \sin^2 \frac{ph}{2} - \sin^2 \frac{qh}{2}, \qquad (22.26)$$

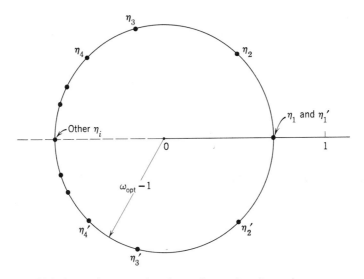

FIG. 22.3. Successive overrelaxation: the η_i for the optimum overrelaxation factor $\omega = \omega_{\text{opt}}$.

of which those of maximum modulus (say, $\pm\lambda_1$) are given by

$$\lambda_1 = \cos h \sim 1 - \frac{h^2}{2}, \qquad \text{as } h \to 0. \qquad (22.27)$$

The corresponding rate of convergence is approximately $h^2/2$.

For the method of successive displacements, there is the dominant eigenvalue $\eta_1^{(1)} = \lambda_1^2$. Hence

$$\eta_1^{(1)} = \cos^2 h \sim 1 - h^2, \qquad \text{as } h \to 0, \qquad (22.28)$$

with a rate of convergence approximately h^2, twice that of the previous method. Thus, asymptotically, the use of successive displacements saves half the computing time. This is sometimes explained heuristically by the fact that in the method of successive displacements one uses new values of the U_i half the time, on the average.

For optimum successive overrelaxation, we get a dominant root from (22.24) as follows:

$$\eta_{\text{opt}} = (1 - \sqrt{1 - \lambda_1^2})(1 + \sqrt{1 - \lambda_1^2})^{-1}$$
$$= (1 - \sin h)(1 + \sin h)^{-1} \tag{22.29}$$

or

$$\eta_{\text{opt}} \sim 1 - 2h, \quad \text{as } h \to 0. \tag{22.30}$$

The rate of convergence is now asymptotically $2h$, larger than that for the method of successive displacements by the factor $2h^{-1}$. This means that asymptotically the computing time will be reduced by the factor $2h^{-1}$, a substantial amount.

For Richardson's method (see Sec. 21.5), the best average rate of convergence which can be attained is approximately h. From (22.30) we see that, even for Čebyšev polynomials of very high degree K, the average rate of convergence h for Richardson's method is only half the rate of convergence of the method of optimum successive overrelaxation. And, as we noted in Sec. 21.5, it takes a degree K as high as n to attain this asymptotic rate reasonably closely.

A moderate problem for current microsecond computers might correspond to $n = 45$, with 1936 interior nodes to be relaxed. To see what convergence factors are actually involved for $n = 45$, note from (22.27) that, since $h = \pi/45$, $\lambda_1 = \cos(\pi/45) = 0.99756$, so that $\eta_1^{(1)} = \lambda_1^2 \doteq 0.99513$. Hence

$$\omega_{\text{opt}} = 2(1 + \sqrt{1 - \lambda_1^2})^{-1} \doteq 2(1 + \sqrt{0.00487})^{-1} \doteq 1.870.$$

Hence the convergence factor for optimum overrelaxation is $\omega_{\text{opt}} - 1 \doteq 0.870$.

The optimal overrelaxation method is approximately $90/\pi \doteq 30$ times faster than the Liebmann process ($\omega = 1$). On SWAC, for example, such a Dirichlet problem for Laplace's equation would require about five hours with $\omega = 1$, but only about ten minutes with a nearly optimal choice of ω. We must add to this the time required to locate such a value of ω (perhaps another ten minutes). A typical nearly optimal value of ω would be 1.9, corresponding to a convergence factor of 0.9.

For the Richardson method, as we saw in Sec. 21.5, the best possible factor is 0.93254 (whose square is 0.870, checking our computation). However, for $K = 20$, we achieve only the factor 0.957.

To summarize, in principle, for $n = 45$ we can attain convergence factors of 0.870 by successive overrelaxation and 0.932 by Richardson's method, but in practice the respective factors are apt to be something like 0.90 and 0.96, showing a still greater advantage for successive overrelaxation. Such an advantage is to be expected, of course, because the method is designed to take advantage of property (A), whereas Richardson's method makes no use of that property.

In the practical use of successive overrelaxation, finding the optimal ω is perhaps the most important problem. This will be discussed further in Sec. 22.2 and in Sec. 25.5. Assume that one deals with a symmetric matrix A with property (A). One important fact to notice is that it is far better to overestimate ω_{opt} a little than to underestimate it by the same

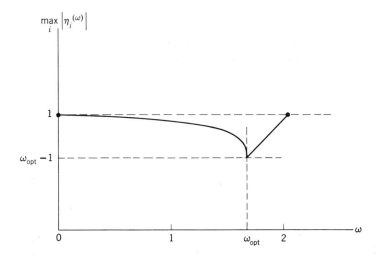

FIG. 22.4. The spectral radius of the successive overrelaxation method for various values of ω.

amount. For it can be shown from (22.16) and (22.19) that the graph of $\eta(\omega) = \max_i |\eta_i^{(\omega)}|$ against ω has the general appearance of Fig. 22.4. Note that $\eta(\omega)$ has an infinite slope for $\omega = \omega_{opt} - 0$, but slope 1 for $\omega \geq \omega_{opt} + 0$.

In theory one can estimate $\eta_1^{(1)} = \lambda_1^2$ by solving the problem in part with $\omega = 1$, and then estimate ω_{opt} from (22.23). For example, one can run a while with $\omega = 1$, and keep track of the size of the residual $R_k = B - AU_k$. Since $\eta_1^{(1)} = \lambda_1^2 < 1$ is the only dominant eigenvalue of $H(1)$, it follows from (21.23) that $R_k \to 0$, and that $R_k \sim \binom{k}{m} \lambda_1^{2k} R_0$, where m is the size of the largest Jordan block associated with λ_1. Hence one can estimate λ_1^2 from the relation

$$\frac{\|R_k\|}{\|R_{k-1}\|} \to \lambda_1^2, \quad \text{as} \quad k \to \infty. \tag{22.31}$$

Any norm would do, of course; one of the authors has used $\|R_k\|_1 = \sum_{i=1}^{N} |R_{k,i}|$, since it is easily computed without the loss of significance possible in computing $\|R_k\|_2 = (\sum_{i=1}^{N} R_{k,i}^2)^{1/2}$.

It is curious that, although iteration with $\omega = 1$ will reveal ω_{opt} eventually by (22.31), iteration with ω slightly larger than ω_{opt} will not. For recall from Fig. 22.3 that when ω is equal to or greater than its optimal value ω_{opt} all the N eigenvalues $\eta_i^{(\omega)}$ are of equal modulus. Now by (21.26) the residual R_k is given by

$$R_k = [AH(\omega)A^{-1}]^k R_0.$$

Recall that $AH(\omega)A^{-1}$ has the same Jordan canonical form as $H(\omega)$. But, assuming for simplicity that all eigenvalues $\eta_i^{(\omega)}$ of $H(\omega)$ correspond to linear elementary divisors, we have

$$R_k = \sum_{i=1}^{N} (\eta_i^{(\omega)})^k X_i, \tag{22.32}$$

where X_i is the eigenvector of $AH(\omega)A^{-1}$ belonging to $\eta_i^{(\omega)}$.

Since the $\eta_i^{(\omega)}$ are complex numbers of equal modulus (for $\omega \geq \omega_{opt}$), the vector R_k of (22.32) will vary almost randomly as $k \to \infty$, except for a drift toward 0 caused by the common value of the $|\eta_i^{(\omega)}| < 1$. Such a process as (22.32) is sometimes used to generate *pseudorandom vectors*, because of the unpredictable character of the sum of a large number N of almost independent directions. In practice $\|R_k\|$ will do such erratic things as increase for a dozen successive values of k, and then drop enormously for one or two values of k.

The preceding discussion of the determination of ω_{opt} has been phrased in terms of R_k. Although the use of R_k is possible in principle, the nature of successive overrelaxation is such that one does not have the vector R_k readily at hand. For the computation of the ith component of $R_k = B - AU_k$ would require the simultaneous use of $U_{k,i}$ and all the components $U_{k,j}$ of U_k which are coupled with $U_{k,i}$, whereas at the time when $U_{k,i}$ is computed one has in the memory some of the "new" components $U_{k,j}$ and some of the "old" components $U_{k-1,j}$. It would therefore be awkward to compute R_k.

Fortunately one can equally well use the vector $Y_{k-1} = U_k - U_{k-1}$ for the determination of ω_{opt}. As formula (22.4) shows, one has the ith component of Y_{k-1} in the memory at the time of computing $U_{k,i}$. It is therefore easy to compute $\| Y_{k-1}\|$. By (21.12) we see that

$$Y_k = [H(\omega)]^k Y_0,$$

and this relation permits one to determine ω_{opt} by the preceding method.

It is theoretically possible to estimate ω_{opt} by iteration with a value of ω

slightly smaller than ω_{opt}. One would determine the dominant eigenvalue $\eta_1^{(\omega)}$ from the iteration, get λ_1^2 from (22.17), and finally get ω_{opt} from (22.23). Although this would be more complicated, it would have the advantage that the iteration with ω near ω_{opt} contributes more to solving the problem than that with $\omega = 1$. How best to determine ω_{opt} is an unsolved problem.

Varga [1959] has extended property (A) in such a way that there can be three or even p different kinds of sets like S_1 and S_2 in the 2-block tridiagonal representation (22.2) of a matrix A. He permits A to take the form

$$A = \begin{bmatrix} D_1 & E_1 & 0 & \cdots & 0 \\ 0 & D_2 & E_2 & \cdots & 0 \\ \cdot & \cdot & \cdot & \cdots & \cdot \\ 0 & 0 & 0 & \cdots & E_{p-1} \\ E_p & 0 & 0 & \cdots & D_p \end{bmatrix},$$

which he calls p-cyclic. He gets an analog of the optimum-ω theory of this section, wherein the exponent $\frac{1}{2}$ in (22.15) is replaced by $1 - 1/p$. There is an application (with $p = 3$) to a regular net in the plane with hexagonal meshes.

Young and Frankel formulated their theories for boundary-value problems where u is prescribed on the boundary. Since many practical boundary-value problems include the specification of u_n on the boundary, or of a linear combination of u and u_n, it would be important to know whether Young's theory can be extended this far. It seems quite likely that it can in part, and a study by Brunings [1957] is a first attempt.

Another question is to consider what happens in Young's theory when one relaxes the equations in an inconsistent order. In his thesis, Young conjectures that no inconsistent order for Laplace's equation has a rate of convergence as great as that common to all consistent orders. Varga [1959a] proves this conjecture. Powers [1955] investigated various orderings for solving the Dirichlet problem over a rectangular network of approximately 100 points. In an experimental approach with $\omega = 1$, she considered a number of orders, both consistent and inconsistent, and counted the number of cycles necessary to reduce the initial error by a factor of the order of 10^{-4}. This measure of convergence rate was not very sensitive, and the results were generally not conclusive. They did show one thing, however: that, although the asymptotic rate of convergence is the same for all consistent orders, the actual reduction of error for $\omega = 1$ after approximately $N/4$ iterations varies greatly among different consistent orders.

The reason for the latter phenomenon may be related to the fact that, although the eigenvalues of $H = H(1)$ are the same for all consistent orders, the matrices H are not all similar. For one consistent order considered above (first all points of odd parity, then all points of even parity), the eigenvalue 0 seems to be associated only with linear elementary divisors (we have not seen a proof), although its multiplicity is approximately $N/2$. However, if one orders the points of a net by rows (like reading a page of English), the eigenvalue 0 has nonlinear divisors of various multiplicities m; for each nonlinear divisor of multiplicity m there is a vector X such that $A^m X = 0$, but $A^{m-1} X \neq 0$. This means that for less than m iterations, the eigenvalue 0 does not achieve its asymptotic state of annihilating approximately half the principal directions. Thus an asymptotic definition of the rate of convergence cannot really apply when there are fewer than m iterations, as there may be for large problems.

DeVogelaere [unpublished] has considered the alternate use of two distinct overrelaxation factors ω, ω' for a special order. There does not appear to be a significant advantage in practice, although the theory is interesting.

Heller [1958] has discussed the question of how many orders σ are consistent.

22.2. Overrelaxation Without Property (A)

The practical success with successive overrelaxation has been so great that people have tried it with matrices which do not satisfy property (A) (see Young [1955]). Although theoretically unjustified at the time, this application of successive overrelaxation turned out to improve the rate of convergence, and the matter is beginning to receive theoretical attention. We shall state one or two of the results of Kahan [1958], which are based mainly on a theorem of Stein and Rosenberg [1948].

Given an arbitrary matrix A with no $a_{ii} = 0$. For the moment, define D to be the diagonal terms of A, E to be the subdiagonal terms, and F to be the superdiagonal terms. Then there is no difficulty in describing successive overrelaxation for the solution of a linear system $AU = B$, by means of formula (22.5).

For any matrix A, any order σ, and any overrelaxation factor ω, the rate of convergence $R(\omega; A, \sigma)$ may be defined whenever the method is convergent, and is differentiable for most values of ω. An optimal choice of ω is one for which $R(\omega; A, \sigma)$ is maximized. This value, ω_{opt}, depends on A and on σ. For fixed A and σ such that the method of successive displacements ($\omega = 1$) converges, the value of $R(1; A, \sigma)$ is determined. Now it would be quite unusual if the value of

$$\delta = \frac{d}{d\omega} R(\omega; A, \sigma), \qquad \text{for } \omega = 1$$

were exactly 0. When it is not zero, some values of ω larger than 1 (if $\delta > 0$) or less than 1 (if $\delta < 0$) will deliver a larger rate of convergence than 1. Hence over- or underrelaxation is *a priori* likely to be useful for any problem. On the other hand, the value of ω_{opt} might be a complicated function of A and of σ. The point of Young's theory is that, when A has property (A), the value of ω_{opt} is independent of σ for a considerable class of orders (called consistent) and, moreover, depends on A only through the dominant root of (22.8).

Consider the class of nonsingular symmetric matrices A for which

$$a_{ij} = a_{ji} \leq 0, \qquad \text{all } i \neq j \qquad (22.33)$$

and for which

$$a_{ii} > 0, \qquad \text{all } i. \qquad (22.34)$$

Conditions (22.33) and (22.34) are satisfied whenever A represents self-adjoint elliptic difference equations of nonnegative type (see Sec. 20.4).

By rescaling the unknowns and dividing through equations, one can make

$$a_{ii} = 1, \qquad \text{all } i, \qquad (22.35)$$

without upsetting (22.33). Then, changing the meaning of E and F, we have $A = -E + I - F$, where E, F represent triangular matrices formed with the absolute values of the elements of A below and above the main diagonal respectively.

Assume we have arranged the equations and unknowns so that the relaxation is carried out in the order $1, 2, \cdots, N$, i.e., so that σ is the identity permutation σ_0. According to Ostrowski's extension of Reich's theorem (Sec. 21.6), the method of successive over- or underrelaxation for a fixed ω ($0 < \omega < 2$) converges if and only if A is a positive definite matrix, i.e., if and only if the roots μ_i of the equation $\det(A - \mu I) = 0$ are all positive. [A positive definite matrix satisfying (22.33) and (22.34) is often called a *Stieltjes matrix*; all the elements of its inverse can be proved to be nonnegative.] But the μ_i satisfy the equation

$$\det(A - \mu I) = \det(-E + I - F - \mu I) = 0. \qquad (22.36)$$

Now, by (22.8), the convergence factors of the method of simultaneous displacements are the roots of

$$\det(-E + \lambda I - F) = 0. \qquad (22.37)$$

Comparing (22.36) and (22.37), we see that the roots λ_i of (22.37) are related to the roots μ_i of (22.36) by

$$\lambda_i = 1 - \mu_i. \qquad (22.38)$$

On the other hand, from (22.37) the numbers λ_i are the eigenvalues of

$E + F$, a matrix of nonnegative elements. According to a theorem of Frobenius (see MacDuffee [1946], p. 28), a largest eigenvalue in modulus of $E + F$ is a real positive eigenvalue λ_1. Hence all $|\lambda_i| < 1$ if and only if $\lambda_1 < 1$. By (22.38), it follows from the last two sentences that all $|\lambda_i| < 1$ if and only if all $\mu_i > 0$. We have therefore proved the following theorem:

THEOREM 22.3. *Assume matrix A satisfies (22.33) and (22.34). If the method of successive under- or overrelaxation converges for any one ω $(0 < \omega < 2)$, then the method of simultaneous displacements converges. Conversely, if the method of simultaneous displacements converges, then the method of successive under- or overrelaxation converges for all ω $(0 < \omega < 2)$.*

We showed essentially the same result in Sec. 22.1 when A had property (A) and was symmetric.

Since all values of ω $(0 < \omega < 2)$ lead to convergence, we now wonder which value is best. Kahan states that $R(\omega; A, \sigma_0) < R(1; A, \sigma_0)$ for $0 < \omega < 1$, and, therefore, that values $\omega < 1$ need never be considered.

Let $\eta_1^{(\omega)}$ be the dominant eigenvalue of the successive overrelaxation scheme. Define

$$\omega_b = \frac{2}{1 + \sqrt{1 - \lambda_1^2}}, \tag{22.39}$$

which would be equal to ω_{opt} for a consistent ordering of a matrix with property (A). In Sec. 22.1, when property (A) held, we showed the relation of $\eta_1^{(\omega)}$ to ω. Kahan [1958, Theorem 3.6.18] proves from assumptions (22.33) and (22.35) that, for all ω $(0 < \omega < 2)$, $|\eta_1^{(\omega)}|$ is larger than the value it would have for a consistent ordering if A had property (A) and the same value of λ_1; i.e.,

$$|\eta_1^{(\omega)}| \geq \omega_b - 1. \tag{22.40}$$

Moreover, he proves that

$$\omega_b - 1 \leq |\eta_1^{(\omega)}| < \sqrt{\omega_b - 1}. \tag{22.41}$$

Now (22.41) implies that the best convergence factor $|\eta_1^{(\omega_{opt})}|$ is fairly close to that obtainable with ω_b, whenever $\omega_b \doteq 2$. Moreover, the best convergence factor is much lower than $|\eta_1^{(1)}|$, when $\omega_b \doteq 2$.

The actual optimal value ω_{opt} of ω is not known. It is not always equal to ω_b. Kahan conjectures (even for nonsymmetric A) that ω_{opt} is the largest value of ω $(0 < \omega < 2)$ for which the dominant eigenvalue $\eta_1^{(\omega)}$ is real and positive, just as is the case when property (A) holds.

It seems clear from this partial survey of present results that much of Young's theory can be extended to matrices without property (A). There are many problems yet to be solved.

A novel heuristic interpretation of successive overrelaxation has been given by Garabedian [1956a]. In this the overrelaxation solution of the Dirichlet problem for the Laplace difference equation is considered as the solution by difference methods of a time-dependent problem for $\partial u/\partial t = L_h(u)$, where L_h is a difference operator different from Laplace's. By his method Garabedian derives the correct asymptotic form of Young's ω_{opt}, as $h \to 0$. One value of Garabedian's contribution is that the method is applicable to various finite-difference analogs of the Laplace operator, whether or not they have property (A). It thus represents another road toward freeing Young's theory from the restriction to property (A), and we shall describe it now.

Consider Young's method of solving the Laplace difference equation over a square net in a region R of the (x, y)-plane, with linear boundary conditions of form $\alpha u + \beta u_n + \gamma = 0$ on C, the boundary of R. Assume we follow a fixed line-after-line order σ of the nodes (x, y). By (22.5), the new values $\{U^{(n+1)}\}$ are obtained from the old values $\{U^{(n)}\}$ as follows:

$$U^{(n+1)}(x, y) = (1 - \omega) U^{(n)}(x, y) + \frac{\omega}{4} [U^{(n+1)}(x - h, y)$$

$$+ U^{(n+1)}(x, y - h) + U^{(n)}(x + h, y) + U^{(n)}(x, y + h)]. \quad (22.42)$$

Let us consider that $U^{(n)}(x, y)$ represents the value at time $t = nk$ of a time-dependent function $U(x, y, t)$. We may then rewrite (22.42) in the form

$$U(x, y, t + k) = (1 - \omega) U(x, y, t) + \frac{\omega}{4} [U(x - h, y, t + k)$$

$$+ U(x, y - h, t + k) + U(x + h, y, t) + U(x, y + h, t)]. \quad (22.43)$$

Following an idea of Young [unpublished], we now formally expand (22.43) in a Taylor's series about (x, y, t), and keep only the leading terms. We get

$$U + kU_t + \cdots = (1 - \omega)U + \frac{\omega}{4} \left[U - hU_x + \frac{h^2}{2} U_{xx} \right.$$

$$+ kU_t - hkU_{xt} + \cdots + U - hU_y$$

$$\left. + \frac{h^2}{2} U_{yy} + kU_t - hkU_{yt} + \cdots \right]. \quad (22.44)$$

Collecting and cancelling terms, and dropping terms of degree higher than 2 in the quantities $h, k, 2 - \omega$, we find that

$$k\left(1 - \frac{\omega}{2}\right) U_t = \frac{\omega}{4} [h^2(U_{xx} + U_{yy}) - hk(U_{xt} + U_{yt})]. \quad (22.45)$$

Now divide through equation (22.45) by $hk(\omega/4)$, and introduce the abbreviations

$$\tau = \frac{1}{2}\frac{1 - \omega/2}{(\omega/4)h} = \frac{2 - \omega}{h\omega}, \qquad \rho = \frac{h}{k}. \tag{22.46}$$

We find that

$$2\tau U_t = \rho(U_{xx} + U_{yy}) - (U_{xt} + U_{yt}). \tag{22.47}$$

The meaning of this formalism is that (22.43) is a difference equation which approximates the time-dependent differential equation (22.47). Now Garabedian assumes that h and k are taken so small, and with such an appropriate ratio ρ (see Sec. 29) that the solution of Young's difference system (22.43) approximately behaves like the true solution of (22.47) in the region R of the (x, y)-plane. We therefore want to choose $\tau = \tau(\omega)$ so that the true solution of (22.47) converges most rapidly, as $t \to \infty$, to the steady-state function $U_0(x, y)$, the solution of $\Delta U = U_{xx} + U_{yy} = 0$ in R, with the same boundary conditions.

To solve (22.47), introduce the variable $s = \rho t + x/2 + y/2$. Write $u(x, y, s) = U(x, y, t)$, and (22.47) takes a form essentially like the equation of wave propagation:

$$u_{xx} + u_{yy} - \tfrac{1}{2}u_{ss} - 2\tau u_s = 0. \tag{22.48}$$

By separating variables, one can show that convergent series of the form

$$u = u_0(x, y) + \sum_{m=1}^{\infty} (a_m e^{-p_m s} + b_m e^{-q_m s}) u_m(x, y) \tag{22.49}$$

are solutions of (22.48), if the u_m are the eigenfunctions of

$$-\Delta u_m = \mu_m u_m, \qquad 0 < \mu_1 \le \mu_2 \le \cdots, \tag{22.50}$$

with $\alpha u + \beta u_n = 0$ on the boundary of R. Here

$$p_m = 2\tau - \sqrt{4\tau^2 - 2\mu_m}, \qquad q_m = 2\tau + \sqrt{4\tau^2 - 2\mu_m}.$$

As $t \to \infty$ and $s \to \infty$, we see from (22.49) that

$$u - u_0 \sim a_1 e^{-p_1 s} u_1(x, y) = a_1 e^{-p_1 \rho t} e^{-p_1 x/2} e^{-p_1 y/2} u_1(x, y),$$

since p_1 is the coefficient with minimum real part of all the numbers p_m and q_m. To get the most rapid convergence, we must choose τ to make the real part of p_1 as large as possible. It is fairly simple to prove that the real part of $p_1 = 2\tau - (4\tau^2 - 2\mu_1)^{1/2}$ is maximized when the radical is 0, i.e., when

$$\tau = \tau_{\text{opt}} = \sqrt{\frac{\mu_1}{2}} \doteq 0.7071\sqrt{\mu_1}. \tag{22.51}$$

Going back to (22.46), we then note that (22.51) calls for the selection of ω as follows:

$$\omega_{\text{opt}} = \frac{2}{1 + h\tau_{\text{opt}}} \doteq 2 - 2h\tau_{\text{opt}} = 2 - \sqrt{2\mu_1}h. \qquad (22.52)$$

As a check on (22.52), consider that R is the square $0 < x < \pi$, $0 < y < \pi$, and that the boundary condition reduces to $u = 0$ on C. Then $u_1(x, y) = \sin x \sin y$, so that $\mu_1 = 2$. Hence $\omega_{\text{opt}} \doteq 2 - 2h$, so that, by (22.24), $\eta_{\text{opt}} \doteq 1 - 2h$, in agreement with (22.30). The rate of convergence is of the order $2h$.

Now this theory of Garabedian's can be valid only for small h, since it is otherwise not reasonable to replace (22.43) by (22.47). Nevertheless it is very useful, for two reasons: (1) the argument can be carried over to other difference formulas without property (A); (2) it expresses ω_{opt}, for small h, approximately as a function of the domain R, the boundary conditions and h.

Concerning (2), we note that, if R and h are changed to αR and αh by a similarity transformation, then μ_1 is changed to μ_1/α^2, so that $\sqrt{\mu_1} h$ is invariant. Hence ω_{opt} is invariant, and depends on the fundamental eigenvalue μ_1 of a region R_1 which is similar to R, but h^{-1} times as large. This conclusion only applies asymptotically, as $h \to 0$. Nevertheless it gives us a reasonable basis for estimating ω_{opt} in practice. There are various methods of estimating μ_1, any of which would be useful here. (See Pólya and Szegö [1951] for a discussion of these.) Since it is better to err by using too high a value for ω_{opt} instead of by using too low a value, it is better to use a slightly low value of μ_1 in (22.52). This is the more difficult side of μ_1 to estimate closely. Perhaps the simplest bound for μ_1 for Dirichlet boundary conditions is

$$\mu_1 \geq \frac{j\sqrt{\pi}}{\sqrt{|R|}}, \qquad (22.53)$$

where $|R|$ is the area of R, and $j \doteq 2.405$ is the first zero of the Bessel function J_0. But (22.53) is not a close bound unless R is nearly circular.

Garabedian states that this discussion applies to problems with arbitrary linear boundary conditions, as long as μ_1 in (22.50) is defined by the corresponding homogeneous conditions. He does not discuss the modification of (22.42) to take care of non-Dirichlet boundary conditions, and it seems to us that this matter should be investigated further. If one has the boundary conditions $\partial u/\partial n = 0$ on all of C, u is determined only up to an arbitrary constant, and we should understand by μ_1 the smallest *positive* eigenvalue of $-\Delta$.

Garabedian applies the present asymptotic method also to explicit successive overrelaxation for the nine-point Laplace difference equation

$$\Delta_h^{(9)}U = 4[U(x - h, y) + U(x, y - h) + U(x + h, y) + U(x, y + h)]$$

$$+ U(x - h, y - h) + U(x - h, y + h) + U(x + h, y - h)$$

$$+ U(x + h, y + h) - 20U(x, y) = 0. \qquad (22.54)$$

He finds that, if one lets

$$\omega = 2(1 + \tau h)^{-1},$$

one gets the following analog to (22.47) for $h = k$:

$$3\Delta U = 2U_{xt} + 3U_{yt} + 5\tau U_t. \qquad (22.55)$$

This leads eventually to $\tau_{\text{opt}} = 5^{-1}(13\mu_1)^{1/2}$, and

$$\omega_{\text{opt}} \doteq 2 - \tfrac{2}{5}(13\mu_1)^{1/2}h \doteq 2 - 1.442\mu_1^{1/2}h,$$

a value very close to that obtained for the five-point formula. For the square considered above, with $\mu_1 = 2$, we then have

$$\eta_{\text{opt}} = \omega_{\text{opt}} - 1 = 1 - 1.442\sqrt{2}h \doteq 1 - 2.04h.$$

The corresponding rate of convergence is $2.04h$, almost identical with that for the five-point formula Δ_h. Thus the number of cycles of iteration required will be approximately the same for successive overrelaxation solutions of $\Delta_h^{(9)}U = 0$ as for $\Delta_h U = 0$. This is quite an important conclusion, because of the much smaller local discretization error of the nine-point formula; see Secs. 20 and 23.

The Garabedian technique can apparently be applied to successive overrelaxation in solving the Dirichlet problem for any finite-difference scheme involving constant coefficients, provided that no interpolation is required at the boundary. However, an attempt to apply it to the method of simultaneous displacements for Laplace's equation (a method described in Sec. 21.4) seems to have been unsuccessful [David Young, oral communication].

22.3. Implicit Methods: Overrelaxation by Lines

In all the relaxation methods considered so far, including Young's, the value of each component of U_k is determined by an explicit linear formula, of which (21.62) is typical. By *explicit* we mean that the kth approximation to the ith component $U_{k,i}$ of U_k can be determined by itself at its proper step of the algorithm, without the necessity of simultaneously determining a group of other components of U_k. It is true that we sometimes recast the formulas for explicit relaxation so that they appear to define all the components of U_k at once, as we did in (21.63), but for explicit methods this is only a notational convenience and not a computational necessity.

In contrast are *implicit* formulas, by which a group of components of U_k are defined simultaneously in such an interrelated manner that it is necessary to solve a linear subsystem for the whole subset of components at once before a single one can be determined. As the extreme example, the basic vector equation $AU = B$ defines all the components of $A^{-1}B$ implicitly. In more realistic examples, groups of from perhaps 10 to 100 unknown components of U_k are defined simultaneously by implicit linear relations.

The iterative solution of an elliptic boundary-value problem $L(u) = 0$ is equivalent or analogous to the time integration of the parabolic equation $u_t = L(u)$ (see Sec. 22.2). Hence implicit methods for elliptic problems were suggested by the discovery by Crank and Nicolson [1947] (see Sec. 13.3) of the stability of such methods for the heat equation $u_t = u_{xx}$, even for large time steps.

In pencil-and-paper computation it is advantageous to use explicit methods, since the solution of a linear algebraic system of order greater than three is already a considerable chore. But with automatic computers, especially those with large memory capacities, it is entirely feasible to employ a subroutine for the solution of 10 to 100 linear equations, and to use this as the means for solving for a group of unknown components simultaneously. This may prove to be the best way to solve a given linear problem with several hundreds or thousands of unknowns. In this section, it is our purpose to consider a certain class of implicit methods and compare them with explicit methods. In Sec. 22.4, more intricate implicit methods will be discussed. (Such methods have been classified by Keller [1958].)

Although problems differ in their sizes (i.e., number of components N), and machines differ in their memory capacities and structures, the typical machine algorithm for solving a large elliptic difference equation on a computer is as follows: There is an intermediate store (magnetic tape or drum) on which the whole field of values of U_{k-1} is stored. For processing, one must transfer the components of U_{k-1} to the high-speed store (now usually a magnetic core). The arithmetic speed of the computer is substantially faster than the time of transfer of a single word between the intermediate and high-speed stores. It is most efficient to transfer the values of U_{k-1} into, and the values of U_k out of, the high-speed store in fairly large blocks. Even so, the time of the entire computation may be essentially the time required to move these blocks between the two classes of storage. This is particularly true with those machines whose buffer storage permits arithmetic calculation to progress at the same time that blocks of information are being transferred in and out of the high-speed memory. Consequently, it may pay to reduce the number of transfers of data to and from the intermediate storage, even at the cost of considerably increasing the complexity of the arithmetic. This consideration has led to the discussion of implicit methods for solving these elliptic problems. The discussion is too recent for results to be definitive, but we can give some indication of their direction.

Consider a two-dimensional working domain $\bar{R}_h$ of nodes (x, y) where $U(x, y)$ is to be determined. In the solution of an elliptic boundary-value problem, the corresponding function values $U(x, y)$ are ordinarily filed by lines in the intermediate store. [A *line* is the set of nodes (x, y) with constant x, or with constant y.] One line of $\bar{R}_h$ may constitute part or all of one track of a magnetic drum, for example. On most machines it is efficient to transfer whole tracks or similar blocks of consecutive data from the intermediate store to high-speed storage. It is therefore natural to consider implicit equations, whereby one determines the values of all the $U(x, y)$ on one line simultaneously and implicitly. Let us study the advantages and disadvantages of such methods, which we shall call *relaxation by lines*.

Assume we are dealing with a difference equation—like the five-point or nine-point formulas—in which a point (x_0, y_0) is coupled only with points (x, y) for $y = y_0$, $y_0 - h$, or $y_0 + h$. Let S_1 be the set of nodes in the first line of $\bar{R}_h$; let S_2 be those in the second line, etc. Then the matrix A can be written in the block-tridiagonal form (22.1), but the D_i are ordinarily not diagonal matrices. If a point (x_0, y_0) is coupled only with points (x, y) for which $x = x_0$, $x_0 - h$, or $x_0 + h$, as in the five-point and nine-point formulas, then each D_i is itself a tridiagonal matrix.

We can denote the block of unknown components $U(x, y)$ within the ith line by a single letter U_i. If there are m lines in $\bar{R}_h$, we get the following block-tridiagonal system of equations:

$$D_1 U_1 + F_1 U_2 \qquad\qquad\qquad\qquad = B_1$$
$$E_1 U_1 + D_2 U_2 + F_2 U_3 \qquad\qquad\qquad = B_2$$
$$\cdot\ \cdot\ \cdot\ \cdot\ \cdot\ \cdot\ \cdot\ \cdot\ \cdot\ \cdot\ \cdot\ \cdot\ \cdot\ \cdot\ \cdot\ \cdot\ \cdot\ \cdot \qquad (22.56)$$
$$D_{m-1} U_{m-1} + F_{m-1} U_m = B_{m-1}$$
$$E_{m-1} U_{m-1} + D_m U_m = B_m.$$

We hope to solve system (22.56) by one of the preceding methods, where the basic units will be blocks like D_2 or F_2. The critical operation will be to find an inverse of a matrix like $D_1, D_2, \cdots, D_m$, or to solve linear systems with such matrices. Ordinarily the matrices D_i will themselves be tridiagonal, and solving a system $TU = B$ with a tridiagonal matrix T is, in principle, easy by elimination.

Once we have basic subroutines for inverting individual blocks in (22.56), how shall we deal with the whole system? We may expect that the system (22.56) is too large to solve by a direct method, as we indicated in Sec. 21 (though not without reservations). We are therefore led to iterative methods. Now the whole set of iterative methods developed in Sec. 21 and in the earlier part of Sec. 22 can be translated into analogous *block-iterative methods*. For some methods, like Richardson's, the details have not been worked out, but the development from the method of simultaneous displacements through successive overrelaxation has been worked on by several authors: Arms, Gates, and Zondek [1956], Keller [1958], and others. We continue to follow the point of view of Friedman [1957].

Although we have derived the blocks in equations (22.56) to correspond to the lines of a two-dimensional network of nodes, a partition of the nodes into other types of sets $S_1, \cdots, S_m$ might also lead to equations of the form (22.56). The important requirement, that the matrix in (22.56) be block-tridiagonal requires that the unknowns of each block S_i be coupled only among themselves or with unknowns of the blocks S_{i-1} or S_{i+1}. For example, one might put several adjacent lines of the net into one block. Or one might take as one block a large rectangle in the middle of an irregularly shaped domain. In both these examples, for Laplace's equation, one can use known formulas for the inverse of the Laplacian operator over a rectangle. Muller [1956] used an analogous idea to propose a faster Monte Carlo method to solve Laplace's equation.

In breaking the full system $AU = B$ into blocks, we are merely partitioning the matrix A, as we did in Sec. 21.2. Here, as before, we propose solving the individual blocks by a direct process. The difference between the present point of view and that of Sec. 21.3 is the manner in which the solution to the entire system $AU = B$ is obtained from the solutions of the separate blocks. In Sec. 21.3 we considered combining the subsolutions into the whole solution by a direct process. In the present section we combine them by an iterative process.

The entire theory of successive pointwise overrelaxation was based on Theorem 22.1, which relates the zeros $\eta_i^{(\omega)}$ of (22.12) to the roots λ_i^P (P for points) of (22.8). Now in the formal matrix operations leading to the proof of Theorem 22.1, no use was made of the fact that the D_i were diagonal matrices. Hence the whole theory applies equally well to the *method of successive overrelaxation by lines*, or by other blocks of points S_i. Thus equation (22.17) can now be interpreted as giving the eigenvalues $\eta_i^{(\omega)}$ for the method of successive overrelaxation by lines in terms of those (call them λ_i^L) for the method of simultaneous displacements by lines. If $|\lambda_i^L| < |\lambda_i^P|$ for all i, we can be sure that successive overrelaxation by lines will be faster than successive overrelaxation by points.

As an example of this implicit method, let us consider the Dirichlet problem for the square treated in Sec. 21.5. Here $\bar{R}_h = R_h$ consists of all points (x, y) with $x, y = h, 2h, 3h, \cdots, (n-1)h$. Let the set S_j consist of the points with $y = jh \ (j = 1, 2, \cdots, n-1)$. There are $(n-1)^2$ interior points in R_h. Consider the method of simultaneous displacements by lines for Laplace's difference equation (five-point formula). In this we determine the U_k by solving the system

$$U_k(x + h, y) + U_{k-1}(x, y + h) + U_k(x - h, y)$$
$$+ U_{k-1}(x, y - h) - 4U_k(x, y) = 0. \quad (22.57)$$

To find the eigenvalues λ of the operator H^L (L for lines) corresponding to (22.57), with zero boundary conditions, we must find $\lambda = \lambda^L$ and $X(x, y)$ such that

$$\lambda X(x + h, y) + X(x, y + h) + \lambda X(x - h, y)$$
$$+ X(x, y - h) - 4\lambda X(x, y) = 0. \quad (22.58)$$

Now, trying $X(x, y) = \sin px \sin qy$, since $nh = \pi$, we find after some reductions that

$$(2\lambda \cos ph + 2 \cos qh - 4\lambda) \sin px \sin qy = 0. \quad (22.59)$$

But (22.59) will be satisfied if

$$\lambda(p, q) = \lambda^L(p, q) = \frac{\cos qh}{2 - \cos ph}, \qquad p, q = 1, \cdots, n-1. \quad (22.60)$$

In (22.60) we have exhibited the $(n-1)^2$ eigenvalues of H^L, i.e., the roots of equation (22.8) corresponding to the $n-1$ lines of the net.

Clearly $|\lambda(p, q)| < 1$ for all p, q, and so the method of simultaneous displacements by lines converges. The maximum modulus of the eigenvalues is

$$\lambda_1^L = \max_{p,q} \lambda(p, q) = \frac{\cos h}{2 - \cos h} \sim 1 - h^2, \qquad \text{as } h \to 0, \quad (22.61)$$

and it is λ_1^L which governs the rate of convergence of this method. The corresponding rate of convergence is h^2. The corresponding eigenvalue, λ_1^P, for the pointwise method of simultaneous displacements, found in Sec. 22.1, is

$$\lambda_1^P = \cos h \sim 1 - \frac{h^2}{2}, \qquad \text{as } h \to 0. \quad (22.62)$$

Thus the method of simultaneous displacements by lines converges at the same rate (for h near 0) as the method of successive displacements by points (see (22.28) above), and twice as fast as the method of simultaneous displacements by points.

Let us now consider successive overrelaxation by lines. The relation (22.24) now takes the form

$$\omega_{\text{opt}} - 1 = \frac{1 - \sqrt{1 - (\lambda_1^L)^2}}{1 + \sqrt{1 - (\lambda_1^L)^2}} \sim 1 - 2\sqrt{2}h, \qquad \text{as } h \to 0,$$

and this is the convergence factor for the method. The corresponding rate of convergence is $2\sqrt{2}h$, a gain by the factor $\sqrt{2}$ over the corresponding pointwise method. It seems doubtful whether this factor $\sqrt{2}$ would compensate for the extra time of solving the implicit equations. The matter would have to be studied for each special problem and machine.

In spite of the modest advantage of the method of successive overrelaxation by lines in the above example, the method has one considerable advantage in principle. Namely, it requires less restriction on the difference equations to derive a block-tridiagonal form than it requires to have property (A). For example, the nine-point difference approximation to Laplace's equation does not have property (A), yet it does take the block-tridiagonal form (22.56) when we use the lines as blocks.

If we make the comparable analysis for the implicit use of the nine-point formula $\Delta_h^{(9)}$ of (20.56), we find that the rate of convergence is asymptotically the same (as $h \to 0$) as that for the five-point formula Δ_h. The equation analogous to (22.59) is

$$(4 \cos ph \cos qh + 8 \cos qh + 8\lambda \cos ph - 20\lambda) \sin px \sin qy = 0.$$

Write $\alpha = \cos ph$, $\beta = \cos qh$ temporarily. We find that the roots of the last equation are

$$\lambda(\alpha, \beta) = \frac{\beta(\alpha + 2)}{5 - 2\alpha}.$$

Hence $\max_{\alpha, \beta} |\lambda(\alpha, \beta)|$, for $-1 < \alpha < 1$, $-1 < \beta < 1$, comes for the α and β nearest 1. Thus $\alpha = \beta = \cos h$, and we have

$$\lambda_{\max} = \frac{(\cos h)(2 + \cos h)}{5 - 2 \cos h} \sim 1 - h^2, \qquad \text{as } h \to 0.$$

Hence the rate of convergence of the method of simultaneous displacements by lines for solving $\Delta_h^{(9)} U = 0$ is approximately h^2. Since this agrees with that found in (22.61), we neither increase nor decrease the rate of convergence in changing from Δ_h to $\Delta_h^{(9)}$. The same conclusion follows for successive overrelaxation for the same implicit formula. The decision as to which formula to use can therefore be made on other grounds, such as accuracy or convenience.

22.4. Implicit Alternating-Direction Methods

In the past few years, two novel variants of the implicit method have been proposed, with the object of obtaining a rate of convergence substantially greater than that of the method of successive overrelaxation. One is the Peaceman-Rachford [1955] method; the other is the Douglas-Rachford [1956] method. We shall here treat the former according to the account of Birkhoff and Varga [1959].

In the historical development of the method of successive overrelaxation, the first paper published was that of Frankel [1950], who developed the theory for the Dirichlet problem for Laplace's equation in a rectangle. The most significant contribution of Young [1954a] (whose thesis was accepted in 1950) was to show that for the Dirichlet problem the theory of Frankel holds also for a general self-adjoint second-order partial differential equation without a term u_{xy}, and for a general region in the (x, y)-plane. Thus the theory for a rectangle properly forecast the theory for a general region.

The Peaceman-Rachford and Douglas-Rachford theories were developed for rectangles, and for these regions show a startling superiority to successive overrelaxation. However, the analysis of Birkhoff and Varga [1959] shows that the reason for this superiority does not carry over to nonrectangular regions nor to general partial difference operators. The actual value of the methods for general regions is still in doubt, and is the subject of current research. The methods will be discussed again in Sec. 30 for mixed parabolic-elliptic problems.

It will first be useful to prove the following general lemma reportedly due to Frobenius.

LEMMA 22.4. *Let the symmetric matrix B have eigenvalues $\beta_1, \cdots, \beta_N$, and let C denote another symmetric matrix of order N, with eigenvalues $\gamma_1, \cdots, \gamma_N$. Then $BC = CB$ if and only if B and C have a common basis of eigenvectors. When $BC = CB$, the matrices BC and CB have eigenvalues $\beta_1\gamma_1, \cdots, \beta_N\gamma_N$, and also share the basis of eigenvectors common to B and C.*

Proof. If B and C have a common eigenvector basis, then there is an orthogonal matrix S such that $S^T BS$ and $S^T CS$ are diagonal matrices, which necessarily commute. Hence

$$S^T BCS = S^T BS(S^T CS) = S^T CS(S^T BS) = S^T CBS,$$

so that $BC = CB$. Clearly $S^T BCS = (\beta_i \gamma_j \delta_{ij})$ has eigenvalues $\beta_i \gamma_i$ and is diagonal, and hence BC shares with B and C the columns of S as an eigenvector basis.

Conversely, if $BC = CB$, choose S so that $S^T BS$ is a diagonal matrix B_1, whose diagonal elements are the β_i. Let $C_1 = S^T CS$, with elements c_{ij}. We can show that $B_1 C_1 = C_1 B_1$. That is, for each i and j, $\beta_i c_{ij} = \beta_j c_{ij}$, so that either $\beta_i = \beta_j$ or $c_{ij} = 0$.

Assume that S was so chosen that any equal eigenvalues β_i are adjacent in B_1. Then we just showed that C_1 is diagonal, except possibly for a square diagonal block of order m corresponding to each eigenvalue β_i of multiplicity m. Corresponding to any diagonal block c_{ii} of order 1 of C_1 are the eigenvalue γ_i and eigenvector e_i, the ith unit vector. But e_i is clearly also the corresponding eigenvector of the diagonal matrix B_1. Corresponding to a diagonal block of C_1 of order $m > 1$, B_1 has a diagonal block of order m of form λI, and so, whatever are the corresponding eigenvectors of C_1, they will also be eigenvectors of B_1. Hence B_1 and C_1 (and therefore B and C) have a common basis of eigenvectors, and the lemma is completely proved.

In the implicit method of Sec. 22.3 we assumed that the working domain $\bar{R}_h$ was partitioned into a fixed collection of subsets S_ν. This is clearly not essential to an iterative technique, and we may inquire whether it might be profitable to vary the decomposition

$$\bar{R}_h = \bigcup_\nu S_\nu$$

at various stages of the solution. In this manner one might hope to improve the convergence, for the following intuitive reason. During any linear iterative process, the error E_k tends to settle into a certain "rut"; i.e., if there is a dominant eigenvalue λ_1, eventually

$$E_k \doteq c\lambda_1{}^k X_1,$$

where X_1 is the corresponding eigenvector. For a significant problem, one usually finds that $|\lambda_1|$ is only slightly less than 1, so that $\|E_k\|$ is making only very slow progress to zero; this is the "rut." Now, if at this stage one changes the iterative process, one will ordinarily acquire a new set of eigenvalues and a new set of eigenvectors. At the moment of change, the vector X will not be an eigenvector of the new process, and one may expect several steps to take place before E_k settles into a new rut. Meanwhile, one may hope to have decreased $\|E_k\|$ considerably.

In one group of proposals for varying the decomposition of $\bar{R}_h$, the net is alternately broken into horizontal lines and vertical lines.

For simplicity, we confine our analysis to the five-point approximation to the Laplace operator in a region R which is the union of squares of the network. Assume we have Dirichlet boundary conditions, and that the net region R_h has N points. We represent this difference operator in the form

$$-h^2 \Delta_h U(x, y) = A\, U(x, y) = (A^H + A^V)\, U(x, y)$$
$$= A^H\, U(x, y) + A^V\, U(x, y), \qquad (22.63)$$

where

$$A^H\, U(x, y) = -U(x - h, y) + 2U(x, y) - U(x + h, y),$$
$$A^V\, U(x, y) = -U(x, y - h) + 2U(x, y) - U(x, y + h). \qquad (22.64)$$

Thus A^H (H for horizontal) and A^V (V for vertical) are symmetric matrices of order N representing one-dimensional second-difference operators on the net function $U(x, y)$, for (x, y) in R_h.

The matrices A^H and A^V are positive definite, for the following reason, stated for A^H. First, by Gerschgorin's theorem (see Milne [1953], p. 169, Theorem 9), each eigenvalue lies in the closed interval [0, 4]. Now, if 0 were an eigenvalue, there would have to be a corresponding nonzero net eigenfunction X such that $A^H X = 0$, with $X = 0$ on C. Such a function would have to have a maximum absolute value on each line of the net. If we fix our attention on any line $y = $ const., and use the fact that by (22.64)

$$X(x, y) = \tfrac{1}{2}[X(x - h, y) + X(x + h, y)],$$

we can easily find that this maximum absolute value can only be zero. This contradiction, which is shown in Sec. 23 to lead to the *maximum principle* in n dimensions, shows that all eigenvalues of A^H are positive, so that the matrix A^H is definite.

In the present notation, the Richardson process (21.37) for solving $AU = B$ can be written in the form

$$U_k = U_{k-1} - \alpha_k[(A^H + A^V)U_{k-1} - B]. \qquad (22.65)$$

In the Peaceman-Rachford [1955] method one uses two implicit variations of the Richardson method. In the first, one replaces (22.65) by

$$U_{k-1/2} = U_{k-1} - \alpha_k(A^H U_{k-1/2} + A^V U_{k-1} - B). \qquad (22.66)$$

Thus a net function $U_{k-1/2}$ is computed by simultaneous over- or under-displacements, implicit by horizontal lines. In the second half of the Peaceman-Rachford process one forms

$$U_k = U_{k-1/2} - \alpha_k(A^H U_{k-1/2} + A^V U_k - B). \qquad (22.67)$$

This is the corresponding form of simultaneous displacements, implicit by vertical lines.

There is no permanent interest in $U_{k-1/2}$, which is merely an auxiliary between U_{k-1} and U_k. If we let $E_r = U_r - A^{-1}B$, and eliminate $U_{k-1/2}$ between (22.66) and (22.67), we find that each full cycle of the process has the effect

$$E_k = P(\alpha_k)E_{k-1}, \tag{22.68}$$

where

$$P(\alpha) = (I + \alpha A^V)^{-1}(I - \alpha A^H)(I + \alpha A^H)^{-1}(I - \alpha A^V). \tag{22.69}$$

Let λ_i^H, λ_i^V denote the eigenvalues of A^H, A^V respectively; we showed above that all are positive and less than or equal to 4. Arrange these so that $\lambda_1^H \leq \lambda_2^H \leq \cdots \leq \lambda_N^H$, etc. Now $P(\alpha)$ is similar to the matrix $Q(\alpha) = (I + \alpha A^V) P(\alpha)(I + \alpha A^V)^{-1}$; i.e., $P(\alpha)$ has the same eigenvalues as

$$Q(\alpha) = (I - \alpha A^H)(I + \alpha A^H)^{-1}(I - \alpha A^V)(I + \alpha A^V)^{-1} = P^H(\alpha)\, P^V(\alpha), \tag{22.70}$$

where $P^H(\alpha) = (I - \alpha A^H)(I + \alpha A^H)^{-1}$, and where $P^V(\alpha)$ is defined analogously.

By the Hamilton-Cayley theorem, any matrix B satisfies its characteristic equation

$$F(B) = c_n B^n + c_{n-1} B^{n-1} + \cdots + c_1 B + c_0 = 0.$$

Since $F(x) = \det(B - xI)$, we see that $c_0 = \det B$, so that $c_0 \neq 0$ when B is nonsingular. Premultiplying $F(B)$ by B^{-1}, and solving for B^{-1}, we find that B^{-1} is a polynomial in B. It follows that, if it is nonsingular, the matrix $(I + \alpha A^H)^{-1}$ is a polynomial in $I + \alpha A^H$, and hence also in A_H. Hence $P^H(\alpha)$ is a polynomial in A^H, and is therefore symmetric for each α for which $(I + \alpha A^H)$ is nonsingular and, in particular, for all positive α. Moreover, it can be shown similarly that the eigenvalues of $P^H(\alpha)$ are $(1 - \alpha\lambda_i^H)(1 + \alpha\lambda_i^H)^{-1}$. All the above statements hold analogously for A^V. Keep $\alpha > 0$.

Let $\|X\|_2$ denote the Euclidean length of a vector X. With this metric, let $\|G\|_2$ denote the norm of the linear transformation with matrix G. That is,

$$\|G\|_2 = \max_{\|X\| \neq 0} \frac{\|GX\|_2}{\|X\|_2}.$$

This is the matrix norm *subordinate* to the vector norm $\|X\|_2$, in the sense of Faddeeva [1950]. When G is symmetric, $\|G\|_2$ can be shown to be equal to the spectral radius of G, the maximum of the moduli of the eigenvalues of G. The eigenvalues of $P^H(\alpha)$ are $(1 - \alpha\lambda_i^H)(1 + \alpha\lambda_i^H)^{-1}$, the maximum modulus of which is either $|1 - \alpha\lambda_1^H|(1 + \alpha\lambda_1^H)^{-1}$ or $|1 - \alpha\lambda_N^H|(1 + \alpha\lambda_N^H)^{-1}$, since, for $x > 0$, $(1 - \alpha x)(1 + \alpha x)^{-1}$ is monotonic for $\alpha > 0$.

Keep $\alpha > 0$ in the following. Let λ, Λ be chosen so that

$$0 < \lambda \leq \lambda_i^H \leq \Lambda < \infty \qquad \text{and} \qquad 0 < \lambda \leq \lambda_i^V \leq \Lambda < \infty,$$

for all i. Let

$$\theta = \theta(\alpha) = \max \left(\frac{|1 - \alpha\Lambda|}{1 + \alpha\Lambda}, \frac{|1 - \alpha\lambda|}{1 + \alpha\lambda} \right). \qquad (22.71)$$

Then

$$\|P^H(\alpha)\|_2 \leq \theta(\alpha), \qquad \|P^V(\alpha)\|_2 \leq \theta(\alpha).$$

It follows from the fundamental properties of a matrix norm that

$$\|Q(\alpha)\|_2 \leq \|P^H(\alpha)\|_2 \|P^V(\alpha)\|_2 \leq \theta(\alpha)^2.$$

Since $(1 - \alpha x)(1 + \alpha x)^{-1}$ is monotonic for $\alpha > 0$, $x > 0$, we have

$$\theta(\alpha) < 1 \qquad \text{for } \alpha > 0.$$

Although $Q(\alpha)$ is in general not symmetric, it is a general theorem proved in Householder [1958] that, for any matrix M and for any norm, $\|M\|$ is greater than or equal to the spectral radius of M, which we denote by $\bar{\lambda}(M)$. Hence $\bar{\lambda}[Q(\alpha)] \leq \theta(\alpha)^2$. Since $P(\alpha)$ is similar to $Q(\alpha)$, we have also $\bar{\lambda}[P(\alpha)] \leq \theta(\alpha)^2 < 1$.

Now, if we choose the α_k to be equal to α, for all k, we see from (22.68) and (21.20) that $E_k \to 0$, as $k \to \infty$. Hence we have proved a theorem:

THEOREM 22.5. *If $\alpha_k \equiv \alpha$, for any constant $\alpha > 0$, the Peaceman-Rachford method converges for any region.*

Theorem 22.5 is due to Sheldon, and a proof is given by Birkhoff and Varga [1959].

With the above definitions it is possible also to give sufficient conditions for the convergence of the Peaceman-Rachford method for nonconstant α_k. Since $\alpha > 0$ and

$$P(\alpha) = (I + \alpha A^V)^{-1} Q(\alpha)(I + \alpha A^V),$$

we have

$$\|P(\alpha)\|_2 \leq \|(I + \alpha A^V)^{-1}\|_2 \|Q(\alpha)\|_2 \|I + \alpha A^V\|_2$$

$$\leq (1 + \alpha\lambda)^{-1} \theta(\alpha)^2 (1 + \alpha\Lambda).$$

That is,

$$\|P(\alpha)\|_2 \leq \frac{1 + \alpha\Lambda}{1 + \alpha\lambda} \theta(\alpha)^2.$$

By (22.68), $\|E_k\|_2 \leq \|P(\alpha_k)\|_2 \|E_{k-1}\|_2$. Hence, if all α_k are chosen so that $\|P(\alpha_k)\|_2 \leq c < 1$, then $\|E_k\|_2 \to 0$. By (22.71) and the last displayed equation, a condition on the α_k sufficient for the convergence of the Peaceman-Rachford method for a general region is that, for all k,

$$\frac{1 + \alpha_k \Lambda}{1 + \alpha_k \lambda} \left[\max \left(\frac{|1 - \alpha_k \Lambda|}{1 + \alpha_k \Lambda}, \frac{|1 - \alpha_k \lambda|}{1 + \alpha_k \lambda} \right) \right]^2 \le c < 1.$$

An equivalent sufficient condition is that both the following inequalities hold:

$$\frac{(1 + \alpha_k \Lambda)(1 - \alpha_k \lambda)^2}{(1 + \alpha_k \lambda)^3} \le c < 1, \qquad \text{for all } k;$$

$$\frac{(1 - \alpha_k \Lambda)^2}{(1 + \alpha_k \lambda)(1 + \alpha_k \Lambda)} \le c < 1, \qquad \text{for all } k.$$

These conditions do not seem to have been investigated, although one condition for variable α_k is stated by Birkhoff and Varga [1959], Theorem 6.

The power of the Peaceman-Rachford method is not apparent from Theorem 22.5, and, for a general net region R_h, it is not known how large the rate of convergence is. When R_h is a net rectangle, however, much more can be proved. We will develop the theory for the square of side π, with $N = (n - 1)^2$ interior nodes, where $nh = \pi$.

For this R_h, we find that A^H and A^V both share the eigenvectors $\sin px \sin qy$ $(p, q = 1, \cdots, n - 1)$, with corresponding eigenvalues

$$\lambda^H_{p,q} = 4 \sin^2 \frac{ph}{2}, \quad \lambda^V_{p,q} = 4 \sin^2 \frac{qh}{2}, \quad p, q = 1, \cdots, n - 1. \quad (22.72)$$

Since the eigenvectors are common to A^H and A^V, we see by Lemma 22.4 that A^H and A^V commute. It follows quite readily that $P(\alpha)$, $P^H(\alpha)$, and $P^V(\alpha)$ all share the same eigenvectors, and that *the eigenvalues of $P(\alpha)$ are*

$$\mu_{p,q}(\alpha) = \frac{1 - \alpha \lambda^H_{p,q}}{1 + \alpha \lambda^H_{p,q}} \frac{1 - \alpha \lambda^V_{p,q}}{1 + \alpha \lambda^V_{p,q}}. \quad (22.73)$$

This permits a much stronger hold on the Peaceman-Rachford algorithm. It should be repeated that the relation $A^H A^V = A^V A^H$ is essential to the proof of (22.73); moreover, *this commutativity is a very exceptional property, occurring only for rectangles* (Birkhoff and Varga [1959]).

From (22.72) and (22.73) we see that

$$\mu_{p,q}(\alpha) = \frac{1 - 4\alpha \sin^2 (ph/2)}{1 + 4\alpha \sin^2 (ph/2)} \frac{1 - 4\alpha \sin^2 (qh/2)}{1 + 4\alpha \sin^2 (qh/2)}. \quad (22.74)$$

From (22.74) we see an enormous difference between the Peaceman-Rachford scheme and that of Richardson (22.65); see Fig. 22.5. As discussed in Sec. 21.5 and illustrated in Fig. 21.3, for the larger values of α, many of the eigenvalues of the Richardson operator exceed 1 in absolute value. There is therefore always a danger of causing great growth in some eigenvectors while trying to diminish the others. But (22.74) shows that the eigenvalues $\mu_{p,q}(\alpha)$ of $P(\alpha)$ are less than 1 in modulus for all positive values of α. Hence an unwanted growth cannot occur, and one should be able to choose the values of α for optimal convergence, without danger of instability.

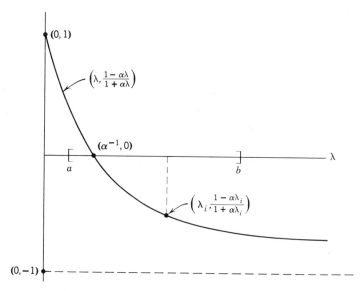

FIG. 22.5. Effect of the Peaceman-Rachford process on components of the error. Contrast with Fig. 21.3.

How should one choose the sequence of values $\{\alpha_k\}$? Suppose we consider a semi-iterative process, i.e., one in which the α_k are chosen in a cyclic order with period K. The corresponding linear operator is $P(\alpha_1)$ $P(\alpha_2) \cdots P(\alpha_K)$. Having selected K, we now have to determine $\alpha_1, \cdots, \alpha_K$ so that the eigenvalues of $P(\alpha_1) P(\alpha_2) \cdots P(\alpha_K)$ are as small as possible in modulus. But, since all the $P(\alpha_k)$ have a common basis of eigenvectors, as shown above, the eigenvalues of $P(\alpha_1) \cdots P(\alpha_K)$ are $\mu_{p,q}(\alpha_1) \cdots \mu_{p,q}(\alpha_K) = \mu'_{p,q}(\alpha_1, \cdots, \alpha_K)$.

If $K \geq n - 1$, we can in principle make $\mu'_{p,q} = 0$ for all p, q by choosing the $n - 1$ different α-values

$$\alpha^{(r)} = \left(4 \sin^2 \frac{rh}{2}\right)^{-1}, \qquad r = 1, 2, \cdots, n - 1. \qquad (22.75)$$

For each $\alpha^{(r)}$ will cause all the corresponding eigenvalues $\mu_{r,q}$ and $\mu_{p,r}$ to vanish $(p, q = 1, \cdots, n - 1)$. [For a rectangular net of $(m - 1)(n - 1)$ points, it would require $m + n - 2$ values of α.] Suppose, however, that $K < n - 1$. Then there is a real problem of approximation—to choose positive numbers $\alpha_1, \cdots, \alpha_K$ so that

$$\max_{\substack{1 \leq p \leq n-1 \\ 1 \leq q \leq n-1}} |\mu'_{p,q}(\alpha_1, \cdots, \alpha_K)| = \min. \tag{22.76}$$

The problem (22.76) is quite difficult since the α_i enter nonlinearly. A basic theory of such nonlinear Čebyšev approximation has been given by Motzkin [1949] and by Tornheim [1950], but the details have apparently not been worked out for (22.76). (See the discussion at the end of this section.)

Peaceman and Rachford [1955] give a procedure for bounding max $|\mu'_{p,q}|$, in the following manner. They approach the problem backward, assigning a number ρ such that they would like to make

$$\max_{p,q} |\mu'_{p,q}(\alpha_1, \cdots, \alpha_K)| \leq \rho, \tag{22.77}$$

and then determining possible K and $\alpha_1, \cdots, \alpha_K$ accordingly. For each α and all p, q one has

$$|\mu_{p,q}(\alpha)| \leq \left| \frac{1 - 4\alpha\tau_p}{1 + 4\alpha\tau_p} \right|, \qquad \tau_p = \sin^2 \frac{ph}{2}. \tag{22.78}$$

Let $a = \sin^2 (h/2)$, and let t assume continuous values in the interval $a \leq t \leq t_0 = 1$.

We first need a lemma.

LEMMA 22.6. *Consider the family of functions defined by* $\phi_\beta(t) = (1 - \beta t)(1 + \beta t)^{-1}$ *on the interval* $t' \leq t \leq t''$, *where* $0 < t' < t''$, *for* $\beta > 0$. *Let*

$$\rho = \min_{\beta > 0} \max_{t' \leq t \leq t''} |\phi_\beta(t)|.$$

Then $\rho < 1$ *and*

$$\frac{t'}{t''} = (1 - \rho)^2(1 + \rho)^{-2}. \tag{22.79}$$

Proof. For any $\beta > 0$, the function $\phi_\beta(t)$ is strictly monotone in the interval $[t', t'']$, with $\phi_\beta(0) = 1$ and $\phi_\beta(+\infty) = -1$. Hence $\rho < 1$. As β increases, $\phi_\beta(t)$ decreases for all $t > 0$. It is therefore clear that $\max_t |\phi_\beta(t)|$ will be minimized for such a β that

$$\phi_\beta(t') = -\phi_\beta(t''). \tag{22.80}$$

[For if (22.80) failed to hold, one could decrease $\max_t |\phi_\beta(t)|$ by a slight change of β.] From (22.80) one can prove at once that the minimizing β is $(t't'')^{-1/2}$, and that

$$\rho = \frac{1 - (t'/t'')^{1/2}}{1 + (t'/t'')^{1/2}} .$$ (22.81)

But (22.79) follows from (22.81), and the lemma is completely proved.

Now let $\rho < 1$ be given. If we let $t_0 = 1$ and $t_1 = (1 - \rho)^2(1 + \rho)^{-2}t_0$, then we know by the lemma that we can choose $\alpha_1 > 0$ such that

$$\left| \frac{1 - 4\alpha_1 t}{1 + 4\alpha_1 t} \right| \le \rho \qquad \text{for } t_1 \le t \le t_0.$$ (22.82)

In the same way, if $t_k = (1 - \rho)^2(1 + \rho)^{-2}t_{k-1}$ $(k = 1, 2, \cdots, K)$, then we can choose $\alpha_k > 0$ such that

$$\left| \frac{1 - 4\alpha_k t}{1 + 4\alpha_k t} \right| \le \rho \qquad \text{for} \qquad t_k \le t \le t_{k-1}, \quad k = 1, 2, \cdots, K. \quad (22.83)$$

Now let $K = K(\rho, a)$ be the least integer such that $t_K \le a$. Since

$$t_K = \left(\frac{1 - \rho}{1 + \rho} \right)^{2K} \le a,$$

we see that

$$K \ge \frac{\log a}{2 \log \left[(1 - \rho)/(1 + \rho) \right]}$$ (22.84)

Now, since $|(1 - 4\alpha t)(1 + 4\alpha t)^{-1}| < 1$ for all $\alpha > 0$, $t > 0$, we see from (22.83) that

$$\left| \prod_{k=1}^{K} \frac{1 - 4\alpha_k t}{1 + 4\alpha_k t} \right| \le \rho \qquad \text{for } a \le t \le 1.$$ (22.85)

But then, by (22.78),

$$\left| \prod_{k=1}^{K} \mu_{p,q}(\alpha_k) \right| \le \rho \qquad \text{for all } p, q.$$ (22.86)

That is, we have found a method of picking K and $\alpha_1, \cdots, \alpha_K$ so that $|\mu'_{p,q}(\alpha_1, \cdots, \alpha_K)| \le \rho$. Although those $\alpha_1, \cdots, \alpha_K$ do not minimize (22.76), they show something of what can be accomplished.

The average rate of convergence R of the K steps is certainly no less than

$$-\frac{1}{K} \log \rho.$$ (22.87)

Since, by the derivation of (22.84),

$$K \doteq \frac{\log a}{2 \log \left[(1 - \rho)/(1 + \rho) \right]},$$

we see that, approximately,

$$R \geq - \frac{2 \log \left[(1 - \rho)/(1 + \rho)\right]}{\log a} \log \rho. \tag{22.88}$$

We should like to maximize the right-hand side of (22.88) by varying ρ. In this way we get the highest average rate of convergence for methods of this sort. Clearly the maximizing value of ρ is independent of a.

A calculation by Young [1956] shows that $\log \left[(1 - \rho)(1 + \rho)^{-1}\right] \log \rho$ is maximized when $(1 - \rho)(1 + \rho)^{-1} = \rho = \sqrt{2} - 1 \doteq 0.414$. Hence this is the best value of ρ to use in this form of the Peaceman-Rachford algorithm. The approximate inequality (22.88) then takes the form

$$R \geq - \frac{2 \log^2 (\sqrt{2} - 1)}{\log a} \doteq - \frac{1.554}{\log a} = - \frac{0.777}{\log \sin (h/2)}. \tag{22.89}$$

Thus, as $h \to 0$, we have asymptotically $R \geq 0.777/\log (1/h)$, a value which is asymptotically far larger than the rate of convergence h of the optimum successive overrelaxation method.

To see the approximate sizes of the rates of convergence, let us fix $h = \pi/45$. Then $\log \sin (h/2) = \log \sin 2° \doteq -3.36$, so that (22.89) gives the lower bound 0.231 for the rate of convergence of the Peaceman-Rachford process. For comparison, successive overrelaxation, implicit by lines, has a rate of convergence $2\sqrt{2}h = 2\sqrt{2}\pi/45 \doteq 0.198$. Thus little is gained by the Peaceman-Rachford process for $n = 45$.

How to determine the best possible α_k and the corresponding rate of convergence seems to be an open problem. However, the principles of such Čebyšev approximations are well known: It is convenient to let $\gamma_i = \alpha_i^{-1}$, and to let $\sigma_r = 4 \sin^2 (rh/2)$. Given K, one seeks $\gamma_1, \cdots, \gamma_K$ such that

$$\max_{p,q} \left| \prod_{i=1}^{K} \frac{\gamma_i - \sigma_p}{\gamma_i + \sigma_p} \frac{\gamma_i - \sigma_q}{\gamma_i + \sigma_q} \right| = \min. \tag{22.90}$$

Now let

$$F(p) = \prod_{i=1}^{K} \frac{\gamma_i - \sigma_p}{\gamma_i + \sigma_p}.$$

The minimization of (22.90) is equivalent to the minimization of

$$\max_{p,q} |F(p) F(q)|;$$

and this (for a square) is equivalent to the minimization of

$$\max_{p} |F(p)| \max_{q} |F(q)| = \max_{p} |F(p)|^2.$$

Hence we have only to solve the problem of minimizing $\max_p |F(p)|$, an ordinary problem in Čebyšev approximation with a nonlinear family of functions $F(p)$ depending on $\alpha_1, \cdots, \alpha_K$. We may replace this by the problem of minimizing

$$\max_{a \le x \le b} |G(x)|, \qquad G(x) = \prod_{i=1}^{K} \frac{\gamma_i - x}{\gamma_i + x}, \qquad (22.91)$$

where $a = \min \sigma_p$, $b = \max \sigma_p$. It is known (Motzkin [1949]) that the minimizing function $G(x)$ oscillates equally between $+\epsilon$ and $-\epsilon$ in the interval $[a, b]$, assuming the maximum absolute value $|G(x_i)| = \epsilon$ exactly $K + 1$ times. In fact, there exist ϵ and x_i such that

$$a = x_1 < x_2 < x_3 < \cdots < x_{K+1} = b,$$

with

$$G(x_1) = \epsilon, \; G(x_2) = -\epsilon, \; G(x_3) = \epsilon, \cdots, \; G(x_{K+1}) = (-1)^{K+1}\epsilon. \quad (22.92)$$

One can determine the x_i and ϵ from (22.92) by solving a set of nonlinear algebraic equations.

Rather similar to the method of Peaceman and Rachford is an implicit scheme by Douglas and Rachford [1956]. The latter uses the same first half-step (22.66), but follows with a second half-step

$$U_k = U_{k-1/2} - \alpha_k A^V (U_k - U_{k-1}). \qquad (22.93)$$

From (22.66) and (22.93), one finds that $E_k = D(\alpha_k)E_{k-1}$, where

$$D(\alpha) = (I + \alpha A^V)^{-1}(I + \alpha A^H)^{-1}(I + \alpha^2 A^H A^V),$$

which is similar to $(I + \alpha A^H)^{-1}(I + \alpha^2 A^H A^V)(I + \alpha A^V)^{-1}$. A theorem analogous to Theorem 22.5 can be proved. For general regions it is an open question as to which converges faster: successive overrelaxation by points, the Peaceman-Rachford scheme, or that of Douglas and Rachford.

The latter two methods look ideally adapted for solving Poisson's equation over a rectangle. Birkhoff and Varga show their utility also for equations of type

$$-\Delta_h U + \sigma U = B,$$

where $\sigma \ge 0$ is constant.

22.5. Summary of Rates of Convergence for a Square

To give a quick comparison of the rates of convergence of the iterative methods of Secs. 21 and 22, we list them for the square of side π, divided into n^2 mesh squares, with $nh = \pi$. There are $(n - 1)^2$ interior nodes R_h. The rates of convergence are valid for the solution of Poisson's equation with Dirichlet boundary conditions (U fixed on boundary). Here the five-point formula $\Delta_h U$ is given by (20.51), and the nine-point formula $\Delta_h^{(9)} U$ is

given by (20.56). Those results which were derived earlier are given a
page reference. The rates of convergence are only the first terms of a
power series in h.

Method	Approximate Rate of Convergence	Page
Simultaneous displacements	$h^2/2$	230
Successive displacements	h^2	255
Richardson (with period K)		
$K \doteq \infty$	h	231
$K \doteq 2n$	$0.89h$	232
$K \doteq n$	$0.78h$	232
$K \doteq n/2$	$0.59h$	232
Optimum successive overrelaxation by points, for Δ_h	$2h$	256
Optimum successive overrelaxation by points, for $\Delta_h^{(9)}$	$2.04h$	266
Simultaneous displacements, implicit by lines (either Δ_h or $\Delta_h^{(9)}$)	h^2	270
Successive displacements, implicit by lines (either Δ_h or $\Delta_h^{(9)}$)	$2h^2$	—
Optimum successive overrelaxation, implicit by lines (either Δ_h or $\Delta_h^{(9)}$)	$2\sqrt{2}h$	271
Peaceman-Rachford	$>0.777/\ln(1/h)$	281
Douglas-Rachford	$>0.535/\ln(1/h)$	—

SECTION 23. DISCRETIZATION AND ROUND-OFF ERRORS

23.1. The Method of Gerschgorin

The best-known method for the appraisal of the discretization error

$$w = U - u \qquad (2.31)$$

involved in the replacement of an elliptic boundary-value problem for the
function u by a difference problem for a function U goes back to a paper
by Gerschgorin [1930]. This method resembles in structure the general
scheme explained in Sec. 7.2, and shares with it the shortcomings mentioned on various occasions: it yields bounds on the discretization error
that can be effectively used in computing only if some bounds on the

derivatives of the unknown function u are available. Lacking such know-ledge, only the order of magnitude of the error with respect to the mesh lengths is furnished. Moreover, the method, at least in its original form, applies only to problems whose data are sufficiently regular to guarantee the boundedness of the derivatives of u that enter the arguments. In spite of these drawbacks, Gerschgorin's technique is important, since it is frequently the only way to get some information on the goodness of a proposed difference procedure.

We shall first describe this method in the case of a particular difference approximation to Dirichlet's problem for Laplace's equation in two dimensions. In Secs. 23.3 and 23.4 it will be shown that the reasoning is capable of a very wide generalization. Let R be an open, bounded, con-nected region with boundary C, and denote by u the solution of the prob-lem

$$\Delta u = 0 \quad \text{in} \quad R, \qquad u = f(x, y) \quad \text{on} \quad C. \qquad (23.2)$$

It is assumed that f and R are sufficiently smooth for this problem to pos-sess a solution continuous in $\bar{R} = R \cup C$. (The uniqueness of u is an immediate consequence of the maximum principle of Sec. 19.5.)

Let R_1 be the subset of points (x, y) of R such that all points of type $(x + \xi h, y)$ and $(x, y + \xi h)$, $|\xi| \leq 1$, lie in $\bar{R}$, and let $R_2 = R - R_1$. At the points of R_1, we approximate Laplace's equation by the difference equation

$$U(x, y) = \tfrac{1}{4}U(x + h, y) + \tfrac{1}{4}U(x - h, y) + \tfrac{1}{4}U(x, y + h) + \tfrac{1}{4}U(x, y - h),$$

$$(x, y) \in R_1. \qquad (23.3)$$

With every point (x, y) of R_2, we associate a different and simpler differ-ence equation obtained by linear interpolation. More precisely: since $(x, y) \in R_2$, at least one grid line through (x, y) meets C at a point (x', y') at distance $h' < h$ from (x, y). Let (x'', y'') be the point of that grid line at distance h on the other side of (x, y), provided this net point lies in $R \cup C$. Otherwise, (x'', y'') is to be the nearest point of C on that side of the grid line. In either case, the distance h'' from (x, y) to (x'', y'') does not exceed h. Then we require the function U to satisfy the following relation analo-gous to (20.67):

$$U(x, y) = \frac{h' \, U(x'', y'') + h'' \, U(x', y')}{h' + h''}, \qquad (x, y) \in R_2. \qquad (23.4)$$

The value of $U(x', y')$ is to be taken as equal to $f(x', y')$. If (x'', y'') is in R, another one of the equations of set (23.3) or (23.4) is associated with it. If $(x'', y'') \in C$, then $U(x'', y'') = f(x'', y'')$. Observe that R_1 and R_2 depend on h only, but not on any particular position of the grid of mesh length h. Thus (23.3) and (23.4) together define a linear difference equation *at every point of R.* This formulation is not intended to imply that the problem should be solved analytically for all points of R, a task difficult even in a rectangle. Our reason for introducing R_1 and R_2 at this time is to prepare the reader for the more general discussion in Secs. 23.2, 23.3, and 23.4. For any fixed grid of mesh length h equations (23.3) and (23.4), together with the boundary condition

$$U(x, y) = f(x, y), \qquad (x, y) \in C, \tag{23.5}$$

constitute a set of as many linear algebraic equations as there are grid points in R. The unknowns of this system are the values of U at the grid points.

It should be noted that in this example equation (23.4) is not a formal approximation to Laplace's equation in particular. The same interpolation scheme near the boundary can be applied to any Dirichlet problem.

Much as equations (23.3) and (23.4) differ, they have one important common feature: they represent $U(x, y)$ as a weighted average with positive weights of the values of U at a certain nearby point set. In somewhat modified form this property will be present, and prove to be decisive, in the generalization to be given later. It leads immediately to the following fundamental discrete analog of the maximum principle of Sec. 19.5:

MAXIMUM PRINCIPLE. *A function U defined in the points of a square grid of mesh length h in R, as well as on C, and satisfying* (23.3) *or* (23.4) *(respectively) at the grid points in R_1 and R_2 is at no interior grid point greater than its maximum on C.*

Proof. Since U is a weighted average with positive weights, the value of U at any interior grid point does not exceed its largest value at the neighboring points that occur in the difference equation valid at that point. If the equation that applies at the point is (23.4), the statement is proved for this grid point. Otherwise, the same argument applies to all four neighbors of the original point, and so forth, until a point with neighbors on C is reached.

Application of the maximum principle to the function $-U(x, y)$ proves that U does not fall below its minimum on C at any grid point in R.

A first important consequence of the maximum principle is the *uniqueness* of the solution of the problem defined by equations (23.3), (23.4), (23.5). In fact, if there are two solutions of (23.3) and (23.4) satisfying the same boundary condition (23.5), then their difference is itself a solution of (23.3) and (23.4) that vanishes everywhere on C. Such a solution must be identically zero by virtue of the maximum-minimum principle. The uniqueness of the solution implies its *existence* in this case. For the determination of U at any given point (x, y) of R requires the solution of a set of linear algebraic equations with as many equations as unknowns.

That for such a system the existence of a solution follows from its uniqueness is an elementary theorem of linear algebra.

It will be convenient to abbreviate the notation and to write (23.3) and (23.4) in the combined form

$$\mathscr{L}(U) = 0. \tag{23.6}$$

Here $\mathscr{L}$ is the linear operator defined by

$$\mathscr{L}(U) = \begin{cases} \frac{1}{4}U(x+h, y) + \frac{1}{4}U(x-h, y) + \frac{1}{4}U(x, y+h) \\ \qquad + \frac{1}{4}U(x, y-h) - U(x, y), \qquad (x, y) \in R_1, \\ \dfrac{h'}{h'+h''} U(x'', y'') + \dfrac{h''}{h'+h''} U(x', y') - U(x, y), \\ \qquad\qquad\qquad\qquad\qquad\qquad (x, y) \in R_2. \end{cases} \tag{23.7}$$

In analogy with what was done earlier (see, e.g., Sec. 7.2), the first step in the appraisal of the discretization error consists in regarding $w = U - u$ as the solution of the discrete problem

$$\mathscr{L}(w) = -\mathscr{L}(u) \qquad \text{in } R,$$
$$w = 0 \qquad\qquad \text{on } C. \tag{23.8}$$

Since $\mathscr{L}$ is a formal approximation to Δ, the quantity $\mathscr{L}(u)$ can be expected to be small for small h. We find indeed, by Taylor's formula,

$$\mathscr{L}(u) = \begin{cases} \dfrac{h^4}{96}[u_{x^4}(x+\theta h, y) + u_{x^4}(x-\theta h, y) + u_{y^4}(x, y+\theta h) \\ \qquad\qquad + u_{y^4}(x, y-\theta h)], \quad (x, y) \in R_1 \\ \dfrac{1}{2}\left[\dfrac{h'h''^2}{h'+h''} u_{x^2}(x - \theta'h'', y) + \dfrac{h''h'^2}{h'+h''} u_{x^2}(x + \theta'h', y)\right], \\ \qquad\qquad\qquad\qquad\qquad (x, y) \in R_2, \end{cases} \tag{23.9}$$

where $0 < \theta < 1, 0 < \theta' < 1$, and the subscripts indicate repeated partial differentiations. In the second of these formulas it has been assumed, for the sake of simplicity, that the points (x'', y''), (x, y), (x', y') have the same ordinate, and that $x'' < x < x'$, since this formula varies in a trivial manner with the configuration of the three points. Now we introduce the decisive assumption that *the derivatives of u occurring in* (23.9) *are bounded in* $\bar{R}$. Then (23.9) leads to

$$|\mathscr{L}(u)| \leq \begin{cases} \frac{1}{24}M_4 h^4, & (x, y) \in R_1 \\ \frac{1}{2}M_2 h^2, & (x, y) \in R_2, \end{cases} \tag{23.10}$$

where M_r denotes an upper bound in $\bar{R}$ for the absolute values of all partial derivatives of order r of $u(x, y)$.

In order to appraise w on the basis of (23.8) and (23.10), we need the following slight modification of the maximum principle:

LEMMA 23.1. *Let v be a function defined in $\bar{R}$ such that $\mathscr{L}(v) \geq 0$ everywhere in a subdomain R^* of R. Then*

$$\sup_{R^*} v \leq \sup_{\bar{R} - R^*} v. \tag{23.11}$$

Proof. $\mathscr{L}(v) \geq 0$ in R^* implies that at every point of R^* the value of v does not exceed the largest value of v in certain neighboring points. If one of these neighbors lies in $\bar{R} - R^*$, the lemma is proved; if all neighbors are in R^* the same argument can be applied to them until a point in $\bar{R} - R^*$ is reached.

Gerschgorin's original argument made use of this maximum principle for the whole domain R. His idea was to construct explicitly a small auxiliary comparison function ϕ such that $\phi \geq 0$ on C and $\mathscr{L}(\phi) \leq -|\mathscr{L}(u)|$ in R. Combination with (23.8) leads then to $\mathscr{L}(\pm w - \phi) \geq 0$ in R, $\pm w - \phi \leq 0$ on C. (By writing $\pm$ we mean that these inequalities are true for the upper as well as for the lower sign.) Hence, by the maximum principle, $\pm w - \phi \leq 0$ in R; i.e., $|w| \leq \phi$, which is the desired estimate. However, in many applications such a function ϕ is difficult to construct, because the definition of $\mathscr{L}$ is not the same in R_1 and in R_2. The construction of ϕ is much easier if $\mathscr{L}(\phi) \leq -|\mathscr{L}(u)|$ is required only in an interior subset of R where $\mathscr{L}$ has a simple structure.

In the present case such a comparison function is easily found in R_1. In fact, let (x_0, y_0) be the center of the circumscribed circle of R and let r be its radius. The function

$$Q(x, y) = r^2 - (x - x_0)^2 - (y - y_0)^2 \tag{23.12}$$

is then nonnegative in R, and

$$\mathscr{L}(Q) = -h^2 \qquad \text{in } R_1, \tag{23.13}$$

as can be readily verified. Hence, by (23.10) and (23.13),

$$\mathscr{L}\left(\frac{M_4}{24} h^2 Q\right) \leq -|\mathscr{L}(u)|, \qquad (x, y) \in R_1, \tag{23.14}$$

and, because of (23.8),

$$\mathscr{L}\left(\pm w - \frac{M_4}{24} h^2 Q\right) \geq 0 \qquad \text{in } R_1. \tag{23.15}$$

The preceding lemma, with $R^* = R_1$, shows then that

$$\sup_{R_1} \left(\pm w - \frac{M_4}{24} h^2 Q \right) \leq \sup_{\bar{R} - R_1} \left(\pm w - \frac{M_4}{24} h^2 Q \right) \leq \sup_{\bar{R} - R_1} |w|,$$

or

$$\sup_{R_1} |w| \leq \sup_{\bar{R} - R_1} |w| + \frac{M_4}{24} h^2 \sup_R Q. \qquad (23.16)$$

This inequality contains *two* unknown quantities: $\sup_{R_1} |w|$ and $\sup_{\bar{R} - R_1} |w|$. We therefore need a second inequality linking these numbers. To find it, we observe that at least one of the two numbers $h'/(h' + h'')$, $h''/(h' + h'')$ does not exceed $\frac{1}{2}$, and that then the corresponding point (x', y') or (x'', y''), respectively, lies on C, where $w = 0$. To fix the ideas, let (x', y') be that point. Then (23.8) and the second inequality in (23.10) imply the relation

$$|w(x, y)| \leq \frac{h'}{h' + h''} |w(x'', y'')| + \frac{M_2}{2} h^2, \qquad (x, y) \in R_2, \quad (23.17)$$

i.e.,

$$\sup_{\bar{R} - R_1} |w| \leq \frac{1}{2} \sup_{R_1} |w| + \frac{M_2}{2} h^2. \qquad (23.18)$$

Solving the simultaneous inequalities (23.16) and (23.18) yields the final inequality

$$|w| \leq 2(\tfrac{1}{24} M_4 h^2 \sup_R Q + \tfrac{1}{2} M_2 h^2) \qquad \text{in } R_1. \qquad (23.19)$$

It is plausible that the foregoing method should be capable of wide generalization. It is desirable to present it in a form that applies to as large a class of difference approximations as possible, rather than to give a separate proof for each problem. There are many variable elements in this class of problem: the differential equation to be approximated, the kind of grid used (square, rectangular, hexagonal, irregular, etc.), the number of dimensions, the difference formula to be used in the chosen grid, and the interpolation technique near the boundary. An extension of Gerschgorin's method which includes so many possibilities must, by necessity, be somewhat condensed in its notation. As always, the generality gained in this way has to be paid for by a slight additional effort of interpretation each time the results are applied to a concrete case.

23.2. An Integral Equation with a Stieltjes Kernel

The best way to denote in a unified way a class of summations that may be extended over sets of points in an unspecified grid, regular or not, is to employ Stieltjes integrals. Almost all difference problems that have

actually been used to approximate Dirichlet problems for elliptic differential equations can be regarded as special instances of an integral
equation with a Stieltjes kernel of the form

$$U(x) = \begin{cases} \int_{\dot{R}} U(y)\, dF(y, x), & x \in R, \\ f(x), & x \in C. \end{cases} \tag{23.20}$$

Here are the explanations of the symbols used in this formula: x and
y are points of n-dimensional Euclidean space. The integration refers
(here and in the sequel) to the first of the two variables in the kernel.
Unless we explicitly specify the contrary, all Stieltjes integrations are
performed over bounded, connected Borel sets. (A set is said to be a Borel
set if it can be constructed from n-dimensional intervals by denumerably
many unions, intersections, and subtractions of sets.) R is open, with
boundary C, and $\bar{R} = R \cup C$. The functions $F(y, x)$ and $f(x)$ are bounded
and Borel-measurable, for $x \in \bar{R}$, $y \in \bar{R}$. [A function $g(x)$ is called
Borel-measurable in $\bar{R}$ if the subset of points in $\bar{R}$ for which $g(x) \leq k$ is a
Borel set, for every k.] The integral is a Lebesgue-Stieltjes integral (Cramér
[1946], p. 80).

The following condition must hold for $F(y, x)$.

CONDITION 1.   *For every set $S \subseteq \bar{R}$ and every $x \in \bar{R}$,*

$$0 \leq \int_S dF(y, x) \leq 1. \tag{23.21}$$

Equations (23.3), (23.4), and (23.5) constitute a simple example of an
equation of type (23.20) satisfying Condition 1. This condition is satisfied
because the coefficients in (23.3) as well as in (23.4) are nonnegative and
have a sum that does not exceed unity. An example of a difference formula that does not satisfy (23.21) is obtained if the two-dimensional
Dirichlet problem

$$\Delta u(x) + \lambda^2\, u(x) = 0, \qquad x \in R,$$
$$u(x) = f(x), \qquad x \in C, \tag{23.22}$$

is approximated by the discrete problem

$$\Delta_h U(x) + \lambda^2\, U(x) = 0, \qquad\qquad\qquad x \in R_1,$$
$$U(x) = \frac{h'\, U(x'') + h''\, U(x')}{h' + h''}, \qquad x \in R_2, \tag{23.23}$$
$$U(x) = f(x), \qquad\qquad\qquad\qquad x \in C.$$

The notation in (23.23) is the same as in Sec. 23.1, except that the letter x now stands where (x, y) was written before. The form of (23.23) that corresponds to (23.20) is

$$
U(x) = \begin{cases}
\dfrac{1}{4 - h^2\lambda^2} U(x^{(1)}) + \dfrac{1}{4 - h^2\lambda^2} U(x^{(2)}) + \dfrac{1}{4 - h^2\lambda^2} U(x^{(3)}) \\
\qquad\qquad + \dfrac{1}{4 - h^2\lambda^2} U(x^{(4)}), \qquad x \in R_1 \\[2mm]
\dfrac{h''}{h' + h''} U(x') + \dfrac{h'}{h' + h''} U(x''), \qquad\qquad x \in R_2 \\[2mm]
f(x), \qquad\qquad\qquad\qquad\qquad\qquad\qquad\quad x \in C,
\end{cases}
$$

where $x^{(i)}$ ($i = 1, 2, 3, 4$) are the four grid points at distance h from x. Obviously Condition 1 is not satisfied for x in R_1 if $\lambda > 0$. Of course, problem (23.22) has a solution for reasonably smooth data, unless λ^2 is an eigenvalue, but whether (23.23) yields an approximation to this solution is a more difficult question. (See Saul'ev [1957] for an affirmative answer by different methods, under certain hypotheses.)

In spite of its generality, formulation (23.20) excludes some applications. Instead of *inter*polating at the boundary, it is also possible to introduce exterior points at which the value of the solution is determined by some *extra*polation scheme (Collatz [1933]). It is doubtless possible to include such methods in the integral equation formulation by extending the definition of $F(y, x)$ and the domain of integration into the whole space.

A formulation similar to, but not identical with, (23.20) was originally introduced by Petrowsky [1934]. There $F(y, x)$ is defined in the whole space E and $\int_E dF(y, x) \equiv 1$. The starting point of that author is a probability interpretation of such integral equations as (23.20). Let us consider a particle at the point x which, at a given instant, either performs a jump so as to land with probability $\int_S dF(y, x)$ in any given set S, or disappears with probability $1 - \int_R dF(y, x)$. (In the example of the preceding section the last quantity is always zero.) A sequence of such jumps is a *random walk* that may terminate at a point of R, or may reach a point of C, after which the walk is considered terminated. Or, finally, it may stay indefinitely in R. If we attribute to each walk that ends at a point y of C the value $f(y)$ and the value zero to the other walks, then *the solution of (23.20), if it exists, is the expected value of $f(y)$ for random walks starting at x, whenever this expected value exists.* Let us demonstrate this fact under the assumption that the probability of a random walk reaching the boundary C in a finite number of steps is 1. The simplification introduced in this manner is not essential. Then there exists a cumulative probability function $P(z, x)$, for

$z \in C$, such that $\int_\Gamma dP(z, x)$ is the probability that a random walk starting from $x \in R$ will terminate on the subset Γ of C. By the law of composition of probabilities,

$$P(z, x) = \int_R P(z, y)\, dF(y, x).$$

The expected value of f, i.e., $\int_C f(z)\, dP(z, x)$, therefore satisfies the integral equation

$$\int_C f(z)\, dP(z, x) = \int_R \int_C f(z)\, dP(z, y)\, dF(y, x), \qquad x \in R.$$

From the definition of $P(z, x)$ it is clear that also

$$\int_C f(z)\, dP(z, x) = f(x) \qquad \text{for } x \in C.$$

Hence $\int_C f(z)\, dP(z, x)$ satisfies (23.20), as claimed.

The probability interpretation of discrete approximations to elliptic differential equations is frequently helpful to the proper understanding of their mathematical properties. It can also be exploited numerically since it opens the possibility of solving the approximating discrete problem numerically by simulating a large number of random walks in a computing machine ("Monte Carlo" method). There exists an extensive literature on this approach. So far, however, these statistical methods have not proved practically useful for the solution of Dirichlet problems. We shall therefore not enter further into this subject.

It is nevertheless interesting to realize that equation (23.20) applies also to random walks that do not take place in a preassigned finite point set. The following is an example of such a walk. Consider a particle in the plane that performs jumps of fixed length h in such a way that all directions are equally probable. The particle starts from a point P in the region R, and the walk terminates when the particle arrives for the first time at a point Q whose distance from the boundary C is less than h. If the function f is prescribed on the boundary, let us assign to this walk the score $f(\bar{Q})$, for some point $\bar{Q}$ of C closest to Q. If R_1 is the subset of R formed by the points at distance h or more from C, the expected value of the score of this random walk satisfies the integral-equation problem

$$U(x, y) = \begin{cases} \dfrac{1}{2\pi} \displaystyle\int_0^{2\pi} U(x + h \cos\theta, y + h \sin\theta)\, d\theta, & (x, y) \in R_1, \\[2ex] f(\bar{x}, \bar{y}), & (x, y) \in R - R_1, \\[1ex] f(x, y), & (x, y) \in C, \end{cases}$$

where $(\bar{x}, \bar{y})$ are the coordinates of $\bar{Q}$. This is clearly a problem of type

(23.20). [The pair of scalars (x, y) corresponds to the vector x in the notation of (23.20).]

The preceding particular integral-equation problem constitutes a formal approximation to Dirichlet's problem for Laplace's equation, for, if the right member of the integral equation is developed in powers of h, we find, for sufficiently regular U, an expression of the form $U + h^2 \Delta U + O(h^4)$. If U is a harmonic function, the integral reduces to $U(x, y)$ itself, in consequence of the mean value theorem (19.61) for harmonic functions. In this sense this integral equation is the best possible approximation to Laplace's equation. This does not mean that the solution U of the integral-equation problem is exactly equal to the solution of the corresponding Dirichlet problem

$$\Delta u = 0 \text{ in } R, \qquad u = f \text{ on } C,$$

because u does not, in general, satisfy the condition imposed on U in $R - R_1$. The only thing we can say is that for this particular approximation to Dirichlet's problem, the discretization error originates entirely in the boundary strip. We shall soon show that the discretization error is here $O(h)$, whereas the difference approximation discussed in Sec. 23.1 involved an error of order $O(h^2)$ [formula (23.19)]. The perfect accuracy of the approximation in R_1 is therefore spoiled by the coarseness of the interpolation at the boundary.

By taking the probability interpretation as a heuristic guide one can construct a whole class of integral equations depending on a small parameter that are formal approximations to Dirichlet's problem for elliptic linear partial differential equations of order two. The treatment of the discretization error to be given now is sufficiently general to include most of these approximations. Deeper studies of these questions can be found in Lüneberg [1930], Petrowsky [1934], Khintchine [1933], and Wasow [1951, 1951a, 1951b].

The existence and uniqueness of a solution $U(x)$ of (23.20) require a proof. In the example of the preceding section, this proof was based on the maximum principle and on facts from linear algebra. In the present general case we must proceed differently. The reasoning below resembles that in Petrowsky [1934]. As shown there, some additional restriction on $F(y, x)$ is needed to guarantee uniqueness. The following condition was introduced by Petrowsky.

CONDITION 2. *Let* $F_1(y, x) = F(y, x)$, $F_r(y, x) = \int_R F_{r-1}(y, z) \, dF(z, x)$, $r > 1$. *Then there exist a positive integer m and a number $\delta < 1$, both independent of x, such that*

$$\int_R dF_m(y, x) \leq \delta, \qquad x \in R.$$

This condition has a simple probability interpretation: By the law of composition of probabilities $F_2(y, x) = \int_R F_1(y, z)\, dF(z, x)$ is the probability that a particle starting from x will after *two* jumps be in the part of $\bar{R}$ where all coordinates are less than the corresponding ones of y. Generally, $F_r(y, x)$ is the analogous probability after r jumps. The above equation therefore represents the hypothesis that the probability for the random walk to be ended after m jumps is *positive*. From this it follows in particular that the probability of random walks of infinite duration (i.e., with infinitely many jumps) is zero. It is easy to verify that Condition 2 is always satisfied in the difference schemes of practical usefulness. Let us illustrate this with the example of the preceding section. Let x be a point in R_2 and assume that x' (say) is on C. As was pointed out in the preceding section, this implies that $h''/(h' + h'') \geq \frac{1}{2}$. But this quantity is precisely the probability of jumping from x to the point x' on C in one jump. If x is in R_1, the first jump of the walk has the probability $\frac{1}{4}$ of ending at the point with coordinates $(x_1 + h, x_2)$, if (x_1, x_2) are the coordinates of x. Since R_1 is bounded, there exists a positive integer r such that $(x_1 + rh, x_2)$ is a point of R_2 or of C. In any case, the probability of leaving R in $r + 1$ jumps is not less than $\frac{1}{2}4^{-r}$. The number r depends on x but, as R is bounded, we have certainly

$$\int_R dF_m(y, x) \leq 1 - \frac{1}{2}\, 4^{-D/h}, \qquad \text{for } m \geq \frac{D}{h} + 1,$$

if D is the diameter of R.

THEOREM 23.2. *If $F(y, x)$ satisfies Conditions 1 and 2, problem (23.20) possesses one and only one bounded and Borel-measurable solution.*

Proof. Suppose, for the moment, that $f(x)$ is nowhere negative. Set

$$U_0(x) = \begin{cases} 0, & x \in R, \\ f(x), & x \in C, \end{cases} \tag{23.24}$$

and

$$U_{r+1}(x) = \begin{cases} \displaystyle\int_{\bar{R}} U_r(y)\, dF(y, x), & x \in R, \\ f(x), & x \in C \end{cases} \qquad r = 0, 1, \cdots. \tag{23.25}$$

Then it follows that

$$U_1(x) = \int_C f(y)\, dF(y, x), \qquad x \in R$$

and, by induction,

$$U_r(x) = \sum_{j=1}^{r} q_j(x), \qquad x \in R, \tag{23.26}$$

with

$$q_1(x) = \int_C f(y)\, dF(y,\, x), \qquad q_{j+1}(x) = \int_R q_j(y)\, dF(y,\, x). \quad (23.27)$$

The $q_j(x)$ are nonnegative, and the $U_r(x)$ therefore form a nondecreasing sequence. Iterating (23.25) m times, we find, for $r > m$,

$$U_{r+1}(x) = \int_R U_{r-m}(x)\, dF_m(y,\, x) + \chi(x), \qquad x \in R, \quad (23.28)$$

where $\chi(x)$ is bounded and nonnegative. In view of Condition 2 and of the nondecreasing character of the sequence $U_r(x)$, we can conclude from (23.28) that

$$0 \le \sup_{x \in R} U_{r+1}(x) \le \delta \sup_{x \in R} U_{r+1}(x) + \sup_{x \in R} \chi(x),$$

and, therefore, that

$$0 \le U_{r+1}(x) \le (1 - \delta)^{-1} \sup_{x \in R} \chi(x), \qquad x \in R.$$

This shows that the monotonic sequence $U_r(x)$ is bounded. Hence the limit $\lim_{r \to \infty} U_r(x) = U(x)$ exists. This function is bounded, Lebesgue-integrable, and satisfies the integral equation (23.20) (see Cramér [1946], p. 74).

If $f(x)$ is partly negative, consider the two problems

$$U^{(1)}(x) = \begin{cases} \displaystyle\int_R U^{(1)}(y)\, dF(y,\, x), & x \in R \\[2mm] \displaystyle\sup_C |f(x)|, & x \in C, \end{cases}$$

$$U^{(2)}(x) = \begin{cases} \displaystyle\int_R U^{(2)}(y)\, dF(y,\, x), & x \in R \\[2mm] \displaystyle\sup_C |f(x)| - f(x), & x \in C, \end{cases}$$

which possess solutions by what has been proved already. The function $U^{(1)} - U^{(2)}$ is then a solution of the original problem.

To prove uniqueness, it suffices to show that $f(x) \equiv 0$ implies $U(x) \equiv 0$. By means of m iterations of (23.25) with $f(x) \equiv 0$, we find

$$U(x) = \int_R U(y)\, dF_m(y,\, x),$$

and hence

$$\sup_{x \in R} |U(x)| \leq \delta \sup_{y \in R} |U(y)|.$$

As $\delta < 1$, this implies indeed $U(x) \equiv 0$.

We shall later need the following generalization of Theorem 23.2.

THEOREM 23.3. *The problem*

$$W(x) = \begin{cases} \int_{\bar{R}} W(y) \, dF(y, x) + g(x), & x \in R, \\ f(x), & x \in C, \end{cases} \tag{23.29}$$

possesses a unique solution, provided that Conditions 1 and 2 hold.

Proof. We may assume without loss of generality that $f(x) \equiv 0$, since this simplification can always be achieved by subtracting equation (23.20)—which is already known to possess a unique solution—from (23.29). The procedure is then almost the same as for the preceding theorem: We set

$$W_0(x) \equiv 0, \quad W_{r+1}(x) = \begin{cases} \int_{R} W_r(y) \, dF(y, x) + g(x), & x \in R, \\ 0, & x \in C. \end{cases}$$

[It makes no difference whether the integral is extended over R or over $\bar{R}$, since the $W_r(x)$ vanish on C.] Then

$$W_r(x) = \sum_{j=1}^{r} s_j(x), \qquad x \in R,$$

with

$$s_1(x) = g(x), \qquad s_{j+1}(x) = \int_{R} s_j(y) \, dF(y, x), \qquad x \in R.$$

If $g(x)$ does not change sign in R, one shows as before that $\lim_{r \to \infty} W_r(x)$ exists and satisfies (23.29) with $f(x) \equiv 0$.

If $g(x)$ is not everywhere in R of the same sign, problem (23.29) can be replaced by the two problems

$$W^{(1)} = \begin{cases} \int_{R} W^{(1)} \, dF - \inf_{R} g, & x \in R, \\ 0, & x \in C, \end{cases}$$

$$W^{(2)} = \begin{cases} \int_{R} W^{(2)} \, dF + g - \inf_{R} g, & x \in R, \\ 0, & x \in C. \end{cases}$$

$W = W^{(2)} - W^{(1)}$ is then a solution of (23.29). The uniqueness follows from the fact, proved before, that the homogeneous problem with $f(x) \equiv 0$ admits only the solution zero.

23.3. An Appraisal of the Solution of the Integral Equation

In this section we shall prove a maximum principle and derive from it some inequalities which are generalizations to Stieltjes integral equations of inequalities obtained in Sec. 23.1 for a particular example. If the operator $\mathscr{L}$ is defined by

$$\mathscr{L}(v) = \int_{\bar{R}} v(y) \, dF(y, x) - v(x), \tag{23.30}$$

the general maximum principle can be formulated as follows:

LEMMA 23.4 (Maximum Principle). *If Condition 1 is satisfied, and if* $R_1 \subset \bar{R}$*, then the inequality*

$$\mathscr{L}(v) \geq \epsilon > 0, \qquad for \ x \in R_1$$

implies that

$$\sup_{R_1} v(x) < \sup_{\bar{R} - R_1} v(x).$$

Proof. If the last inequality were false, we should have, for every x in R,

$$v(x) \leq \sup_{R_1} v \int_{R_1} dF(y, x) + \sup_{\bar{R} - R_1} v \int_{\bar{R} - R_1} dF(y, x) - \epsilon \leq \sup_{R_1} v - \epsilon,$$

which is absurd.

The statement and proof of Lemma 23.1 in Sec. 23.1 do not strictly form a particular case of Lemma 23.4. Since in Lemma 23.1 we were dealing with finite sums rather than with a Stieltjes integral, the positive lower bound ϵ could there be dispensed with. The next lemma prepares the ground for the use of a comparison function, as in Sec. 23.1.

LEMMA 23.5. *Let* $F(y, x)$ *be a function satisfying Condition* 1*, and let* K_1 *be a constant such that*

$$|\mathscr{L}(v)| \leq K_1, \qquad x \in R_1 \subset \bar{R}. \tag{23.31}$$

If $q(x)$ *is a nonnegative function in* $\bar{R}$ *such that*

$$\mathscr{L}(q) \leq -1, \qquad x \in R_1, \tag{23.32}$$

then

$$\sup_{R_1} |v| \leq K_1 \sup_{R_1} q + \sup_{\bar{R} - R_1} |v|. \tag{23.33}$$

Proof. Let K_1^* be a constant with $K_1^* > K_1$. It follows from (23.31) and (23.32) that

$$\mathscr{L}(\pm v - K_1^* q) \geq K_1^* - K_1 > 0, \qquad x \in R_1, \qquad (23.34)$$

and therefore, by Lemma 23.4, that

$$\sup_{R_1} (\pm v - K_1^* q) < \sup_{\bar{R} - R_1} (\pm v - K_1^* q) \leq \sup_{\bar{R} - R_1} |v|.$$

Hence

$$\sup_{R_1} |v| \leq K_1^* \sup_{R_1} q + \sup_{\bar{R} - R_1} |v|,$$

and (23.33) follows by letting K_1^* tend to K_1.

As in Sec. 23.1, we need a second inequality linking $\sup_{R_1} |v|$ and $\sup_{\bar{R} - R_1} |v|$. In the application to the discretization error, v vanishes on the boundary, and $R_2 = R - R_1$ is a strip near the boundary characterized by the property that not all the contributions to $\int_R dF(y, x)$ come from the interior R of $\bar{R}$, when $x \in R_2$. This motivates the hypotheses of the next lemma.

LEMMA 23.6. *Let*

$$|\mathscr{L}(v)| \leq K_2 \qquad for \ x \in R - R_1, \qquad (23.35)$$

and assume that, in addition to the hypotheses of Lemma 23.5,

$$v(x) = 0 \qquad for \ x \in C, \qquad (23.36)$$

and that

$$\int_{\bar{R}} dF(y, x) \leq k < 1 \qquad for \ x \in R - R_1. \qquad (23.37)$$

Then

$$|v(x)| \leq \frac{1}{1 - k} (K_1 \sup_{\bar{R}} q + K_2) \qquad for \ x \in R. \qquad (23.38)$$

Proof. Because of inequality (23.35), we can use (23.30) to prove that

$$|v(x)| \leq \int_{\bar{R}} v(y) \, dF(y, x) + K_2, \qquad x \in R - R_1.$$

Application of (23.36) and (23.37) leads to

$$\sup_{\bar{R} - R_1} |v| \leq k \sup_{R_1} |v| + K_2, \qquad (23.39)$$

or

$$\sup_{\bar{R} - R_1} |v| \leq k \sup_{\bar{R} - R_1} |v| + K_2, \qquad (23.40)$$

depending on whether the upper bound of $v(x)$ is greater in R_1 or in $R - R_1$. The inequality (23.33) combined with (23.39) or with (23.40) constitutes, in either case, a system of two simultaneous inequalities for $\sup_{R_1} |v|$ and $\sup_{\hat{R}-R_1} |v|$. An easy calculation leads, in either case, to inequalities that imply (23.38).

23.4. Appraisal of the Discretization Error

Let $u(x)$ be the solution of the problem

$$L(u) = 0, \qquad x \in R,$$
$$u = f(x), \qquad x \in C, \qquad (23.41)$$

where

$$L(u) = \frac{1}{2} \sum_{i,k=1}^{n} a_{ik}(x) \frac{\partial^2 u}{\partial x_i \, \partial x_k} + \sum_{j=1}^{n} b_j(x) \, u_j(x) + c(x)u \qquad (23.42)$$

is an elliptic differential expression in R. The data of this problem should be such that it possesses a unique solution. If U is the solution of problem (23.20), the difference $w = U - u$ solves the problem

$$w(x) = \begin{cases} \displaystyle\int_{\hat{R}} w(y) \, dF(y, x) + \mathscr{L}(u), & x \in R, \\[2mm] 0, & x \in C. \end{cases} \qquad (23.43)$$

This much is true regardless of any relation between the discrete and the differential problems. If we wish w to be small, $\mathscr{L}(u)$ has to be small. In the example of Sec. 23.1 we had $\mathscr{L}(u) = O(h^2)$, where h was the mesh length, which is considered a small parameter in this context. Whenever $\mathscr{L}$ is defined in terms of a regular grid, a mesh length h is the natural parameter to use. However, as we have seen, our present theory includes operators $\mathscr{L}$ of a much more general nature. It is therefore advisable at this stage not to make any commitment as to the geometric interpretation of the parameter in $\mathscr{L}$. We consider a family of kernels $F(y, x; \mu)$ involving a parameter μ, and try to define properties of $F(y, x; \mu)$ which will make $\mathscr{L}(u)$ tend to zero with μ with a preassigned order of magnitude. The relation between the parameter μ in this general formulation and the mesh length, whenever the approximation is based on a regular grid, must be investigated in each individual problem. Since in most applications the definition of $F(y, x)$ has to be modified in a strip near the boundary, we divide R into an interior region R_1 and a strip $R - R_1 = R_2$ near the boundary, and require different properties from $F(y, x; \mu)$ according as $x \in R_1$ or $x \in R_2$.

Taylor's formula for $u(y)$ about the point x, up to terms of degree $p - 1$, can be written

$$u(y) = P(y, x) + \frac{1}{p!} \left[\sum_{j=1}^{n} (y_j - x_j) \frac{\partial}{\partial \tilde{x}_j} \right]^p u(\tilde{x}), \qquad x, y \in \bar{R}. \qquad (23.44)$$

The function $P(y, x)$ is a polynomial in the components $y_j - x_j$, ($j = 1$, $2, \cdots, n$) of $y - x$ of degree $p - 1$ at most. The symbols $\tilde{x}_j$, $\tilde{x}$ in the remainder term are to be treated as variables in the indicated differentiations and are then to be replaced by a certain (unknown) point in R. The points x and y may lie anywhere in R or even on the boundary C if the partial derivatives of order $p - 1$ are continuous at these points.

CONDITION 3. (a) *There is an integer $p > 0$ such that for the solution $u(x)$ of the problem (23.41) the function $P(y, x)$ defined in (23.44) satisfies the integral equation*

$$P(x, x) - \int_{\bar{R}} P(y, x) \, dF(y, x; \mu) = 0, \qquad x \in R_1.$$

(b) *There exist positive constants B_1 and α such that*

$$\frac{1}{p!} \int_{\bar{R}} \left(\sum_{j=1}^{n} |y_j - x_j| \right)^p dF(y, x; \mu) \le B_1 \mu^{\alpha}, \qquad x \in R_1. \qquad (23.45)$$

To illustrate the meaning of this condition, let us assume that $L(u) = 0$ in R_1 is replaced by an approximating difference equation of the form

$$L_h(U) \equiv \sum_{s=0}^{N} c_s \, U(x + m_s h) = 0, \qquad (23.46)$$

where the c_s are scalar functions of x and h, and the m_s are n-dimensional vectors with integral components m_{s_i}. Let $m_0 = 0$. In Motzkin and Wasow [1953] it is proved that there exist expressions of the form (23.46) that approximate $L(u)$ in the formal sense and which are of *positive type*, i.e., for which in R

$$c_s > 0, \qquad \text{for } s = 1, 2, \cdots, N, \qquad c_0 < 0. \qquad (23.47)$$

Now, to say that (23.46) is a formal approximation to $L(u)$ means that, after division by a suitable normalization factor, the formal Taylor expression of the left member of (23.46) about x begins with the expression $L(U)$. This condition is expressed by the equations

$$\sum_{s=0}^{N} c_s - c(x) = 0, \qquad (23.48)$$

$$\sum_{s=1}^{N} c_s m_{s_j} h - b_j(x) = 0, \qquad j = 1, \cdots, n, \qquad (23.49)$$

$$\sum_{s=1}^{N} c_s m_{s_i} m_{s_k} h^2 - a_{ik}(x) = 0, \qquad i, k = 1, \cdots, n; \qquad (23.50)$$

see (20.6). If (23.46) is written in the form

$$U(x) = \sum_{s=1}^{N} \frac{c_s}{-c_0} \, U(x + m_s h), \qquad (23.46a)$$

it is seen from (23.47) and (23.48) that this is a special case of the integral relation

$$U(x) = \int_{\tilde{R}} U(y)\, dF(y, x; \mu).$$

Here $F(y, x)$ satisfies the inequalities (23.21) of Condition 1, provided

$$c(x) \leq 0 \quad \text{in } R, \tag{23.51}$$

a condition that is frequently imposed in the theory of problem (23.41) since, without it, a solution may fail to exist.

Equations (23.48), (23.49), (23.50) imply that, if U is replaced by any indefinitely differentiable function $v(x)$ in (23.46) and expanded about x, the contribution of the constant, linear, and quadratic terms combines into $L(v)$. This means that Condition 3a is satisfied with $p = 3$ for any solution of $L(u) = 0$. The left member of inequality (23.45) then becomes

$$\frac{1}{6} \sum_{s=1}^{N} \left(\sum_{j=1}^{n} |m_{s_j}| \right)^3 h^3 \frac{c_s}{-c_0}.$$

This is less than $B_1 h^3$ for some constant B_1. However, the constant α can be defined only after the relation between h and μ is fixed. This is a matter of definition and is irrelevant for the meaning of the final result.

Throughout the discussion of this illustrative example it must be borne in mind that an equation of the form (23.46) can be used only in R_1, unless R is a region bounded by hyperplanes of the grid. Also, the grid neighborhood of x formed by the points $x + m_s h$, $s = 1, \cdots, N$, may have to be chosen very large if (23.46) is to be of positive type. In such cases the mesh length h must be taken very small if there is to exist a subdomain R_1 such that $x + m_s h$ lies in $\tilde{R}$ whenever x lies in R_1.

CONDITION 4. *For $x \in R_2$ relations similar to those of Condition 3 are valid with constants q, B_2, β taking the places of p, B_1, α respectively.*

The meaning of Condition 4 may be illustrated by the interpolation formula (23.4). This relation is satisfied by all linear functions; hence we may take $q = 2$. For this example, the inequality of Condition 4 analogous to (23.45) becomes

$$\frac{1}{2}\left[(h'')^2 \frac{h'}{h' + h''} + (h')^2 \frac{h''}{h' + h''} \right] = \frac{1}{2} h' h'' < \frac{1}{2} h^2.$$

[Observe that the notation in (23.4) does not agree with that of the present section. The point (x, y) of (23.4) is now denoted by x and its coordinates by (x_1, x_2). The only contributions to the integral in (23.45) come from the points $(x_1 + h', x_2)$ and $(x_1 - h'', x_2)$.] Hence B_2 can be taken equal to $\frac{1}{2}$.

The next condition is a weak point of this theory, because it is too restrictive for many applications.

CONDITION 5. *All derivatives of orders p and q of the solution $u(x)$ of problem (23.41) are bounded in $\bar{R}$.*

A realistic theory should be applicable to regions with corners. But at a corner, the higher derivatives of $u(x)$ are, in general, unbounded. The influence of such corners on the discretization error will be briefly discussed in Sec. 23.5.

From the preceding hypotheses we immediately obtain an appraisal for the function $\mathscr{L}(u)$: Let M_r denote an upper bound in $\bar{R}$ for the absolute values of all partial derivatives of order r of $u(x)$. In the expression for $\mathscr{L}(u)$, as defined in (23.30), replace $u(y)$ by the right member of (23.44). This leads to

$$\mathscr{L}(u) = -u(x) + \int_{\bar{R}} P(y, x)\, dF(y, x; \mu)$$

$$+ \frac{1}{p!} \int_{\bar{R}} \left[\sum_{j=1}^{n} (y_j - x_j) \frac{\partial}{\partial \tilde{x}_j} \right]^p u(\tilde{x})\, dF(y, x; \mu).$$

By (23.44) we have $u(x) = P(x, x)$, so that the sum of the first two terms in the right member above is zero, in consequence of Condition 3*a*. Hence

$$|\mathscr{L}(u(x))| \leq M_p \frac{1}{p!} \int_{\bar{R}} \left(\sum_{j=1}^{n} |y_j - x_j| \right)^p dF(y, x; \mu) \leq M_p B_1 \mu^{\alpha}.$$

An analogous inequality holds for $x \in R_2$ and, hence,

$$|\mathscr{L}(u(x))| \leq \begin{cases} M_p B_1 \mu^{\alpha}, & x \in R_1 \\ M_q B_2 \mu^{\beta}, & x \in R_2, \end{cases} \tag{23.52}$$

which is the natural generalization of (23.10).

Since we wish to apply Lemma 23.6, inequality (23.37) must be satisfied; i.e., we need

CONDITION 6.

$$\int_{R} dF(y, x; \mu) \leq k < 1, \qquad x \in R_2,$$

with k independent of μ.

Finally, we must find a function $q(x)$ of the type introduced in Lemma 23.5. This function must be expected to depend on the parameter μ and, in general, it will turn out to be unbounded, as μ tends to zero. To arrive at an appraisal of the discretization error that tends to zero with μ, it is necessary to impose a restriction on the growth of $q(x)$.

CONDITION 7. *There exists a function $q(x)$, nonnegative in R, such that*

$$\mathscr{L}(q) \leq -1, \qquad x \in R_1.$$

Here $q(x)$ may depend on μ, but there exists a positive integer $\gamma < \alpha$ such that

$$Q(x) = q(x)\mu^\gamma$$

remains bounded as $\mu \to 0$. (See Condition 3 for the definition of α.)

The construction of such functions $q(x)$ or $Q(x)$ is discussed below. Formula (23.12) defines such a function Q for the example treated there.

The desired appraisal of the discretization error w is now an immediate consequence of Lemma 23.6.

THEOREM 23.7. *If Conditions 1 through 7 are satisfied, the discretization error inherent in the approximation of Dirichlet's problem (23.41), (23.42) by the integral equation (23.20) satisfies the inequality*

$$|U(x) - u(x)| \leq \frac{1}{1-k} \left(M_p B_1 \mu^{\alpha - \gamma} \sup_R Q(x) + M_q B_2 \mu^\beta \right).$$

We still have to examine the existence of functions $Q(x)$ satisfying Condition 7. A detailed analysis of this question would lead us too far. If $F(y, x; \mu)$ satisfies the conditions of Petrowsky [1934], as it does in all applications with $\int_R dF \equiv 1$ known to the authors, the existence of a positive function $q(x)$ for which $\mathscr{L}(q) = -1$ has been proved in Wasow [1951a]. This function is the mean duration of a random walk in R with the transition probability distribution $F(y, x; \mu)$. If the differential equation to be approached is that of Laplace, then, as was proved in Wasow [1951a], this particular choice of $q(x)$ satisfies the asymptotic inequality

$$q(x) \leq \pi^{-1} \Gamma^{2/n} \left(\frac{n+2}{2} \right) V^{2/n} \mu^{-2} [1 + o(1)],$$

in which n is the dimension of the space and V is the n-dimensional volume of R. The parameter μ in this equation has to satisfy the assumption in Petrowsky [1934]. If $F(y, x; \mu)$ is defined in a regular orthogonal grid of mesh length h, one may take $\mu = h$. More generally, let $\|y - x\|_2$ be the Euclidean distance from x to y. Then

$$\int_R \|y - x\|_2^2 \, dF(y, x; \mu) = \mu^2 + o(\mu^2)$$

on the basis of Petrowsky's hypotheses, so that μ^2 is approximately the mean square step length of the random walk defined by $F(y, x; \mu)$. (See Wasow [1951a], p. 467; the parameter there called μ is the square of our present μ.)

The construction of some function $q(x)$ satisfying Condition 7 and free from unknown infinitesimals like $o(1)$ is quite simple for difference operators of the particular form

$$\Delta_h U = h^{-2} \left[\sum_{s=1}^{2n} U(x + m_s h) - 2n\, U(x) \right]$$

with

$$m_1 = (1, 0, \cdots, 0), \quad m_2 = (-1, 0, \cdots, 0), \cdots, m_{2n} = (0, \cdots, -1).$$

This is the natural extension to n dimensions of the operator Δ_h defined for two dimensions in (20.51). The corresponding operator $\mathscr{L}$, according to definition (23.30), is

$$\mathscr{L} \equiv \frac{h^2}{2n} \Delta_h. \tag{23.53}$$

Clearly Δ_h is a formal approximation to Laplace's operator. Let r be the radius of the smallest sphere circumscribed about R, and let x^0 be its center. The function

$$q(x) = h^{-2} \left[r^2 - \sum_{i=1}^{n} (x_i - x_i^0)^2 \right]$$

is positive in R, and

$$\mathscr{L}(q) = -1.$$

This function satisfies Condition 7 with $\mu = h$, $\gamma = 2$. $Q(x) = \mu^2 q(x)$ is the direct generalization of the function $Q(x)$ defined in (23.12) for the two-dimensional case.

A similar construction is possible for many operators of the form (23.46) that are of positive type and satisfy (23.48), (23.49), (23.50). The corresponding operator $\mathscr{L}$ differs from L_h in (23.46) by the normalization factor $-1/c_0$ [see (23.46a)]. In Motzkin and Wasow [1953] it is shown that the solutions of (23.49), (23.50) that satisfy the inequalities (23.47) are of the form

$$c_s = k_s(x, h)h^{-2}, \quad s = 1, 2, \cdots, N,$$

where the $k_s(x, h)$ are positive and bounded in $\bar{R}$, as $h \to 0$. [See also (20.7) and following.] Hence, by (23.48),

$$c_0 = c(x) - \sum_{s=1}^{N} k_s(x, h)h^{-2},$$

so that $\mathscr{L}(U)$ is of the form

$$\mathscr{L}(U) = -\frac{1}{c_0} L_h(U) = h^2 \rho(x, h) L_h(U), \tag{23.54}$$

where $\rho(x, h)$ is positive and bounded, provided $c(x) \leq 0$ and h is suffi-ciently small. The function $\rho(x, h)$ must be calculated for each problem separately. For $L_h = \Delta_h$ formula (23.53) shows that $\rho(x, h) = (2n)^{-1}$.

Let us try to find a function $q(x)$ of the form

$$q(x) = C_1 h^{-2}\left\{\delta - \sum_{i=1}^{n} [\beta_i(x_i - x_i^0) + \gamma_i(x_i - x_i^0)^2]\right\}$$

with constants $C_1 > 0$, $\delta, \beta_i, x_i^0, \gamma_i$ to be determined. By means of the relations (23.48), (23.49), (23.50), and (23.54), we find

$$\mathscr{L}(q) = C_1 \rho(x, h)\left\{c(x) q(x) - \sum_{i=1}^{n} [\gamma_i a_{ii} + b_i(2\gamma_i(x_i - x_i^0) + \beta_i)]\right\}.$$

By a suitable choice of the parameters in $q(x)$, it is often possible to satisfy Condition 7. For example, if the functions b_i do not change sign in R, we may take $\beta_i = 2 \max_R |x_i - x_i^0|$ sgn b_i, $\gamma_i = 1$, x^0 = center of the sphere circumscribed about R, and $\delta = (2n + 1)r^2$ (r = radius of circum-scribed sphere). We then have

$$q(x) = C_1 h^{-2}\left\{(2n + 1)r^2 - \sum_{i=1}^{n} [2 \max_R |x_i - x_i^0| \text{ sgn } b_i (x_i - x_i^0)\right.$$

$$\left. + (x_i - x_i^0)^2]\right\} \geq C_1 h^{-2}[(2n + 1)^2 r^2 - 2nr^2 + r^2] > 0.$$

Moreover, in view of (23.51),

$$\mathscr{L}(q) \leq -C_1 \rho(x, h) \sum_{i=1}^{n} a_{ii},$$

so that Condition 7 is satisfied if C_1 is taken sufficiently large, and if we set $\mu = h$, $\gamma = 2$.

Another construction of a function $q(x)$ for certain special cases is con-tained in Collatz [1955], p. 286.

Actually, the precise form of $q(x)$ is not very important, as long as its existence can be established. The importance of Theorem 23.7 lies mostly in the qualitative insight into the discretization error which it gives us, because the bounds M_p, M_q for the derivatives of u are unknown, even if they exist. The usual way of overcoming this difficulty is to substitute difference quotients for the partial derivatives of $u(x)$ in the determination of the constants M_p, M_q. But Milne [1953] has shown that the appraisals so obtained are not always reliable, particularly near the boundary C. If nothing is known about M_p and M_q, Theorem 23.7 suggests that the function $F(y, x; \mu)$ should be constructed so that

$$\alpha - \gamma = \beta,$$

since no great advantage can be expected from using a very precise approximation in R_1, unless it is matched by an equally refined interpolation at the boundary, and vice versa.

We conclude this section with a list of the values of the constants $\alpha, \beta, p, q, B_1, B_2, k$ for some of the simplest approximation methods in two dimensions. In all four of these examples $\mu = h$ and $\gamma = 2$.

(1) *Approximation of Δ by Δ_h in R_1.*

$$\alpha = 4, \qquad p = 4, \qquad B_1 = \tfrac{1}{24}.$$

This was proved in Sec. 23.1.

(2) *Let*

$$\Delta_h{}^\times U \equiv \frac{1}{2h^2} \left[U(x_1 + h, x_2 + h) + U(x_1 - h, x_2 + h) \right.$$

$$\left. + U(x_1 + h, x_2 - h) + U(x_1 - h, x_2 - h) - 4U(x_1, x_2) \right]$$

and approximate ΔU in R_2 by $\Delta_h^{(9)} = \tfrac{2}{3}\Delta_h + \tfrac{1}{3}\Delta_h{}^\times$. Then, since problem (23.41) is $\Delta u = 0$ [see (20.57)],

$$\alpha = 8, \qquad p = 8, \qquad B_1 = 0.00129.$$

(3) *Interpolation of order zero at the boundary.* Let R_2 be the strip of R at distance less than h from C and set $U(x_1, x_2) = U(\bar{x}_1, \bar{x}_2)$ in R_2, where $(\bar{x}_1, \bar{x}_2)$ is some point on C at distance less than h from (x_1, x_2). Then

$$\beta = 1, \qquad q = 1, \qquad B_2 = 1, \qquad k = 0.$$

(4) *Interpolation of order one at the boundary.* This is the interpolation formula described by formula (23.4). Hence

$$\beta = 2, \qquad q = 2, \qquad B_2 = \tfrac{1}{2}, \qquad k = \tfrac{1}{2}.$$

(5) *Interpolation of order two for Laplace's operator.* Let R_2 be defined as in (3). Proceeding counterclockwise from the positive x_1-axis, denote by h_1, h_2, h_3, h_4 four numbers equal to the distance from (x_1, x_2) to a point of C or the mesh length h, whichever is smaller, in each of the four coordinate directions. Then approximate Δu by a linear combination of U at the five points (x_1, x_2), $(x_1 + h_1, x_2)$, $(x_1, x_2 + h_2)$, $(x_1 - h_3, x_2)$, $(x_1, x_2 - h_4)$ that approximates ΔU up to terms of the highest possible order. This leads to the following definition of $F(y, x; \mu)$ [see (20.69)]:

$$\int_{\bar{R}} dF(y, x; \mu) = \left(\frac{1}{h_1 h_3} + \frac{1}{h_2 h_4} \right)^{-1} \left[\frac{U(x_1 + h_1, x_2)}{h_1(h_1 + h_3)} + \frac{U(x_1, x_2 + h_2)}{h_2(h_2 + h_4)} \right.$$

$$\left. + \frac{U(x_1 - h_3, x_2)}{h_3(h_3 + h_1)} + \frac{U(x_1, x_2 - h_4)}{h_4(h_4 + h_2)} \right].$$

The Taylor expansion of $u(y)$ about x up to quadratic terms is

$$P(y, x) = u(x) + u_{x_1}(x)(y_1 - x_1) + u_{x_2}(y_2 - x_2) + \tfrac{1}{2}[u_{x_1x_1}(x)(y_1 - x_1)^2$$
$$+ 2u_{x_1x_2}(x)(y_1 - x_1)(y_2 - x_2) + u_{x_2x_2}(x)(y_2 - x_2)^2],$$

where the subscripts indicate partial differentiation. By means of a short calculation, one verifies that

$$\int_{\bar{R}} dF(y, x; \mu) = 1,$$

$$\int_{\bar{R}} P(y, x)\, dF(y, x; \mu) = u(x) + \left(\frac{1}{h_1 h_3} + \frac{1}{h_2 h_4}\right)^{-1} \Delta u(x) = u(x),$$

since equation (23.41) is $\Delta u = 0$, and therefore

$$\mathscr{L}[P(y, x)] = u(x) - u(x) = 0.$$

If the terms of degree three had been included in the definition of $P(y, x)$, the condition $\mathscr{L}[P(y, x)] = 0$ would not have been satisfied. The proper choice for q is therefore $q = 3$. Moreover, $|y_1 - x_1| + |y_2 - x_2| \leq h$ for each of the four points that contribute to the integral

$$\frac{1}{3!} \int_{\bar{R}} (|y_1 - x_1| + |y_2 - x_2|)^3\, dF(y, x; \mu).$$

Hence the last expression does not exceed

$$\frac{1}{6} h^3 \int_{\bar{R}} dF(y, x; h) = \frac{h^3}{6}.$$

In other words, $B_2 = \tfrac{1}{6}$, and therefore, if we set $\mu = h$, we have $\beta = 3$.

Finally, at least one of the four points that contribute to $\int_{\bar{R}} dF(y, x; \mu)$ is on C, for $x \in R_2$. Assume, for instance, that $(x_1 + h_1, x_2)$ is on C and that $h_2 = h_3 = h_4 = h > h_1$. Then the weight factor of $U(x_1 + h_1, x_2)$ in $\int_{\bar{R}} dF$ is

$$\left(\frac{1}{h_1 h_3} + \frac{1}{h_2 h_4}\right)^{-1} \frac{1}{h_1(h_1 + h_3)} = \left(\frac{1}{h_1 h} + \frac{1}{h^2}\right)^{-1} \frac{1}{h_1(h_1 + h)}$$

$$= \left(\frac{h}{h_1 + h}\right)^2 \geq \frac{1}{4}.$$

If exactly two of the points, say, those corresponding to h_1 and h_2, are on C, we may assume, in order to fix the ideas, that $h_1 \geq h_2$, and then

$$\left(\frac{1}{h_1 h_3} + \frac{1}{h_2 h_4}\right)^{-1}\left[\frac{1}{h_1(h_1 + h_3)} + \frac{1}{h_2(h_2 + h_4)}\right] \geq \frac{h_2}{h_1} \frac{h}{h_1 + h} \geq \frac{1}{2}.$$

The other possible combinations can be similarly treated with the result that k can be taken equal to $\frac{3}{4}$. Summarizing, we have

$$\beta = 3, \qquad q = 3, \qquad B_2 = \tfrac{1}{6}, \qquad k = \tfrac{3}{4}.$$

23.5. Summary of Some Further Results Concerning Discretization Errors for Linear Dirichlet Problems

(a) **Reduction of the Discretization Error by Extrapolation to** $\mu = 0$. Let $U(x, \mu)$ be the approximate solution of a problem whose exact solution is $U(x) = U(x, 0)$. If $U(x, \mu)$ is differentiable with respect to μ at $\mu = 0$, i.e., if

$$U(x, \mu) = u(x) + u_1(x)\mu + o(\mu), \tag{23.55}$$

then a knowledge of two approximations $U(x, \mu_1)$ and $U(x, \mu_2)$ with

$$\mu_2 = \theta\mu_1, \qquad 0 < \theta < 1,$$

enables us to calculate the linear combination

$$\frac{U(x, \mu_2) - \theta U(x, \mu_1)}{1 - \theta} = u(x) + o(\mu_1), \tag{23.56}$$

which is a better approximation to $U(x)$, as far as the order of magnitude of the error is concerned. If $U(x, \mu)$ possesses higher continuous derivatives with respect to μ at $\mu = 0$, several approximations can be linearly combined in an obvious manner to yield still better approximations.

This method was suggested by Richardson [1910], and was called by him *the deferred approach to the limit*. It frequently leads to striking improvements of numerical results in the solution of differential equations by finite differences. (See Richardson [1910], Richardson and Gaunt [1927], Salvadori [1951].) All these applications deal with problems in regions simple enough to make boundary interpolation unnecessary, namely, intervals or rectangles.

In Wasow [1955] examples are given indicating that this extrapolation technique is valueless for the solution of Dirichlet problems in domains with curved boundaries, unless an interpolation scheme is used that is more refined than would otherwise be necessary.

For example, the solution of Dirichlet's problem for Laplace's equation with the help of the first-order interpolation formula (23.4) of Sec. 23.1 involves, as we have seen, an error of order $O(h^2)$, so that we have

$$U(x) \equiv U(x, h) = u(x) + u_1^*(x, h)h^2. \tag{23.57}$$

This is, however, not sufficient for the application of the extrapolation method. With $h_2{}^2 = \theta h_1{}^2$, we have

$$\frac{U(x, h_2) - \theta U(x, h_1)}{1 - \theta} = u(x) + \frac{u_1{}^*(x, h_2) - u_1{}^*(x, h_1)}{1 - \theta} h_2{}^2,$$

and there is no reason to assume that the factor of $h_2{}^2$ in the second right-hand term will be small for small h_1. On the contrary, simple one-dimensional examples suggest that $U(x, h)$ in (23.57) is, in general, not a differentiable function of h^2 at $h = 0$ (see Wasow [1955]).

The nature of the difficulty caused by interpolation at the boundary can be illustrated by a very simple example. Let R be the one-dimensional interval $|x| < 1$, and consider the boundary-value problem

$$u'' = 0 \quad \text{for } |x| < 1, \qquad u(-1) = -1, \qquad u(1) = 1,$$

with the obvious solution $u(x) = x$. Now we replace this problem by a discrete problem in a net of mesh length h, *without insisting that the points* $x = \pm 1$ *be net points*. Then interpolation at the end points is necessary, and the simplest treatment is the interpolation of order zero in which the values of $u(x)$ prescribed at the end points are assigned to the nearest grid points. Thus we are led to the difference problem

$$\tfrac{1}{2}U(x + h) + \tfrac{1}{2}U(x - h) - U(x) = 0, \qquad \text{for } |x| \le 1 - h,$$

$$U(x) = 1, \qquad \text{for } 1 - h < x \le 1,$$

$$U(x) = -1, \qquad \text{for } -1 \le x < -1 + h.$$

This is the formulation employed in our preceding general theory, in which the position of the net was not specified. The set R_1 is the interval $|x| \le 1 - h$, and R_2 consists of the two intervals $1 - h < x < 1, -1 < x < -1 + h$. In order to simplify the argument, let us restrict the variable x to points that are multiples of h, so that $x = 0$ is a point of the net of mesh length h that has x as a net point. Let $1 - \delta \ (0 \le \delta < h)$ be the net point of $|x| \le 1$ nearest to $x = 1$. Then the solution of the difference problem is

$$U(x) \equiv U(x, h) = \frac{x}{1 - \delta} = x + \frac{\delta x}{(1 - \delta)h} h \qquad \text{for } |x| \le 1 - h.$$

Now δ is a discontinuous periodic function of h with a jump of size h whenever $h = 1/m$ (m an integer). Hence δ/h has jumps of size unity, so that $U(x, h)$ is not of the form (23.55), and extrapolation does not improve the approximation. This example is admittedly artificial, since boundary interpolation is not necessary in one-dimensional problems, but it is extremely plausible that the same phenomenon presents itself in more dimensions, where interpolation cannot be avoided.

The size of the discontinuous jumps of the discretization error depends on the method of boundary interpolation employed, and it is always possible to reduce these jumps so as to make Richardson's extrapolation procedure feasible. For instance, if Δu is approximated by $\Delta_h U$ in the interior of a two-dimensional domain and if the interpolation technique (5) of Sec. 23.4 is chosen at the boundary, Richardson's extrapolation increases the order of the discretization error from $O(h^2)$ to $O(h^3)$. A proof of this fact is contained in Wasow [1955]. It is an open question whether it is economical to apply this complicated procedure or, instead, to be content with a simpler treatment of the boundary in a finer net without extrapolation.

(b) Appraisals of the Discretization Error from the Data Alone. The principal weakness of our theory—i.e., the presence of the derivatives of the unknown solution u in the appraisals—has stimulated some mathematicians to investigate the discretization error on the basis of the data alone. We collect here, without proofs, some of these results. They are theoretically interesting, but probably without great numerical usefulness.

When R is a rectangle in the (x, y)-plane with commensurable sides, the solution of the problem

$$\Delta_h U = 0 \text{ in } R, \qquad U = f(x, y) \text{ on } C$$

can be explicitly represented either as a trigonometric polynomial or, if the boundary values are sufficiently smooth, as a convergent Fourier series. As h tends to zero, this trigonometric representation tends to the well-known Fourier series representation of the solution $u(x, y)$ of the corresponding continuous Dirichlet problem. A careful analysis of this passage to the limit leads to an appraisal of the discretization error $U - u$ in terms of the properties of the boundary function $f(x, y)$.

A first such result was obtained by Wasow [1952] on the assumption that $f(x, y)$ is continuous and possesses bounded third derivatives on each closed side of the rectangle. If R is the square $0 < x < a,\ 0 < y < a$, Wasow finds that

$$|U - u| \leq (1.4A_2 + 0.43A_3 a)h^2,$$

where A_2 is the maximum of the modulus of the second tangential derivatives of f at the vertices of C, and A_3 is an upper bound for the modulus of the third tangential derivative of f on C. The corresponding formula for general rectangles is of the same structure but somewhat longer.

It should be observed that the error is of the order $O(h^2)$, although the hypotheses are weaker than those necessary for finding appraisals of this order by the theory of the preceding section. There, bounded *fourth* derivatives of u in $\bar{R}$ were required.

Walsh and Young [1953] have obtained further results. They prove, also by means of trigonometric series, that

$$|U - u| \leq Mh,$$

provided:

(i) f is continuous on C;
(ii) the first derivative of f is piecewise continuous;
(iii) the second derivative of f exists, except at a finite number of points, and is bounded.

(A function is called *piecewise continuous* on C if it is continuous except for a finite number of jump discontinuities.) For the constant M, an explicit expression is given in terms of the sides of the rectangle, the jumps of the derivative of f, and bounds on f and its first two derivatives.

There are many more appraisals in Walsh and Young [1953]. They show for instance that, instead of appraising the discretization error in a rectangle in terms of the derivatives of the boundary values, the modulus of continuity of f, i.e., the function

$$\omega(\delta) = \sup |f(P_1) - f(P_2)|, \qquad \overline{P_1P_2} < \delta, \qquad P_1 \in C, \qquad P_2 \in C,$$

can be introduced. The inequality they obtain is too involved to reproduce here. It implies, in particular, that $|U - u| \leq M^*h^{2/7}$ if f satisfies a Lipschitz condition. The constant M^* depends on $\omega(\delta)$.

Appraisals of a different kind are derived in Walsh and Young [1954]. There they limit themselves to closed (but arbitrary) subdomains of the rectangle, thus permitting a considerable improvement of the results. For instance, the error is of order $O(h^2)$ if the conditions (i) and (ii) above are satisfied, and if the first derivative of f is of bounded variation.

It is known (Phillips and Wiener [1923], and Courant, Friedrichs, and Lewy [1928]) that U tends to u, as $h \to 0$, under the sole hypothesis that f is continuous, and one might conjecture that there is some order of magnitude of the discretization error that applies to the whole class of harmonic functions in R with continuous boundary values. This conjecture is wrong, however. Walsh and Young [1954] conclude their investigations with an interesting example which shows that the convergence of U to u can be *arbitrarily slow*.

(c) Piecewise Analytic Boundary Data. Condition 5 of Sec. 23.4 is very undesirable, because it limits the validity of the theory of that section to problems with boundary data so smooth that the derivatives of orders p and q of the solution u are bounded in $\bar{R}$. In physical problems, the boundary and the prescribed boundary values are almost always piecewise analytic. [In one dimension, a function $f(s)$ of a real variable s is called *piecewise* *analytic* in an interval $0 \le s \le L$ if it is continuous in $0 \le s \le L$ and if the interval can be divided into a finite number of subintervals such that $f(s)$ is analytic in each closed subinterval. An arc is called piecewise analytic if its parametric representation in terms of the arc length can be given by two piecewise analytic functions $x(s)$, $y(s)$.] At the points of C where the boundary data are not analytic the pertinent derivatives of u are usually unbounded, so that the method of Sec. 23.4 is inapplicable.

Various results partly overcoming this difficulty have been obtained by Wasow [1957] and Laasonen [1957a]. We shall give a brief account of Laasonen's results. These are limited to Dirichlet's problem for Laplace's equation in two dimensions and to approximations of Δ by the operator Δ_h. We consider only the boundary treatment described under (3) in Sec. 23.4 (interpolation of order zero), although Laasonen treats also the improved interpolation method (4). Laasonen proves that the presence of acute angles at the boundary does not affect the order of magnitude of the discretization error, which is $O(h)$, except possibly in an infinitesimal neighborhood of the boundary. However, for interior angles $\pi\alpha$ with $\alpha \ge 1$, Laasonen's method yields an error bound of the order $O(h^{1/\alpha - \epsilon})$ with arbitrary positive ϵ. It is not known what is the best possible result for such angles. By different methods Wasow [1957] has proved that the order $O(h)$ is still correct if the boundary is an analytic curve without corners and the boundary values are piecewise analytic. There is some numerical evidence that re-entrant angles may actually modify the order of magnitude of the discretization error globally.

A simplifying feature of Laplace's problem in two dimensions is that it permits the application of methods from the theory of analytic functions. This makes it possible, in particular, to determine the asymptotic behavior of the solution $u(x, y)$ of the differential equation problem near analytic corners. (See Lehman [1959] for a treatment of more general elliptic partial differential equations.) It can be stated roughly that a harmonic function at an analytic corner (the meaning of this expression should be clear from the foregoing discussion) of interior angle $\pi\alpha$ $(0 < \alpha \le 2)$ behaves like

$$n(x, y) = u_1(x, y) + \begin{cases} O(r^{1/\alpha}), & \text{if } \alpha \ne 1/m \\ O(r^m \log r), & \text{if } \alpha = 1/m \end{cases} \quad m \text{ an integer,} \quad (23.58)$$

where $u_1(x, y)$ is indefinitely differentiable at the corner. Here r designates the distance from the corner. This relation may be formally differentiated as often as desired (see Wasow [1957a]). This result is more than sufficient for the study of the problem under discussion. Laasonen [1957a] takes advantage of such asymptotic formulas to construct a function $Q^*(x, y)$ to take the place of the simple function $Q(x, y)$ of formula (23.12). This considerably more complicated function $Q^*(x, y)$ is nonnegative and satisfies the inequality

$$\mathscr{L}(Q^*) \leq -\text{const. } h^{-\sigma}|\mathscr{L}(u)|, \tag{23.59}$$

analogous to (23.14), in a domain obtained from R by removing infinitesimal neighborhoods of the corners. Here σ is a certain positive number which determines the order of magnitude of the final result. Observe that $|\mathscr{L}(u)|$ is usually unbounded as $h \to 0$, but that formula (23.58) enables us to calculate its order of growth near the corners. Once such a function Q^* has been constructed, Gerschgorin's original argument applies without change. The details may be found in Laasonen's paper.

(d) **Nonhomogeneous Differential Equations.** Some modifications are necessary to extend the general formula of Theorem 23.7 to the nonhomogeneous differential equation $L(u) = \phi(x)$, where $L(u)$ is the linear second-order differential operator defined in formula (23.42). Let us assume that the boundary value problem

$$\begin{aligned} L(u) &= \phi(x), &\quad x \in R, \\ u &= f(x), &\quad x \in C, \end{aligned} \tag{23.60}$$

has been replaced by a discrete problem of the form

$$\begin{aligned} \mathscr{L}(U) &= \Phi(x), &\quad x \in R, \\ U &= f(x), &\quad x \in C. \end{aligned} \tag{23.61}$$

The operator $\mathscr{L}$ is defined by (23.30), and Conditions 1 and 2 are supposed to be satisfied. The discretization error $w = U - u$ is the solution of the problem

$$\begin{aligned} \mathscr{L}(w) &= \Phi(x) - \mathscr{L}(u), &\quad x \in R, \\ w &= 0, &\quad x \in C, \end{aligned}$$

or

$$w(x) = \begin{cases} \displaystyle\int_{R} w(y)\, dF(y, x) + \mathscr{L}(u) - \Phi(x), &\quad x \in R, \\ 0, &\quad x \in C, \end{cases} \tag{23.62}$$

analogous to (23.43). Generally speaking, $w(x)$ will be small, in view of Lemma 23.6, whenever $|\mathscr{L}(u) - \Phi(x)|$ is small throughout R. In principle, $\mathscr{L}(u) - \Phi(x)$ could be made as small as we please, even zero, by choosing $\mathscr{L}$ or $\Phi(x)$ suitably. But this means begging the question, since the solution $u(x)$ of (23.60) is unknown. It is true that Conditions 3 and 4 also were formulated in terms of the unknown solution $u(x)$, but all approximation operators in actual use are constructed so that Conditions 3 and 4 are satisfied for *all* solutions of $L(u) = \phi(x)$, a construction which does not presuppose an explicit knowledge of these solutions.

Since the more general formulation of the method in terms of Stieltjes integrals is somewhat awkward for the nonhomogeneous equation, we explain the argument only for the operator defined by (23.46) and (23.54), combined with some similarly accurate interpolation method at the boundary. In view of (23.54) and the conditions (23.48), (23.49), (23.50), we have then for any sufficiently smooth function $v(x)$

$$\mathscr{L}(v) = h^2 \rho(x, h) L(v) + h^3 \sigma(x, h), \qquad x \in R_1, \qquad (23.63)$$

where

$$|\sigma(x, h)| \leq M_3 A_1. \qquad (23.64)$$

Here M_3 denotes the least upper bound for the absolute values of all third-order partial derivatives of v in R, and A_1 is a constant depending on L only. If L_h can be taken as an even function of h, the remainder term in (23.63) may be taken of order h^4. However, still better formal approximations, such as $\Delta^{(9)}$ in example (2), Sec. 23.4, are not practicable for nonhomogeneous problems, because they are valid, at best, only for a special choice of the right member $\Phi(x)$.

Now we define $\Phi(x)$ in (23.61) by

$$\Phi(x) = \phi(x)h^2 \rho(x, h) \qquad (23.65)$$

and obtain

$$|\mathscr{L}(u) - \Phi(x)| \leq M_3 A_1 h^3, \qquad x \in R_1, \qquad (23.66)$$

if u is a solution of $L(u) = \phi(x)$.

In R_2 we may interpolate with accuracy of order zero [example (3), Sec. 23.4], if we want to match the precision of (23.66). Occasionally interpolation of order one [example (4), Sec. 23.4] may be indicated. For interpolation of order zero we have

$$|\mathscr{L}(v)| \leq M_1 B_2 h, \qquad x \in R_2$$

and therefore, using (23.65),

$$|\mathscr{L}(u) - \Phi(x)| \leq M_1 B_2 h + \max_R |\phi| B_3 h^2. \qquad (23.67)$$

Finally, we may assume that the problem admits a nonnegative comparison function $q(x)$ satisfying (23.32), and such that

$$|q(x)| \leq h^{-2} B_4, \qquad x \in R. \qquad (23.68)$$

The existence of such a function follows from the theory of Petrowsky [1934], mentioned in Sec. 23.4. Inserting (23.66) and (23.67) into (23.62), we find then from Lemma 23.5 the appraisal

$$|w(x)| \leq (M_3 B_1 B_4 + M_1 B_2)h + \max_R |\phi| B_3 h^2$$

for the discretization error. Thus the presence of the term Φ in the right member of the differential equation does not affect the error much. If a formal approximation of order $O(h^2)$ had been employed, which is not always possible with a formula of positive type, the contribution of the right member to the error, being of the order $O(h^2)$ itself, would not have altered the order of magnitude of the error.

23.6. Green's Function for Discrete Dirichlet Problems

Green's function is a very valuable tool for the study of elliptic differential equations. Its finite-difference analog is easily defined, but to explore the asymptotic properties of this finite analog, as the mesh length tends to zero, is a less simple task. In this section two such studies, McCrea and Whipple [1940] and Wasow [1957], will be briefly described, omitting most of the proofs. Again, the analysis will be limited to Laplace's operator Δ in two dimensions and to the finite-difference operator defined by Δ_h in the interior and by interpolation of order zero at the boundary. For another treatment of Green's function for Δ_h, see Saltzer [1958].

We begin by recalling the definition of Green's function for Laplace's operator and the boundary condition $u = 0$ on C. Let $u(x, y)$ be the solution of the problem

$$\Delta u = \phi(x, y) \text{ in } R, \qquad u = 0 \text{ on } C. \qquad (23.69)$$

It is shown in classical potential theory that there exists a function of four variables $G(x, y; \xi, \eta)$, depending on R but not on $\phi(x, y)$, such that

$$u(x, y) = \iint_R G(x, y; \xi, \eta) \, \phi(\xi, \eta) \, d\xi \, d\eta. \qquad (23.70)$$

This function G, called *Green's function for the problem* (23.69), is exceedingly useful for the theoretical analysis of problem (23.69).

For the sake of simplicity, let us assume that R is a bounded domain with a piecewise analytic boundary C. This is amply sufficient for the existence of Green's function. For abbreviation, let P and Q denote the points (x, y) and (ξ, η) respectively, and write $G(P, Q)$ for $G(x, y; \xi, \eta)$. Let $\overline{PQ}$ denote the Euclidean distance from P to Q. It can be proved (Courant and Hilbert [1953]) that Green's function is uniquely characterized by the following properties:

(i) $G(P, Q)$ is harmonic with respect to P, except for $P = Q$;

(ii) $G(P, Q) = -(1/2\pi) \log \overline{PQ} + \psi(P, Q)$, where $\psi(P, Q)$ is a bounded function of P in R;

(iii) $G(P, Q) = 0$ for P on C and $P \neq Q$.

From these properties a number of others can be easily derived, such as:

(iv) $G(P, Q) > 0$, P in R;

(v) $G(P, Q) = G(Q, P)$;

(vi) $\psi(P, Q)$ is harmonic with respect to P (and, therefore, with respect to Q), and $\psi(P, Q) = (1/2\pi) \log \overline{PQ}$, for P on C.

The theory of Green's function is by no means trivial. The properties of its analog for the discrete problem are, however, fairly obvious. Consider the problem

$$\Delta_h U = \phi(x, y) \text{ in } R_h, \qquad U = 0 \text{ on } C. \tag{23.71}$$

This is a system of linear algebraic equations for the values of U at the points of R_h. From Sec. 23.1 we know that the solution exists and is unique. This solution is a linear function of the values of ϕ at the grid points, and, hence, we can write

$$U(P) = h^2 \sum_{Q \in R_h} G_h(P, Q) \, \phi(Q). \tag{23.72}$$

The factor h^2 has been extracted in order to bring out the analogy with formula (23.70), which is clearly the formal limit of (23.72), as $h \to 0$. Up to this point, no property of Δ_h has been used that is not common to all linear finite difference equations in a bounded domain that possess a solution. If (23.71) is regarded as a system of N equations for the values of $U(P)$ at the N points of R_h, then the N^2 values of $h^2 G_h(P, Q)$ form a matrix which is the inverse of the coefficient matrix in the system for $U(P)$. Since the latter is symmetric, at least for the operator Δ_h, we have

(v*) $G_h(P, Q) = G_h(Q, P)$.

By applying (23.71) and (23.72) to the particular function $\phi(Q) = \delta(Q, Q')$, where

$$\delta(Q, Q') = \begin{cases} 0, & Q \neq Q' \\ 1, & Q = Q', \end{cases}$$

it is seen that $G_h(P, Q)$ is the solution of the problem

(i*) $\Delta_{h,P} G_h(P, Q) = h^{-2} \delta(P, Q)$, $P \in R_h$;

(iii*) $G_h(P, Q) = 0$, $P \in C_h$.

The subscript P in the symbol $\Delta_{h,P}$ means that the operator is to be applied with respect to the variable P.

The function $G_h(P, Q)$ shares with $G(P, Q)$ the property of being positive in R_h. For $G_h(P, Q)$ cannot be constant, because of (i*). If it is negative or zero anywhere in R_h, there must be a point $P = P_0$ in R_h where

$G_h(P, Q)$, as a function of P for fixed Q, has a minimum, while $G_h(P_j, Q) > G_h(P_0, Q)$ for at least one of the four neighbors P_j $(j = 1, \cdots, 4)$ of P_0 in the grid. However, the difference equation in (i*) implies that

$$G_h(P_0, Q) \geq \sum_{j=1}^{4} G_h(P_j, Q)$$

and, therefore, $G_h(P_0, Q)$ must also exceed at least one of the four values $G_h(P_j, Q)$, which is a contradiction to the minimum property of P_0.

In view of the analogy between G and G_h it is natural to conjecture that G_h tends to G, as $h \to 0$, at least for $P \neq Q$. That this is actually the case can be proved by constructing a function in the net that plays the same role for the operator Δ_h as the function $-(1/2\pi) \log \overline{PQ}$ does for Δ. A function that differs from $-(1/2\pi) \log \overline{PQ}$ by a function that is harmonic in the whole plane is sometimes called a *fundamental solution* of Laplace's equation. The particular fundamental solution $-(1/2\pi) \log \overline{PQ}$ can be shown to be the only one that tends to zero at infinity. To find an analogous function for the discrete problem, we have to construct a solution of (i*) that tends to zero at infinity.

Now, it is not difficult to solve the problem defined by equations (i*) and (iii*) when R is a rectangle in the grid. One way of doing this is based on finite Fourier series, in strict imitation of the way Green's function for the continuous operator Δ is calculated in a rectangle. For our purpose it is sufficient to take R as the square $|x| \leq a\pi$, $|y| \leq a\pi$, and to set $Q = 0$. The function $\delta(P, 0)$, as an even function, can be represented as a linear combination of the even eigenfunctions

$$U_{mn}(x, y) = \cos \frac{(2m - 1)x}{2a} \cos \frac{(2n - 1)y}{2a}, \quad m, n = 1, 2, \cdots, \frac{a\pi}{h} - 1$$

of the operator Δ_h in R. (We assume that h is limited to values such that $a\pi/h$ is an integer.) The coefficients c_{mn} in the expansion

$$\delta(P, 0) = \sum_{m,n=1}^{a\pi/h-1} c_{mn} U_{mn}(P) \tag{23.73}$$

can be calculated from the orthogonality relations for the functions U_{mn}. Insertion of (23.73) into (i*) with $Q = 0$, substitution of

$$\gamma_{h,a}(P) = \sum_{m,n=1}^{a\pi/h-1} a_{mn} U_{mn}(P) \tag{23.74}$$

for $G_h(P, 0)$, and subsequent comparison of coefficients lead to explicit expressions for the coefficients a_{mn}.

One might then expect that letting a tend to infinity in (23.74) would yield a fundamental solution. Actually, however, $\lim_{a \to \infty} \gamma_{h,a}(P) = \infty$. Hence, in order to obtain a finite limit, McCrea and Whipple [1940] subtract from $\gamma_{h,a}(P)$ a suitably chosen constant depending on h and a and tending to infinity with a. This results in a representation as a finite Fourier series of a function $\gamma_h(P)$ which is a fundamental solution of Δ_h. By means of some nontrivial transformations, this sum is replaced by the integral representation

$$\gamma_h(x, y) = \frac{1}{2\pi} \int_0^\pi \frac{1 - \cos(y\lambda/h)\, e^{-|x|\mu/h}}{\sinh \mu}\, d\lambda, \qquad (23.75)$$

where μ is the function of λ defined for $0 < \lambda < \pi$ by the equation

$$\cos \lambda + \cosh \mu = 2$$

and the condition $\lim_{\lambda \to 0} \mu/\lambda = 1$, which specifies the branch of this multivalued function. For the details of these calculations, we refer to the paper by McCrea and Whipple.

Next, the authors derive the asymptotic expression

$$\gamma_h(x, y) = \frac{1}{2\pi} \log \sqrt{x^2 + y^2} + \frac{1}{2\pi} \log h + \frac{1}{4\pi}(\log 8 + 2\gamma) + O\left(\frac{h^2}{x^2 + y^2}\right),$$

where γ is Euler's constant, which shows that

$$g_h(P, Q) = -\gamma_h(x - \xi, y - \eta) + \frac{1}{2\pi} \log h + \frac{1}{4\pi}(\log 8 + 2\gamma)$$

is a solution of (i*) with the asymptotic representation

$$g_h(P, Q) = \frac{1}{2\pi} \log \overline{PQ} + O\left(\frac{h^2}{\overline{PQ}^2}\right). \qquad (23.76)$$

It is now an easy matter to derive from (23.76) a similar asymptotic representation for Green's function $G_h(P, Q)$, since the difference

$$\psi_h(P, Q) = G_h(P, Q) - g_h(P, Q) \qquad (23.77)$$

satisfies the difference equation

$$\Delta_{h,P}\, \psi_h(P, Q) = 0, \qquad P \in R_h, \qquad (23.78)$$

and the boundary condition

$$\psi_h(P, Q) = -g_h(P, Q), \qquad P \in C_h. \qquad (23.79)$$

Here (23.78) and (23.79) are approximations to the equations

$$\Delta_P\, \psi(P, Q) = 0, \qquad P \in R,$$

$$\psi(P, Q) = \frac{1}{2\pi} \log \overline{PQ}, \qquad P \in C \qquad (23.80)$$

for the function ψ introduced in property (ii) of Green's function. In view of (23.76), (23.79), and (23.80), the function $\psi_h(P, Q)$ differs from $\psi(P, Q)$ by $O(h)$, for $P \in C_h$, provided Q is bounded away from C, uniformly in h. To the resulting difference problem for $\psi_h - \psi$:

$$\Delta_h(\psi_h - \psi) = \Delta_h\psi \text{ in } R_h, \qquad \psi_h - \psi = O(h) \text{ on } C_h,$$

the theory of Sec. 23.4 can be applied. If C is so smooth that $\Delta_h\psi = O(h)$ (for instance, if C is representable by four times continuously differentiable functions of the arc length), we can conclude that

$$\psi_h - \psi = O(h), \qquad P \in R_h. \tag{23.81}$$

Hence, by means of property (ii) and formulas (23.76), (23.77), and (23.81), we conclude that

$$G_h(P, Q) = G(P, Q) + O(h),$$

provided Q is subjected to the further restriction that

$$\overline{PQ} \geq \text{const. } \sqrt{h} > 0.$$

We summarize this result in a theorem.

THEOREM 23.8. *Let R be a bounded, finitely connected, open region in the plane with a four times continuously differentiable boundary C. Let $G(P, Q)$, $G_h(P, Q)$ denote the Green's functions defined in this section. Then*

$$G_h(P, Q) - G(P, Q) = O(h),$$

uniformly for $P \in R_h$, if Q is bounded away from C independently of h, and $\overline{PQ} \geq \text{const. } \sqrt{h} > 0$.

Instead of basing the proof on the theory of Sec. 23.4, the method of Laasonen [1957a] could have been utilized with the result that for piecewise analytic regions $G_h - G = O(h^p)$, where $p = 1$ or $1/\alpha - \epsilon$ according as the largest interior angle $\alpha\pi$ at a corner of C is or is not less than π. The additional restriction that P must be bounded away from the corners of C has to be imposed now.

23.7. Discretization Error for the Neumann and Third Boundary-Value Problems

Almost all the literature on discretization error has been devoted to the Dirichlet problem. Yet in practice one very often solves boundary-value problems with Neumann boundary conditions on at least part of the boundary. For example, a line of symmetry for the Dirichlet problem leads to the boundary condition $u_n = 0$ on this line, and so yields a mixed boundary-value problem.

To assist the reader in getting started, we should like to mention papers by Batschelet [1952] and Giese [1958] which do treat the discretization error for boundary conditions not of Dirichlet type. Batschelet's paper is a long one, applying the general method of Gerschgorin outlined above to the third boundary-value problem. Assuming bounded derivatives of order four for the solution of the continuous problem, Batschelet devises a numerical finite-difference method, and proves that the discretization error is $O(h)$, as $h \to 0$.

Giese's paper deals with the Neumann problem for a rectangle, employing the Fourier-series method presented by Wasow [1952] for the Dirichlet problem. Giese uses the difference formula Δ_h of (20.51) and a centered difference approximation to the normal derivative u_n on the boundary. He shows that, if the prescribed values of u_n are twice continuously differentiable on each edge of the rectangle, then the discretization error is $O(h^2 \log h)$, as $h \to 0$.

23.8. Round-off Error in Solving the Dirichlet Difference Problem

As we have noted before, the bounds of Gerschgorin and his successors for the discretization error are applicable only when the regions and boundary conditions are well behaved. However, the same point of view can be applied without exception to a study of the round-off error in solving the difference equations themselves. This may, in fact, be the most practically useful application of the lemmas of the Gerschgorin type.

Let U be a solution of the difference equation

$$L_h(U) = G \qquad \text{in } R_h, \tag{23.82a}$$

$$U = F \qquad \text{on } C_h. \tag{23.82b}$$

Here L_h is any finite-difference operator.

In solving the system (23.82) on a digital computer, it is ordinarily necessary to replace the values of U, F, and G by *digital numbers*, i.e., by terminating fractions with base β (usually $\beta = 2$ or 10). Suppose one is calculating in fixed point, with s places to the right of the radical (decimal or binary) point. Then U can be expressed only to the nearest multiple of β^{-s}, and this is the source of the *round-off error*.

Let V be the digital-valued net function that is actually stored in the machine as a near solution of (23.82). We have that

$$L_h(V) = G + e \qquad \text{in } R_h, \tag{23.83a}$$

$$V = F + d \qquad \text{on } C_h. \tag{23.83b}$$

Here e and d are the *residuals* of the equations (23.82) with respect to the approximate solution V. Hence, in a sense, the vector pair e, d is a perfect representation of the error in V as a solution of (23.82), and it may be unwise to use anything more subtle than a norm of e, d to describe this error.

On the other hand, one is usually asked how much V may differ from the true solution U of (23.82). To answer this, one defines the *round-off error* W by

$$W = V - U. \qquad (23.84)$$

Subtracting (23.82) from (23.83), we see that

$$L_h(W) = e \qquad \text{in } R_h, \qquad (23.85a)$$

$$W = d \qquad \text{on } C_h. \qquad (23.85b)$$

Thus the round-off error is the solution of (23.85). If the operator L_h is of nonnegative type with diagonal dominance, we can follow the Gerschgorin theory to bound $|W|$ in R, as follows. In analogy with (23.32), let Q_h be any solution of the inequality

$$L_h(Q_h) \le -1 \qquad \text{in } R_h,$$
$$Q_h = 0 \qquad \text{on } C_h. \qquad (23.86)$$

We will prove the following theorem:

THEOREM 23.9. *Let L_h be of nonnegative type with diagonal dominance (defined in Sec. 20.4). Write $L_h(U)$ so that*

$$L_h[U(P)] = \sum_{P'} \sigma(P, P')\, U(P'),$$
$$\text{with} \quad \sigma(P, P') \ge 0 \ (P \ne P') \quad \text{and} \quad \sigma(P, P) < 0.$$

Suppose that U, V are, respectively, the solutions of (23.82), (23.83). Then, for all P in R_h,

$$|W(P)| = |V(P) - U(P)| \le \max_{C_h} |d| + Q_h(P) \max_{R_h} |e|. \qquad (23.87)$$

Proof. The proof is like that of Sec. 23.1. Let $\epsilon = \max_{R_h} |e|$, and let $\delta = \max_{C_h} |d|$. Then $|L_h(W)| \le \epsilon$, so that $-\epsilon \le L_h(W) \le \epsilon$. Since $L_h(Q_h) \le -1$, one sees that $L_h(\epsilon Q_h) \le -\epsilon$, whence

$$L_h(\epsilon Q_h - W) \le 0 \qquad \text{in } R_h.$$

Let E denote a function equal to 1 at all points of $R_h \cup C_h$. By the hypothesis of diagonal dominance, since $\sigma(P, P) < 0$, we know that $L_h(\delta E) \le 0$. Let $S = \epsilon Q_h + \delta E - W$. Then it follows that

$$L_h(S) = -\rho \le 0 \qquad \text{in } R_h,$$

where the function $\rho = \rho(P)$ is defined by this statement, and

$$S \geq 0 \qquad \text{on } C_h. \tag{23.88}$$

But

$$-\rho(P) = L_h[S(P)] = \sigma(P, P) \, S(P) + \sum_Q \sigma(P, Q) \, S(Q).$$

Hence, for each P in R_h with neighbors Q,

$$S(P) = -\sum_Q \frac{\sigma(P, Q)}{\sigma(P, P)} \, S(Q) - \frac{\rho(P)}{\sigma(P, P)}$$

$$\geq -\sum_Q \frac{\sigma(P, Q)}{\sigma(P, P)} \, S(Q) \geq \min_Q S(Q), \tag{23.89}$$

since $-\sigma(P, Q)/\sigma(P, P) \geq 0$, and $-\sum_Q \sigma(P, Q)/\sigma(P, P) \leq 1$. It follows from (23.88) and (23.89) by an obvious argument that $S \geq 0$ in R_h, whence

$$\epsilon Q_h + \delta E - W \geq 0 \qquad \text{in } R_h.$$

In a similar fashion one can prove that

$$\epsilon Q_h + \delta E + W \geq 0 \qquad \text{in } R_h.$$

From the last two equations it follows that

$$|W| \leq \epsilon Q_h + \delta E \qquad \text{in } R_h, \tag{23.90}$$

proving the theorem.

Theorem 23.9 was stated as a bound on $\max_{P \in R_h} |W(P)|$, i.e., as a bound on the "maximum" norm $\|W\|_\infty$, where, for any function X defined on R_h, we define

$$\|X\|_\infty = \max_{R_h} |X(P)|.$$

From inequality (23.90) and well-known properties of the pth-power norms $\|\cdot\|_p$ $(p = 1, 2, \infty)$, one can show that

$$\|W\|_p \leq \delta \|E\|_p + \epsilon \|Q_h\|_p \qquad \text{for } p = 1, 2, \infty.$$

In particular, for the Euclidean norm defined by

$$\|X\|_2 = \left(\sum_P [X(P)]^2 \right)^{1/2},$$

we know that $\|E\|_2 = \sqrt{N}$, and can obtain the following theorem.

THEOREM 23.10. *Under the hypotheses of Theorem 23.9, it follows that*

$$\|W\|_2 \leq \sqrt{N} \max_{C_h} |d| + \|Q_h\|_2 \max_{R_h} |e|, \tag{23.91}$$

where N is the number of points in R_h.

Theorem 23.10 is probably less useful than Theorem 23.9 for error bounds, but it will make possible a convenient comparison of the Gerschgorin technique with the results obtained below when L_h is not of nonnegative type.

For fixed h, functional values approximating $F(P)$ in (23.82) are selected and fixed throughout the calculation. It is always possible to select them so that

$$\delta = \max_{C_h} |d| \le \tfrac{1}{2}\beta^{-s}. \tag{23.92}$$

No matter how carefully we solve (23.82), for small h the values of e are ordinarily much larger, for the following reason. Consider, for example, the equation $\Delta_h U = 0$, where we write

$$\Delta_h U(P) = 4\,\frac{\tfrac{1}{4}[U(E) + U(N) + U(W) + U(S)] - U(P)}{h^2}.$$

Because of the necessity of rounding $U(P)$ to the nearest multiple of β^{-s}, $U(P)$ differs from the average of its four neighboring values by some number approximately equal to $\tfrac{1}{2}\beta^{-s}$. Hence $\Delta_h U(P)$ is approximately equal to $2h^{-2}\beta^{-s}$, and we expect that

$$\epsilon = \max_{R_h} |e| \doteq 2h^{-2}\beta^{-s}. \tag{23.93}$$

A similar error is to be expected when L_h is a more general elliptic operator of nonnegative type with diagonal dominance.

Since ordinarily $h \ll 1$, we shall henceforth ignore δ in comparison with ϵ, and find from (23.93) that the bound (23.87) for the round-off error $|W|$ is approximately

$$2 \max_{R_h} Q_h(P)\, h^{-2}\beta^{-s} \sim C_2 h^{-2}\beta^{-s}, \qquad \text{as } h \to 0. \tag{23.94}$$

Here we have used the fact that $\max Q_h(P)$ converges to some constant $C_2/2$, as $h \to 0$, a consequence of the convergence of $Q_h(P)$ to a limit $Q(P)$, as $h \to 0$ (see Wasow [1951b]). Then the round-off error $V - U$ at each point P is of the order $O(h^{-2})$, in comparison with the order $O(h^2)$ for the discretization error $U - u$ in the previous theory of this section (under the necessary stringent hypotheses).

Suppose we know the constants C_1, C_2 involved in the bound for the total error $V - u$, where

$$|V - u| \le |U - u| + |V - U| \le C_1 h^2 + C_2 h^{-2}\beta^{-s}.$$

We can look for the h to minimize this bound for $|V - u|$. We find that the h for which $C_1 h^2 + C_2 h^{-2}\beta^{-s}$ is least is $h^* = (C_2\beta^{-s}/C_1)^{1/4} \doteq \beta^{-s/4}$, and that when $h = h^*$

$$|V - u| \le 2\sqrt{C_1 C_2}\,\beta^{-s/2} \doteq \beta^{-s/2}. \tag{23.95}$$

These approximate equalities are based on the assumption that C_1, C_2 are roughly of the magnitude of 1.

To get a feeling for the numerical values involved in (23.95), let R be the square $0 < x < \pi$, $0 < y < \pi$ considered in Sec. 21.5, and let L_h be the five-point Laplacian difference operator $-\Delta_h$ of (20.51). Let $u = \sinh x \sin y$, so that $M_4 = \cosh \pi < 12$, where M_4 was defined after (23.10). Now the function

$$Q_1(x, y) = \frac{\pi^2}{8} - \frac{1}{4}\left(x - \frac{\pi}{2}\right)^2 - \frac{1}{4}\left(y - \frac{\pi}{2}\right)^2$$

in R is equal to $\frac{1}{4}Q$, for Q as in (23.12). Moreover, Q_1 dominates the unique solution Q_h of the form of (23.86) in which the inequality sign is replaced by an equality. That is,

$$\left.\begin{array}{r} \frac{1}{4}\max\limits_{R} Q = \\[2mm] \max\limits_{R_h} Q_h \leq \end{array}\right\} \max\limits_{R} Q_1 = Q_1\left(\frac{\pi}{2}, \frac{\pi}{2}\right) = \frac{\pi^2}{8} < \frac{5}{4}.$$

[By separation of variables Mitchell [1954] solves the equation $-\Delta_h Q_h = 1$ in a square, and obtains the approximation (in our notation)

$$\max\limits_{R_h} Q_h \doteq \frac{1}{4}(0.294)\pi^2 \doteq 0.0735\pi^2,$$

which is, of course, lower than our above upper bound $\pi^2/8 = 0.125\pi^2$.]

For later reference we note that, as $h \to 0$,

$$\|Q_h\|_2^2 < \|Q_1\|_2^2 = \sum_{R_h} [Q_1(P)]^2$$

$$\sim h^{-2} \int\int_R [Q_1(x, y)]^2 \, dx \, dy < h^{-2} \int\int_D [Q_1(x, y)]^2 \, dx \, dy,$$

where D is the circle where $Q_1(P) \geq 0$. Since the radius of D is $\pi/\sqrt{2}$, we have

$$\|Q_1\|_2^2 < 2\pi h^{-2} \int_0^{\pi/\sqrt{2}} \left(\frac{\pi^2}{8} - \frac{1}{4}r^2\right)^2 r \, dr$$

$$= \left[\frac{4\pi h^{-2}}{3}\left(\frac{r^2}{4} - \frac{\pi^2}{8}\right)^3\right]_0^{\pi/\sqrt{2}}$$

$$= \frac{\pi^7 h^{-2}}{384} \doteq 7.8 h^{-2}.$$

Hence it is reasonable to use the bound

$$\|Q_h\|_2 < 2.8 h^{-1}. \tag{23.96}$$

Since there is no interpolation at the boundary, we omit the term involving M_2 in (23.19), and we find from that formula that

$$C_1 = \tfrac{1}{12}M_4 \sup_R Q < \tfrac{1}{12} \cdot 12 \cdot 5 = 5,$$

and we see from (23.94) that $C_2 = 2 \cdot \tfrac{5}{4}$. Taking $\beta^{-s} = 10^{-10}$, it follows from the development up to (23.95) that $h^* = (2^{-1}\,10^{-10})^{1/4} = 2^{-1/4}10^{-2.5} \doteq 0.003$, with a corresponding error from (23.95):

$$|V - u| \le 5\sqrt{2}\,10^{-5} \doteq 7 \cdot 10^{-5},$$

provided that one can solve the difference equations with minimum round-off error.

With $h = h^* = 0.003$, one has a network with about $(1000)^2 = 10^6$ interior nodes—too many to handle with current machines. For more practical values of h, such as 0.05 (corresponding to about 3600 interior nodes), the round-off error bound $C_2h^{-2}\beta^{-s}$ is much smaller than the discretization error bound C_1h^2. Thus we conclude that *round-off is probably negligible in comparison with the discretization error in ordinary computation with finite-difference methods for elliptic problems.* This conclusion becomes even more valid when, as often happens, the hypotheses under which $|U - u| = O(h^2)$ are not satisfied, and there is a still larger discretization error.

Theorem 23.9 was based entirely on the operator L_h being of nonnegative type with diagonal dominance. It is reasonable to ask what can be said when L_h does not satisfy this condition. Such a problem arises when L_h corresponds to an elliptic operator $L(u)$ involving a term in u_{xy} (see Sec. 20.6). It also arises when one solves an eigenvalue problem like

$$-\Delta_h U = \mu_h U \qquad \text{in } R_h,$$
$$U = 0 \qquad \text{on } C_h,$$

since the fact that $\mu_h > 0$ destroys the diagonal dominance of $L_h = \Delta_h + \mu_h I$. [See the remarks following (23.22).]

What can now be done to bound the size of the round-off error W of (23.85), given e and d? For the Dirichlet problem, we have been thinking of W as being defined on the set $R_h \cup C_h$, assuming the values d on C_h. For the present purpose it is preferable to consider W as defined on the set R_h, and to consider the values d as contributing to the right-hand side of (23.85a). Thus, for example, suppose the point P of R_h has its "eastern" neighbor E in C_h, and that no other neighbor is in C_h. Then, for P in R_h,

$$\sum_Q \sigma(P, Q)\, W(Q) + \sigma(P, P)\, W(P) = e(P). \tag{23.97}$$

We transfer the term $\sigma(P, E) W(E) = \sigma(P, E) d(E)$ to the right-hand side of (23.97), and write

$$\sum_{Q \neq E} \sigma(P, Q) W(Q) + \sigma(P, P) W(P) = e(P) - \sigma(P, E) d(E).$$

We redefine $L_h(W)$ to include only homogeneous terms in W, and redefine e to include all terms like $\sigma(P, E) d(E)$. Designating the new e by e_1, we have

$$L_h(W) = e_1, \tag{23.98}$$

where both W and e_1 are defined on R_h.

Take any norm function, and suppose that $\|e_1\|$ is known. The problem is: how big is $\|W\|$? We can easily give a representation for a bound when L_h has an inverse, L_h^{-1}, as it certainly will for a definite operator. Let

$$\|L_h^{-1}\| = \max_{\|X\|=1} \|L_h^{-1}X\| = (\min_{\|Y\|=1} \|L_h Y\|)^{-1}.$$

Then it is seen from (23.98) that

$$\|W\| \leq \|L_h^{-1}\| \|e_1\|. \tag{23.99}$$

In general, bounds on $\|L_h^{-1}\|$ are not easy to find, but sometimes it is possible, even though the hypotheses of Theorem 23.9 fail to hold. In such cases (23.99) replaces (23.87).

To illustrate (23.99) and compare it with (23.87) in a very special case where $\|L_h^{-1}\|$ is known, let L_h be the operator Δ_h, and let R_h be the set of lattice points in the square $0 < x < \pi$, $0 < y < \pi$. Let $h = \pi/n$. Now $\sigma(P, Q) = 1/h^2$, for $Q = E, N, W, S$. Hence,

$$e_1(P) = \begin{cases} e(P), & P \text{ not next to } C_h, \\ e(P) - \dfrac{1}{h^2} \sum d(Q), & P \text{ next to } C_h. \end{cases} \tag{23.100}$$

The sum in (23.100) is taken over the one or two neighbors of P on C_h.

The operator Δ_h is symmetric, hence also Δ_h^{-1}. If we take the Euclidean norm, then for any symmetric matrix X, $\|X\|_2 = \max_i |\lambda_i(X)|$, where the $\lambda_i(X)$ are the eigenvalues of X. Hence $\|\Delta_h^{-1}\|_2$ is the maximum eigenvalue of Δ_h^{-1}; this is μ_h^{-1}, where μ_h is the least eigenvalue of Δ_h. But, as shown in equation (21.52a), $\mu_h = 8h^{-2} \sin^2 (h/2) \sim 2$, as $h \to 0$. Hence $\|\Delta_h^{-1}\|_2 \to \frac{1}{2}$, as $h \to 0$. It follows from (23.99) that, for $h \doteq 0$,

$$\|W\|_2 \leq \tfrac{1}{2}\|e_1\|_2 \quad \text{(approximately).} \tag{23.101}$$

It is difficult to compare formulas involving different norms. But a formula in the Gerschgorin theory which is comparable with (23.101) is

$$\max_{R_h} |W(P)| \leq \tfrac{5}{4} \max_{R_h} |e(P)|, \tag{23.102}$$

obtained by putting the bound for $Q_h(P)$ found after (23.95) into (23.87), and ignoring d. Since (23.101) and (23.102) involve different norms, it should not be concluded that (23.101) is better than (23.102).

23.9. Probabilistic Estimate of Round-off Error

One may suspect that the approximate bound (23.101) for the round-off error W is excessively pessimistic because it implicitly assumes that all the error components $e_1(P_i)$ have the same sign. Can we get an essentially better bound if we assume a random distribution of the errors $e_1(P_i)$?

To study this question, let us assume that each residual $e_1(P_i)$ may be represented as an independent selection from a random normal population with mean 0 and variance σ^2. This is probably not an unreasonable assumption in practice. (See Sec. 5.1.) It follows that the normalized value of the squared length of e_1, $\sigma^{-2}\|e_1\|_2{}^2 = \sigma^{-2}\Sigma_{i=1}^{N}e^2(P_i)$, has a χ^2 distribution with N degrees of freedom. Hence the expected value of $\sigma^{-2}\|e_1\|_2{}^2$ is N, and its variance is $2N$ (see Wilks [1943]). Since moreover, for $N > 50$, χ^2 has nearly a normal distribution, we may say that with a probability more than 0.997

$$N - 3\sqrt{2N} \leq \sigma^{-2}\|e_1\|_2{}^2 \leq N + 3\sqrt{2N}, \qquad N > 50.$$

It follows that, with the same probability,

$$(N - 3\sqrt{2N})^{1/2} \leq \sigma^{-1}\|e_1\|_2 \leq (N + 3\sqrt{2N})^{1/2}, \qquad N > 50.$$

With a little transformation we find that

$$\sqrt{N}\left(1 - \frac{3\sqrt{2}}{2\sqrt{N}}\right) \leq \sigma^{-1}\|e_1\|_2 \leq \sqrt{N}\left(1 + \frac{3\sqrt{2}}{2\sqrt{N}}\right), \qquad N > 50,$$

approximately, and hence that

$$\sqrt{N} - \tfrac{3}{2}\sqrt{2} \leq \sigma^{-1}\|e_1\|_2 \leq \sqrt{N} + \tfrac{3}{2}\sqrt{2}, \qquad N > 50,$$

or

$$(\sqrt{N} - 2.2)\sigma \leq \|e_1\|_2 \leq (\sqrt{N} + 2.2)\sigma, \qquad N > 50, \quad (23.103)$$

with probability more than 0.997.

Now let M denote L_h^{-1}, assumed to be symmetric and positive definite. Let

$$0 < \mu_N \leq \mu_{N-1} \leq \cdots \leq \mu_1$$

be the eigenvalues of M. By (23.98), the round-off error W is given by

$$W = Me_1. \qquad (23.104)$$

Hence the deterministic upper bound (23.99) yields the estimate

$$\|W\|_2 \leq \mu_1\|e_1\|_2, \qquad (23.105)$$

and (23.103) says that, with probability 0.997,

$$\|W\|_2 \leq \mu_1 \sigma(\sqrt{N} + 2.2), \qquad N > 50. \qquad (23.106)$$

In (23.105) no allowance was made for the possible variations in the signs of the $e_1(P_i)$. What can we do with a probabilistic treatment?

Write $e_1(P_i)$ as e_{1i}. From (23.104) we see that

$$w_i = \sum_{j=1}^{N} m_{ij} e_{1j},$$

whence

$$E(w_i) = \sum_{j=1}^{N} m_{ij} E(e_{1j}) = 0,$$

where E denotes the expectation function. Moreover,

$$E(w_i^2) = \sum_{j=1}^{N} m_{ij}^2 E(e_{1j}^2) = \sigma^2 \sum_{j=1}^{N} m_{ij}^2. \qquad (23.107)$$

From (23.107) we find that

$$E(\|W\|_2^2) = E\left(\sum_{i=1}^{N} w_i^2\right) = \sum_{i=1}^{N} E(w_i^2) = \sigma^2 \sum_{i,j=1}^{N} m_{ij}^2.$$

Define

$$\nu^2 = [\nu(M)]^2 = \sum_{i,j=1}^{N} m_{ij}^2.$$

Since $[\nu(M)]^2$ is the trace of $M^T M = M^2$, it follows that $[\nu(M)]^2 = \mu_1^2 + \cdots + \mu_N^2$. Hence

$$E(\|W\|_2^2) = \sigma^2(\mu_1^2 + \cdots + \mu_N^2).$$

Although we could analyze the distribution of $\|W\|_2^2$ in detail, for present purposes it suffices to note that the probable size of $\|W\|_2$ is approximately

$$\sqrt{E(\|W\|_2^2)} = \sigma(\mu_1^2 + \cdots + \mu_N^2)^{1/2}. \qquad (23.108)$$

It remains to compare (23.108) with (23.105). For this purpose we need specific values of the μ_i. As usual, we take for an example the operator $L_h = -\Delta_h$ corresponding to the Dirichlet difference problem over the square $0 < x < \pi,\ 0 < y < \pi$, with $N = (n-1)^2$ interior points. Then, as shown in Sec. 21.5, the eigenvalues μ_i of $L_h^{-1} = -\Delta_h^{-1}$ are the numbers

$$\frac{h^2}{4}\left(\sin^2 \frac{ph}{2} + \sin^2 \frac{qh}{2}\right)^{-1}, \qquad p,q = 1, \cdots, n-1, \qquad h = \frac{\pi}{n}.$$

These numbers range from $h^2/8$ up to approximately $\frac{1}{2}$.

We need to approximate

$$\nu^2 = \mu_1^2 + \cdots + \mu_N^2 = \sum_{p,q=1}^{n-1} \frac{h^4}{[4\sin^2(ph/2) + 4\sin^2(qh/2)]^2}.$$

It is easy to show that

$$v^2 = \sum_{p,q=1}^{n-1} \frac{h^4}{\left[(ph)^2 + (qh)^2\right]^2} + O(h^2), \qquad \text{as } h \to 0,$$

$$\sim \sum_{p,q=1}^{\infty} \frac{1}{(p^2 + q^2)^2}, \qquad \text{as } h \to 0.$$

Hence

$$\lim_{h \to 0} v^2 = \frac{1}{(1+1)^2} + \frac{2}{(1+4)^2} + \frac{2}{(1+9)^2} + \frac{1}{(4+4)^2}$$

$$+ \frac{2}{(1+16)^2} + \frac{2}{(4+9)^2} + \frac{2}{(1+25)^2} + \frac{2}{(4+16)^2}$$

$$+ \frac{1}{(9+9)^2} + \frac{2}{(9+16)^2} + r,$$

where

$$r < \iint\limits_{\substack{x^2+y^2>17 \\ x>0 \\ y>0}} \frac{dx\,dy}{(x^2 + y^2)^2} = \frac{\pi}{68} < 0.04620.$$

Hence

$$\lim_{h \to 0} v^2 = 0.39862 + \theta(0.04620), \qquad 0 < \theta < 1. \qquad (23.109)$$

From (23.108) and (23.109), we see that, for $h \doteq 0$, we have

$$\sqrt{E(\|W\|_2{}^2)} = \sigma\sqrt{0.39862 + \theta(0.04620)} \doteq 0.65\sigma, \qquad 0 < \theta < 1. \tag{23.110}$$

Since, by (23.103), $\sigma \doteq \|e_1\|_2/\sqrt{N}$, we finally have

$$\sqrt{E(\|W\|_2{}^2)} \doteq \frac{0.65\|e_1\|_2}{\sqrt{N}}. \tag{23.111}$$

Result (23.111) should be compared with the following consequence of (23.103) when $L_h = -\Delta_h$:

$$\|W\|_2 \le \tfrac{1}{2}\|e_1\|_2. \tag{23.101}$$

Roughly speaking, the probabilistic bound is $1/\sqrt{N} \doteq h/\pi$ times the absolute bound.

If this same factor h/π should apply also to the maximum norm, we might expect from (23.102) that, with reasonable probability,

$$E(\max_{R_h} |W(P)|) \le Ch \max_{R_h} |e(P)|, \qquad C = \text{const.} \tag{23.112}$$

We might therefore conjecture that with high probability the round-off error for the Dirichlet problem is $O(h^{-1})$, as $h \to 0$, rather than the $O(h^{-2})$ bound found in Sec. 23.8. It would be good to have machine experiments to test this conjecture.

Another probabilistic treatment of round-off error for Laplace's equation over a rectangle is given by Abramov [1953], who assesses the cumulative effect of round-off on an iterative solution of the difference equations.

SECTION 24.   THE MEMBRANE EIGENVALUE PROBLEM

24.1. Introduction

So far in the sections on elliptic partial differential equations, we have spoken mostly of boundary-value problems for linear operators L. But quite frequently physical problems lead to eigenvalue problems of the form $Lu = \lambda u$ in R, with various homogeneous boundary conditions. In Sec. 18 we listed two such eigenvalue problems as typical of those arising in practice.

In Sec. 20 we mentioned various mathematical problems which are raised by the discretization of elliptic partial differential equations. For the most part these apply also to eigenvalue problems, in which one seeks to approximate one or more values of λ, and possibly also the corresponding eigenfunctions u. The problems of selecting a net and the corresponding difference equations are solved the same way for both boundary-value and eigenvalue problems; the ideas of Sec. 20 apply equally well to both. The remaining two problems concern the solution of the discretized problem, and the estimation of the discretization error.

Both these problems are important, and neither is really well solved for eigenvalue problems, even when L is the Laplacian. We shall start with the second problem, and deal with the discretization errors in Secs. 24.1 through 24.7, returning to the solution of the discretized problem in Sec. 24.8.

In one respect, eigenvalue problems furnish a simpler problem in regard to discretization error. An eigenvalue λ is only one number to watch, and the error in this scalar is the discretization error. If one is also interested in the eigenfunction, the problem is at least as complicated as that for boundary-value problems, of course.

For a general treatment of variational approaches to the eigenvalue problem, see Gould [1957].

From various mathematical and physical principles, one can get upper and lower bounds for the eigenvalues λ of $Lu = \lambda u$ in R (see Pólya and

Szegö [1951] and Sec. 24.3). It is natural to inquire whether finite-difference methods can furnish such upper and lower bounds, and whether such bounds can be made arbitrarily close without excessive labor. For the time being, we shall assume that our computations are carried out with exact arithmetic, and thus ignore round-off questions. We shall confine ourselves to one so-called *membrane eigenvalue problem*, partly because it is representative of simple elliptic eigenvalue problems, and partly because few results are available for other problems.

Our membrane eigenvalue problem involves the determination of numbers λ^k (k = superscript) for which there exist functions $u^k(x, y)$, not identically zero, with

$$-\Delta u^k(x, y) = \lambda^k u^k(x, y) \qquad \text{in } R, \qquad (24.1a)$$

$$u^k = 0 \qquad\qquad \text{on } C. \qquad (24.1b)$$

Here, as in Sec. 18, we assume R to be a bounded plane region whose boundary C consists of a finite number of piecewise-analytic simple closed curves. A treatment of this problem is found in Courant and Hilbert [1953], pp. 297 ff., and in Tamarkin and Feller [1941]. It is known that the eigenvalues are all positive and have no finite limit point; we may therefore number them so that

$$0 < \lambda^1 \le \lambda^2 \le \lambda^3 \le \cdots \le \lambda^k \le \lambda^{k+1} \le \cdots. \qquad (24.2)$$

It is also known that we may pick the u^k to be *orthonormal*, in the sense that

$$\int\int_R u^k u^l \, dx \, dy = \delta_{kl} = \begin{cases} 1, & k = l, \\ 0, & k \ne l. \end{cases} \qquad (24.3)$$

When $\lambda^k \ne \lambda^l$, the second relation in (24.3) is a consequence of (24.1) and Green's theorem. If $\lambda^k = \lambda^l$, one chooses u^k, u^l so that (24.3) holds.

Let K_1 be the class of functions w such that w_{xx}, w_{xy}, w_{yy} are continuous in R with $w = 0$ on C, and such that ww_{xx} and ww_{yy} are Lebesgue-integrable on the set $\bar{R} = R \cup C$. Let K, which can be shown to contain K_1, be the class of functions w, continuous in $\bar{R}$, with a piecewise continuous gradient $\nabla w = (w_x, w_y)$ in R and $w = 0$ on C, with $|\nabla w|^2$ Lebesgue-integrable on $\bar{R}$.

It is known that the Rayleigh quotient

$$\rho(w) = \frac{\displaystyle\int\int_R |\nabla w|^2 \, dx \, dy}{\displaystyle\int\int_R w^2 \, dx \, dy} \qquad (24.4)$$

satisfies the inequality $\rho(w) \geq \lambda^1$, for w in K, and that it is stationary at each value λ^k ($k = 1, 2, \cdots$) when $w = u^k$ (see Sec. 19.2). In particular,

$$\lambda^1 = \min_{w \in K} \rho(w), \tag{24.5}$$

a fact of considerable use. For any function in K_1, we can use Green's theorem to rewrite $\rho(w)$ in the form

$$\rho(w) = -\frac{\displaystyle\iint_R w\,\Delta w\,dx\,dy}{\displaystyle\iint_R w^2\,dx\,dy}, \tag{24.6}$$

a form which will often be useful to us. It turns out that the function in K which minimizes (24.5) is always in class K_1.

24.2. Upper Bounds by Difference Methods

If $v_1, \cdots, v_n$ are linearly independent functions in K, form $v = \Sigma_{i=1}^n \alpha_i v_i$. Then $\rho(v)$ is a certain quotient of two quadratic forms in the scalars α_i:

$$\rho(v) = F(\alpha_1, \cdots, \alpha_n).$$

For fixed functions v_i, as one varies the α_i there are certain stationary values of $F(\alpha_1, \cdots, \alpha_n)$; call them μ^k, where

$$\mu^1 \leq \mu^2 \leq \cdots \leq \mu^n.$$

The μ^k are roots of a matrix eigenvalue problem of form $AV = \mu BV$, where A and B are symmetric matrices. In fact, let

$$F(\alpha_1, \cdots, \alpha_n) = \frac{\displaystyle\iint_R |\nabla v|^2\,dx\,dy}{\displaystyle\iint_R v^2\,dx\,dy} = \frac{\displaystyle\sum_{i,j=1}^n a_{ij}\alpha_i\alpha_j}{\displaystyle\sum_{i,j=1}^n b_{ij}\alpha_i\alpha_j}. \tag{24.7}$$

It is seen that

$$a_{ij} = \iint_R (\nabla v_i)^T(\nabla v_j)\,dx\,dy, \qquad b_{ij} = \iint_R v_i v_j\,dx\,dy.$$

That the matrices $A = [a_{ij}]$ and $B = [b_{ij}]$ are positive definite follows from (24.7). The μ^k are roots of $\det(A - \mu B) = 0$, as is proved, for example, in Courant and Hilbert [1953], and the reader is advised to be sure he is acquainted with the ideas set forth in Chap. 1 of that book.

A proof of the following important theorem will be found in Poincaré [1890]:

THEOREM 24.1. *For* $k = 1, 2, \cdots, n,$

$$\lambda^k \leq \mu^k. \tag{24.8}$$

There is a finite analog of the Poincaré theorem, which we shall use in Sec. 24.6 but which we shall not prove. In this the λ^k are themselves roots of an algebraic eigenvalue problem.

Theorem 24.1 is very useful in finding upper bounds for eigenvalues. The case $n = 1$, which states that $\lambda^1 \leq \rho(v)$ for all v in K, was mentioned before. In principle, one can select any n-parameter linear family of functions in K, and determine the finite eigenvalues μ^k associated with the function F of equation (24.7). The μ^k will then be upper bounds for the λ^k. This is essentially the *Rayleigh-Ritz method*. In practice, the difficulty is to find functions v_j that satisfy the boundary condition (24.1*b*).

For regions R that are precisely unions of meshes of a square net, Pólya [1954] has proposed the use of finite-difference methods for this, as follows. Let $u(P)$ be defined at each node P of a square net R_h, and let u be continued inside each elementary square mesh of the net by bilinear interpolation based on the values at the corners of the mesh. For example, if the corners of the square S_h are $(0, 0)$, $(h, 0)$, (h, h), $(0, h)$, then Pólya defines

$$u(x, y) = h^{-2}[u_{hh}xy + u_{00}(h - x)(h - y)$$
$$+ u_{h0}x(h - y) + u_{0h}(h - x)y] \tag{24.9}$$

for $0 \leq x \leq h$, $0 \leq y \leq h$, where $u_{hh} = u(h, h)$, etc. Since this form of interpolation is actually linear on each link of the net, it provides a function u which is continuous in $\bar{R}$, and whose gradient is piecewise continuous. If we select $u(P)$ to vanish at boundary nodes, we obtain a function u in K for arbitrary choices of $u(P)$, P in R_h.

Clearly these u form a linear family of functions, with as many parameters as there are points of R_h. Theorem 24.1 is applicable, and yields upper bounds μ^k for the λ^k ($k = 1, \cdots, n$).

To see what sort of matrix problem we get here, we have only to compute

$$\iint\limits_{R} u^2 \, dx \, dy \qquad \text{and} \qquad \iint\limits_{R} |\nabla u|^2 \, dx \, dy$$

as quadratic forms in the $u(P)$, for P in R_h.

Over the one mesh square S_h cited earlier, we obtain the relation

$$\iint\limits_{S_h} u^2 \, dx \, dy = \iint\limits_{S_h} h^{-4}(u_{hh}xy + \cdots)^2 \, dx \, dy$$

$$= \frac{h^2}{9}(u_{00}{}^2 + u_{h0}{}^2 + u_{hh}{}^2 + u_{0h}{}^2)$$

$$+ \frac{h^2}{9}(u_{00}u_{h0} + u_{h0}u_{hh} + u_{hh}u_{0h} + u_{0h}u_{00})$$

$$+ \frac{h^2}{18}(u_{00}u_{hh} + u_{h0}u_{0h}). \tag{24.10}$$

Summing expression (24.10) over all meshes of the net leads to the fact that

$$\iint\limits_{R} u^2 \, dx \, dy = \tfrac{1}{18} \sum_{P \in R_h} h^2 \, u(P)[8u(P) + 2u(E) + 2u(N) + 2u(W)$$

$$+ 2u(S) + \tfrac{1}{2}u(NE) + \tfrac{1}{2}u(NW) + \tfrac{1}{2}u(SW) + \tfrac{1}{2}u(SE)]. \tag{24.11}$$

Here the sum is extended over all points P of R_h, and we use the abbreviations $u(E)$, $u(NW)$, etc., to denote values of $u(x, y)$ at the eight node neighbors of P, according to the scheme of Fig. 20.2.

In a similar way one can find that

$$\iint\limits_{S_h} u_x{}^2 \, dx \, dy = \tfrac{1}{3}(u_{00}{}^2 + u_{h0}{}^2 + u_{hh}{}^2 + u_{0h}{}^2) - \tfrac{1}{3}(u_{00}u_{hh} + u_{h0}u_{0h})$$

$$- \tfrac{2}{3}(u_{00}u_{h0} + u_{0h}u_{hh}) + \tfrac{1}{3}(u_{00}u_{0h} + u_{h0}u_{hh}).$$

Adding a similar term for $\iint\limits_{S_h} u_y{}^2 \, dx \, dy$, we show that

$$\iint\limits_{S_h} |\nabla u|^2 \, dx \, dy = \tfrac{2}{3}(u_{00}{}^2 + u_{h0}{}^2 + u_{hh}{}^2 + u_{0h}{}^2)$$

$$- \tfrac{1}{3}(u_{00}u_{h0} + u_{h0}u_{hh} + u_{hh}u_{0h} + u_{0h}u_{00})$$

$$- \tfrac{2}{3}(u_{00}u_{hh} + u_{h0}u_{0h}). \tag{24.12}$$

Summing (24.12) over the net, we find that

$$\iint\limits_{R} |\nabla u|^2 \, dx \, dy = \tfrac{1}{3} \sum_{P \in R_h} u(P)[8u(P) - u(E) - u(N) - u(W) - u(S)$$

$$- u(NE) - u(NW) - u(SW) - u(SE)], \tag{24.13}$$

again with the notation convention of Fig. 20.2.

Having the two quadratic forms (24.11), (24.13), to find the stationary values of $F(\alpha)$ in (24.7), we can form the matrix eigenvalue problem det $(A - \mu B) = 0$. This is equivalent to finding μ such that the linear system $(A - \mu B)U = 0$ has a nontrivial solution U. If one differentiates the forms with respect to each $u(P)$, it is found that we get the difference equation problem

$$-\Delta_h^* U = \mu M U, \tag{24.14}$$

where we define

$$\Delta_h^* U(P) = (3h^2)^{-1}[U(E) + U(N) + U(W) + U(S) + U(NE)$$
$$+ U(NW) + U(SE) + U(SW) - 8U(P)] \tag{24.15}$$

and where

$$MU(P) = \tfrac{1}{36}[16U(P) + 4U(E) + 4U(N) + 4U(W) + 4U(S)$$
$$+ U(NE) + U(SW) + U(NW) + U(SE)]. \tag{24.16}$$

Symbolically, as after (20.51), we can write (24.14), (24.15), (24.16) in the form

$$-\frac{1}{3h^2}\begin{bmatrix} 1 & 1 & 1 \\ 1 & -8 & 1 \\ 1 & 1 & 1 \end{bmatrix} U = \frac{\mu}{36}\begin{bmatrix} 1 & 4 & 1 \\ 4 & 16 & 4 \\ 1 & 4 & 1 \end{bmatrix} U. \tag{24.17}$$

Among finite-difference problems, the eigenvalue problem (24.17) is unusual in structure, in that the operator M differs from the identity I. But, if we solve (24.17) exactly, we obtain upper bounds for all λ^k of (24.2).

24.3. A Standard L-Shaped Membrane

To compare various eigenvalue estimates numerically, it is useful to have a standard region. For various reasons which will become clear later, a rectangle is too simple a domain. To have a nonconvex region, we select R to be the L-shaped union of three unit squares (see Sec. 18.6 and Fig. 18.8). Although the eigenvalues λ^k of this region are not known, calculations done by Forsythe [1954], Gerberich and Sangren [1957], and Sangren and J. H. Alexander [unpublished] have given a good idea of the value of the fundamental eigenvalue λ^1. De Vogelaere [private communication] makes the informal conjecture, based on machine experiments, that

$$9.63968 < \lambda^1 < 9.63972, \tag{24.18}$$

whereas Forsythe [1954] obtained the value $\lambda^1 \doteq 9.636$ by extrapolation from earlier machine experiments. According to similar extrapolations of Forsythe [1954] for the second eigenvalue λ^2,

$$\lambda^2 = 15.2. \tag{24.19}$$

It would be desirable to have guaranteed close bounds for several λ^k.

To get an idea of the bounds for λ^1 obtainable analytically with only pencil-and-paper calculations, let us consider upper bounds first. In terms of the axes of Fig. 18.8, we can use the test function $w(x, y)$ defined by $x(1 - x)(y + 1)$ for $x \geq y$, and by symmetry for $x < y$. This w is in class K. An elementary but tedious calculation shows that $\rho(w) = \frac{140}{11} = 12.8^-$. Hence, since (24.5) shows that $\lambda^1 \leq \rho(w)$, we have

$$\lambda^1 < 12.8.$$

Better results could be obtained (Ritz's method) by appropriately selecting a finite number of parameters $a_0, a_1, a_2, \cdots$ in a test function

$$w(x, y) = x(1 - x)(y + 1)(a_0 + a_1 x + a_2 y + \cdots), \qquad x \geq y.$$

For the L-shaped region, upper bounds for λ^1 can probably be made very close, with sufficient labor. However, for general regions, there is no systematic program for generating a good test function w because it is difficult to satisfy (24.1b).

Now λ^1 can be shown from (24.5) to be less than the fundamental eigenvalue for any region contained in R. From the right triangle bounded by the lines $x = 1$, $y = 1$, $x + y = 0$, whose fundamental eigenfunction is (see Courant and Hilbert [1953], pp. 301–2)

$$u^1 = \sin \frac{\pi}{2}(x + 1) \sin \pi(y + 1) + \sin \pi(x + 1) \sin \frac{\pi}{2}(y + 1),$$

we get the bound

$$\lambda^1 < \frac{5\pi^2}{4} \doteq 12.33. \tag{24.20}$$

For λ^1, Pólya's method of Sec. 24.2 can be applied to the L-shaped region for $h = \frac{1}{2}, \frac{1}{3}, \frac{1}{4}$, etc. For $h = \frac{1}{2}$, this is a simple desk computation, and yields the bound

$$\lambda^1 < 11.71.$$

In principle, the Ritz and Pólya upper bounds can be made arbitrarily close, with computation of an appropriate algebraic eigenvalue problem on an automatic digital computer. In practice, the calculations are not difficult, although they would be lengthy for high precision.

Lower bounds are more difficult, because the basic and useful variational principle $\lambda^1 = \min \rho(w)$ always yields upper bounds for λ^1. By comparison of R with the circumscribed square of side 2, we find that

$$\lambda^1 > \frac{\pi^2}{2} \doteq 4.94. \tag{24.21}$$

By the so-called Rayleigh-Faber principle (Pólya and Szegö [1951]), we know that λ^1 exceeds the corresponding eigenvalue for a circle of the same area as R. This tells us that

$$\lambda^1 > 6.05. \tag{24.22}$$

A variational principle complementary to the one which states that $\lambda^1 = \min \rho(w)$ has been stated by Barta [1937], by Duffin [1947], and has been discussed by Redheffer [1957]. It states that, for any test function v such that $v(x, y) > 0$ in $\bar{R}$, and $-\Delta v > 0$ everywhere in R, we have

$$\min_{(x,y)\in R} \left(\frac{-\Delta v}{v}\right) \leq \lambda^1. \tag{24.23}$$

Although (24.23) is theoretically capable of furnishing arbitrarily good bounds, it is not easy to find a good function v, and we have not applied this bound (24.23) to the L-shaped membrane.

See Protter [1958, 1959] for another method of obtaining lower bounds for λ^1 analytically.

24.4. Lower Bounds from Difference Equations: Weinberger's Method

A powerful and elegant method for getting lower bounds for the λ^k was given by Weinberger [1956]. As we present it, it applies only to the fundamental eigenvalue of the membrane problem, but in a later paper Weinberger [1958] has extended the method to more general operators and to higher eigenvalues.

Let R be any bounded, connected, open set in the (x, y)-plane, whose boundary we denote by $\dot{R}$. We now define a region R^* which is a union of squares of the net, and which is somewhat bigger than R; i.e., R^* contains every point (x, y) such that $(x + \alpha, y + \beta)$ belongs to R for some α, β with $0 \leq \alpha \leq h, 0 \leq \beta \leq h$ (see Fig. 24.1). Let R_h^* consist of all the interior nodes of R^*. Thus R_h^* is a net region in our usual sense, but by its definition it extends a distance at least h to the left and below R, and, moreover, it cannot conform closely to the boundary $\dot{R}$ of R at places where $\dot{R}$ has narrow convolutions.

Let $U(x, y)$ be any real-valued function defined on all the nodes of the plane, vanishing at all nodes on and outside the net boundary of R_h^*.

Let

$$D_h(U) = \sum_{(x,y)} \{[U(x + h, y) - U(x, y)]^2 + [U(x, y + h) - U(x, y)]^2\}, \tag{24.24}$$

where the sum is taken over all nodes of the plane. This is the net analog of the Dirichlet integral $D(u) = \iint |\nabla u|^2 \, dx \, dy$.

Consider the finite Rayleigh quotient

$$\rho_h^*(U) = \frac{D_h(U)}{\sum_{(x,y)} h^2 [U(x, y)]^2}.$$

Regard the set of nonzero values $U(x, y)$ as a vector U in a finite-dimensional space. Then $[D_h(U)]/h^2$ is a quadratic form in U, which we may write in the form

$$\frac{D_h(U)}{h^2} = U^T A U,$$

where A is a symmetric, positive-semidefinite matrix. Hence

$$\rho_h^*(U) = \frac{U^T A U}{U^T U}.$$

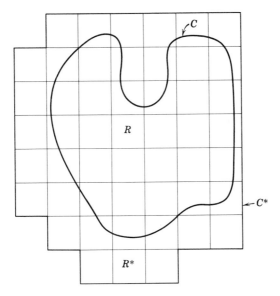

FIG. 24.1. The region R^* of Weinberger.

As mentioned in Sec. 24.2, the stationary values of $\rho_h^*(U)$ are the eigenvalues of A. In particular, the minimum of $\rho_h^*(U)$ is the least eigenvalue of A. Finally, the reader can show from the definition of A that $AU = (2h^2)^{-1} \nabla D_h(U) = -\Delta_h(U)$. Hence *the minimum value of* $\rho_h^*(U)$ *is precisely the least eigenvalue* λ_h^{*1} *of the net eigenvalue problem* (24.26) *below.* That is,

$$\lambda_h^{*1} = \min_U \frac{D_h(U)}{\sum_{(x,y)} h^2 [U(x, y)]^2}, \qquad (24.25)$$

where this and the following sums are taken over all net nodes (x, y) in the plane. This is a discrete analog of the fact that λ^1 is the minimum of the $\rho(w)$ of (24.4).

Weinberger now demonstrates the following theorem.

THEOREM 24.2. *Let $\lambda_h{}^{*1}$ be the least eigenvalue of the net eigenvalue problem*

$$-\Delta_h U = \lambda_h U \qquad in\ R_h^* \tag{24.26a}$$

$$U = 0 \qquad on\ C_h^*, \tag{24.26b}$$

where $\Delta_h U$ is defined in (20.51). Let λ^1 be the least eigenvalue of the problem (24.1). *Then $\lambda_h{}^{*1} < \lambda^1$.*

Proof. Let $u(x, y)$ be the eigenfunction of problem (24.1) belonging to λ^1. Extend $u(x, y)$ to vanish outside R, and let $U(x, y; \alpha, \beta) = u(x + \alpha, y + \beta)$, for $0 \le \alpha \le h$, $0 \le \beta \le h$. By our choice of R_h^*, the function $U(x, y; \alpha, \beta)$ is eligible to be put into the minimum principle (24.25), for each fixed pair α, β. Hence

$$\lambda_h{}^{*1}h^2 \sum_{(x,y)} [u(x + \alpha, y + \beta)]^2 \le \sum_{(x,y)} \{[u(x + \alpha + h, y + \beta)$$
$$- u(x + \alpha, y + \beta)]^2 + [u(x + \alpha, y + \beta + h) - u(x + \alpha, y + \beta)]^2\}. \tag{24.27}$$

Now integrate (24.27) over the square $0 \le \alpha \le h$, $0 \le \beta \le h$. We get, for the left side of (24.27),

$$\lambda_h{}^{*1}h^2 \sum_{(x,y)} \int_0^h \int_0^h [u(x + \alpha, y + \beta)]^2 \, d\alpha \, d\beta = \lambda_h{}^{*1}h^2 \iint_R u^2 \, dx \, dy. \tag{24.28}$$

For the first term on the right side of (24.27), we have

$$\sum_{(x,y)} \int_0^h \int_0^h [u(x + \alpha + h, y + \beta) - u(x + \alpha, y + \beta)]^2 \, d\alpha \, d\beta$$

$$= \iint_R [u(x + h, y) - u(x, y)]^2 \, dx \, dy$$

$$= \iint_R \left[\int_0^h u_x(x + \gamma, y) \, d\gamma \right]^2 dx \, dy$$

$$\le \iint_R \left(h \int_0^h [u_x(x + \gamma, y)]^2 \, d\gamma \right) dx \, dy \quad \text{(by Schwarz's inequality)}$$

$$= \int_0^h d\gamma \, h \iint_R [u_x(x + \gamma, y)]^2 \, dx \, dy$$

$$= \int_0^h d\gamma \, h \iint_R [u_x(x, y)]^2 \, dx \, dy = h^2 \iint_R u_x{}^2(x, y) \, dx \, dy.$$

Adding a similar bound for the second term on the right side of (24.27), we find that

$$\lambda_h^{*1} h^2 \int \int_R u^2 \, dx \, dy \leq h^2 \, D(u),$$

whence

$$\lambda_h^{*1} \leq \frac{D(u)}{\int \int_R u^2 \, dx \, dy} = \lambda^1. \tag{24.29}$$

This completes Weinberger's ingenious proof of Theorem 24.2.

If, as $h \to 0$, the region R^* and its boundary C^* converge in an appropriate sense to R and its boundary C, respectively, it is to be expected that $\lambda_h^{*1} \to \lambda^1$ and, hence, that Weinberger's theorem will yield lower bounds for λ^1 which can be made arbitrarily close for sufficiently small h. Such approximation of R, C by R^*, C^* is possible for the regions R defined in Sec. 18, since they are bounded by piecewise analytic curves.

The fact that C^* is approximately at the distance h from R on the left and bottom sides means that the fundamental eigenvalue λ^{*1} of the continuous problem for R^* may be expected to be less than λ^1 by a term of order $O(h)$. For we may heuristically think of R^* as being roughly similar to R, but $1 + h$ times as wide, and a similar region $1 + h$ times as wide as R has exactly $(1 + h)^{-2}\lambda^1$ as its fundamental membrane eigenvalue. Now there are reasons to believe that λ_h^{*1} differs from λ^{*1} by $o(h)$ (see Sec. 24.5). If so, we may expect that

$$\lambda_h^{*1} = \lambda^{*1} + o(h) = (1 + h)^{-2}\lambda^1 + o(h)$$
$$= \lambda^1 - 2\lambda^1 h + o(h), \tag{24.30}$$

Thus Weinberger's bound, while rigorous, is probably low by a term of size $O(h)$. If the diameter of R is about 2, with present computers we might use an h near $\frac{1}{25}$ (yielding 2500 points in R_h^*); we might then expect Weinberger's bounds to be low by something like 4%. If $\lambda^1 \doteq 10$, as with the L-shaped membrane of Sec. 24.3, from Theorem 24.2 we may expect lower bounds near $\lambda^1 - 0.4$. The authors know of no actual computation to verify this.

If R should have a cut in it, the formation of R^* essentially erases the cut, and causes λ_h^{*1} to be smaller than λ^1 by $O(1)$.

Related to Weinberger's work are some researches of Hersch [1955] and of Hersch, Pfluger, and Schopf [1956] on upper and lower bounds for domain functionals by difference methods. We shall not review these here. One of the most interesting aspects of these papers is the utilization of real-valued functions defined not only on the nodes of a square net but also sometimes on the meshes or on the links. Hersch et al. also deal with vector-valued functions on a grid, as does Synge [1951, 1957].

24.5. Asymptotic Lower Bounds from Difference Equations

Forsythe has studied the relation between λ^k and $\lambda_h{}^k$, where a discrete problem is taken over a net region R_h that matches R as closely as possible, in the hope of finding close lower bounds for the λ^k. The hope arose from a look at rectangular regions R which are unions of meshes of a square net. Suppose, as did Forsythe [1954], that R is a rectangle with commensurable sides π/p, π/q. It is easily verified that $u^{(m,n)} = \sin mpx \sin nqy$ is an eigenfunction of both $-\Delta$ and $-\Delta_h$; it is more convenient to use a double superscript temporarily instead of the single superscript k. Now, for the differential equation one has

$$\lambda^{(m,n)} = (mp)^2 + (nq)^2;$$

and, as $h \to 0$ over values of h for which R is a union of squares of the net,

$$\lambda_h^{(m,n)} = \frac{\sin^2(mph/2) + \sin^2(nqh/2)}{(h/2)^2}$$

$$= \lambda^{(m,n)} - \left[\frac{(mp)^4 + (nq)^4}{12}\right]h^2 + O(h^4), \qquad \text{as } h \to 0. \quad (24.31)$$

Hence $\lambda_h^{(m,n)} < \lambda^{(m,n)}$ for all (m, n) and all h, and one can use $\lambda_h^{(m,n)}$ as a lower bound for $\lambda^{(m,n)}$. Moreover, $\lambda^{(m,n)} - \lambda_h^{(m,n)} = O(h^2)$. If the rectangle were typical, close lower bounds could be expected from ordinary difference methods.

Unfortunately the rectangle is not typical, and the investigation has never settled the relation of $\lambda_h{}^k$ to λ^k for nontrivial regions and large values of h. However, certain asymptotic results have been proved, which lead to lower bounds for λ^k for all sufficiently small h when R is convex. We shall summarize these investigations in the following.

We shall first need to know the analytic behavior of the eigenfunctions $u^k(x, y)$ of $-\Delta$ in R, assumed to be an open region bounded by C, a finite number of piecewise analytic simple closed curves. We demand that all corners of C be *strictly convex*; i.e., at any point on C where distinct analytic curves meet, the interior angle is to be less than π (equality not permitted). The following is needed:

THEOREM 24.3. u^k is an analytic function of x as well as of y in R.
For a proof, see Bernstein [1950], p. 179.

THEOREM 24.4. u^k is analytic on C, excluding the corners.
For a proof of a much more general result, see Morrey and Nirenberg [1957].

THEOREM 24.5. *Let* $P = (x_P, y_P)$ *be a corner of* C, *with interior angle* $\pi/\alpha\ (\alpha > 1)$. *Let* $r^2 = (x - x_P)^2 + (y - y_P)^2$. *Then, for* $m = 0, 1, 2, \cdots$, *for* $k = 1, 2, \cdots$, *and for* (x, y) *in* R, *we have*

$$\frac{\partial^m u^k(x, y)}{\partial x^\mu \, \partial y^\nu} = r^{\alpha - m} f_{m,k}(x, y), \qquad \mu + \nu = m,$$

where $f_{m,k}$ *is continuous in* x *and* y *at* P.

Proof. A proof of Theorem 24.5 has been given by Lehman [1959], Theorem 3.4, based on methods introduced in Lehman [1957]. Related ideas were used by Wasow [1957a]. The supposed proofs of Theorems 24.4 and 24.5 in Forsythe [1954, 1955] are incorrect.

The assertion of Theorem 24.5 is that u^k behaves locally at a corner P like a nonzero solution w of $\Delta w = 0$ in a circular sector of angle π/α, with $w = 0$ on the straight sides of the sector. One such function would be $w(r, \theta) = r^\alpha \sin \alpha\theta$, where r, θ are polar coordinates centered at P.

The following lemma follows from Theorem 24.5:

LEMMA 24.6. *For* $k, l = 1, 2, \cdots$, *the functions* $u_{xx}^k u_{xx}^l$, $u_x^k u_{xxx}^l$, $u^k u_{xxxx}^l$, $u_{yy}^k u_{yy}^l$, $u_y^k u_{yyy}^l$, *and* $u^k u_{yyyy}^l$ *are Lebesgue-integrable in* $\bar{R}$. *The Lebesgue integrals* $\int_C u_x^k u_{xx}^l \, dy$ *and* $\int_C u_y^k u_{yy}^l \, dx$ *exist. Equivalently, these integrals may be interpreted as improper Riemann integrals.*

Proof. By Theorems 24.3 and 24.4 the integrands are all analytic and, hence, integrable, in every closed subregion of $R \cup C$ not containing the corners. By Theorem 24.5, the functions $u_{xx}^k u_{xx}^l, \cdots, u^k u_{yyyy}^l$ are $O(r^{2\alpha - 4})$ at each corner. Since $1 < \alpha$, they are $O(r^{-2+\epsilon})$ for some $\epsilon > 0$, and are hence plane-integrable in R. Similarly, the line integrals exist.

It follows from Lemma 24.6 that (24.4) and (24.6) are equivalent forms of the Rayleigh quotient $\rho(u)$.

We now set up a square net R_h inside R, and add to it certain points of C as neighbors of the irregular interior points, following the treatment in Sec. 20.9 (interpolation of degree two). For any net function $U(P)$ defined in $\bar{R}_h = R_h \cup C_h$, with $U(P) = 0$ for P in C_h, we let $\Delta^{(h)} U$ be the Shortley-Weller form of the Laplace difference operator, defined in (20.69). Now the matrix $A^{(h)}$ corresponding to the operator $-\Delta^{(h)}$ is not symmetric, and this prevents our describing the eigenvalues of $-\Delta^{(h)}$ as stationary values of a quadratic form. We therefore introduce the symmetrized operator $\bar{\Delta}_h$ corresponding to the symmetric matrix $A = \frac{1}{2}[A^{(h)} + A^{(h)T}]$. The eigenvalues $\bar{\lambda}_h^k$ of $-\bar{\Delta}_h$ are the stationary values of the Rayleigh quotient

$$\rho_h(U) = \frac{-\sum_P U(P)\, \bar{\Delta}_h\, U(P)}{\sum_P [U(P)]^2}. \tag{24.32}$$

It is these eigenvalues $\bar{\lambda}_h^k$ of $-\bar{\Delta}_h$ which we shall compare with the eigenvalues λ^k of $-\Delta$. It can be proved that $\bar{\lambda}_h^k \to \lambda^k$, as $h \to 0$.

To state the theorems relating $\bar{\lambda}_h^k$ with λ^k, announced by Forsythe [1956a], we need a few more definitions. Let τ be the angle between the x-axis and the positive direction of the tangent line to C. As a function of arc length s on C, $\tau = \tau(s)$ is piecewise continuously differentiable. Let v, w denote any two eigenfunctior s of $-\Delta$; by Theorem 24.5, their inner normals v_n, w_n are continuous on C. We define a formal inner product (v, w) as follows:

$$12(v, w) = \int\int_R (v_{xx}w_{xx} + v_{yy}w_{yy}) \, dx \, dy + \int_C v_n w_n \sin^2 2\tau \, d\tau. \quad (24.33)$$

It must be noted that (v, w) is not necessarily an inner product in the Hilbert-space sense, unless R is convex, since (v, v) may be negative. The first integral in (24.33) is finite by Lemma 24.6. The second is a finite Lebesgue-Stieltjes or Riemann-Stieltjes integral. Since $v_n = w_n = 0$ at each corner of C (Theorem 24.5), there is no contribution to the second integral at a corner of C, and we may rewrite the second integral in the equivalent form

$$\int_C v_n(s) \, w_n(s) \sin^2 [2\tau(s)] \, \tau'(s) \, ds, \quad (24.34)$$

a Riemann integral with the corners ignored.

Now let the eigenfunctions u^k of $-\Delta$ be so normalized that

$$\int\int_R (u^k)^2 \, dx \, dy = 1, \quad k = 1, 2, \cdots. \quad (24.35)$$

Corresponding to a multiple eigenvalue $\lambda^k = \lambda^{k+1} = \cdots$, choose the eigenfunctions to be orthogonal in the sense that (24.3) holds. Let the infinite symmetric matrix D have elements $d_{ij} = (u^i, u^j)$ in the sense of (24.33). We now define a sequence γ_k of real numbers, as follows. If λ^k is a simple eigenvalue of $-\Delta$, let $\gamma_k = d_{kk}$. If $\lambda^k = \lambda^{k+1} = \cdots = \lambda^{k+m-1}$ is an m-fold multiple eigenvalue of $-\Delta$, define $\gamma_k \geq \gamma_{k+1} \geq \cdots \geq \gamma_{k+m-1}$ to be the m (real) eigenvalues of the corresponding m-rowed principal minor of D, i.e., of $[d_{ij}]$, $i, j = k, k + 1, \cdots, k + m - 1$.

We can now state the principal result:

THEOREM 24.7. *Let R, an open region with strictly convex corners, be bounded by C, the union of a finite number of piecewise analytic simple closed curves. Define h, λ^k, $\bar{\lambda}_h^k$, and γ_k as above. Then for $k = 1, 2, \cdots$, one has*

$$\bar{\lambda}_h^k \leq \lambda^k - \gamma_k h^2 + o(h^2), \quad as \; h \to 0. \quad (24.36)$$

The proof of Theorem 24.7 is given in Sec. 24.6.

If R not only has strictly convex corners but also is a convex region, then $d\tau(s) \geq 0$ for all s, and every principal minor of D is positive definite. To see this, note that, for any real numbers $x, \cdots, x_{pr}$, not all zero,

$$\sum_{i,j=p}^{r} d_{ij} x_i x_j = \left(\sum_{i=p}^{r} x_i u^i, \sum_{j=p}^{r} x_j u^j \right) = (z, z)$$

$$= \tfrac{1}{12} \iint_R (z_{xx}^2 + z_{yy}^2) \, dx \, dy + \tfrac{1}{12} \int_C z_n^2 \sin^2 2\tau \, d\tau > 0.$$

From the positive definiteness, it follows that all $\gamma_k > 0$. We therefore have deduced the following corollary to the last theorem:

THEOREM 24.8. *Let R, a convex open region with strictly convex corners, be bounded by C, a piecewise analytic simple closed curve. Then, with the above notation, $0 < \gamma_k < \infty$, and for each $k = 1, 2, \cdots$, there exists $h_0(k) > 0$ such that*

$$\bar{\lambda}_h^k < \lambda^k, \qquad \text{if } h \leq h_0(k). \tag{24.37}$$

Theorem 24.7 is the best possible asymptotic result, in the sense that for the rectangle discussed in (24.31), the coefficient of h^2 is actually the γ_k corresponding to (m, n). Thus (24.36) is an equality for such a rectangle.

24.6. Proof of Theorem 24.7

It now remains to prove Theorem 24.7. Let R continue to satisfy the hypotheses of that theorem.

LEMMA 24.9. *Let w, together with its first and second derivatives, be continuous in $\bar{R}$. Suppose w, w_x, and w_y all vanish on C. Then*

$$h^2 \sum_{P \in R_h} w(P) = \iint_R w \, dx \, dy + o(h^2), \qquad \text{as } h \to 0. \tag{24.38}$$

Proof. By the hypotheses on w, for P within a distance h of C, $|w(P)| \leq \sigma h^2$, $\sigma = $ constant. Hence we can ignore both the integral and the sum over irregular meshes adjoining the boundary, as these would contribute a total of $O(lh)(\sigma h^2) = o(h^2)$, where $l = $ length of C.

Now for any one square mesh S_h of side h, let $\frac{1}{4} \Sigma w_i$ denote the average of the four corner values. By expanding $w(x, y)$ about the center O of the mesh, we can show that

$$\tfrac{1}{4} \sum_i w_i = w_O + \tfrac{1}{8} h^2 (w_{xx} + w_{yy})_O + o(h^2), \qquad \text{as } h \to 0, \tag{24.39}$$

where w, w_{xx}, and w_{yy} are evaluated at O. In the same way, we compute that

$$\iint_{S_h} w \, dx \, dy = h^2 w_O + \tfrac{1}{24} h^4 (w_{xx} + w_{yy})_O + o(h^4), \qquad \text{as } h \to 0. \quad (24.40)$$

From (24.39) and (24.40) we see that

$$\frac{h^2}{4} \sum_i w_i = \iint_{S_h} w \, dx \, dy + \tfrac{1}{12} h^4 (\Delta w)_O + o(h^4), \qquad \text{as } h \to 0. \quad (24.41)$$

If we sum (24.41) over all full squares of the net, which are $O(1/h^2)$ in number, we get (24.38), except for the term

$$\frac{h^2}{12} \sum (\Delta w)_O h^2,$$

which, as a Riemann sum for the integration of the continuous function Δw over $\bar{R}$, is

$$\frac{h^2}{12} \left[\iint_R \Delta w \, dx \, dy + o(1) \right], \qquad \text{as } h \to 0. \quad (24.42)$$

By the divergence theorem (24.47) with $p = w_x$, $q = w_y$, since w_x and w_y vanish at C, the term (24.42) is $o(h^2)$, and the lemma is proved completely.

In the quadrature formula (24.38), if $w = 0$ but $\nabla w \neq 0$ on C, the error term would be $O(h^2)$. The error becomes $o(h^2)$ because ∇w vanishes on C.

LEMMA 24.10. *If u^i, u^j are two normalized eigenfunctions of $-\Delta$, then*

$$\sum_{P \in R_h} u^i(P) \, u^j(P) h^2 = \delta_{ij} + o(h^2), \qquad \text{as } h \to 0. \quad (24.43)$$

Proof. Let $w = u^i u^j$. Then w is analytic in R, while

$$\nabla w = u^i \nabla u^j + u^j \nabla u^i \to 0, \qquad \text{as } P \to C.$$

Moreover, $w = 0$ on C. Then Lemma 24.10 follows from Lemma 24.9 and (24.3).

LEMMA 24.11. *Let v, w be two normalized eigenfunctions of $-\Delta$ in R. Define (v, w) as in (24.33). For each node (x, y), let*

$$\Theta u(x, y) = u_{xxxx}(x + \theta h, y) + u_{yyyy}(x, y + \theta' h), \quad (24.44)$$

where θ, θ' depend on x, y, with $-1 < \theta < 1$, $-1 < \theta' < 1$.
Then

$$\tfrac{1}{24} \sum (v \Theta w + w \Theta v) h^2 = (v, w) + o(1), \qquad \text{as } h \to 0, \quad (24.45)$$

where the sum is taken over all regular interior nodes of R_h which are more distant than h from a corner of C.

Proof. The sum is taken over such nodes that Θv, Θw are finite. The proof has two parts. First, one proves that the sum in (24.45) equals

$$\tfrac{1}{24}\iint\limits_{R} v(w_{xxxx} + w_{yyyy})\, dx\, dy + \tfrac{1}{24}\iint\limits_{R} w(v_{xxxx} + v_{yyyy})\, dx\, dy + o(1),$$

$$\text{as } h \to 0. \quad (24.46)$$

Second, one shows that (24.46) equals the right-hand side of (24.45).

The first part can be proved by application of the Lebesgue convergence theorem. Lemma 24.6 can be used to show that the convergence of $v\Theta w$ to $v(w_{xxxx} + w_{yyyy})$ is dominated by a summable function. Details are parallel to those in the proof of Lemma 6 of Forsythe [1954], and are omitted.

In transforming (24.46) to (24.45), one uses the divergence theorem twice in the form

$$\iint\limits_{R}(p_x + q_y)\, dx\, dy = \int\limits_{C}(p\, dy - q\, dx). \quad (24.47)$$

Lemma 24.6 justifies (24.47) for the functions p and q used below.

If we let $p = vw_{xxx} + wv_{xxx}$, $q = vw_{yyy} + wv_{yyy}$, we find that (24.46) takes the form

$$-\tfrac{1}{24}\iint\limits_{R}(v_x w_{xxx} + v_y w_{yyy})\, dx\, dy - \tfrac{1}{24}\iint\limits_{R}(w_x v_{xxx} + w_y v_{yyy})\, dx\, dy + o(1),$$

$$(24.48)$$

since the line integral vanishes. A second application of the divergence theorem, with $p = v_x w_{xx} + w_x v_{xx}$, $q = v_y w_{yy} + w_y v_{yy}$, transforms (24.48) into

$$\tfrac{1}{12}\iint\limits_{R}(v_{xx} w_{xx} + v_{yy} w_{yy})\, dx\, dy + \tfrac{1}{24}\Gamma + o(1), \quad (24.49)$$

where

$$\Gamma = \int\limits_{C}[(v_y w_{yy} + w_y v_{yy})\, dx - (v_x w_{xx} + w_x v_{xx})\, dy].$$

To finish the proof, we have only to prove that

$$\Gamma = 2\int\limits_{C} v_n w_n \sin^2 2\tau\, d\tau. \quad (24.50)$$

Since v, w are analytic in $\bar{R}$, corners excepted, and satisfy equation (24.1), on C one has that $v_{yy} = -v_{xx}$, $w_{yy} = -w_{xx}$. Hence

$$\Gamma = \int\limits_{C}[v_{yy}(w_y\, dx + w_x\, dy) + w_{yy}(v_y\, dx + v_x\, dy)]. \quad (24.51)$$

Let s denote arc length, and let primes denote d/ds. Differentiating the relations (u is v or w)

$$u_x = -u_n \sin \tau, \qquad u_y = u_n \cos \tau, \qquad (24.52)$$

we find that on C

$$u_x' = -u_n' \sin \tau - u_n \tau' \cos \tau = u_{xy} \sin \tau + u_{xx} \cos \tau,$$
$$u_y' = \quad u_n' \cos \tau - u_n \tau' \sin \tau = u_{xy} \cos \tau + u_{yy} \sin \tau. \qquad (24.53)$$

Changing u_{xx} to $-u_{yy}$, and then solving (24.53) for u_{yy} on C, we find

$$u_{yy} = u_n' \sin 2\tau + u_n \tau' \cos 2\tau.$$

Since $dx = ds \cos \tau$ and $dy = ds \sin \tau$, from (24.52) we obtain

$$\int_C v_{yy}(w_y \, dx + w_x \, dy) = \int_C (v_n' \sin 2\tau + v_n \tau' \cos 2\tau)(w_n \cos 2\tau) \, ds. \qquad (24.54)$$

Similarly,

$$\int_C w_{yy}(v_y \, dx + v_x \, dy) = \int_C (w_n' \sin 2\tau + w_n \tau' \cos 2\tau)(v_n \cos 2\tau) \, ds. \qquad (24.55)$$

Adding (24.54) and (24.55), we find that

$$\Gamma = 2\int_C v_n w_n \cos^2 2\tau (\tau' \, ds) + \int_C (v_n w_n)' \sin 2\tau \cos 2\tau \, ds. \qquad (24.56)$$

Integrating by parts, we see that

$$\int_C (v_n w_n)' \sin 2\tau \cos 2\tau \, ds = \tfrac{1}{2} \int_C (v_n w_n)' \sin 4\tau \, ds$$
$$= \tfrac{1}{2} \Big[v_n w_n \sin 4\tau \Big]_C - 2\int_C v_n w_n \tau' \cos 4\tau \, ds. \qquad (24.57)$$

Since $\cos^2 2\tau - \cos 4\tau = \sin^2 2\tau$, and since $\tau' \, ds = d\tau(s)$, substitution of (24.57) into (24.56) shows that (24.50) holds, completing the proof of the lemma.

We shall need some perturbation theory of the eigenvalues of symmetric matrices.

LEMMA 24.12. *Let* $A = A^T$, $B = B^T$, $C = A - B$ *have the following* (real) *eigenvalues:*

$$A: \quad \alpha_1 \le \alpha_2 \le \cdots \le \alpha_n,$$
$$B: \quad \beta_1 \le \beta_2 \le \cdots \le \beta_n,$$
$$C: \quad \gamma_1 \le \gamma_2 \le \cdots \le \gamma_n.$$

Then for $i = 1, 2, \cdots, n$

$$\alpha_i - \beta_n \le \gamma_i \le \alpha_i - \beta_1. \tag{24.58}$$

Proof. Consider $B_1 = B - \beta_1 I$, a positive-semidefinite matrix whose eigenvalues are $\beta_i - \beta_1 \ge 0$. By Courant and Hilbert [1953], p. 33, the eigenvalues of $A - B_1$ (which are $\gamma_i + \beta_1$) are respectively less than or equal to those of A (which are α_i). Hence $\gamma_i + \beta_1 \le \alpha_i$, proving half of (24.58). The other half is proved similarly.

Lemma 24.12 also follows from a general result of Lidskiĭ [1950] and Wielandt [1955].

THEOREM 24.13 (Rellich). *Let $A(\epsilon)$ be a symmetric matrix of order n whose elements are regular analytic functions of ϵ, for small real $|\epsilon|$. Then the eigenvalues $\lambda_k(\epsilon)$ are regular analytic at $\epsilon = 0$. Also, for real ϵ, it is possible to choose an eigenvector set $\{u_k(\epsilon)\}$, $k = 1, 2, \cdots, n$, so that each $u_k(\epsilon)$ is regular analytic at $\epsilon = 0$.*

For proof, refer to Rellich [1953]. Being analytic, two eigenvalues $\lambda_i(\epsilon)$ and $\lambda_j(\epsilon)$, not identically equal, can only have isolated coincidences near $\epsilon = 0$. Hence, except at isolated points, normalized eigenvectors $u_i(\epsilon)$ of roots $\lambda_i(\epsilon)$ which are not identically multiple roots are uniquely determined up to their signs. At an isolated coincidence ϵ the choice of $u_i(\epsilon)$, known to be possible by Theorem 24.13, can then be made solely by continuity. We shall make use of this to determine the derivatives of $\lambda_i(\epsilon)$.

THEOREM 24.14. *Suppose $\lambda_k(0)$ is an eigenvalue of $A(0)$ of multiplicity $m \ge 1$, with a corresponding m-dimensional invariant subspace Σ. Let vectors $p_1, \cdots, p_m$ form any orthonormal basis of Σ. Define the following matrix $V = [v_{ij}]$ of order m:*

$$v_{ij} = p_i^T A'(0) p_j, \qquad i, j = 1, \cdots, m.$$

Let the eigenvalues of V be $\gamma_1, \cdots, \gamma_m$.

Then, with appropriate numbering, the derivatives at $\epsilon = 0$ of the m eigenvalues $\lambda_k(\epsilon)$ are given by

$$\lambda_k'(0) = \gamma_k, \qquad k = 1, \cdots, m. \tag{24.59}$$

Proof. Since λ_k and u_k are regular analytic, if properly chosen, we may differentiate the relation $A(\epsilon) u_k(\epsilon) = \lambda_k(\epsilon) u_k(\epsilon)$ at $\epsilon = 0$, to get

$$A u_k' + A' u_k = \lambda_k' u_k + \lambda_k u_k'.$$

Premultiplying by u_k^T, and remembering that $u_k^T A = \lambda_k u_k^T$, we obtain

$$u_k^T(0) A'(0) u_k(0) = \lambda_k'(0). \tag{24.60}$$

It remains to show that (24.60) implies (24.59). For a similar proof for operators, see Courant and Hilbert [1953], pp. 346–348.

The quantities γ_i and $\lambda_k'(0)$ are independent of the coordinate system. If λ_k has multiplicity m, we remarked after Theorem 24.13 that we must select the m vectors $u_k(0)$ in (24.60) to be limits, as $\epsilon \to 0$, of the $u_k(\epsilon)$. Let us assume the coordinates have been fixed so that $A(0)$ is in a diagonal form J, and so that the m-fold root $\lambda_k(0)$ corresponds to the matrix $\lambda_k I_m$ in the upper left-hand corner of J. Then Σ is spanned by the first m coordinate vectors.

If we expand $A(\epsilon)$ by Taylor's theorem, we have

$$A(\epsilon) = J + \epsilon A'(0) + O(\epsilon^2), \qquad \text{as } \epsilon \to 0.$$

Now $A(\epsilon)$ has m unit eigenvectors $u_k(\epsilon)$ which must approach a basis of Σ, as $\epsilon \to 0$, by Theorem 24.13. The components of $u_k(\epsilon)$, except for the first m, must be $O(\epsilon)$, since they go to zero with ϵ and are analytic. Ignoring terms in ϵ^2, which by Lemma 24.12 must be negligible for the purpose of deriving (24.63) below, let us partition $A(\epsilon)$ into four submatrices, as follows:

$$A(\epsilon) = \begin{bmatrix} \lambda_k I_m + \epsilon A_{11}' + \cdots & \epsilon A_{12}' + \cdots \\ \epsilon A_{21}' + \cdots & J_1 + \epsilon A_{22}' + \cdots \end{bmatrix} \begin{matrix} (m) \\ (n-m). \end{matrix}$$
$$\qquad\qquad (m) \qquad\qquad\quad (n-m)$$

Let $u_k = u_k(\epsilon)$ be partitioned correspondingly:

$$u_k(\epsilon) = \begin{bmatrix} U_0 + U_1 \epsilon + \cdots \\ U_2 \epsilon + \cdots \end{bmatrix} \begin{matrix} (m) \\ (n-m). \end{matrix}$$

Moreover $\lambda_k(\epsilon) = \lambda_k + \lambda_k' \epsilon + \cdots$. Fix k.

Now

$$A(\epsilon) u_k(\epsilon) = \begin{bmatrix} \lambda_k U_0 + \epsilon(A_{11}' U_0 + \lambda_k U_1) + \cdots \\ \epsilon(A_{21}' U_0 + J_1 U_2) + \cdots \end{bmatrix}, \tag{24.61}$$

while

$$\lambda_k(\epsilon) u_k(\epsilon) = \begin{bmatrix} \lambda_k U_0 + \epsilon(\lambda_k' U_0 + \lambda_k U_1) + \cdots \\ \epsilon \lambda_k U_2 + \cdots \end{bmatrix}. \tag{24.62}$$

Equating powers of ϵ in (24.61) and (24.62), we see, among other things, that

$$A_{11}' U_0 = \lambda_k' U_0. \tag{24.63}$$

Hence U_0, the vector formed by the first m components of $\lim_{\epsilon \to 0} u_k(\epsilon)$, must be an eigenvector of A_{11}', which is the matrix V for the coordinate system considered. Since the later components of $u_k(0) = \lim_{\epsilon \to 0} u_k(\epsilon)$ are 0, we see that $U_0^T U_0 = 1$, whence

$$u_k^T(0) A'(0) u_k(0) = U_0^T A_{11}' U_0 = U_0^T V U_0 = U_0^T \gamma_k U_0 = \gamma_k.$$

The last equality, with (24.60), implies (24.59), and this completes the proof of Theorem 24.14.

Proceeding now to the proof of Theorem 24.7, we let

$$y = \sum_{i=1}^{n} t_i u^i \qquad (24.64)$$

be a test function to be set into the finite Rayleigh quotient $\rho_h(y)$ of (24.32). Here $u^1, \cdots, u^n$ are eigenfunctions of $-\Delta$, and $t_1, \cdots, t_n$ are real parameters to be varied until $\rho_h(y)$ is stationary. This use of the solutions of the differential equation as test functions for the finite-variational problem is the essence of this method as well as that of Weinberger [1956, 1958]. The idea was used much earlier by Collatz [1938]. We assume that h is so small that these eigenfunctions u^i of $-\Delta$, when restricted to R_h, form linearly independent vectors. That this is possible follows from (24.70) and (24.71) below. Let the stationary values of $\rho_h(y)$ be $\mu_h{}^k$. By the finite analog of Theorem 24.1,

$$\lambda_h{}^k \le \mu_h{}^k, \qquad k = 1, \cdots, n. \qquad (24.65)$$

We shall now relate the $\mu_h{}^k$ to the λ^k.

By (24.32)

$$\begin{aligned}
\rho_h(y) &= \frac{-\sum_P y(P)\, \bar{\Delta}_h\, y(P)}{\sum_P [y(P)]^2} \\
&= \frac{-\sum_P y(P)\, \Delta^{(h)}\, y(P)}{\sum_P [y(P)]^2}, \qquad \text{by definition of } \bar{\Delta}_h. \qquad (24.66)
\end{aligned}$$

The sums are taken over all points of R_h.

We know from (20.52) that at each regular interior node (x, y) of R_h,

$$\Delta^{(h)} w(x, y) = \Delta w(x, y) + \frac{h^2}{12}\, \Theta w, \qquad (24.67)$$

where Θw was defined in (24.44). Hence, setting expression (24.64) into (24.66) and using (24.67), we find that

$$\begin{aligned}
\rho_h(y) &= \frac{-\sum_{i,j=1}^{n} t_i t_j \sum_P u^i(P)\, \Delta^{(h)}\, u^j(P)}{\sum_{i,j=1}^{n} t_i t_j \sum_P u^i(P)\, u^j(P)} \\
&= \frac{-\sum_{i,j=1}^{n} t_i t_j \sum_P u^i(P)[\Delta u^j(P) + (h^2/12)\Theta\, u^j(P)]}{\sum_{i,j=1}^{n} t_i t_j \sum_P u^i(P)\, u^j(P)}. \qquad (24.68)
\end{aligned}$$

The above sums are taken over the regular interior nodes (defined in Sec. 20.9) of R_h. The omission of the irregular nodes can contribute only a term $o(h^2)$ to $\rho_h(y)$. Now the numerator of (24.68) can be simplified, since $-\Delta u^j = \lambda^j u^j$, and we also wish to write the quadratic forms symmetrically. We find that

$$\rho_h(y) = \frac{\displaystyle\sum_{i,j=1}^{n} m_{ij} t_i t_j}{\displaystyle\sum_{i,j=1}^{n} n_{ij} t_i t_j},$$

where

$$m_{ij} = m_{ji} = \left(\frac{\lambda^i + \lambda^j}{2}\right) \sum_P u^i(P)\, u^j(P) h^2$$

$$- \frac{h^2}{24} \sum_P [u^i(P)\Theta\, u^j(P) + u^j(P)\Theta\, u^i(P)]h^2; \quad (24.69)$$

$$n_{ij} = n_{ji} = \sum_P u^i(P)\, u^j(P) h^2. \quad (24.70)$$

Now, by Lemma 24.10,

$$n_{ij} = \delta_{ij} + o(h^2), \qquad \text{as } h \to 0, \quad (24.71)$$

whereas by Lemma 24.11

$$m_{ij} = \delta_{ij}\lambda^i - h^2(u^i, u^j) + o(h^2),$$

or

$$m_{ij} = \delta_{ij}\lambda^i - h^2 d_{ij} + o(h^2). \quad (24.72)$$

The stationary values of $\rho_h(y)$ are the values of μ such that

$$\det (M - \mu N) = 0, \quad (24.73)$$

where $M = [m_{ij}]$, $N = [n_{ij}]$. Knowing the expressions (24.72), (24.73) for M, N, the rest of the proof of Theorem 24.7 follows from the perturbation theory of eigenvalues of a symmetric matrix.

The roots μ of (24.73) are the eigenvalues of $N^{-1/2} M N^{-1/2}$. By Lemma 24.12 with $A = I$ and $B = [-o(h^2)]$, the eigenvalues of N are $1 + o(h^2)$, whence those of $N^{-1/2}$ are also $1 + o(h^2)$. Hence

$$N^{-1/2} M N^{-1/2} = [\delta_{ij}\lambda^i - h^2 d_{ij} + o(h^2)]. \quad (24.74)$$

By Lemma 24.12, again, the eigenvalues μ of $N^{-1/2} M N^{-1/2}$ are equal to the eigenvalues ν^i of the matrix

$$Q \equiv [\delta_{ij}\lambda^i - h^2 d_{ij}], \quad (24.75)$$

plus terms of order $o(h^2)$.

But, letting $\epsilon = h^2$, we can examine the eigenvalues of $Q = Q(h^2)$ with the help of previous theorems. For $\epsilon = 0$ the eigenvalues are λ^i, and by

Theorem 24.13 each root v^k is a regular analytic function of h^2. For a multiple zero $\lambda^k = \lambda^{k+1} = \cdots = \lambda^{k+m-1}$, we have by Theorem 24.14 that

$$v^i = \lambda^i - \gamma_i h^2 + O(h^4), \qquad i = k, \cdots, k + m - 1,$$

where $-\gamma_i$ was defined after equation (24.35) as the appropriate eigenvalue of the principal minor of the matrix $[(dq_{ij}/dh^2)_{h=0}] = [-d_{ij}]$ involving the rows and columns of $[\delta_{ij}\lambda_i]$ included in the multiple root. In particular, for a simple zero,

$$v^k = \lambda^k - d_{kk}h^2 + O(h^4).$$

Now the roots μ of $N^{-1/2}MN^{-1/2}$ differ from the v^i by a term $o(h^2)$ ($h \to 0$). But these roots μ differ by $o(h^2)$ from the μ_h^k of (24.65). Hence

$$\bar{\lambda}_h^k \leq \mu_h^k = v^k + o(h^2) = \lambda^k - \gamma_k h^2 + o(h^2), \qquad \text{as } h \to 0.$$

Thus finally we have proved Theorem 24.7.

24.7. Experiments with L-Shaped Membrane

In Theorems 24.7 and 24.8 convexity entered in two ways. First, R had to have strictly convex corners in order that such integrals as $\iint(u_{xx}^2 + u_{yy}^2)\,dx\,dy$ exist, where u is an eigenfunction of $-\Delta$. This in turn leads to the finiteness of the γ_k in (24.36). Although it is not proved, it is our conjecture that strict convexity of the corners is necessary in order that $\bar{\lambda}_h^k - \lambda^k = O(h^2)$, as $h \to 0$. Second, given strictly convex corners, convexity of R is a sufficient condition that the γ_k be positive, so that ultimately all $\bar{\lambda}_h^k$ approach λ^k from below, as $h \to 0$.

In order to learn the behavior of some eigenvalue for a nonconvex region, various calculations of λ_h^1 and λ_h^2 have been made for the L-shaped membrane of Sec. 18.6 and Sec. 24.3. (We may now drop the bar over λ, since there are no irregular interior points.) The numbers displayed in Table 24.1 are taken from unpublished experiments of Sangren and Alexander. For other data see Gerberich and Sangren [1957]. The values for $1/h = 2, 3, 4, 5, 6, 7, 8, 9, 16$ have been confirmed by the authors. Observe that these λ_h^1 seem to decrease eventually, as h decreases, so that lower bounds for λ^1 cannot be expected directly from these numbers.

De Vogelaere [private communication] conjectures that λ_h^1 has an asymptotic series with leading terms

$$\lambda_h^1 = \lambda^1 + ah^{4/3} + bh^2 + ch^{8/3} + dh^2\log h + \cdots, \qquad \text{as } h \to 0, \quad (24.76)$$

(including powers of $h^{2/3}$ and of h, and some confluent terms). The exponent 2/3 is α, where $\pi/\alpha = 3\pi/2$ is the interior angle at the nonconvex corner. For one thing, the sum $\Sigma u^1 \Delta_h u^1 h^2$ and the corresponding integral $\iint_R u \Delta u\,dx\,dy$ differ by $O(h^{4/3})$, as $h \to 0$. For another, De Vogelaere has been able to explain the data of Sangren and Alexander quite well by fitting them with a finite series like (24.76), terminating with $dh^2 \log h$. It was in such a way that he estimated the value (24.18) for λ^1.

TABLE 24.1

h	$\lambda_h{}^1$
1/2	9.07180
1/3	9.52514
1/4	9.64143
1/5	9.67860
1/6	9.69083
1/7	9.69384
1/8	9.69316
1/9	9.69100
1/10	9.68829
1/11	9.68547
1/12	9.68273
1/13	9.68014
1/14	9.67774
1/15	9.67553
1/16	9.67351
. . . .	
1/30	9.65743

The values of $\lambda_h{}^2$ behave quite differently from those in Table 24.1. The following numbers, taken from Forsythe [1954], have not been verified, and must be considered only as indicative:

TABLE 24.2

h	$\lambda_h{}^2$
1/2	12.00000
1/3	13.73700
1/4	14.37340
1/5	14.67081
1/6	14.83259
1/7	14.93003
1/8	14.99315

Note that in Table 24.2 $\lambda_h{}^2 \uparrow$, as $h \downarrow$. Now the net eigenfunction defined on the nodes of the L-shaped region was found to be zero along the line of symmetry $x + y = 0$ of the region (see Fig. 18.8), and zero nowhere else. Hence the same function is the fundamental net eigenfunction for the convex trapezoidal region which is half the L. (See Courant and Hilbert

[1953], pp. 297 ff. for a discussion of nodal lines in general.) It seems likely therefore that $\lambda_h{}^2$ for the L-shaped region is $\lambda_h{}^1$ for the trapezoid. Since the trapezoid is convex, we know by Theorem 24.8 that ultimately its fundamental eigenvalue increases to its limit. It therefore appears highly probable that for Table 24.2, $\lambda_h{}^2 \uparrow \lambda^2$, as $h \downarrow 0$. Even more, it looks from Table 24.2 as though $\lambda_h{}^2 = \lambda^2 - Ah^2 + \cdots \doteq 15.2 - 13.2h^2 + \cdots$.

If the value 14.99315 were a lower bound for λ^2, which is probably about 15.2, the bound would be low by 0.2. From the Weinberger theorem of Sec. 24.3, one might expect to find an eigenvalue $\lambda_{1/8}^*$ lower than λ^2 by approximately $15/8 \doteq 1.9$. So, the numerical analyst is now given the choice between a *proven* lower bound near 13.3 and a *surmised* lower bound near 15.0. This is illustrative of the gap between the *art* and *science* of numerical analysis.

24.8. Numerical Solution of the Finite Eigenvalue Problem

We now revert to the first problem mentioned in Sec. 24.1, the numerical solution of the large algebraic eigenvalue problem involved in solving

$$-\Delta_h U = \lambda_h U \qquad \text{in } R_h,$$
$$U = 0 \qquad \text{on } C_h. \tag{24.77}$$

For simplicity we suppose that R_h is a *regular* net region, i.e., that there are no irregular interior nodes. Hence we shall take $\Delta_h U$ as in (20.51). Given R_h, we are to determine one or more λ_h, and usually also the corresponding net functions U, to satisfy (24.77).

If we let $\mu = 4 - h^2\lambda_h$, then (24.77) takes the form

$$AU = U(E) + U(N) + U(W) + U(S) = \mu U(P), \qquad P \text{ in } R_h,$$
$$U = 0, \qquad P \text{ on } C_h, \tag{24.78}$$

where A is defined by (24.78). For small h and for the few least eigenvalues λ_h, the eigenvalues μ are slightly less than 4.

Thus we have the problem of solving the matrix eigenvalue problem $AU = \mu U$, where A is a symmetric matrix of nonnegative elements. One feels pretty confident about how to solve such an eigenvalue problem numerically when A is a symmetric dense matrix of such a low order N that one can hold the whole matrix A in intermediate storage (see Wilkinson [1954] and Givens [1954, 1957]). For such a problem a recommended method is that of Givens, in which A is stored completely, and then reduced by certain orthogonal transformations to a similar tridiagonal matrix A_1, from which the eigenvalues may be obtained in various ways. Finally, one may determine the eigenvector (in the rotated coordinate system) corresponding to each eigenvalue μ by solving the singular system $(A_1 - \mu I)U_1 = 0$.

Although Wilkinson [1958] has shown that one must be quite careful in solving this system, he also has shown how to do it, and the computational problem is regarded as solved.

If we look at (24.78), however, it is possible to store all elements of A when N^2 is in the range of 10^3 to 10^6, depending on the machine. For any machine capable of such storage, in whatever part of the range, it is probable that equations (24.78) will arise with N in the range of 10^3 to 10^6, and hence with N^2 well beyond the feasible range. Hence the above program is not feasible for equations (24.78).

The problem, then, is to solve (24.78) while storing little more than the N elements of a net function U, e.g., kN elements, where k is a small integer. Our discussion in Sec. 21.2 is highly relevant to this problem, except that now we have not only the linear problem of determining U but also the additional nonlinear problem of determining μ. It seems almost certain that we must determine μ by successive approximations.

If m is approximately, but not exactly, equal to μ, then we may hope to get an approximate eigenvector by solving a linear system

$$(A - mI)U = V,   \tag{24.79}$$

where V is some almost arbitrary vector. For, if $\mu_1, \cdots, \mu_N$ are the eigenvalues of A, with corresponding orthonormal eigenvectors $U_1, \cdots, U_N$, then $(A - mI)^{-1}$ has the same eigenvectors with eigenvalues $(\mu_i - m)^{-1}$. Hence, if $V = \Sigma_{i=1}^{N} \sigma_i U_i$, the true solution of (24.79) is

$$U = (A - mI)^{-1}V = \sum_{i=1}^{N} \frac{\sigma_i U_i}{\mu_i - m}.   \tag{24.80}$$

If $|m - \mu_k|$ is less than $|m - \mu_i|$ $(i \neq k)$, then $(\mu_k - m)^{-1}$ dominates the other $(\mu_i - m)^{-1}$, and the solution of (24.79) is closer to the direction of U_k than V is.

We then will expect to get an improved value of the approximate eigenvalue m by using the Rayleigh quotient $U^T A U / U^T U$. With this improved m, we could solve (24.79) again for a still better U. This will be the nature of our process, and the key to its use is the solution of (24.79).

The pure mathematician may worry that we will not be able to solve (24.79) when m is close to an eigenvalue μ of A, since $A - mI$ is nearly singular. Let him be reassured that there is no difficulty. If σ_k is substantially nonzero, the only action made necessary by the smallness of $\mu_k - m$ is a scaling down of the vector solution. On the other hand, the numerical analyst worries that V may be orthogonal to the desired eigenvector U_k, so that the term in the desired U_k may disappear from (24.80). (See Wilkinson [1958] for a technique applicable to small matrices A.)

As a variant of the algorithm, one might solve (24.79) r times ($r \geq 2$) with the same value of m, using the result of the previous solution each time as a new right-hand side V. Thus, effectively, one would be determining

$$U = (A - mI)^{-r}V.$$

The advantage would be greatest if the method of solving (24.79) were elimination, because an iterated elimination involves little more time than one elimination. A method of this type has been called *gebrochene Iteration* by Wielandt [1944]. We prefer the term *inverse iteration*, since the method corresponds to the power method described below for the inverse matrix $(A - mI)^{-1}$.

The convergence properties of these methods have been studied by Crandall [1951] and by Ostrowski [1958, 1959].

In solving (24.79) we have the whole choice of methods outlined in Secs. 21 and 22, and more. Elimination methods are certainly conceivable; the considerations here seem to be identical with those of Sec. 21.2 and, although the matter has not been fully investigated, we doubt that elimination will be feasible unless R is a rectangle or other simple shape; and, even for a rectangle, the storage may be troublesomely large.

One then turns to iterative processes. Here there are two major subcases. If one is searching for an *end* eigenvalue of A—corresponding to the least or largest eigenvalue of $-\Delta_h$—the matrix $A - mI$ will be approximately semidefinite. But, if λ is an interior eigenvalue of A, $A - mI$ will be a symmetric indefinite matrix, and all of its diagonal elements will be of one sign. In Sec. 21.6 we noted that, for a symmetric matrix with the latter property, the method of successive point displacements will converge if and only if $A - mI$ is a semidefinite matrix (Theorems 21.1 and 21.2). Hence we can use successive point displacements only for the end eigenvalues. It is probable that Reich's Theorem 21.1 goes over to block methods also, so that one would expect success from the implicit methods only when dealing with end eigenvalues.

For the end eigenvalues, we have had very good success with Young's method of successive point overrelaxation, as a practical code on SWAC. This was the method used in computing several of our values in Table 24.1. A few details will be given in Sec. 25.

For the end eigenvalues, one can also use the classical iterative process described in Wilkinson [1954], named the *power method* by Bodewig [1956] and others. In this one starts with a vector U^0, and forms $U^1 = AU^0, \cdots,$ $U^{k+1} = AU^k$, until the direction of U^k settles down. The limit of the normalized U^k is the eigenvector belonging to the largest eigenvalue μ of A in modulus—in this case the positive one nearest 4, corresponding to the least root λ_h^1. A slight modification will yield the root corresponding to λ_h^N. The ratio of $\|U^{k+1}\|$ to $\|U^k\|$ (any norm) yields the eigenvalue μ, which may be improved with the Rayleigh quotient. Although many more iterations will be required with the power method than with inverse iteration, the iterations are so simple that the convergence may be faster. The extension of the power method to other eigenvalues of A usually involves one of two techniques. (i) One might "deflate" A (see, for example, Feller and Forsythe [1951]) to a dense matrix that lacks the eigenvalue μ—clearly impractical here; or (ii) one might continue the power method while maintaining the U^k orthogonal to eigenvectors already found. The latter will require storage of all the previously found eigenvectors—possibly a practical procedure for a very few vectors only.

An approach to solving (24.79) for intermediate eigenvalues of A without storing more than the vector U might be to use the iterative method of Kaczmarz [1937]. For a general nonsingular system of equations $CU = B$ (C not symmetric), Kaczmarz proposes that one start with an arbitrary vector U^0. Consider that the equation $CU = B$ represents the solution $C^{-1}B$ as the intersection of N hyperplanes Π_i, one for each equation. One projects U^0 orthogonally onto Π_1 to get U^1, then U^1 onto Π_2 to get U^2, etc. Continuing in cyclic order, one can prove that always $U^k \rightarrow C^{-1}B$, as $k \rightarrow \infty$.

If the ith hyperplane Π_i is $\sum_{j=1}^N C_{ij}U_j = b_i$, then in the projection onto Π_i, one moves from the point U^{i-1} with components U_j^{i-1} to the point U^i with components U_j^i, where

$$U_j^i = U^{i-1} + t_i C_{ij}, \tag{24.81}$$

with

$$t_i = \frac{b_i - \sum\limits_{j=1}^N C_{ij} U_j^{i-1}}{\sum\limits_{j=1}^N C_{ij}^2}. \tag{24.82}$$

The Kaczmarz method can easily be applied to system (24.79). One vector Z_P orthogonal to the hyperplane Π_P, corresponding to node P, has components 1 at each of the interior nodes E, N, W, S, and $-m$ at the node P. Thus each step of the process involves a relaxation of up to five nearby components of U at once. The factor t_P controlling the displacement in the direction Z_P, given by (24.82), is a simple function of the residual at P and the coefficient m. The method should not be much more difficult to code than the method of successive displacements. However, it seems probable that, when the latter method converges, it converges much faster than the Kaczmarz method. Hence one should probably not use the Kaczmarz algorithm for an end eigenvalue.

The authors know of no experience with the Kaczmarz method in this setting. It is almost certain that an acceleration scheme would be essential with it. As each full cycle of the Kaczmarz process represents one step of a linear iterative process in the sense of Sec. 21.3, the asymptotic behavior is known in principle, and this should permit the design of useful accelerations.

SECTION 25. SOLVING ELLIPTIC PARTIAL DIFFERENCE EQUATIONS ON AN AUTOMATIC DIGITAL COMPUTER

For technologically important problems associated with elliptic partial differential equations, the associated difference equations now ordinarily involve a large number of interior nodes. For this reason their solution is usually carried out with an automatic digital computer. In our discussions of the solution of such difference equations in the preceding sections, we have made occasional reference to the use of such computers. In this section we shall augment these references with other practical considerations. Because of the rapid development of automatic computers, it will be possible to give only rather tentative and limited discussions.

25.1. Obtaining the Equations in a Digital Computer

In the pencil-and-paper solution of elliptic problems by finite-difference methods, solving the difference equations is far more troublesome than obtaining the equations. With automatic digital computers the situation is quite different. The capacity and speed of electronic computers permit the use of far more interior nodes than with desk methods. Hence there are far more equations to be obtained and solved.

So far most analytical thought has gone into the question of how to solve the increased number of equations. The methods of the preceding sections are of a simple iterative nature which are easy to code for a computer. Although their running may take a long or short computer time, depending on various factors, the amount of human effort involved in solving them is not exceptionally great.

On the other hand, obtaining the greatly increased number of equations usually adds a great deal of human labor. The reason is basically that, whereas the solution of equations can proceed entirely within the machine, obtaining the equations entails a transition from a blueprint outside the machine to a representation of difference equations inside the computer. Such a transition cannot make full use of the real power of the new machines—their arithmetic organs. A very substantial human effort is needed to locate the boundary, designate the type of boundary condition, determine the nature and location ·of the net, and so on. Until these mundane details have been automated, the programmer will find that most of his time will go into dealing with them.

In Sec. 25.1 we shall sketch one method for obtaining difference equations to represent Laplace's equation for a bounded plane region R. In this we assume that the region R is the connected union of squares and half-squares of a square net, and that one desires to solve a Dirichlet problem in

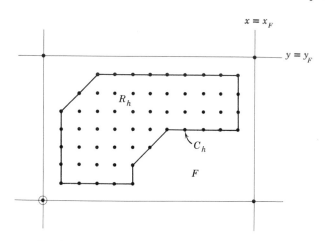

FIG. 25.1. The rectangle D inclosing the net region R_h.

R. (By a half-square we mean a right triangle whose vertices are adjacent nodes of a square.) No other assumption is made about the shape of the boundary C of R. The following ideas are based on a code written by William Gragg, Jr. for the IBM 650 computer at Stanford University.

Suppose that R is contained in a closed rectangle D with sides parallel to the coordinate axes, and let D have height y_F and width x_F (see Fig. 25.1). Select the origin at the corner of D so that the nodes (x, y) of D are characterized by the relations $0 \leq x \leq x_F$ and $0 \leq y \leq y_F$. We shall devote one cell of the storage of our computer to each node (x, y) in D, and, for brevity, shall simply call it the *cell* (x, y). The cell (x, y) might, for example, be machine address $100x + y$. The cells (x, y) of D fall into three classes:

1. Those in the interior R_h of the net region, for which we shall later determine the unknown value $U(x, y)$ by use of a *relaxation code*.

2. Those on the net boundary C_h, which hold the fixed boundary values $U(x, y)$ of the Dirichlet problem.

3. Those in $F = D - (R_h \cup C_h)$, which play no role in the Dirichlet problem, but which will nevertheless later be examined by the relaxation code.

The first task is to get the boundary value $U(x, y)$ into each cell (x, y) of C_h, and to *tag* the value $U(x, y)$ so that the relaxation code will know that (x, y) is a boundary point. We assume that the input facilities of the computer are used for this. For a tag, one sometimes makes the number in cell (x, y) negative, while using its absolute value $U(x, y) \geq 0$ as the boundary value for the Dirichlet problem. (If the original boundary values include negative numbers, they can all be made positive by the addition of a suitable positive constant, without essentially changing the Dirichlet problem.) Another type of tag is to force one binary digit of the word in cell (x, y) to be 1—usually the least significant or the most significant digit. The relaxation code must include instructions to ignore the tags, of course.

If C_h has a simple structure and if the boundary values $U(x, y)$ are correspondingly simple, one can write a simple routine which will generate the boundary values in the storage of the computer, perhaps starting only from the coordinates of the corners of C_h.

Now the points of R_h and of F are ordinarily much more numerous than those of C_h, and they need not have input values $U(x, y)$ associated with them. It would therefore be unnecessarily wasteful to use the input to identify these cells (x, y), and to do so would be a prohibitive chore for the programmer when D has thousands of nodes. One must therefore prepare a machine code which tags all the points of F, so that the relaxation code will ignore them. One simple way of tagging the points of F is first to tag those of R_h (with a different tag from that of C_h), and then to tag all the remaining points F of D. (One can use the same tag for F as for C_h.) Finally, one erases the tags in R_h.

We therefore now need a method of temporarily tagging all the points of R_h, given that the points of C_h are already tagged. Because of the possibly complicated shape of R_h, it is not easy for the code to tell directly whether a point is in R_h or in F. We make use of the assumption that R is a connected union of squares, and assume even more—that each pair of nodes in R_h can be joined by a *chain* (an arc consisting of vertical and horizontal links in R_h). Now the net boundary of R_h must be C_h. Hence, if any net neighbor Q of a point P in R_h is not in C_h, Q must be in R_h.

We start the *tagging code* at a point (x, y) known to be in R_h. The code builds up R_h as the union of all chains starting from (x, y). We shall describe the code by means of a *flow chart*. The steps are to be followed in numerical order unless it is stated otherwise.

1. START. Let the variable r take the value x. Let the variable s take the value y.

2. Tag (r, s) as a member of R_h.

3. Is $(r + h, s)$ tagged as a member of either R_h or C_h?

(a) If the answer is yes, go to step 4.

(b) If the answer is no, increase the value of the variable r by h, and go to step 2.

4. Is $(r - h, s)$ tagged as a member of either R_h or C_h?

(a) If the answer is yes, go to step 5.

(b) If the answer is no, decrease the value of the variable r by h, and go to step 2.

5. Is $(r, s + h)$ tagged as a member of either R_h or C_h?

(a) If the answer is yes, go to step 6.

(b) If the answer is no, increase the value of the variable s by h, and go to step 2.

6. Is $(r, s - h)$ tagged as a member of either R_h or C_h?

(a) If the answer is yes, go to step 7.

(b) If the answer is no, decrease the value of the variable s by h, and go to step 2.

7. Since every neighbor of (r, s) is already tagged, this chain is over. To try to start a new chain, consider all the points of D ordered in a simple array: $P_1, \cdots, P_n$. Let the integer variable i take the value 1 and go to step 8.

8. Is the point P_i tagged as a member of R_h?

(a) If the answer is no, increase the value of the variable i by 1, and go to step 9.

(b) If the answer is yes, go to step 10.

9. Is $i = n + 1$?

(a) If the answer is yes, we have exhausted the points of D, and have therefore tagged all the points of R_h. HALT.

(b) If the answer is no, return to step 8.

10. Does P_i have an east, north, west, or south neighbor which is untagged?

(a) If the answer is yes, let the variable (r, s) take values corresponding to the coordinates of P_i, and go to step 3.

(b) If the answer is no, increase the value of the variable i by 1, and go to step 9.

After the completion of the tagging code described above, every point of R_h is tagged. As we noted earlier, we next tag the points of F, which are identified as not having tags, and then erase the tags of R_h. The way is now completely prepared for a relaxation code, which will pick up the cells (x, y) of D in turn. If the cell (x, y) is tagged as a member of F or C_h, the cell will be ignored. If the cell is not tagged, it is a member of R_h, and the particular relaxation process is carried out on $U(x, y)$. For example, in the method of successive displacements of Sec. 21.6, $U(x, y)$ will be given the value that is the average of $U(x + h, y)$, $U(x, y + h)$, $U(x - h, y)$, and $U(x, y - h)$. One will have to devise convergence criteria, and so on, but there is no logical difficulty in writing the relaxation code once the preparatory codes have tagged all the points of F.

The tagging codes can easily be modified to deal with boundary conditions of the type $u_n = 0$. It only requires the use of several more types of tags to identify the type of points in C_h. The codes can also be modified to deal with problems in three or more dimensions.

25.2. Obtaining the Difference Equations When C is Curved

Obtaining the difference equations becomes much more complicated when the region R is no longer the union of squares or half-squares of the net. We now sketch a code proposed in 1956 by Forsythe and Kenneth Ralston at U.C.L.A. for obtaining difference equations corresponding to the Dirichlet problem for Laplace's equation in the plane. It was sketched in Forsythe [1956a].

Assume that the region is bounded by a simple closed curve C which is *piecewise quadratic*, a term implicitly defined below. Such a curve is complicated enough to handle a great number of practical situations. For example, engineering drawings often show boundaries made up of straight lines, with corners faired with circular arcs. Let R be inclosed in a rectangle D, as in Sec. 25.1. Let D be divided into n disjoint polygons D_i whose union is D (see Fig. 25.2). Let D_i be described as the set of points (x, y) satisfying a finite number $h_i + k_i$ (usually 3 or 4) of linear inequalities of the form

$$L_j(x, y) \leq 0, \qquad j = 1, 2, \cdots, h_i,$$

$$L_j(x, y) < 0, \qquad j = h_i + 1, \cdots, k_i,$$

where each L_j is a linear nonhomogeneous function of x and y. Let the part of the curve C in the polygon D_i be designated by the equation $Q_i(x,y) = 0$, where Q_i is a quadratic nonhomogeneous function of x and y. In particular, fix Q_i so that in D_i the region R (interior of C) is the set of (x, y) with $Q_i(x, y) < 0$ $(i = 1, 2, \cdots, n)$. Assume that the D_i are so chosen that, if any two neighboring nodes P, Q are in R_h, then the entire link joining P to Q is in R. (This restriction can be modified at the cost of considerable complication.) Suppose, finally, that the boundary values of $U(x, y)$ on $C \cap D_i$ are given by $f_i(x, y)$, a function which can be computed.

In this proposal it is assumed that one inputs the coefficients of the functions L_j, Q_i, and f_i, together with the values of n and h. The code is to generate a square net, and compute values for the coefficients of the Shortley-Weller approximation (20.69) to Laplace's equation wherever the simple formula (20.51) will not apply.

Like the code of Sec. 25.1, this method also involves several subroutines. But now we have a direct method of determining whether a given point (x, y) is in R_h or not, namely, by determining which region D_i the point is in, and then checking the sign of $Q_i(x, y)$.

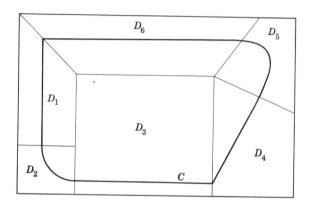

FIG. 25.2. Obtaining difference equations for a region with curved boundary C.

In a first sweep through the lattice points of D, the program tags each *boundary node* (lattice point on C) and each *exterior node*, i.e., lattice point in neither R nor C. In a second sweep, it examines the remaining lattice points of D (the *interior nodes*), and tags the *irregular interior nodes* —the interior nodes which are in R but which have at least one neighbor which is an exterior node. These are the points that will require special attention in the relaxation code, since they are in R_h but need special coefficients. In the second sweep, the code also computes the boundary value $f_i(x, y)$ at each boundary node (x, y), and stores it in the corresponding cell (x, y).

In the third sweep, the code examines the interior nodes in the order in which the relaxation code will examine them. A special part of storage is set aside for the coefficients of irregular points. Whenever the code comes to an irregular interior node P in this third sweep, it examines each of its four neighbors in turn, and learns which are in the exterior. For each Q which is in the exterior, the code learns the distance from P to C along the link PQ by a detailed examination of the regions and the Q_i. Thus it finds the lengths h_E, h_N, h_W, h_S of the four "legs" from P to its neighbors or to C, as the case may be. Finally, it enters formula (20.69) to get appropriate coefficients. Whenever a neighbor of P is on the boundary, the corresponding value of $f_i(x, y)$ is multiplied into the appropriate coefficient to avoid having to store a boundary neighbor of any irregular interior point. This avoids the storage conflict caused, for example, by the fact that the point C_h "north" of the point (x, y) of R_h may not be the same as the point of C_h "west" of $(x + h, y + h)$. Finally, the irregular interior node P is given one of a number of tags, revealing its relation to the boundary. The relevant coefficients are all stored in a part of the memory reserved for them, in a preassigned order which will be known to the relaxation code.

At this stage, the tagging code is finished. The relaxation code can now take over and proceed to solve the equations. Regular interior points are treated with a formula corresponding to the simple 5-point formula (20.51). The irregular points are met in a known order, and have been tagged. The tag might, for example, reveal that all the neighbors are in R_h except the eastern neighbor, which is on C_h. Suppose that the relaxation formula is

$$U(P) = \sigma(E)\, U(E) + \sigma(N)\, U(N) + \sigma(W)\, U(W) + \sigma(S)\, U(S).$$

The code goes to the special part of storage referred to, and takes the next four coefficients in order. It knows that these are, respectively, $\sigma(E)\, U(E)$, $\sigma(N)$, $\sigma(W)$, and $\sigma(S)$. It can then proceed to calculate a new value of $U(P)$.

A code embodying these ideas in part has been written by Neal Reinders for the UNIVAC scientific computer type 1103AF. Floating-point arithmetic was used, in part to deal with scaling problems arising when both h_E and h_W become small, or both h_N and h_S.

Ralston's proposed code could also deal with a boundary condition of type $\alpha u + \beta u_n + \gamma = 0$ on a straight boundary segment parallel to the x- or y-axis.

Our concept of tagging was developed on SWAC, a four-address binary machine, and it caused very little loss of time in carrying out the subsequent relaxation. On other machines the use of tags can be more costly. On a ten-digit decimal machine, for example, devoting one digit to a tag uses 10% of the arithmetic information in a word. Moreover, it may be harder to remove the tag for the arithmetic operations and to restore it later if a machine does not have suitable digit-extraction commands. For a convex region, some programmers use a table of the first and last nodes to be relaxed in each line, with the understanding that these nodes are irregular interior points. There are an embarrassing number of other possible coding devices.

25.3. Plans for an Integrated Industrial Program

In 1957 an association of IBM 704 computer users called SPADE felt the need for a comprehensive set of programs for solving systems of elliptic and parabolic partial differential equations. A Committee on Partial Differential Equations was formed and was steered by the so-called SCOPE subcommittee. A very ambitious group of machine programs was planned, and has been partially prepared. It is too early to report whether the project will succeed in its entirety. It seems worth while in any case to mention the objectives of the plan. The work was stimulated by an unpublished report of H. Reichenbach, part of which was referred to in Sec. 20.4.

It was decided to write as many as possible of the programs in the FORTRAN II algebraic language, so that the programs could later be easily used with other computers. This is an important step towards the goal of writing all computer programs in a single internationally standardized algebraic language. A program written in such an algebraic language can be the input to a machine translator code whose output is a code in machine language that will carry out the numerical manipulations called for in the algebraic formulation.

The goal of the SCOPE project is to handle problems involving systems of up to ten simultaneous partial differential equations in one or two space variables, plus possibly a time-like variable. The equations and the boundary conditions are permitted to be nonlinear. However, the user must provide his own numerical analysis, since the program does not anticipate the behavior of nonlinear partial differential equations.

The work was divided into four phases:

Phase 1. *Generation of the mesh.* In codes of phase 1 the input is to be information necessary to determine the boundary, the interfaces, and the mesh constants. The boundary can be arcs of conic sections or segments of straight lines. The output is to be a sequence of *point records*—coordinates of mesh points and a list of the *neighbors* of each point in some form.

Phase 2. *Coefficient generation routines.* Following various methods, most of which are discussed in Sec. 20, the codes of phase 2 are to generate difference equations for all points of the working domain. The input will be the output of phase 1, plus information supplied by the user.

Phase 3. *Iteration routines.* These are to be routines for the solution of the algebraic difference equations generated in phase 2. Various of the methods outlined in Secs. 21 and 22 are to be available.

Phase 4. *Coordinating routines.* These routines are needed to coordinate the codes of phases 1, 2, and 3 to solve specific problems.

25.4. Use of Graded Nets

In most boundary-value problems the region R is not uniform in its character. There are usually parts of R where the solution u varies slowly, and parts where it varies rapidly. The entire interest in the solution may be in the behavior of u near one corner, which might, for example, represent the region of maximum stress. Suppose we wish to use a square net. To reveal the solution in sufficient detail in the interesting region, it may be necessary to take a net there with a very small mesh constant h.

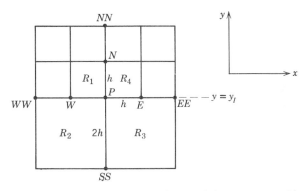

FIG. 25.3. Section of the interface of a graded square net without a transition band. The interface is the line $y = y_I$.

If this value of h were maintained throughout all of R, it might result in far more equations than the computer could handle.

These considerations have led to the use of *refined* or *graded nets*, in which a very fine net is used in the interesting regions of R, while a coarse net is used elsewhere. Techniques for dealing with graded nets with pencil-and-paper calculation have been summarized by Allen [1954], and we shall only touch on the subject here.

The principal problem with graded nets is obtaining the equations at the *interfaces* between different nets. To keep adjoining nets reasonably compatible, it is customary to double h at each interface. Thus two nets might meet at the interface WW–EE of Fig. 25.3. Points like SS are in the interior of the coarse net, and the corresponding difference equation is set up according to the formulas of Sec. 20 with a mesh constant $2h$. Similarly, points like N are in the fine net, and their equations are easily found, with a mesh constant h. But the points P and E are representative of the two types of points on the interface, and they are troublesome to handle without loss of accuracy.

A number of ways of defining the equations at the troublesome points

P and E have been used. Although they may differ slightly in the ease of obtaining the equations and solving them with a computer, the difference cannot be great. The choice of a method for defining the equations seems, therefore, to depend on which yields the least discretization error. (A theory of bounding discretization errors in general is given in Sec. 23.)

For illustration we consider Laplace's equation, and suppose that the simple five-point formula (20.51) is being used in the interior of both the fine net and the coarse net. The question then is, how to define equations

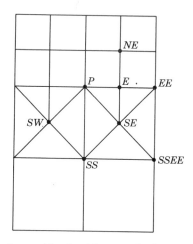

Fig. 25.4. Use of a transition band between the fine net and the coarse net.

corresponding to points like P and E in Fig. 25.3. We mention three possible methods:

Method 1: Treat P as an ordinary point of the coarse net, with the four neighbors EE, NN, WW, SS. Obtain the value $U(E)$ as an average of the two values $U(P)$ and $U(EE)$.

Method 2: Follow the variational method of Sec. 20.5.

Method 3: Introduce new nodes at the mid-points of the large squares just "south" of the interface (see Fig. 25.4). Treat P as an ordinary point of the coarse net, as in method 1, and treat E as an ordinary point of the fine net, with neighbors EE, NE, P, SE. Use formula (20.53) at SE, with the four neighbors P, SS, $SSEE$, EE.

There are other methods like method 3, in which a finite-difference analog of the Laplacian operator is set up at each interior node. For example, at point E, the difference operator might involve the five neigh-bors EE, NE, P, SS, and $SSEE$.

It is possible to analyze the discretization error for these various methods, following the general approach of Gerschgorin, as generalized in Sec. 23. We shall sketch such analyses for methods 3 and 1 only. We assume that interpolation at the boundary is done so carefully that it does not decrease the order of magnitude of the error due to the discretization in the interior of R. The exact notation of Sec. 23 is applicable only to method 3, in which every interior node is treated by use of either $\Delta_h U$ or $\Delta_h^\times U$. For method 3, using the error expressions in Sec. 20.7 and the notation of Conditions 3 and 7, Sec. 23.4, we have ($h = \mu$)

$$\alpha = 4, \qquad p = 4, \qquad \gamma = 2,$$

so that $|U(x, y) - u(x, y)| = O(h^2)$.

To study the discretization error in method 1, we shall have to modify the notation of Sec. 23 slightly. Let the interface be the line $y = y_I$. Define the finite-difference operator L_h according to the following:

$$L_h(U) = (2h)^{-2}[U(x + 2h, y) + U(x, y + 2h) + U(x - 2h, y)$$
$$+ U(x, y - 2h) - 4U(x, y)], \quad (25.1)$$

for $y \leq y_I$, when (x, y) is not a point of type E in Fig. 25.3. Let

$$L_h(U) = \tfrac{1}{2}[U(x + h, y) + U(x - h, y) - 2U(x, y)], \quad (25.2)$$

for (x, y) of type E. Finally, let

$$L_h(U) = h^{-2}[U(x + h, y) + U(x, y + h) + U(x - h, y)$$
$$+ U(x, y - h) - 4U(x, y)], \quad (25.3)$$

for $y > y_I$. Note that L_h is of nonnegative type in every case.

Now, if one were to introduce the operator $\mathscr{L}$ of (23.6) or (23.30), one would lose the opportunity of using a different power of h in (25.2) from that in (25.1) or (25.3). If one carries out the analysis of discretization error without $\mathscr{L}$, one follows the pattern of Sec. 23.8.

It turns out that we could prove that $|U(x, y) - u(x, y)|$ is of order $O(h^2)$, as $h \to 0$, provided we could exhibit an upper bound, independent of h, to the problem

$$L_h(Q) = -1 \quad \text{in } R_h,$$
$$Q = 0 \quad \text{in } C_h. \quad (25.4)$$

For, if U solves $L_h(U) = 0$, and if $\Delta u = 0$, then $|L_h(u - U)| = |L_h(u)| \leq Kh^2$, by (25.1), (25.2), (25.3). But then, since L_h is of nonnegative type, one can use Qh^2 as a comparison function for $u - U$, so that

$$|u - U| \leq (\max_{\tilde{R}} Q)Kh^2. \quad (25.5)$$

No published study of the function Q is known to the authors, but it seems very probable that an upper bound can be found for Q in (25.4). An announcement that $|u - U| = O(h^2)$ for method 1 has been made by Arms [1957]. It would be desirable to have a detailed analysis available.

25.5. Successive Overrelaxation: Estimating ω

The easiest to code of all reasonably successful methods for solving difference equations with property (A) is the method of successive over-relaxation by points described in Sec. 22. Take any five-point homogeneous difference equation with Dirichlet boundary conditions:

$$L_h U(P) \equiv \sigma(E) U(E) + \sigma(N) U(N) + \sigma(W) U(W) + \sigma(S) U(S)$$
$$- \sigma(P) U(P) = 0, \qquad P \text{ in } R_h, \quad (25.6)$$
$$U = \text{prescribed function on } C_h.$$

For example, if there were no irregular interior point in R_h, and if L_h were the five-point Laplacian operator (20.51), then we would have (with $h = 1$)

$$L_h U(P) = \Delta_h U(P) = U(E) + U(N) + U(W) + U(S) - 4U(P). \quad (25.7)$$

Assume $\sigma(P) > 0$ in (25.6).

As in Sec. 25.1, the points of R_h and C_h are imbedded in a rectangle D. In the successive overrelaxation process the nodes of D are repeatedly scanned in a cyclic order, usually line after line. By means of the tags placed by the tagging codes described earlier, the program recognizes points not in R_h, and leaves the corresponding cells unchanged. When a point of R_h is reached, the program forms the *residual* $L_h U(P)$ according to (25.6). If fixed-point operations are used, it may be important to avoid intermediate overflows by alternating the additions and subtractions. For example, in (25.7) one might form $\Delta_h U(P)$ in the order

$$\Delta_h U(P) = U(E) - U(P) + U(N) - U(P)$$
$$+ U(W) - U(P) + U(S) - U(P). \quad (25.8)$$

The use of (25.8) may also save the loss of one or two binary digits with floating-point arithmetic. Finally, for the general problem (25.6), a new value of $U(P)$ is computed by the formula

$$\text{new } U(P) = U(P) + \omega[\sigma(P)]^{-1}L_h U(P), \quad (25.9)$$

where ω is the overrelaxation factor ($1 \leq \omega < 2$). One then goes on to the next point of D. At the end of one sweep of D, the new net function U will have been obtained from the U at the end of the previous sweep by means of formula (22.5). For $\omega = 1$, the present method is precisely the method of successive displacements of Sec. 21.6.

The theory of Sec. 22 assures us that the method of successive overrelaxation will converge for all ω such that $0 < \omega < 2$, and that the most rapid convergence occurs for a value called ω_{opt}, with $1 < \omega_{\text{opt}} < 2$. It is extremely important to use a value of ω near ω_{opt}. In one SWAC run, for example, the time for reduction of the initial error by the factor 10^{-6} required 13 minutes for a field of about 2000 interior nodes by use of ω slightly larger than ω_{opt}, whereas the use of $\omega = 1$ would have required over 5 hours. As shown in Sec. 22, the use of ω slightly larger than ω_{opt} is less costly in time than the use of ω slightly smaller than ω_{opt}.

The programmer therefore faces one substantial problem in the use of successive overrelaxation—how to determine an ω which is quite close to ω_{opt} and preferably on the high side. Moreover, this ω must be known in a relatively short computer time—certainly in rather less than the time it would take to solve the problem (25.6) with any reasonable guess of ω. Obviously, if one is solving a sequence of Dirichlet problems with slightly varying regions, the value of ω_{opt} will change only slowly, and one can make good guesses based on experience. But a real problem faces the occasional computer who needs to get a good value of ω quickly. Non-linear boundary-value problems will surely require the frequent determination of ω_{opt} without prior knowledge.

Three approaches to determining ω_{opt} have occurred to the authors, and will be discussed in detail below. In the first, one runs for a number of cycles with the method of successive displacements ($\omega = 1$). In the second, one varies ω over values near ω_{opt}. In the third, one tries to approximate the least eigenvalue of a related problem with homogeneous boundary conditions. None of these methods has yet proved itself to be outstandingly successful, and it may even be true that determining ω_{opt} is as hard a problem as solving (25.6). More research is needed in this area.

Let U_k denote the vector of values of $U(P)$ after the kth sweep. Let $Y_{k-1} = U_k - U_{k-1}$. As we remarked in the discussion following formula (22.32), the vectors Y_k are easily accessible to the relaxation program and, moreover,

$$Y_k = [H(\omega)]^k Y_0. \tag{25.10}$$

Here $H(\omega)$ is the matrix that controls the nature of the linear iteration; except for the parameter ω, it is the H of formula (21.22). Assume that the dominant eigenvalue $\eta_1^{(1)}$ of $H(1)$ is real, which is true under various hypotheses—for example, when the matrix corresponding to (25.6) is symmetric. Now carry out the method of successive displacements ($\omega = 1$) for a number of cycles (sweeps). By the theory reviewed in Sec. 21.3, the direction of the vector Y_k will approach the direction of the eigenvector X of $H(1)$ belonging to the dominant eigenvalue $\eta_1^{(1)}$. It follows that, for any norm function,

$$\lim_{k \to \infty} \frac{\|Y_{k+1}\|}{\|Y_k\|} = \eta_1^{(1)}. \tag{25.11}$$

Finally, by (22.23), since $\lambda_1^2 = \eta_1^{(1)}$ by (22.14), we can compute ω_{opt} by the formula

$$\omega_{opt} = \frac{2}{1 + \sqrt{1 - \eta_1^{(1)}}}. \tag{25.12}$$

In some experiments on SWAC, Forsythe [1956a] ran the original problem with $\omega = 1$, and computed the "first-power norm" $\| Y_k \|_1$; here for any vector Z one defines

$$\| Z \|_1 = \sum_{P \in R^{\star}} |Z(P)|. \tag{25.13}$$

The value of the quotient

$$Q_k = \frac{\| Y_{k+1} \|_1}{\| Y_k \|_1} \tag{25.14}$$

was computed at each cycle of the iteration. It appeared that Q_k increased monotonically. Since, by (25.11), $\lim_k Q_k = \eta_1^{(1)}$, one would estimate $\eta_1^{(1)}$ as the apparent limit of Q_k, and then compute ω_{opt} from (25.12). Convergence acceleration techniques looked feasible. Although it was never done, it looked reasonably easy to automate this algorithm.

Further experiments [unpublished] have been made by James Ortega at Stanford University during the year 1958–59. Although it is too early for final conclusions, they indicate two things:

1. In some problems it takes a prohibitively long running time before the value of Q_k in (25.11) gets near its limiting value.

2. It is often difficult sufficiently early in the running to deduce the limiting value of Q_k by Aitken's δ^2-process for accelerating the convergence of the sequence Q_k (see Householder [1953] for a description of Aitken's process). Thus convergence acceleration looks less successful than was thought previously. Consequently, the authors now have less confidence that running with $\omega = 1$ is a desirable method for estimating ω_{opt}.

The second approach to locating ω_{opt} approximately is to carry out the process of successive overrelaxation with various values of ω suspected to be near ω_{opt}, and compare the results in some way. Under the reasonable assumption that one can guess the value of ω_{opt} before the computation to an accuracy something like 0.1 or 0.2, this approach has the advantage that the test calculations are themselves already advancing the solution of the boundary-value problem fairly rapidly, whereas use of $\omega = 1$ is known to solve the problem much more slowly. But how can one tell which value of ω is best?

Experience shows that the sequence of values of $\| Y_k \|$ in any norm is a rather irregular sequence, for ω near ω_{opt}. The probable reason, indicated at the end of Sec. 22.1, is that $H(\omega)$ has many eigenvalues of equal or nearly equal modulus. If one could afford to wait long enough, one could find the best value of ω as the value for which $\| Y_k \|$ tends to 0 most rapidly. But the approach of $\| Y_k \|$ to 0 is irregular, and cannot usually be measured accurately in the short time available. Moreover, it seems to require repeated running with the same start. Hence, one looks for other properties of the sequence, especially properties which might be observed without starting the iteration over.

It is too early to offer a definitive answer as to what properties will work. In Ortega's experiments, there is some indication that the sequence Q_k of (25.14) is relatively smooth for $\omega < \omega_{\text{opt}}$, while it is relatively rough for ω near or slightly larger than ω_{opt}. Here a sequence is called *smooth* when its differences are relatively low in magnitude, and *rough*, when its differences are large in magnitude. We therefore suggest very tentatively that this property of roughness may help the early determination of ω_{opt} with reasonable accuracy.

As an example of the behavior of the quotients Q_k, consider the L-shaped region of Fig. 18.8, with a square net corresponding to $h = \frac{1}{10}$. There are 261 points in R_h, for which we solve the problem $\Delta_h U = 0$. Take the boundary value to be 1 on the boundary set $\{(x, y): x = -1 \text{ and } 0 \leq y \leq 1\}$, and equal to 0 elsewhere. Let the initial values of $U(P)$ be 0 on R_h. In Table 25.1 we give the values of Q_k for $k = 2(1)20$, as computed by Ortega for various values of ω. The entry for $k = \infty$ is a four-decimal approximation to the limit of Q_k for $\omega < \omega_{\text{opt}}$; for $\omega > \omega_{\text{opt}}$, the sequence Q_k has no limit and, instead, we print the limiting value of the geometric mean of the first K values of Q_k, as $K \to \infty$.

In the last row of Table 25.1, we give the ratio $\rho_k = \| Y_k \|_1 / \| Y_1 \|_1$, for $k = 20$ and the various ω. This ρ_{20} is minimized by $\omega = 1.612$, a bit lower than ω_{opt}. For $k = 15$, ρ_{15} is minimized by $\omega = 1.6$. It is not until $k \doteq 30$ that the minimum comes for ω near $1.641 \doteq \omega_{\text{opt}}$. The iteration was effectively finished at $k = 45$, for ω anywhere in the interval $(1.6, 1.7)$.

In the row labeled r, we give the number of changes of sign of the first differences $Q_k - Q_{k-1}$, for each value of ω. The value of r is a crude measure of the roughness of the sequence Q_k. It will be observed that r increases considerably as ω increases through values near $\omega_{\text{opt}} \doteq 1.641$. (We have calculated the value of ω_{opt} from the value of $\lambda_{1/10}$ in Table 24.1.)

In the other two common norms of numerical analysis, the maximum norm and Euclidean norm, the roughness effect is less clear.

The first approach to determining ω_{opt} mentioned above was simply the *power method* of computing the dominant eigenvalue of the matrix $H(1)$. (See Wilkinson [1954] for a discussion of the power method, there called the "basic iterative method.") The power method is often rather slow to converge, and this slowness is, indeed, the main observed defect of our first approach. A third approach to determining ω_{opt} is to use more powerful algorithms in an attempt to obtain the eigenvalue $\eta_1^{(1)}$ more quickly. Let us assume for simplicity that we are dealing with the Laplacian difference operator (25.7) with no irregular interior points in R_h. By

TABLE 25.1. Values of Q_k for various ω; $\omega_{opt} = 1.641$

ω k	1.0	1.5	1.6	1.612	1.648	1.696	1.8
2	0.7244	0.7136	0.7340	0.7368	0.7458	0.7591	0.8028
3	0.7915	0.7671	0.7874	0.7900	0.7985	0.8107	0.8308
4	0.8311	0.7822	0.8049	0.8085	0.8197	0.8364	0.8786
5	0.8562	0.7941	0.8132	0.8171	0.8294	0.8479	0.8959
6	0.8734	0.7983	0.8104	0.8129	0.8230	0.8434	0.9011
7	0.8858	0.8036	0.8061	0.8106	0.8263	0.8471	0.9016
8	0.8951	0.8174	0.8037	0.8049	0.8107	0.8345	0.8986
9	0.9023	0.8385	0.7933	0.7970	0.8144	0.8364	0.8986
10	0.9080	0.8434	0.7950	0.7953	0.8002	0.8261	0.8900
11	0.9126	0.8430	0.7869	0.7860	0.8004	0.8321	0.8927
12	0.9163	0.8416	0.7882	0.7870	0.7962	0.8302	0.8948
13	0.9194	0.8414	0.7843	0.7835	0.8019	0.8327	0.8922
14	0.9221	0.8435	0.7993	0.7917	0.7931	0.8305	0.8970
15	0.9248	0.8469	0.8050	0.7996	0.8059	0.8370	0.9206
16	0.9262	0.8512	0.8086	0.8031	0.8028	0.8356	0.9082
17	0.9279	0.8564	0.8266	0.8168	0.8005	0.8245	0.9167
18	0.9293	0.8628	0.8450	0.8398	0.8276	0.8500	0.9265
19	0.9307	0.8705	0.8602	0.8566	0.8349	0.8513	0.9158
20	0.9319	0.8791	0.8803	0.8722	0.8510	0.8470	0.9032
∞	0.9521	0.8467	0.7696	0.7518	0.6480	0.6960	0.8000
r	0	2	6	4	12	13	9
ρ_{20}	0.1051	0.0258	0.0167	0.0163	0.0179	0.0303	0.1151

Theorem 22.1, the dominant eigenvalue $\eta_1^{(1)}$ of $H(1)$ is equal to λ_1^2, where λ_1 is the dominant root of the determinant (22.8). This λ_1 is the convergence factor of the method of simultaneous displacements for the problem (25.7). As shown after equation (21.52a), λ_1 is the largest in modulus of the eigenvalues of the matrix $[-h^2(-\Delta_h)]/4$. It can be shown that

$$\lambda_1 = \frac{1 - h^2\mu_1}{4}, \qquad (25.15)$$

where $\mu_1 > 0$ is the least eigenvalue of $-\Delta_h$. That is, there is a vector X such that

$$-\Delta_h X = \mu_1 X \qquad \text{in } R_h,$$
$$X = 0 \qquad \text{in } C_h, \tag{25.16}$$

and μ_1 is the least number with this property. Thus ω_{opt} is a function of μ_1, and a simple computation shows that

$$\omega_{\text{opt}} = \frac{2}{1 + \sqrt{(h^2\mu_1/2) - (h^4\mu_1^2/16)}}. \tag{25.17}$$

In the third approach, then, one concentrates on finding a good estimate for μ_1 as quickly as possible, and then uses it in (25.17) to estimate ω_{opt}. We shall reserve our comments on finding μ_1 for Sec. 25.8.

25.6. Successive Overrelaxation: Time Required

After the programmer has a good method for determining ω_{opt}, or at least a good guess of the right value, the rate of convergence of the method is known from the fact that the eigenvalues of $H(\omega_{\text{opt}})$ are equal in modulus to $\omega_{\text{opt}} - 1$. One then knows approximately how many sweeps of the successive overrelaxation process are needed to solve the boundary-value problem.

An important practical question is how long such a computation will take on a given digital computer. This is fortunately easy to estimate if R_h is not too intricately shaped, since the total time per sweep is very close to the time required for relaxing one single point of R_h, multiplied by the number of points in R_h. The reason is that the logical operations required at the beginning of each new sweep and each new row are few when prorated over the number of ordinary interior points to be treated.

We now give a list of the times required for relaxing one single point of R_h, as determined by actual codes for several automatic digital computers. Each of the codes was written to solve the Dirichlet problem for the Laplacian operator (25.7) in a region with no irregular interior points. Hence there is a minimum of "red tape" connected with one point of R_h. Any code for problems with variable coefficients or other complications would necessarily run a good deal slower.

On SWAC in 1956 the time per point was 4 milliseconds. The 4 milliseconds were divided approximately equally between arithmetic operations and transfer of blocks of data to and from the magnetic drum (the fast-access store was small).

On a basic IBM 650 computer without index registers, core storage, or magnetic tapes the time per point was about 94 milliseconds. The program was hand-coded to yield optimum access to the drum, but this saved time only on some of the operations. Index registers would undoubtedly reduce this figure considerably.

On an IBM 797 computer at Stanford (not commercially available), the time per point was about 17 milliseconds.

On a UNIVAC scientific computer 1103AF, in a code referring only to core storage, the corresponding time per point was about 1.5 milliseconds, as coded by Neal Reinders of the Lockheed Missiles and Space Division.

Roughly, on any of these machines, the relaxation of one point seems to require 20 to 30 addition times. The greater power of the four-address addition command of SWAC yields little time advantage for this problem over the one-address or two-address commands of the 650 and 1103AF.

If presently available magnetic tapes were used for storage, one would have to add approximately 1 millisecond per point to the arithmetic operations to allow for the read-write and the rewind operations. (This time has been computed for a Burroughs 220 computer.)

To get a feeling for the total times required to solve a problem, let R be the π-by-π square considered in Sec. 22.5, and consider a mesh with $h = \pi/n$. In solving the Dirichlet problem for the five-point Laplace difference operator by successive overrelaxation, the rate of convergence is approximately $2h = 2\pi/n$. Suppose we wish to reduce the error to $10^{-6} \doteq e^{-13.8}$ times the initial error. We must "de-e-fold" the error 13.8 times, and each de-e-folding takes $n/(2\pi)$ sweeps.

We conclude that we will need $13.8n/(2\pi) \doteq 2.2n$ sweeps to solve the problem to the desired accuracy. And each sweep will require approximately $(n - 1)^2$ relaxations of individual points of R_h.

Thus, to approximate the time to solve the problem using optimum successive overrelaxation by points on a given machine, we multiply the time per point by a factor approximately equal to $2.2n^3$. Since there are $N = (n - 1)^2$ points involved, we may say that, to solve a Dirichlet problem involving N points, we will need approximately $2.2N^{3/2}$ individual relaxation times. (But we must recognize that the square is relaxed faster than most shapes with the same number of nodes—perhaps faster than any other.)

To see what computations are economically feasible, we consider what values of n can be dealt with on three computers. If we have one hour of SWAC time, we determine n by solving the equation $(0.004)2.2n^3 = 3600$. We find $n = 74$, or $n^2 = 5500$. We can thus expect in the hour to solve a Dirichlet problem for a square region involving 5500 points, which is the order of magnitude of SWAC's magnetic drum memory.

If we have 3 hours on an IBM 650 (more because a cheaper machine!), the corresponding calculation yields $n \doteq 39$, with $n^2 \doteq 1500$, a number of points which can be easily held on the 650 drum of 2000 cells.

If we have 1 hour of time on the UNIVAC scientific 1103AF, the corresponding figure is $n \doteq 103$, with $n^2 \doteq 10,600$, a number which slightly exceeds an 8192-word core storage. Note that the figure $n = 103$ is in close agreement with the estimate $n = 10^2$ of Table 3.3 for one hour's relaxation with the IBM 709 computer, a machine with comparable speed, though somewhat faster.

One might, in practice, have to double these times because of the difficulty of determining ω_{opt} accurately.

25.7. Other Methods for Solving Difference Equations

For machine experience with the Richardson method of Sec. 21.5, see Young and Warlick [1953]. For machine experience with the several other methods discussed in Secs. 21 and 22 for solving elliptic difference-equation problems, there is little literature yet available, and the authors have had no personal experience. The reader is advised to watch for articles comparing successive overrelaxation with successive overrelaxation by lines, or with the Peaceman-Rachford and Douglas-Rachford methods.

One comment may be made. Whenever one deals with the Dirichlet problem for Laplace's difference equation over a rectangular net region R_h (or a line, which is a special case), one can give an explicit formula for the solution in terms of boundary values. This can be derived by Fourier methods, for example, or by the methods of Sec. 21.2. With the enormous storage available in the newer computers, it is quite likely that one can store enough data to be able to compute rapidly the solution for a whole line or, indeed, for several lines. This makes the class of methods involving line relaxation much more feasible than formerly. It is quite possible that successive overrelaxation by lines, for example, may not cost any more computer time per point than successive overrelaxation by points. Hence the factor $\sqrt{2} \doteq 1.4$ of higher rate of convergence given in Sec. 22.5 for the former method may represent a gain of 40% in computer speed. And, if we can use blocks of several lines at one time, still greater savings may be expected.

25.8. Solving Eigenvalue Problems on a Computer

We now give a few comments on the solution on a digital computer of the finite eigenvalue problem posed in Sec. 24.8. Our experience has been limited to the use of successive overrelaxation for the determination of an end eigenvalue of $-\Delta_h$, in fact, the largest eigenvalue μ of A in (24.78). Our method has been to start with a guess at μ—call it m. We then proceed as though to solve the boundary-value problem

$$(A - mI)U = 0 \quad \text{in } R_h,$$
$$U = 0 \quad \text{on } C_h. \tag{25.18}$$

Since $U(P) \equiv 0$ in R_h is a solution of (25.18), it is not possible to start the relaxation with $U \equiv 0$ in R_h, for such values would never change. We start with some crude approximation to the true U, for example, $U(P) \equiv 1$ on R_h, with $U(P) = 0$ on C_h (with appropriate fixed-point scaling).

1. We then take a few cycles of the method of successive displacements ($\omega = 1$) for solving (25.18).
2. We then re-estimate μ from the finite Rayleigh quotient

$$\mu \doteq \rho(U) = \frac{U^T A U}{U^T U},\tag{25.19}$$

where U is the current value of the $U(P)$ in the solution.

We then return to step (1) with $\rho(U)$ replacing m in (25.18). After alternating between steps (1) and (2) until we seem to have μ correct to a couple of decimals, it is time to look for the optimum value of ω.

Assuming that one of the methods of Sec. 25.5 furnishes an adequate value of ω, one then proceeds to step (3):

3. Take a few cycles of the method of successive overrelaxation for solving (25.18).

We now alternate steps (3) and (2) until m seems to have converged to μ. At the very end it is a good idea to take a sweep or two with $\omega = 1$, to smooth the eigenvector U. This smoothing is useful at the end of boundary-value problems, also, since optimum overrelaxation leaves the values of U rather rough.

The reason for using $\omega = 1$ at the start is to keep U fairly smooth until the Rayleigh quotient has a chance to settle down.

Essentially the same method has been used by Reinders to get the fundamental eigenvalue of the operator $\Delta^{(h)}$ of (20.69), when the boundary C is curved. Care was taken that both h_E and h_W were never small together, nor both h_S and h_N. Since $\Delta^{(h)}$ is not quite symmetric, the Rayleigh quotient is not quite so meaningful as with the symmetric operator Δ_h. Nevertheless the method worked well. For the theory of the use of Rayleigh quotients in the eigenvalue problem for a nonsymmetric matrix A, see Ostrowski [1959].

25.9. Solving the Neumann Problem on a Computer

Occasionally a programmer is asked to solve a pure Neumann problem, i.e., a boundary-value problem in which the boundary condition prescribes a value of the normal derivative u_n. This raises a number of problems which have not been solved. We have only one piece of advice to the programmer.

Assume that one is dealing with a Neumann problem for difference equations for which a solution is known to exist. Then there must exist an infinity of solutions, all differing by an additive constant. A programmer's first reaction is to make the solution unique by imposing one additional restriction. For example, he might insist that $U(x, y) = 0$ for some one (x, y).

It is not necessary to pin the solution down at all. We proved in Sec. 21.6 that the method of successive displacements will converge to some solution of the problem anyway, since the matrix A will be semidefinite. In the case of Laplace's five-point operator Δ_h, for example, the rate of convergence to such a solution is actually governed by the first *nonzero eigenvalue* of the operator. It can be shown that, if one constrains the function $U(x, y)$ at any point not on a node of the first nonzero eigenvalue of the operator $-\Delta_h$, the result will be to reduce this eigenvalue. (This is a consequence of a separation theorem for the eigenvalues of a symmetric matrix; see Forsythe and Motzkin [1952].) This will slow the convergence of the process. It is therefore better to leave the net function free to go to whatever values it wants to. A constant can be subtracted from the solution after it has been found, if desired.

4

INITIAL-VALUE PROBLEMS IN MORE THAN
TWO INDEPENDENT VARIABLES

SECTION 26. THE EQUATION OF WAVE PROPAGATION

26.1. The Differential Equation

The differential equation

$$u_{tt} - \Delta u = 0, \tag{26.1}$$

where Δu is Laplace's operator

$$\Delta u = u_{xx} + u_{yy} \quad \text{or} \quad \Delta u = u_{xx} + u_{yy} + u_{zz},$$

depending on whether the number of space dimensions is 2 or 3, is the natural generalization of the equation $u_{tt} - u_{xx} = 0$ treated in Sec. 4. The simplest initial-value problem consists in prescribing the value of u as well as that of its time derivative at the time $t = 0$. In a problem in the plane, for instance, u would have to satisfy the initial conditions

$$u(x, y, 0) = f(x, y), \quad u_t(x, y, 0) = g(x, y). \tag{26.2}$$

The explicit representation of the solution for the corresponding problem on the line, given in (4.1), has its counterpart here, but the formula is now far less simple (see Courant and Hilbert [1937], Chap. 3, Sec. 6.2). We shall give, instead, a solution by means of Fourier series for the problem in two space dimensions. To that end, we must first show that the solution at a given point (x, y, t) depends only on the data in a finite portion of the initial plane $t = 0$, or, in other words, that the concept of domain of dependence extends to problems in two space dimensions.

The domain of dependence for the point (x_0, y_0, t_0) turns out to be the circle $(x - x_0)^2 + (y - y_0)^2 \leq t_0^2$, i.e., the circle cut out from the (x, y)-plane by the circular cone of central angle $\pi/2$ that has its vertex at

(x_0, y_0, t_0) and its axis parallel to the t-axis. To show that $u(x, y, t)$ is not affected by changes in the initial data outside the circle of dependence; it suffices, in view of the superposition principle, to prove that, if the initial data are identically zero in this circle, the solution $u(x, y, t)$ vanishes at (x_0, y_0, t_0). The proof can be based on applying the divergence theorem of integral calculus to an integral over the region R bounded by the cone and the (x, y)-plane. The expression $u_t(u_{tt} - \Delta u)$ satisfies the identity

$$2u_t(u_{tt} - \Delta u) = -2(u_t u_x)_x - 2(u_t u_y)_y + (u_x^2 + u_y^2 + u_t^2)_t.$$

Since the right member is a divergence expression, its integral over the conical solid R can be replaced by a surface integral extended over the surface of R and involving only the first derivatives of u. For $t = 0$ we have, by assumption, $u = u_t = 0$ and, therefore, also $u_x = u_y = 0$, so that the only contribution to the surface integral comes from the lateral surface M of R. Hence, if u is the solution of our initial-value problem, we have

$$0 = \iint_M [(u_x^2 + u_y^2 + u_t^2)\, dx\, dy - 2u_t u_x\, dy\, dt - 2u_t u_y\, dt\, dx].$$

The equation of the cone is $(x - x_0)^2 + (y - y_0)^2 - (t - t_0)^2 = 0$. In spherical coordinates r, θ, ϕ centered at (x_0, y_0, t_0), the unit normal vector on M has the components $\cos\theta/\sqrt{2}$, $\sin\theta/\sqrt{2}$, $1/\sqrt{2}$. Therefore the last integral can be written

$$\frac{1}{\sqrt{2}} \iint_M [(u_x^2 + u_y^2 + u_t^2) - 2u_t u_x \cos\theta - 2u_t u_y \sin\theta]\, dS,$$

where dS denotes the surface element on M. The integrand of this integral is nonnegative, since the integral can be written

$$\frac{1}{\sqrt{2}} \iint_M [(u_x - u_t \cos\theta)^2 + (u_y - u_t \sin\theta)^2]\, dS.$$

If this is to vanish, and if the partial derivatives of u are continuous, the equations

$$u_x - u_t \cos\theta = 0, \qquad u_y - u_t \sin\theta = 0$$

must hold everywhere on M. But the left members of these equations are, respectively, proportional to the directional derivatives of u in two directions tangential to M—those parallel to the (x, t)- and (y, t)-planes. If these vanish, all directional derivatives of u tangential to M must vanish, and, in view of the prescribed initial conditions, we can conclude that u is identically zero on M.

The foregoing argument does not yet prove that the circle $(x - x_0)^2 + (y - y_0)^2 \leq t_0^2$ is the correct domain of dependence, since the solution might conceivably depend on some smaller region only. It is true, however, that a change of the initial data on or inside this circle will in general modify the solution at the vertex of the cone. A proof of this fact can be given by deriving an explicit expression for the solution, but this would lead us too far from our main topic (see Courant and Hilbert [1937], Chap. 3, Sec. 6.5).

The cone M through a point (x, y, t), the so-called *characteristic cone*, here plays the role of the characteristic lines $x \pm t =$ const. of the corresponding problem in one space dimension. If the initial data are prescribed on a region D of the (x, y)-plane, the solution of the initial-value problem is uniquely determined at all points (x, y, t) such that the corresponding characteristic cone intersects the (x, y)-plane in points of D only. Without essential loss of generality, we may take D to be the square

$$0 \leq x \leq \pi, \qquad 0 \leq y \leq \pi.$$

This choice permits us to solve the initial-value problem by means of Fourier sine series. The resemblance to the arguments of Sec. 4 is so great that we may be brief in the details.

Assume that the initial conditions are

$$u(x, y, 0) = f(x, y), \qquad u_t(x, y, 0) = 0, \tag{26.3}$$

and that $f(x, y)$ possesses a Fourier series

$$f(x, y) = \sum_{m,n=1}^{\infty} a_{mn} \sin mx \sin ny \tag{26.4}$$

with

$$\sum_{m,n=1}^{\infty} |a_{mn}| < \infty. \tag{26.5}$$

By separation of variables, one finds readily that

$$u(x, y, t) = \sum_{m,n=1}^{\infty} a_{mn} \cos (\sqrt{m^2 + n^2}\, t) \sin mx \sin ny \tag{26.6}$$

is a formal solution of the initial-value problem. Condition (26.5) assures the uniform convergence of the series (26.6), but it is not strong enough to guarantee that the function $u(x, y, t)$ represented by (26.6) satisfies the differential equation. An obvious sufficient condition for this to be the case is the inequality $\sum_{m,n=1}^{\infty} (m^2 + n^2) |a_{mn}| < \infty$. It can be shown that, if the differential problem possesses a solution with a convergent Fourier series, this series is given by (26.6), but we shall not pursue this matter here. The case that $u_t(x, y, 0) = g(x, y) \neq 0$ can be reduced to the special initial-value problem (26.3), as in Sec. 4.

26.2. The Simplest Difference Approximation

To write the difference equation to be studied in reasonably condensed form, let us introduce the abbreviation $\delta_{zh}f(z)$ for the central difference quotient

$$\delta_{zh}f(z) = h^{-1}\left[f\left(z + \frac{h}{2}\right) - f\left(z - \frac{h}{2}\right)\right].$$

Then

$$\delta_{tk}^2 U - \delta_{xh_1}^2 U - \delta_{yh_2}^2 U = 0 \qquad (26.7)$$

is the most natural finite-difference analog of the differential equation (26.1) in two space dimensions. We assume that the increments k, h_1, h_2 are submultiples of π. With (26.7) we associate the initial conditions

$$U(x, y, 0) = f(x, y), \quad k^{-1}[U(x, y, k) - U(x, y, 0)] = g(x, y). \qquad (26.8)$$

The problem (26.7), (26.8) can be solved stepwise for $t = k, 2k, \cdots$, in an explicit manner. We proceed to solve it analytically in the particular case that $g(x, y) \equiv 0$ in order to study its convergence and stability properties. The formal result is a series of the form

$$U(x, y, t) = \sum_{m,n=1}^{\infty} a_{mn}\, \gamma_{mn}(t) \sin mx \sin ny, \qquad (26.9)$$

where $\gamma_{mn}(t)$ turns out to be

$$\gamma_{mn}(t) = \frac{\cos \mu_{mn}(t - k/2)}{\cos (\mu_{mn} k/2)}. \qquad (26.10)$$

Here μ_{mn} is a solution of the following transcendental equation for μ:

$$k^{-2} \sin^2 \frac{\mu k}{2} - h_1^{-2} \sin^2 \frac{m h_1}{2} - h_2^{-2} \sin^2 \frac{n h_2}{2} = 0. \qquad (26.11)$$

If $\gamma_{mn}(t)$ is bounded, uniformly in m and n, the series (26.9) converges and solves our problem. The condition

$$k^2(h_1^{-2} + h_2^{-2}) \le \lambda^2 < 1, \qquad (26.12)$$

which corresponds to the restriction $k/h < 1$ imposed in the one-dimensional problem, guarantees the boundedness of $\gamma_{mn}(t)$, for it implies that

$$\sin^2 \frac{\mu_{mn} k}{2} \le k^2(h_1^{-2} + h_2^{-2}) \le \lambda^2,$$

and therefore that

$$|\gamma_{mn}(t)| \le \frac{1}{\sqrt{1 - \lambda^2}}.$$

The condition $\lambda < 1$ is, moreover, a sufficient condition for the convergence of U to u, as k, h_1, and h_2 tend to zero. In fact, this passage to the limit reduces equation (26.11) to

$$\mu^2 = m^2 + n^2,$$

from which one concludes by the implicit function theorem that

$$\lim_{k,h_1,h_2 \to 0} \mu_{mn} = \sqrt{m^2 + n^2}.$$

Since the series in (26.9) converges uniformly, the passage to the limit may be performed termwise and leads to the series (26.6) for u.

Is the condition (26.12) necessary for convergence of U to u? If $\lambda = 1$, the present methods fail, as they did in the one-dimensional case, but for $\lambda > 1$ it can be easily shown that convergence of U to u is an exceptional occurrence. To that end, we observe that, in the stepwise numerical solution of the difference equation, the solution at a grid point depends only on those grid points of the plane $t = 0$ that lie inside a certain rhombus. Let us assume, for instance, that we wish to calculate the solution at the point $x = 0$, $y = 0$, $t = sk$. (This particular choice of x and y simplifies the notation but does not cause any loss of generality.) Then this rhombus has the vertices $\pm sh_1$, $\pm sh_2$. The domain of dependence for the differential equation is, however, the circle $x^2 + y^2 \le s^2 k^2$. The inequality (26.12) is precisely the condition that the circle lie inside the rhombus. If the inequality (26.12) for λ is reversed, there will be parts of the circle of dependence where the initial values of the differential problem can be arbitrarily changed without affecting the solution of the difference equation.

It is clear that our result can be simply extended to any number of space dimensions. In m dimensions, condition (26.12) must be replaced by

$$k^2 \sum_{j=1}^{m} h_j^{-2} < 1. \tag{26.13}$$

If all h_j are equal to the same number h, this inequality becomes

$$\frac{k}{h} < \frac{1}{\sqrt{m}}. \tag{26.14}$$

It therefore grows more burdensome as the number of dimensions increases.

The same restrictions on the mesh size guarantee the *stability* of the difference scheme. The proof by means of finite Fourier interpolation series resembles so much the one given in Sec. 5.2 that no elaboration of this point is necessary.

SECTION 27. CHARACTERISTICS IN SEVERAL DIMENSIONS

To introduce the general concept of characteristics for more than two independent variables, we return to the notation of Sec. 6. Let us assume that x, y, and z are the independent variables (extension to more than three variables does not add any essentially new features), and that we are dealing with a system of n first-order differential equations in the n unknown functions u^i ($i = 1, 2, \cdots, n$), say,

$$\sum_{i=1}^{n} (a^{vi}u_x^{\ i} + b^{vi}u_y^{\ i} + c^{vi}u_z^{\ i}) + d^v = 0, \qquad v = 1, 2, \cdots, n, \quad (27.1)$$

where the a^{vi}, b^{vi}, c^{vi}, d are given functions of x, y, z and the u^i. In matrix and vector notation, this system can be rewritten as

$$Au_x + Bu_y + Cu_z + d = 0. \tag{27.2}$$

Multiplication by any nonsingular matrix T changes (27.2) into an equivalent system

$$A^*u_x + B^*u_y + C^*u_z + d^* = 0, \tag{27.3}$$

where

$$A^* = TA, \qquad B^* = TB, \qquad C^* = TC, \qquad d^* = Td. \tag{27.4}$$

In Sec. 6 it was shown that, for hyperbolic systems in two independent variables, T can be determined in such a manner that

$$A^* - MB^* = 0, \tag{27.5}$$

where M is a *diagonal* matrix. The proper analog of relation (27.5) is here (when written in a more symmetric form)

$$QA^* + RB^* + SC^* = 0, \tag{27.6}$$

where Q, R, and S are diagonal matrices. Let us investigate whether T can actually be found so that (27.6) is true. If $T = [t^{v\mu}]$, and q^v, r^v, s^v are the diagonal elements of Q, R, and S, (27.6) becomes, in view of (27.4),

$$\sum_{\mu=1}^{n} (q^v t^{v\mu}a^{\mu i} + r^v t^{v\mu}b^{\mu i} + s^v t^{v\mu}c^{\mu i}) = 0, \qquad v, i = 1, 2, \cdots, n. \quad (27.7)$$

For fixed v, this is a system of n linear homogeneous equations in $t^{v1}, \cdots, t^{vn}$, which possesses nontrivial solutions if and only if the three numbers $q = q^v$, $r = r^v$, $s = s^v$ satisfy the *characteristic equation*

$$\det(qA + rB + sC) = 0. \tag{27.8}$$

If a solution of (27.8) has been found, corresponding values $t^{r1}, \cdots,$ t^{rn} can be determined from (27.7).

The simplest case is that in which (27.8) possesses n real nontrivial solution triples $(q^1, r^1, s^1), \cdots, (q^n, r^n, s^n)$ such that the corresponding sets $t^{1\mu}, t^{2\mu}, \cdots, t^{n\mu}, \mu = 1, \cdots, n$, form a nonsingular matrix T. Then the system is called *totally hyperbolic*, and the differential equation system can be reduced to a form (27.3) so that (27.6) is satisfied.

What does this mean geometrically? The expression in parentheses in (27.1) can be regarded as the scalar product of the three-dimensional vectors (a^{vi}, b^{vi}, c^{vi}) and $(u_x^{\ i}, u_y^{\ i}, u_z^{\ i})$. At a fixed point, this scalar product is proportional to the directional derivative of u^i in the direction of the vector (a^{vi}, b^{vi}, c^{vi}). Now consider a particular one of the equations (27.1); i.e., consider a fixed v. This equation has thus n different directions associated with it, corresponding to the n values of i. This is still true after the transformation of the system by T, but now the n directions of the vectors $(a^{*vi}, b^{*vi}, c^{*vi})$, $i = 1, \cdots, n$, lie all in one plane. In fact, the equation

$$q^v a^{*vi} + r^v b^{*vi} + s^v c^{*vi} = 0,$$

which is one of the n^2 scalar relations that compose (27.6), means that $(a^{*vi}, b^{*vi}, c^{*vi})$ are the components of a vector orthogonal to the vector (q^v, r^v, s^v) which is independent of i (but which may vary with the solution u considered, if the differential system is nonlinear).

In other words: *After the transformation by T, each differential equation of the system contains directional derivatives in one plane only.* These planes are not uniquely determined by the differential equation and its solution u. For equation (27.8) defines a one-parameter family of directions at a point. The family of planes perpendicular to these directions envelop the *characteristic cone* at that point. This cone can be considered the analog of the characteristic directions introduced in the two-dimensional case. The characteristic cone consists, in general, of n branches. The proper generalization of the characteristic curves are now the *characteristic strips*, i.e., curves whose tangents are generators of the local characteristic cone, with associated surface elements such that these elements are everywhere tangent to the local characteristic cone. Surfaces that are composed of characteristic strips are called *characteristic surfaces*, or simply *characteristics*. If the differential equations are linear, the characteristics are the same for all solutions.

The theory of characteristics is very important for the further study of hyperbolic differential equations, but this is beyond the scope of this book. The simplification of the differential equation after multiplication by T is, however, less helpful here than in the case of two variables, and there is no uniquely defined canonical form. In fact, many of the more recent studies of the existence and uniqueness of solutions for hyperbolic systems do not make much use of the theory of characteristics.

To illustrate the foregoing explanations, let u be a solution of the differential equation of wave propagation in two space dimensions, $u_{tt} - u_{xx} - u_{yy} = 0$, and define (u^1, u^2, u^3) by

$$u^1 = u_x, \qquad u^2 = u_y, \qquad u^3 = u_t. \qquad (27.9)$$

Then there corresponds to every u a solution of the system

$$u_t^1 - u_x^3 = 0,$$
$$u_t^2 - u_y^3 = 0, \qquad (27.10)$$
$$u_t^3 - u_x^1 - u_y^2 = 0.$$

If $u(x, y, 0) = f(x, y)$ and $u_t(x, y, 0) = g(x, y)$ are prescribed, the corresponding initial conditions for (27.10) are

$$u^1 = f_x, \qquad u^2 = f_y, \qquad u^3 = g. \qquad (27.11)$$

The system (27.10) also possesses solutions that are not obtainable from a solution u of the wave equation by means of (27.9). But if $(u^1, u^2\ u^3)$ is a solution of (27.10) satisfying initial conditions of the particular form (27.11), then $u_y^1 - u_x^2 = 0$ for $t = 0$. Also, $\partial(u_y^1 - u_x^2)/\partial t = 0$ for all t, in consequence of the first two equations in (27.10). Therefore $u_y^1 - u_x^2 = 0$ for all t, and this equation and the first two equations of (27.10) imply that (u^1, u^2, u^3) is the gradient of some scalar u. The third of equations (27.10) then shows that u solves the equation of wave propagation. In view of this relationship, it is reasonable to expect that the characteristic cone of (27.10) will have that of equation (26.1) as one branch. If we identify t with the variable previously called z, the matrices A, B, C of (27.2) become, for the system (27.10),

$$A = \begin{bmatrix} 0 & 0 & 0 \\ 0 & 0 & 1 \\ 1 & 0 & 0 \end{bmatrix}, \qquad B = \begin{bmatrix} 0 & 0 & -1 \\ 0 & 0 & 0 \\ 0 & 1 & 0 \end{bmatrix}, \qquad C = \begin{bmatrix} 0 & 1 & 0 \\ -1 & 0 & 0 \\ 0 & 0 & -1 \end{bmatrix},$$

and the characteristic equation (27.8) is

$$s(q^2 + r^2 - s^2) = 0.$$

The triples (q, r, s) satisfying this equation are the directions normal to the characteristic cone at its vertex. Hence, this cone consists of the one already met, in a different context, in Sec. 26 and the line through the vertex parallel to the t-axis.

SECTION 28. A METEOROLOGICAL FORECAST PROBLEM

The earth's lower atmosphere can be considered as a mixture of dry air, which behaves like a perfect gas, with water substance in its solid, liquid, and vapor phases. The atmosphere moves over the quite irregular surface of our rotating planet, exchanging some of its water substance and some of its momentum with the solid and liquid parts of the earth. There is also an exchange of heat energy with the earth, and some with outer space through radiation. Hence the meteorological behavior of the atmosphere could only be completely described by hydrodynamical equations of viscous fluid motion, thermodynamical equations of phase transformation within moist air, stress equations of momentum transfer, and equations of radiative heat transfer. Some of these equations may not even be known—for example, those describing thermodynamical processes not in equilibrium. Those that are known are nonlinear.

Any reasonably tractable mathematical model of the meteorological behavior of the atmosphere is bound to be simplified. In one model the atmosphere is assumed to consist of nonviscous dry air, moving adiabatically and insulated against any transfer of heat energy or momentum outside itself. The state of the atmosphere at each point P and time t is described by a vector wind velocity v, pressure p, density ρ, and temperature T. The determining equations are those expressing the conservation of energy, mass, and momentum, and the equation of state. The boundary conditions involve the intricate shape of the earth's surface, and some statement about the "top" of the atmosphere. Initial conditions are postulated from some sample of approximately simultaneous observations of the atmosphere.

To discuss this model, it is useful to take a spherical coordinate system rotating with the earth. Let λ be longitude, ϕ latitude, and r radial distance, and let vectors be written in the order of their eastward, northward, and upward components. Denote the wind velocity by $\mathbf{v} = (u, v, w)$, and let $\mathbf{g} = (0, 0, -g)$ denote the force of gravity on a unit mass. Let $\boldsymbol{\Omega} = (0, \Omega \cos \phi, \Omega \sin \phi)$ be the angular velocity of the earth's rotation with respect to the stars. Let the symbol D/Dt denote Euler's *material time derivative*

$$\frac{D}{Dt} = \frac{\partial}{\partial t} + \mathbf{v} \cdot \nabla. \tag{28.1}$$

Because of our choice of rotating coordinates, the Eulerian equation of momentum conservation (28.2) includes the so-called *Coriolis* force $-2\Omega \times \mathbf{v}$, which is so important that it exerts the principal control over the wind direction in extratropical latitudes. See, for example, Holmboe, Forsythe, and Gustin [1945]. The momentum equation is

$$\frac{D\mathbf{v}}{Dt} = -\frac{1}{\rho}\nabla p + \mathbf{g} - 2\Omega \times \mathbf{v}, \qquad (28.2)$$

where $\mathbf{a} \times \mathbf{b}$ denotes the vector product.

The equation of energy conservation (first law of thermodynamics) is

$$c_p \frac{DT}{Dt} = \frac{1}{\rho}\frac{Dp}{Dt}, \qquad (28.3)$$

where c_p is the specific heat of dry air at constant pressure.

The equation of continuity (conservation of mass) may be written

$$\frac{D\rho}{Dt} = -\rho\nabla \cdot \mathbf{v}, \qquad (28.4)$$

where $\nabla \cdot \mathbf{v} = \text{div } \mathbf{v}$ is the divergence of the wind field.

The equation of state is that of a perfect gas:

$$p = \rho RT, \qquad (28.5)$$

where R is a certain constant.

If one replaces $\mathbf{v}$ by (u, v, w), and replaces the material derivatives in (28.2), (28.3), (28.4) by use of (28.1), one gets six nonlinear scalar equations for u, v, w, p, ρ, T as functions of λ, ϕ, r, t. The system (28.2)–(28.5) constitutes the *primitive equations*.

28.1. Forecasting Directly from the Primitive Equations

In principle, to forecast the weather, one could replace the rewritten system (28.2)–(28.5) by finite-difference equations of explicit type over a spherical network, and solve them as a marching problem in time. Indeed, this was essentially the program of a monumental work by Richardson [1922]. The difficulties are discussed heuristically by Charney [1949] and by Charney, Fjörtoft, and von Neumann [1950], as follows. The equation system (28.2)–(28.5) is so general that it describes atmospheric motions other than the meteorologically significant ones, namely, sound waves and gravity waves. Now, whereas the large-scale meteorological waves have a velocity less than 60 miles per hour, the gravity waves and sound waves move up to about 750 miles per hour. For an explicit finite-difference method involving space increments h and a time increment k to yield a solution converging as $h, k \to 0$ to that of (28.2)–(28.5), the arguments of Sec. 26.2 and of Sec. 28.4 make it plausible that one must have

$$\frac{k}{h} < \tfrac{1}{750}\,(\text{miles per hour})^{-1}. \qquad (28.6)$$

For otherwise the values at time $t + k$ of the variables at a lattice point (λ, ϕ, r) would be independent of the values at time t at lattice points (λ', ϕ', r') from which real sound waves could propagate to (λ, ϕ, r) during the time increment k. To obtain sufficient meteorological detail, it is essential that h be no more than about 125 miles. Then, by (28.6), one must have k less than $\frac{1}{6}$ hour, or 10 minutes.

It is presumed that a choice of k/h violating (28.6) would result in instability of an explicit computational scheme, just as instability is associated with a lack of convergence in other problems treated in this book. Thus the numerical solution of the primitive equations (28.2)–(28.5) would appear to require a new integration for each 10 minutes in time. This would require a nearly impossible amount of computing for machines available up to the present.

Although the increasing speed of computing machines may soon permit numerical integration of (28.2)–(28.5) in ten-minute time slices, there is a second and more fundamental difficulty. Namely, the fine structure of the variation of v, p, ρ, and T due to sound and gravity waves could not possibly be represented on a space grid with a mesh constant of 125 miles. Hence these variations would appear as apparently random perturbations on the meteorological waves. But, since the grid points are so few, it would be extremely difficult to filter the sound and gravity waves out of the solution of the system (28.2)–(28.5), and yet, unless they were filtered out, it would be quite impossible to observe the meteorologically significant structure of v, p, T, and ρ.

28.2. Modified Approaches to Forecasting

The basic approach of Charney and his collaborators to numerical weather prediction has been to filter the sound and gravity waves out of the equations of motion. This means to simplify the system (28.2)–(28.5) so that it admits meteorological waves but not sound or gravity waves. There have been many different approaches to this, of varying complexity, and the field is still developing. Since the primary considerations are meteorological and, hence, outside the scope of this book, only a brief indication will be made of the source of the equations used.

By taking the curl $(\nabla \times)$ of both sides of equation (28.2), and transforming the resulting equation, one finds the *vorticity equation*

$$\frac{D}{Dt}(\zeta + 2\Omega) = (\zeta + 2\Omega) \cdot \nabla v - (\nabla \cdot v)(\zeta + 2\Omega) - \nabla(\rho^{-1}) \times \nabla p; \quad (28.7)$$

see Bjerknes et al. [1933]. Here $\zeta = \nabla \times v$ is the (vector) *vorticity* of the wind field v with respect to the earth, while 2Ω is the vorticity of the earth's rotation. The sum $\zeta + 2\Omega$ is called the (vector) *absolute vorticity* of the air.

The importance of (28.7) is that the terms on the right-hand side are frequently small. In one useful model employed by Charney, Fjörtoft, and von Neumann [1950], they are treated as identically zero, and the vertical component of (28.7) takes the form

$$\frac{D}{Dt}(\zeta + 2\Omega \sin \phi) = 0, \tag{28.8}$$

where ϕ is latitude, and ζ is the vertical component of $\boldsymbol{\zeta}$. Equation (28.8) is called the *nondivergent vorticity equation*. We give a two-dimensional treatment adapted from Charney and Phillips [1953].

For convenience it is usual to map a large region of the earth's surface conformally on a plane with rectangular x, y coordinates. Let $m = m(x, y)$ be the local mapping factor, i.e., the number of length units on the map corresponding to a length unit on the earth; in ordinary units $m \ll 1$. Assume the wind $\mathbf{v} = (u, v)$ to be horizontal and adequately represented by a stream function $\psi = \psi(x, y)$, with

$$u = -m\psi_y, \qquad v = m\psi_x. \tag{28.9}$$

(The meteorologist ordinarily works on a constant pressure surface, and adopts the formulas

$$u = -mf^{-1}\Phi_y, \qquad v = mf^{-1}\Phi_x,$$

where $f = 2\Omega \sin \phi$ and Φ denotes the geopotential of the pressure surface. The nonmeteorologist need not be concerned with this particular choice of stream function.)

Now, for ζ expressed in terms of length units on the earth, we see from (28.9) that

$$\zeta = mv_x - mu_y$$
$$= m^2(\psi_{xx} + \psi_{yy}) + m(m_x\psi_x + m_y\psi_y).$$

Since $m^2\psi_{xx} = m^2\psi_x(\psi_{xx}/\psi_x)$ and $mm_x\psi_x = m^2\psi_x(m_x/m)$, we see that the terms $m^2\psi_{xx}$ and $mm_x\psi_x$ are respectively proportional to the relative changes in ψ_x and in m. In useful map projections, the relative change in m is much less than that in $\psi_x = v/m$ or in ψ_y. Hence, with good approximation,

$$\zeta = m^2(\psi_{xx} + \psi_{yy}) = m^2 \Delta\psi, \tag{28.10}$$

where, as usual, Δ denotes $\partial^2/\partial x^2 + \partial^2/\partial y^2$.

Introduce the notation
$$\eta = \zeta + 2\Omega \sin \phi. \tag{28.11}$$

Now, by (28.1) and (28.9), in earth units,

$$\frac{D}{Dt} = \frac{\partial}{\partial t} - m\psi_y\left(m\frac{\partial}{\partial x}\right) + m\psi_x\left(m\frac{\partial}{\partial y}\right)$$
$$= \frac{\partial}{\partial t} - m^2\psi_y\frac{\partial}{\partial x} + m^2\psi_x\frac{\partial}{\partial y}. \tag{28.12}$$

But then we can express (28.8) in the form

$$\frac{\partial \eta}{\partial t} = m^2(\eta_x \psi_y - \eta_y \psi_x) = m^2 J(\eta, \psi), \tag{28.13}$$

where J denotes the Jacobian operator.

Combining (28.10), (28.11), and (28.13), we get the following pair of equations, since $\partial(2\Omega \sin \phi)/\partial t = 0$:

$$\eta = m^2 \Delta \psi + 2\Omega \sin \phi,$$

$$\Delta\left(\frac{\partial \psi}{\partial t}\right) = J(\eta, \psi). \tag{28.14}$$

As an alternative to the system (28.14), we can write down an equivalent system

$$\Delta \psi = m^{-2}(\eta - 2\Omega \sin \phi), \tag{28.15a}$$

$$\frac{\partial \eta}{\partial t} = m^2 J(\eta, \psi). \tag{28.15b}$$

Although equivalent, the two systems (28.14) and (28.15) lead to different computational schemes; both have been used for numerical weather prediction. One of these will be mentioned after we treat the special case of one space dimension.

28.3. One-Dimensional Model

In the simplest model of the weather to be considered, we assume that the wind $\mathbf{v} = (U, v)$ consists of a small north-south perturbation $v = v(x, t)$ on a prevailing constant west wind U. Since v is independent of y, the system (28.14) reduces to a single partial differential equation in time and in one space dimension x. (In this section we let x, y denote distance on the earth.) Since the perturbation technique is used, we derive a linear equation; i.e., we consider all nonlinear terms in v and its derivatives as negligible.

We have $\zeta = v_x - U_y = v_x$. Then, by (28.1) and (28.8),

$$0 = \frac{D(\zeta + 2\Omega \sin \phi)}{Dt} = \left(\frac{\partial}{\partial t} + U\frac{\partial}{\partial x} + v\frac{\partial}{\partial y}\right)(v_x + 2\Omega \sin \phi)$$

$$= v_{xt} + Uv_{xx} + v(2\Omega \sin \phi)_y$$

$$= v_{xt} + Uv_{xx} + \beta v,$$

where $\beta = 2\Omega r^{-1} \cos \phi$, and r is the earth's radius. Thus we have the equation

$$v_{xt} + Uv_{xx} + \beta v = 0, \tag{28.16}$$

to be solved for $v(x, t)$ for $0 \le x \le L$ and $t > 0$. The initial conditions are the values of $v(x, 0)$ for $0 \le x \le L$.

If we let $\xi = x - Ut$, $\tau = 4\beta t$, and $v(x, t) = \omega(\xi, \tau)$, equation (28.16) reduces to the so-called *telegrapher's equation*

$$\omega_{\xi\tau} + \tfrac{1}{4}\omega = 0, \tag{28.17}$$

to be solved for $\omega(\xi, \tau)$ for $0 \le \xi \le L$ and $\tau > 0$, given $\omega(\xi, 0)$ for $0 \le \xi \le L$.

Although enormously simplified, the one-dimensional weather equation (28.17) raises a basic question which appears in more sophisticated models also—namely, what is a properly posed forecast problem, in the sense that initial data determine a unique solution? If one is to forecast at all with (28.17), one must solve (28.17) for $\omega(\xi_0, \tau_0)$ for some $\tau_0 > 0$, given $\omega(\xi, 0)$ for certain values of ξ. Moreover, meteorologists are accustomed to forecasting quantities like $\omega(\xi_0, \tau_0)$, given values of $\omega(\xi, 0)$ only for $-\xi_1 \le |\xi - \xi_0| \le \xi_1$, where ξ_1 is some constant of the order of magnitude of $U\tau_0/4\beta$. On the other hand, since the characteristics of (28.17) are the lines $\xi = \text{const.}$, $\tau = \text{const.}$, it is clear from the considerations of Sec. 6.4 that knowledge of $\omega(\xi, 0)$ even for all ξ in $(-\infty, \infty)$ permits no inference whatever concerning $\omega(\xi, \tau_0)$ for $\tau_0 > 0$. (For some unknown discontinuity could be propagated along a characteristic separating $\tau = 0$ from $\tau = \tau_0$.) Thus forecasting from (28.17) appears to be impossible in principle.

There are two ways out of this dilemma. In the first place, since the earth is round, we can demand that

$$\omega(\xi, \tau) = \omega(\xi + L, \tau), \tag{28.18}$$

where L is the earth's circumference at the latitude ϕ. In Forsythe [1950a] it is then proved that the initial values $\omega(\xi, 0)$ for $0 \le \xi \le L$ determine $\omega(\xi, \tau)$ uniquely for all $\tau > 0$. It is unusual to find a hyperbolic equation with boundary values on only one characteristic; but with the added condition (28.18) of the periodicity of $\omega(\xi, \tau)$ the initial-value problem is properly posed. The solution $\omega(\xi, \tau)$ can be represented either as a Fourier series or by a Stieltjes integral of the form

$$\omega(\xi, \tau) = \int_0^L G(\xi - \sigma, \tau) \, d\omega(\sigma, 0), \tag{28.19}$$

where G is a certain Green's function for (28.17); see Forsythe [1950a].

The periodic solution (28.19) for $\omega(\xi, \tau)$ requires knowledge of $\omega(\xi, 0)$ for all values of ξ around the earth. Nevertheless, meteorologists believe that $\omega(\xi_0, \tau)$ can be forecast for τ corresponding to approximately a day without knowledge of $\omega(\xi, 0)$ for ξ remote from ξ_0. To support them, a careful study of (28.19) would show that $\omega(\xi_0, \tau)$ depends only very slightly on $\omega(\xi, 0)$ for remote ξ, *for those functions* $\omega(\xi, 0)$ *observed in practice.* Such a study was included in the report of Charney and Eliassen [1949], and represents the second way out of the dilemma mentioned above. Armed with this knowledge, we can approximately predict $\omega(\xi_0, \tau_0)$ from values of $\omega(\xi, 0)$ given for ξ extending only part way around the earth from ξ_0.

Charney and Eliassen [1949] have also given a solution similar to (28.19) for a more complicated one-dimensional model. In none of these one-dimensional models does it seem necessary or advantageous to replace the differential equation by a difference equation. Instead, one can tabulate the appropriate Green's function $G(\xi, \tau)$ once and for all for suitable values of ξ, τ, and then use it to evaluate $\omega(\xi, \tau)$ by a numerical approximation of the integral (28.19) or its analog. Thus difference methods do not seem necessary for the one-dimensional model.

28.4. Two-Dimensional Model

Let us return to the systems (28.14) and (28.15) for two space dimensions and time. As before, let x, y denote rectangular coordinates on a plane map of a portion of the earth. As with the one-dimensional equation (28.17), one would like to use the system (28.14) or (28.15) to forecast $\psi(x_0, y_0, t_0)$ for some $t_0 > 0$, given certain values of $\psi(x, y, 0)$ in a bounded region R of the (x, y)-plane at time $t = 0$. And, as with (28.17), it is mathematically impossible to do this. To see this heuristically, let us concentrate henceforth on system (28.15), which we repeat for convenience:

$$\Delta\psi = m^{-2}(\eta - 2\Omega \sin \phi), \tag{28.15a}$$

$$\frac{\partial\eta}{\partial t} = m^2 J(\eta, \psi). \tag{28.15b}$$

If η is known in R, and ψ is known on the boundary C of R, then ψ can be computed in R from the Poisson equation (28.15a). It therefore appears necessary that the boundary conditions for solving (28.15) permit knowledge of ψ on C at all times, and knowledge of η in R at all times. But recall that the physical origin of the system (28.15) is the condition (28.8), which states that the scalar vorticity $\eta = \zeta + 2\Omega \sin \phi$ is conserved in the fluid motion. Hence η is determined uniquely by its value at any point on the same air trajectory. Thus, whenever a parcel of air enters R, one must know the corresponding value of η. Since the vector air velocity is proportional to $(-\psi_y, \psi_x)$, one sees that fluid is entering R at precisely those points of C where the tangential derivative $d\psi/ds$ of ψ is positive, if s increases in the positive direction around C (the direction with R at the left).

In summary, following Charney, Fjörtoft, and von Neumann [1950], we expect that the appropriate boundary conditions for (28.15) are:

$\psi(x, y, t)$ is prescribed for (x, y) on C and all t;   (28.20a)

$\eta(x, y, t)$ is prescribed for those (x, y) on C and those t
for which the tangential derivative $d\psi/ds \geq 0$.   (28.20b)

As an initial condition, of course,

$\psi(x, y, 0)$ is prescribed for all (x, y) in R.   (28.20c)

The above argument is only heuristic but, in the absence of a general theory for such quasilinear systems, it seems quite plausible.

Without a general theory of such problems, it is not even certain that the mixed initial-value–boundary-value problem (28.15), (28.20) has a unique solution. Recently, however, Sensenig [1959] has proved the existence of a unique solution when the region R is a half-plane, and we shall assume its unique existence also for the rectangular region R considered below. How shall such a solution be calculated? Integral representations like (28.19) no longer appear feasible, and it seems advisable to apply the method of finite differences.

Let us set up a square network in the (x, y)-plane with space mesh constant h, and introduce a time interval k. Let k/h be abbreviated λ (λ is no longer longitude). Let the region R be a rectangle which is the union of mesh squares. The net region R_{hk} in space-time then consists of a set of points $(mh, nh, \mu k)$ for $m = 0, 1, \cdots, m_0$, $n = 0, 1, \cdots, n_0$, $\mu = 0, 1, 2, \cdots$. Let $\Psi(x, y, t)$ and $H(x, y, t)$, defined on R_{hk}, be the net functions approximating ψ and η respectively. Let C_{hk} denote the net boundary. What difference equations shall one use?

From the considerations of Sec. 20 it is natural to replace (28.15a) by

$$h^{-2}[\Psi(x + h, y, t) + \Psi(x, y + h, t) + \Psi(x - h, y, t) + \Psi(x, y - h, t)$$
$$- 4\Psi(x, y, t)] = m^{-2}[H(x, y, t) - 2\Omega \sin \phi], \quad (28.21)$$

where m^2 and ϕ depend on x, y. Everyone seems to agree on using (28.21).

The diversity of proposals comes in setting up an analog of (28.15b). Charney and Phillips [1953], p. 79, use the following as a basic difference equation:

$$(2k)^{-1}[H(x, y, t + k) - H(x, y, t - k)]$$
$$= -m^2(2h)^{-2}[H(x + h, y, t)$$
$$- H(x - h, y, t)][\Psi(x, y + h, t) - \Psi(x, y - h, t)] - [H(x, y + h, t)$$
$$- H(x, y - h, t)][\Psi(x + h, y, t) - \Psi(x - h, y, t)]. \quad (28.22)$$

(For other versions, see Sec. 28.5.) The expression (28.22) is used for nodes (x, y) interior to R and for times $t \geq k$. Since $H(x, y, -k)$ is unknown, the authors modify (28.22) at $t = 0$ by employing a one-sided forward time difference

$$k^{-1}[H(x, y, k) - H(x, y, 0)]$$

for the left side of (28.22). For points (x, y) on C_{hk}, some of the points $(x \pm h, y, t)$ or $(x, y \pm h, t)$ are outside R_{hk}, and (28.22) must be modified again. Where necessary on C_{hk} to avoid outside points, central differences like $(2h)^{-1}[H(x + h, y, t) - H(x - h, y, t)]$ are replaced in (28.22) by one-sided differences like

$$h^{-1}[H(x, y, t) - H(x.- h, y, t)] \quad \text{or} \quad h^{-1}[H(x + h, y, t) - H(x, y, t)].$$

The same is done with differences of Ψ.

Each basic time step of the Charney-Phillips computational scheme is as follows. Assume that $H(x, y, t - k)$, $H(x, y, t)$, and $\Psi(x, y, t - k)$ are stored for all (x, y) in $R_{hk} \cup C_{hk}$.

1. First, (28.21) is solved for $\Psi(x, y, t)$ at all interior grid points (x, y), using $\Psi(x, y, t - k)$ as an initial guess and then erasing the values of $\Psi(x, y, t - k)$ in the memory. (Young's method of successive overrelaxation was actually used.) The boundary values $\Psi(x, y, t)$ are furnished by the boundary condition (28.20a).

2. The new values $H(x, y, t + k)$ are obtained from (28.22) at all interior grid points (x, y). Next, the presence of inflow or outflow at the nodes of C_{hk} is determined by appropriate centered differences of $\Psi(x, y, t)$ along C_{hk}. At points of C_{hk} where there is inflow, $H(x, y, t + k)$ is obtained from the boundary condition (28.20b). At points of C_{hk} where there is outflow, $H(x, y, t + k)$ is obtained from one of the modified forms of (28.22) in which certain one-sided differences of H are used. Thus there are a number of awkward special cases, and it is well known in the use of automatic computers that the resulting special formulas are apt to cause more difficulty than the whole code for the regular points.

Details of storage, computational speed, and apparent accuracy in practice are discussed by Charney and Phillips.

As with the one-dimensional model, conditions (28.20a) and (28.20b) require furnishing boundary values of the basic weather variables being forecast, right up to the instant of time for which the forecast is being prepared! So, once again, forecasting becomes impossible in principle. As with the earlier model, there are two ways out of the dilemma. First, one could presumably solve a version of (28.15) written for the full surface of the earth, with only the initial condition (28.20c). Although this is not known to have been proved, such a problem is probably correctly posed and uniquely solvable. The main objection is the practical one that we do not have weather data densely enough around the whole world to furnish adequate initial data for (28.20c). And, even if we did, such a large area might require larger and faster computers than are currently available for such work.

A second way out of the dilemma is actually used. Fictitious but plausible values of $\eta(x, y, t)$ and $\psi(x, y, t)$ are set into equations (28.20a) and (28.20b) where needed, and it is presumed that the effects of these wrong values will be propagated into R only slowly. [We know from (28.8), for example, that η moves with the speed of the air.] If the boundary C is sufficiently remote from the areas whose forecast is especially desired, and if the forecast period is not too long, experience indicates that the forecast quantities are relatively insensitive to the choice of the fictitious values on C. As with the one-dimensional model, the lack of sensitivity is probably valid only for fairly smooth patterns of η and ψ.

In treating the computational stability of the marching process (28.22), Charney and his collaborators relied on heuristic arguments suggesting plausible values of h and k, and then justified the choices by observing the numerical behavior of the numbers actually computed. The heuristic arguments were based on a common *perturbation approach*. In this one perturbs the equation (28.22) to obtain a linear system, and then treats the variable coefficients of the linear system as constants. The stability of the resulting system of linear difference equations with constant coefficients is tested by the so-called *von Neumann* technique discussed in Secs. 12.1 and 29. That is, one puts a trial solution of the form $e^{i(\alpha x + \beta y + \gamma t)}$ into the difference equations, and sees whether the trial solution will have exponential growth, as $t \to \infty$. If it does not, the h, k being tested do permit a stable solution of the difference equations. The test must be made for all values of the coefficients of the linearized system and, since for the nonlinear system (28.22) these coefficients of the perturbed system depend on the solution Ψ, H, it might be necessary, in principle, to go back and forth several times between solving the system and testing for stability.

The following is an oversimplification of the heuristic stability analysis given by Charney, Fjörtoft, and von Neumann [1950]. In the difference equation system (28.21), (28.22), it is H whose stepwise integration carries the history of the motion. Hence we will perturb H in equation (28.22), and treat Ψ and its differences like constants. (This is the oversimplification!) For brevity, we write

$$\Psi(x, y + h, t) - \Psi(x, y - h, t) = \delta_y \Psi,$$

and similarly introduce $\delta_x\Psi$, $\delta_y H$, $\delta_x H$, $\delta_t H$. In the new notation, (28.22) becomes

$$\frac{\delta_t H}{2k} = -m^2\left(\frac{\delta_x H}{2h}\frac{\delta_y \Psi}{2h} - \frac{\delta_y H}{2h}\frac{\delta_x \Psi}{2h}\right). \qquad (28.23)$$

By (28.26) below, we can write (28.23) in the form

$$\frac{\delta_t H}{2k} = m\left(U\frac{\delta_x H}{2h} + V\frac{\delta_y H}{2h}\right),$$

or

$$\delta_t H = m\lambda(U\,\delta_x H + V\,\delta_y H).$$

Now let the perturbed value of H be denoted by $H + H'$. Then the perturbation equation is

$$\delta_t H' = m\lambda(U\,\delta_x H' + V\,\delta_y H').$$

Setting in the trial solution

$$H' = e^{i(\alpha x + \beta y + \gamma t)}$$

and canceling H', one finds for constant U, V that

$$\omega - \omega^{-1} = 2ia,$$

$$a = m\lambda(U\sin\alpha h + V\sin\beta h),$$

where $\omega = e^{i\gamma k}$. If H' is not to exhibit exponential growth, we must have for both roots ω that $|\omega| \leq 1$. That is, for both roots of

$$\omega^2 - 2ai\omega - 1 = 0,$$

one must have $|\omega| \leq 1$. Necessary and sufficient for $|\omega| \leq 1$ is that $|a| \leq 1$. But, for certain values of α, β (depending on h), we will have $\sin \alpha h \doteq \sin \beta h \doteq 1$. Hence, for stability, it seems necessary and sufficient that

$$m\lambda(|U| + |V|) \leq 1. \qquad (28.24)$$

But $|U| + |V|$ is bounded by $\sqrt{2}\max|\mathbf{v}|$, except for the effect of differencing. Hence we expect that the following condition (28.25) is sufficient for stability:

$$\lambda = \frac{k}{h} < \frac{1}{\sqrt{2}m\max|\mathbf{v}|} = \frac{1}{\sqrt{2}m^2\max|\nabla\psi|}, \qquad (28.25)$$

where the maximum is taken over the whole region under consideration. (The scale factor m is present merely to adjust h and $\mathbf{v}$ to the same length units.) For a more careful, yet still heuristic, derivation of the sufficiency of (28.25), see Charney, Fjörtoft, and von Neumann [1950], p. 244.

In the difference equation (28.22), the value $H(x, y, t + k)$ depends on the values of $H(x, y)$ at times t or $t - k$ at the four points $(x \pm h, y \pm h)$. These four points are the vertices of a square S in the (x, y)-plane. Condition (28.25) states that for stability it is sufficient that the time interval k be so short that no air which is outside S at time t can reach (x, y) by time $t + k$. The restriction (28.25) is comparatively severe, and, for the 300-km space separations used by Charney and Phillips [1953, p. 79], required use of time intervals k no longer than 70 minutes. Thus a 24-hour forecast needed about 24 separate time steps, each involving the solution of a boundary-value problem for the Poisson equation. It would be very desirable to find some way of permitting a longer time interval K. Condition (28.25) is analogous to conditions (7.7) and (26.12) derived earlier.

28.5. "Upwind" Difference Equations

In the meteorological literature it is assumed that solutions of such difference systems as (28.21), (28.22) will approximately represent the solution of the corresponding differential equation problem, provided only that the computation proves to be numerically stable. The authors know of no counterexample to this assumption, and yet it is not satisfying to a mathematician. The relation between stability and convergence of the finite-difference solution to the continuous solution will be analyzed for certain linear systems in Sec. 29, under suitable restrictions. But no such theory has apparently been available for nonlinear systems with three independent variables x, y, t.

Recently, however, mathematicians at New York University have investigated the stability and convergence of meteorological equations closely resembling those considered in the two-dimensional model treated above. The brief summary given here is based on a 1957 lecture by Professor Eugene Isaacson. In the first place, Sensenig [1959] proved the existence and uniqueness of a smooth solution to a system closely resembling (28.15), (28.20), for the special case where R is a half-plane. So let us assume now that a sufficiently differentiable and unique solution of (28.15), (28.20) exists for the rectangular region R considered above. Then the method of the New York University group provides a small but significant modification of the difference equations (28.22), and proves the convergence of the solution of the modified difference equations to the solution of the continuous problem (28.15), (28.20). Moreover, the modification of the difference equations removes the necessity of having various special forms of (28.22) near the boundary of R. Finally, the modified difference equations seem to permit a closer difference analog of the boundary condition (28.20b).

The essential idea here is the analog of that described in Sec. 7.1, viz., the use of one-sided differences to approximate space derivatives of the vorticity. Equation (28.21) is unaltered, and is used as by Charney and Phillips [1953] to solve for $\Psi(x, y, t)$ for all values of x, y in the net, given the boundary values of Ψ and the interior values of H(x, y, t).

Now let the wind components be estimated by the following difference expressions:

$$
\begin{aligned}
U = U(x, y, t) &= -m(2h)^{-1}[\Psi(x, y + h, t) - \Psi(x, y - h, t)], \\
V = V(x, y, t) &= m(2h)^{-1}[\Psi(x + h, y, t) - \Psi(x - h, y, t)].
\end{aligned}
\tag{28.26}
$$

Then in place of (28.22), one writes difference equations with one-sided differences. These differ according to the sign of U and V. When $U \geq 0$, $V \geq 0$ one has

$$
\begin{aligned}
k^{-1}[\mathrm{H}(x, y, t + k) &- \mathrm{H}(x, y, t)] \\
&= -m\, U(x, y, t)h^{-1}[\mathrm{H}(x, y, t) - \mathrm{H}(x - h, y, t)] \\
&\quad -m\, V(x, y, t)h^{-1}[\mathrm{H}(x, y, t) - \mathrm{H}(x, y - h, t)].
\end{aligned}
\tag{28.27}
$$

If $U(x, y, t) < 0$, one replaces the backward difference $h^{-1}[\mathrm{H}(x, y, t) - \mathrm{H}(x - h, y, t)]$ in (28.27) by the forward difference $h^{-1}[\mathrm{H}(x + h, y, t) - \mathrm{H}(x, y, t)]$. Similarly, if $V(x, y, t) < 0$, one uses a forward difference in the y direction. Thus equation (28.27) can assume four different forms, depending on the signs of U and V. We say, for short, that in (28.27) one always employs "upwind differences."

In using (28.22), it is necessary to have a value of H(x, y, t) at each point P of C_{hk} where there is outflow, in order to furnish values of the central differences of H for the interior neighbor of P. In using (28.27), it is ordinarily unnecessary to have a value of H(x, y, t) at such points P of outflow, for P will be downwind of its neighbor. Hence, ordinarily one need never compute H(x, y, t) for any point of outflow on C_{hk}, and thus (28.27) will ordinarily be applied only at interior points of R. It is in this sense that equation (28.27) seems to match the boundary condition (28.20b) much better than the difference equation (28.22) and its sundry modifications at outflow points of C_{hk}. [We use the word "ordinarily" because it might happen that the sign of U or V could change between a point of C_{hk} and its neighbor in the interior. In this rare event, some unimportant artificial convention could be used to introduce a value for H(x, y, t) on C_{hk}.]

A theoretical advantage of the upward difference method is that by its use one can rigorously prove stability and also the convergence of Ψ to ψ and H to η, as h, $k \to 0$, provided that one maintains the relation

$$
\lambda = \frac{k}{h} \leq \{\max\,[|m\, U(x, y, t)| + |m\, V(x, y, t)|]\}^{-1},
\tag{28.28}
$$

where the maximum is taken over all points x, y, t of R_{hk}. Note that (28.28) implies (28.24) also.

The germ of the proof is that (28.27) can be rewritten in the form

$$H(x, y, t + k) = \lambda m\, U(x, y, t)\, H(x - h, y, t)$$
$$+ [1 - \lambda m\, U(x, y, t) - \lambda m\, V(x, y, t)]\, H(x, y, t)$$
$$+ \lambda m\, V(x, y, t)\, H(x, y - h, t), \qquad (28.29)$$

if $U(x, y, t) \geq 0$, $V(x, y, t) \geq 0$. If $U < 0$ or $V < 0$, (28.29) takes corresponding other forms. But, in any case, $H(x, y, t + k)$ is a weighted average of the values $H(x - h, y, t)$, $H(x, y - h, t)$, $H(x, y, t)$, with nonnegative weights. That is, (28.27) is what we have called a difference approximation of positive type; see Sec. 14.1.

The stability and convergence of the upwind method then can be proved like Theorems 14.1 and 14.2 for parabolic equations. Although this is a very important result, it will be omitted here. Certain important lemmas necessary for the present quasilinear problem have been supplied by Montvila [1958].

Apparently, the upwind difference method of this section has not been tested in actual machine computation. It would be interesting to learn whether the increased elegance and mathematical rigor afforded by upwind differences are matched by corresponding decreases in the discretization error and in the complexity of the machine codes.

28.6. Three Space Dimensions

Some further developments in numerical weather prediction have been in the direction of introducing a third space dimension. As pointed out in Sec. 3, a true network in three space dimensions and time would overtax the capacities of current automatic computers. For this reason, Charney and his collaborators have confined their work to a small number n of separate layers at different altitudes. Such models are called $[2 + (n - 1)/n]$-dimensional! Without going into detail, it may be noted that the equations are similar to the system (28.15), and have been treated by difference equations analogous to (28.21), (28.22). One new element occurs in these models, however: the difference equation corresponding to (28.21) can become hyperbolic in certain subregions of R. This introduces the possibility of inconsistent difference-equation systems with zero determinant! There exists a mathematical literature on partial differential equations that are elliptic in some regions and hyperbolic in others. Very recently the possibilities of solving such equations by means of finite differences has begun to be explored, but an exposition of this work here would be premature.

SECTION 29. A GENERAL DISCUSSION OF
THE FOURIER METHOD FOR DIFFERENCE AND
DIFFERENTIAL EQUATIONS

29.1. The Problem

Most of the arguments based on Fourier analysis which we have met in this book can be extended to a very wide class of difference and differential equations with constant coefficients. The presentation given here follows to a large extent a paper by Lax and Richtmyer [1956], but we shall continue to look for statements based on the norm $\|f\| = \max_x |f(x)|$ rather than on the mean square norm.

We consider a set of p linear partial differential equations for p functions $u_1, \cdots, u_p$, depending on the $d + 1$ variables $x_1, \cdots, x_d, t$. The differential equations are of the first order with respect to t. They are homogeneous and have constant coefficients. To avoid very long formulas, we shall consistently use vector and matrix notation. Thus, u will denote the p-dimensional vector with components $u_1, \cdots, u_p$, while x will be the d-dimensional vector with components $x_1, \cdots, x_d$. Furthermore, let z be the d-dimensional vector $z_1, \cdots, z_d$, and consider a p-by-p matrix $A(z)$ whose elements are polynomials in the components of z. If D designates the symbolic vector with components $\partial/\partial x_1, \cdots, \partial/\partial x_n$, it is clear that $A(D)$ is a convenient condensed way of writing a system of p^2 linear differential operators with constant coefficients. We shall deal with systems of differential equations of the form

$$u_t = A(D)u, \qquad (29.1)$$

where the subscript t designates, as usual, differentiation with respect to t. Differential equations involving higher derivatives with respect to t can be reduced to a system of the form (29.1) by introducing the intermediate derivatives as new unknown functions. Observe that we do not specify at this point whether the system is hyperbolic, parabolic, or elliptic.

If we wish to solve such differential systems by means of Fourier series, the domain R in the x space in which the initial data are prescribed must be rectangular. No essential generality is lost if we assume R to be the domain

$$R: \quad -\pi < x_j < \pi, \qquad j = 1, \cdots, d. \qquad (29.2)$$

Let there be prescribed the initial condition

$$u(x, 0) = f(x) \qquad \text{in } R, \qquad (29.3)$$

where $f(x)$ is a p-dimensional vector function. We shall limit the investigation to functions $f(x)$ that are smooth enough to possess a convergent multiple Fourier series in R. The more general theory of Lax and Richtmyer [1956] requires less of $f(x)$, but it does not aim at statements on uniform convergence. The algebraic complexities are greatly reduced when this Fourier series is written in complex form. To this end let m be a d-dimensional vector whose components $m_1, \cdots, m_d$ are integers; then we can write

$$f(x) = \sum_m e^{im \cdot x} c_m. \tag{29.4}$$

This formula is to be interpreted as follows: c_m is a p-dimensional vector depending on the d integers $m_1, \cdots, m_d$; the symbol $m \cdot x$ denotes the scalar product $m_1 x_1 + \cdots + m_d x_d$, and the summation is to be extended over all vectors m with integral components—positive, negative or zero.

As lateral boundary conditions, i.e., as conditions on u at the boundary of R for $t > 0$, we have so far usually required that u be zero there. In the present, more general context, this is not always a condition that can be satisfied by manipulating with Fourier series in a straightforward manner. We impose, instead, the requirement that *the solution* $u(x, t)$ *be periodic with period 2π in every space variable $x_j, j = 1, \cdots, d$*. If $f(x)$ is continued into the whole x-space as a periodic function, we can then interpret our problem as a pure initial-value problem with a periodic initial function given in the whole x-space.

For the special differential equations previously studied by means of Fourier analysis, this new initial-value problem contains the old one with lateral boundary values zero. For let us assume that the problem is to find a solution of (29.1) with a prescribed initial function in the domain R^* defined by the inequalities $0 \leq x_j \leq \pi$, and such that u vanishes on the boundary of R^*. Then we may extend the definition of $f(x)$ into all of R by requiring that it be an *odd* function of each x_j. Now we continue $f(x)$ into the whole space as a function of period 2π in each x_j. The solution $u(x, t)$ of this problem without lateral boundary conditions will, in general, not share the oddness property of the initial function. In the special case, however, that the matrix $A(z)$ is an *even* function of each z_j, it does follow that $u(z, t)$ is an odd function, at least if the solution of the initial-value problem is unique.

To see this, let x^* denote the vector obtained from x by replacing one particular x_j by its negative. If we set $u^*(x, t) = u(x^*, t)$, the function $u^*(x, t)$ satisfies the system

$$u_t^* = A(D^*)u^*,$$

where D^* is the symbolic vector obtained from D by replacing $\partial/\partial x_j$

with $-\partial/\partial x_j$. Under the assumption made, $A(D) = A(D^*)$, whence $u^*(x, t)$ satisfies the original differential equation (29.1). The initial value of $u^*(x, t)$ is $f(x^*)$, which equals $-f(x)$. Therefore we must have $u^*(x, t) = -u(x, t)$. Now, if $u(x, t)$ is a continuous function of x, the fact that it is odd and of period 2π in each x_j implies that it vanishes whenever one x_j assumes the values 0 or π. The condition that $A(z)$ be even is satisfied in the simple problems of the heat equation and the equation of wave propagation that served as the main illustrative examples in previous sections.

Most difference equations proposed for the approximation of the differential equation can be written in the form

$$\mathcal{L}(U) \equiv \sum_{\nu=0,1} \sum_{\alpha_1,\cdots,\alpha_d} P^{(\nu)}_{\alpha_1,\cdots,\alpha_d} U(x_1 + \alpha_1 h_1, \cdots, x_d + \alpha_d h_d, t + \nu k) = 0.$$

$$(29.5)$$

We proceed to explain the notation in this formula: $k, h_1, \cdots, h_d$ are small positive quantities, the mesh lengths in the t direction and in the coordinate directions of the x space respectively. The numbers $\alpha_1, \cdots, \alpha_d$ are integers—positive, negative, or zero—and the summation is extended over some unspecified but finite range of these numbers. $U(x, t)$ is a p-dimensional vector function, and each $P^{(\nu)}_{\alpha_1,\cdots,\alpha_d}$ is a p-by-p matrix with elements depending on $k, h_1, \cdots, h_d$, but not on x and t.

The equation $\mathcal{L}(U) = 0$ must be such that it defines the values of U at the grid points for the time $t + k$ uniquely, whenever the values of U at the level t are given. Equation (29.5) contains all two-level schemes, explicit and implicit, and even certain three-level schemes, such as the DuFort-Frankel method (Sec. 15), which can be brought into the form (29.5) by a change of variables (see Lax and Richtmyer [1956], Sec. 19).

To simplify the notation, we introduce the assumption that the h_j are given functions of k, tending to zero with k:

$$\lim_{k \to 0} h_j(k) = 0, \qquad j = 1, \cdots, d.$$

Also it is convenient, though not necessary, to restrict h_j to values that are submultiples of π. Finally, only combinations of values of t and k for which t/k is an integer will be considered.

The difference equation (29.5) can be regarded as constituting a system of linear equations for the values of U at $t + k$ in terms of those at t. The number of these equations is $(2\pi/h_1) \cdot (2\pi/h_2) \cdots (2\pi/h_d)$.

29.2. Explicit Solution by Infinite Fourier Series

Both the differential and the difference problems can be solved in the standard manner by Fourier series. To do this for the differential equation, we begin with the observation that

$$\frac{\partial}{\partial x_j} e^{ix\cdot m} = im_j e^{ix\cdot m},$$

and therefore, if a is a p-dimensional vector independent of x,

$$A(D)e^{ix\cdot m}a = A(im)e^{ix\cdot m}a.$$

Hence, if $a = a(t)$ is a vector function of t, the function $e^{ix\cdot m}\, a(t)$ solves (29.1) if $a(t)$ is a solution of the equation

$$\frac{da}{dt} = A(im)a. \qquad (29.6)$$

This is a system of p linear scalar differential equations for the components of the vector a. In the theory of differential equations, it is proved that the general solution of (29.6) can be written in exactly the same form as for a single scalar differential equation of this type, namely,

$$a(t) = e^{tA(im)}c,$$

where c is an arbitrary constant vector and $e^{tA(m)}$ is the matrix defined by the universally convergent series

$$e^{tA(im)} = 1 + \frac{tA(im)}{1!} + \frac{[tA(im)]^2}{2!} + \cdots.$$

Hence $e^{im\cdot x}e^{tA(im)}c$ is a solution of (29.1), for any c.

Let c_m now have the same meaning as in (29.4). It follows from the superposition principle that

$$u(x, t) = \sum_m e^{im\cdot x}e^{tA(im)}c_m \qquad (29.7)$$

is, at least formally, a solution of our differential problem. Note that c_m must be placed *after* $e^{tA(im)}$, since the latter expression is a matrix.

We now must impose conditions on $f(x)$ and $A(D)$ which make (29.7) a genuine solution, i.e., conditions guaranteeing that the series converges, that its derivatives satisfy the differential equation, and that $\lim_{t\to 0+} u(x, t) = f(x)$. To formulate such conditions, we introduce the following norms for vectors $b = (b_1, \cdots, b_p)$ and matrices $B = [b_{jk}]$:

$$\|b\|_\infty = \max_{1\le j\le p} |b_j|, \qquad \|B\|_\infty = \max_{1\le j\le p} \sum_k |b_{jk}|. \qquad (29.8)$$

It is easy to show that the quantities so defined are norms in the accepted sense of the definition. Moreover,

$$\|Bb\|_\infty \le \|B\|_\infty \|b\|_\infty, \qquad (29.9)$$

and $\|B\|_\infty$ is the smallest number such that (29.9) is true for all vectors b (see Faddeeva [1950], Chap. 1, Sec. 5).

The norm $\|b\|_\infty$ can be shown to be the limiting value (as $\gamma \to \infty$) of the γth power norm

$$\|b\|_\gamma = \left(\sum_{j=1}^{p} |b_j|^\gamma \right)^{1/\gamma} ;$$

i.e., $\lim_{\gamma \to \infty} \|b\|_\gamma = \|b\|_\infty$. This justifies our use of the subscript on $\|b\|_\infty$. The subscript on $\|B\|_\infty$ is used to indicate the association of the matrix norm $\|B\|_\infty$ with the vector norm $\|b\|_\infty$.

The series in (29.7) is certainly convergent if the initial function is such that

$$\sum_m \|c_m\|_\infty < \infty, \tag{29.10}$$

and if the matrix $A(D)$ satisfies the condition

$$\|e^{tA(im)}\|_\infty \le p(t) < \infty \tag{29.11}$$

uniformly in m. In fact,

$$\|e^{im \cdot x} e^{tA(im)} c_m\|_\infty \le p(t) \|c_m\|_\infty,$$

so that (29.10) and (29.11) imply the uniform and absolute convergence of (29.7). The condition (29.10) could have been replaced by some milder conditions, but only at the price of considerable complication. The inequality (29.11), however, is necessary if the problem is to be well posed in the sense of Sec. 1. For, otherwise, there exist solutions of the forms $e^{ix \cdot m} e^{tA(im)} c_m$ whose norm is arbitrarily large while their initial value c_m is arbitrarily small. Thus the solution does not depend continuously on the initial values in such cases.

The termwise spatial derivatives of the series do not necessarily converge everywhere. The stronger smoothness requirements for $f(x)$, if $u(x, t)$ is to be a genuine solution of the differential equation, vary with the problem. We shall not go into a discussion of this point here.

The solution of the difference-equation problem with the same initial function $f(x)$ can also be found by separation of variables: A function of the special form $e^{ix \cdot m} a^*(t)$ is now a solution of (29.5), if $a^*(t)$ solves the difference equation

$$\sum_{\nu=0,1} \sum_{\alpha_1 \cdots \alpha} e^{i(m_1 \alpha_1 h_1 + \cdots + m_d \alpha_d h_d)} P^{(\nu)}_{\alpha_1 \cdots \alpha_d} a^*(t + \nu k) = 0. \tag{29.12}$$

This equation must possess a solution, because otherwise the difference equation (29.5) would not always be solvable, contrary to our assumption. Since (29.12) is of the form $H^{(1)}_m a^*(t + k) + H^{(0)}_m a^*(t) = 0$, where $H^{(0)}_m$

and $H_m^{(1)}$ are p-by-p matrices, the general solution of (29.12) for all t values that are multiples of k is

$$a^*(t) = E_m^{t/k}c, \qquad \text{for } t/k \text{ an integer.}$$

Here E_m is the matrix $[-H_m^{(1)}]^{-1} H_m^{(0)}$ and c is an arbitrary constant vector. In most problems it is easy to calculate the matrix E_m explicitly. We shall soon see that its properties are decisive for the study of the approximating qualities of the difference equation.

The formal series solution of the difference problem is now

$$U(x, t) = \sum_m e^{im \cdot x} E_m^{t/k} c_m, \tag{29.13}$$

in close formal analogy to (29.7). To ensure convergence of the series (29.13), we impose—in addition to the requirement (29.10) on the Fourier coefficients of the initial function $f(x)$—the analog of condition (29.11), i.e.,

$$\|E_m^{t/k}\|_\infty \leq q_k(t) < \infty, \tag{29.14}$$

where the right-hand side is independent of m, but not necessarily of k.

29.3. Convergence of $U(x, t)$ to $u(x, t)$

So far the two problems under consideration have been totally unrelated. We now ask for additional conditions which guarantee that $U(x, t)$ tends to $u(x, t)$, as $k \to 0$. It is natural to require that the difference equation be a formal approximation to the differential equation, i.e., that

$$\lim_{k \to 0} \mathscr{L}(\phi) = \phi_t - A(D)\phi, \qquad \text{uniformly for } x \in R, \qquad 0 \leq t \leq T,$$
$$\tag{29.15}$$

for any vector function $\phi(x, t)$ for which the partial derivatives occurring in the right member are continuous. Here, and below, convergence of a vector or a matrix means convergence of all its components or elements.

Condition (29.15) is equivalent to a set of limit relations for the matrices occurring in the difference equation (29.12). Of these we note especially the formula

$$\lim_{k \to 0} k \sum_{\alpha_1 \cdots \alpha_d} e^{i(m_1\alpha_1 h_1 + \cdots + m_d\alpha_d h_d)} P_{\alpha_1 \cdots \alpha_d}^{(1)} = I. \tag{29.16}$$

It can be obtained by applying (29.15) with $\phi(x, t) = te^{im \cdot x}c$, and then setting $t = 0$.

We shall now show that condition (29.15) alone is sufficient to make each term in series (29.13) tend to the corresponding term in (29.7). Since $e^{im \cdot x} e^{tA(im)}c$ is, for every constant vector c, a solution of the differential equation (29.6), we have

$$\mathscr{L}(e^{im \cdot x} e^{tA(im)}c) = w_m(x, t, c, k),$$

where

$$\lim_{k \to 0} w_m(x, t, c, k) = 0, \qquad \text{uniformly in } x \text{ and } t. \qquad (29.17)$$

Subtracting this from the equation

$$\mathscr{L}(e^{im \cdot x} E_m^{t/k} c) = 0,$$

we see that

$$\mathscr{L}[e^{im \cdot x}(E_m^{t/k} - e^{tA(im)})c] = -w_m(x, t, c, k).$$

For $x = 0$, the left member of the last equation is of the same form as the left member of (29.12), with $a^*(t)$ replaced by $(E_m^{t/k} - e^{tA(im)})c$. Setting $t = 0$ also, we obtain the equation

$$\sum_{\alpha_1 \cdots \alpha_d} e^{i(m_1 \alpha_1 h_1 + \cdots + m_d \alpha_d h_d)} P_{\alpha_1 \cdots \alpha_d}^{(1)} (E_m - e^{kA(im)})c = -w_m(0, 0, c, k).$$

Hence, by virtue of (29.16) and (29.17),

$$\lim_{k \to 0} k^{-1}(E_m - e^{kA(im)})c = 0.$$

Since this must be true for every vector c, we conclude that

$$\lim_{k \to 0} k^{-1}(E_m - e^{kA(im)}) = 0. \qquad (29.18)$$

We next show that (29.18) implies the formula

$$\lim_{k \to 0} (E_m^{t/k} - e^{tA(im)}) = 0, \qquad \text{for } t/k \text{ an integer.} \qquad (29.19)$$

To this end we first observe that for fixed m the matrix $e^{tA(im)}$ is obviously uniformly bounded in $0 \le t \le T$. If $n = t/k$, it follows from (29.19) that E_m^n is also bounded, uniformly in n, for $0 \le nk \le T$. Let K_m be a common bound for these two matrices. Now we apply the easily verifiable matrix identity

$$G^n - H^n = \sum_{j=0}^{n-1} G^j (G - H) H^{n-1-j},$$

valid for any G and H, to the particular matrices $G = E_m$, $H = e^{kA(im)}$, and obtain

$$\|E_m^n - e^{nkA(im)}\|_\infty \le \|E_m - e^{kA(im)}\|_\infty n K_m,$$

which shows that (29.18) implies (29.19).

This completes the proof that the Fourier series for the solution U of the difference equation tends *termwise* to the series for u, as $k \to 0$. Observe that this is true no matter how k is related to the special increments h_j, $j = 1, \cdots, d$, as long as the latter also tend to zero.

It is important to realize that the foregoing argument does *not* prove the convergence of U to u. If $f(x)$ happens to be a trigonometric polynomial, i.e., if its Fourier series terminates, this conclusion can be drawn, of course, but if the Fourier series involved are infinite, some additional assumption is needed. We have just seen that $E_m^{t/k}$ is a bounded function of k for fixed m, and (29.14) means that this matrix is a bounded function of m for fixed k. However, if $E_m^{t/k}$ is not uniformly bounded in both these variables, the termwise passage to the limit in the series for U is not always correct. To make this passage to the limit legitimate, it is sufficient to impose the decisive stronger condition that there be a constant q such that

$$\|E_m^{t/k}\|_\infty \leq q, \qquad 0 \leq t \leq T, \qquad (29.20)$$

for *all* m and *all* $k \leq k_0$. Now we can reason as in Sec. 4.5: The series (29.13) is uniformly convergent for all $k \leq k_0$ and $0 \leq t \leq T$. Its terms are continuous functions of k at $k = 0$. Hence termwise passage to the limit, as $k \to 0$, is permitted.

As an illustration, consider the implicit scheme (15.2) for the solution of the heat equation $u_t - u_{xx} = 0$. Here $p = d = 1$, and E_m is the scalar

$$E_m = \frac{h^2 - 4(1 - \sigma)k \sin^2 (mh/2)}{h^2 + 4\sigma k \sin^2 (mh/2)}.$$

This quantity is numerically less than or equal to 1 if and only if

$$2(1 - 2\sigma)k - h^2 \leq 0.$$

In this case, (29.20) is satisfied. Otherwise, the solution U of the difference equation may actually fail to converge to u, as in the special case $\sigma = 0$, $k/h^2 > \frac{1}{2}$, discussed in Sec. 12.

The result of this section is summarized in the following theorem.

THEOREM 29.1.   *Let $f(x)$ be a periodic function of $x_1, \cdots, x_d$ with the Fourier series (29.4), and assume that $\Sigma_m \|c_m\|_\infty < \infty$. Denote by u and U, respectively, the solutions of the differential and difference equations (29.1) and (29.5). Let the difference equation be a formal approximation to the differential equation in the sense of equation (29.15), and suppose that the differential problem is well posed. If the increments k and h_j, $j = 1, \cdots, d$, tend to zero in such a way that the matrix $E_m^{t/k}$ defined in this section is uniformly bounded in m, for $0 \leq t \leq T$, then U tends to u in this passage to the limit.*

29.4. Stability

To study the stability of the difference scheme, in the sense of Sec. 5, nothing more restrictive than boundedness should be required of the initial function $f(x)$. The finite trigonometric series used for a similar purpose in Sec. 5 are now more suitable than the infinite Fourier series for the study of the solution U. Accordingly, we restrict the domain of x to the grid points, and replace (29.4) by the finite representation

$$f(x) = \sum_m e^{im \cdot x} c_m{}^*. \tag{29.21}$$

Here the components of the vector m satisfy the inequalities $|m_j| \leq \pi/h_j$, and

$$c_m{}^* = \frac{h_1 \cdots h_d}{(2\pi)^d} \sum_x e^{-im \cdot x} f(x), \tag{29.22}$$

the summation to be extended over all grid points in R.

The solution of our difference problem at the grid points can be found by separation of variables, as in the case of infinite Fourier series, and one finds the representation by the finite sum

$$U = \sum_m e^{im \cdot x} E_m^{t/k} c_m{}^*, \qquad \text{for } t/k \text{ an integer.} \tag{29.23}$$

To save notation, we have again used the letter U, although the quantity so designated may fail to coincide with our previous function U at points off the grid. Inserting (29.22) into (29.23), one obtains the representation

$$U(x, t) = \sum_\xi G(x, t, \xi) f(\xi), \tag{29.24}$$

with

$$G(x, t, \xi) = \frac{h_1 \cdots h_d}{(2\pi)^d} \sum_m e^{im(x - \xi)} E_m^{t/k}. \tag{29.25}$$

Here ξ runs over all grid points of R, and (x, t) is restricted to the grid points of the (x, t)-space for which x is in R and $t > 0$.

If the fundamental inequality (29.20) is satisfied, (29.25) implies that

$$\|G(x, t, \xi)\|_\infty \leq q,$$

because the number of terms in the summation of (29.25) is $(2\pi)^d/(h_1 \cdots h_d)$. Inserted into (29.24), this yields

$$\|U(x, t)\|_\infty \leq \frac{(2\pi)^d}{h_1 \cdots h_d} \max_\xi \|f(\xi)\|_\infty q. \tag{29.26}$$

Inequality (29.26) *implies the stability of the difference procedure* according to the definition adopted in Sec. 5, at least if the h_j do not shrink faster than some power of k, for it means that the cumulative departure due to round-off errors not exceeding ϵ at any one grid point is, at worst, of the order $O(\epsilon h_1^{-1} \cdots h_d^{-1})$.

The preceding appraisal of the departure is certainly very pessimistic, and probably even wasteful, as an absolute upper bound. It is, however, likely that the order of magnitude of the round-off departure actually does increase with the number of dimensions.

29.5. How to Test for Stability and Convergence

The condition (29.20), which guarantees convergence and stability, is easy to check if $p = 1$, i.e., if E_m is a scalar, for then it simply means that $|E_m|$ must satisfy the inequality

$$|E_m| \leq 1 + O(k).$$

For $p > 1$, the relation

$$\| E_m^{t/k} \|_\infty \leq \| E_m \|_\infty^{t/k}$$

shows that

$$\| E_m \|_\infty \leq 1 + O(k) \tag{29.27}$$

is a *sufficient* condition for the validity of (29.20). However, there are problems of practical importance where (29.20) is true, whereas (29.27) is not (see, e.g., Lax and Richtmyer [1956], Sec. 17). The following observations are then sometimes useful.

There is a matrix norm, different from $\| B \|_\infty$, that is important in matrix algebra, the so-called *spectral norm*, which we shall denote by $\| B \|_2$, It can be defined as the square root of the largest eigenvalue of the matrix B^*B, where B^* is obtained from B by taking the transpose of B and then replacing every element by its complex conjugate. (If B is nonsingular, it can be shown that all eigenvalues of B^*B are real and positive; see Householder [1953].) This is the proper norm to employ if the magnitude of a vector v with components $v_1, \cdots, v_p$ is measured by its Euclidean (2nd power) length $\| v \|_2 = (|v_1|^2 + \cdots + |v_p|^2)^{1/2}$, for one has always

$$\| Bv \|_2 \leq \| B \|_2 \| v \|_2,$$

and there exist vectors for which the equality sign holds. (For a proof of this and other properties of the spectral norm, we refer to Householder's book and to Faddeeva [1950].)

The two norms $\| B \|_\infty$ and $\| B \|_2$ are related by the inequalities

$$\frac{1}{\sqrt{p}} \| B \|_2 \leq \| B \|_\infty \leq \sqrt{p} \, \| B \|_2, \tag{29.28}$$

which we shall now prove. Let b_{jk} be the elements of B. Then the inequality $\| Bv \|_2 \leq \| B \|_2 \| v \|_2$ says that

$$\sum_{j=1}^{p} \left| \sum_{k=1}^{p} b_{jk} v_k \right|^2 \leq \| B \|_2^2 \sum_{k=1}^{p} |v_k|^2; \tag{29.29}$$

hence

$$\left| \sum_{k=1}^{p} b_{jk} v_k \right|^2 \leq \| B \|_2^2 \sum_{k=1}^{p} |v_k|^2$$

for all j. With the particular vector

$$v_k = \begin{cases} |b_{jk}|/b_{jk}, & \text{for } b_{jk} \neq 0, \\ 0, & \text{for } b_{jk} = 0, \end{cases}$$

the last inequality becomes

$$\left(\sum_{k=1}^{p} |b_{jk}| \right)^2 \leq p\|B\|_2^2, \qquad j = 1, 2, \cdots, p.$$

Since the maximum of the left member with respect to j is precisely $\|B\|_\infty^2$, the second inequality of (29.28) is proved. To prove the first inequality, substitute into (29.29) some vector v for which the equality sign holds. Then the equality sign will hold as well with any multiple of v. Therefore it can be assumed, without loss of generality, that $\Sigma_{j=1}^{p}|v_j|^2 = 1$. Since this implies that $|v_j| \leq 1, j = 1, \cdots, p$, we conclude from (29.29) that

$$\|B\|_2^2 \leq \sum_{j=1}^{p} \left(\sum_{k} |b_{jk}| \right)^2 \leq p \max_{i} \left(\sum_{k} |b_{ik}| \right)^2 = p\,\|B\|_\infty^2,$$

which was to be proved.

In view of (29.28), the boundedness of $\|(E_m^{t/k})\|_2$ and the boundedness of $\|E_m^{t/k}\|_\infty$ are equivalent conditions. Since $\|E_m^{t/k}\|_2 \leq \|E_m\|_2^{t/k}$, stability and convergence are assured, if

$$\|E_m\|_2 \leq 1 + O(k). \qquad (29.30)$$

Sometimes (29.30) is true, whereas (29.27) is not, and vice versa.

Further criteria for stability and convergence can be found in Lax and Richtmyer [1956]. There it is shown that it is often sufficient to calculate— or appraise—the modulus of the numerically largest eigenvalue of E_m, the so-called *spectral radius* $S(E_m)$ of E_m. It is easy to see that the condition

$$S(E_m) \leq 1 + O(k) \qquad (29.31)$$

is necessary for the validity of (29.20). In fact, since the eigenvalues of $E_m^{t/k}$ are the (t/k)th powers of those of E_m, there exists a vector v_1, an eigenvector of $E_m^{t/k}$, such that

$$\|E_m^{t/k}v_1\|_\infty = S(E_m)^{t/k}\|v_1\|_\infty.$$

On the other hand,

$$\|E_m^{t/k}v\|_\infty \leq \|E_m^{t/k}\|_\infty \|v\|_\infty$$

for *any* vector. Hence,

$$S(E_m)^{t/k} \leq \|E_m^{t/k}\|_\infty.$$

If the left member is bounded, (29.31) must be true. In Lax and Richtmyer [1956] it is shown that, for a wide class of matrices E_m, the relation (29.31) is not only necessary but also sufficient for the validity of (29.20).

SECTION 30. THE METHOD OF PEACEMAN
AND RACHFORD

30.1. General Formulation

The procedure described in Sec. 22.4 for the iterative solution of elliptic problems is applicable to parabolic problems as well. We will discuss it here from this viewpoint.

Let us assume that we are dealing with a differential equation of the form (29.1), with periodic initial conditions, as in Sec. 29. The stepwise solution of the corresponding difference equation $\mathscr{L}(U) = 0$ consists in the successive solution of systems of linear algebraic equations giving the values of U at $t + k$ in terms of its values at t. Since $\mathscr{L}$ does not depend on t, the left members of this system of equations are the same at every step. Therefore, if we denote by C the operator that changes $U(x, t)$ into $U(x, t + k)$, we can symbolically write $U(x, nk) = C^n f(x)$.

The basic idea of Peaceman and Rachford [1955] can now be described as follows. Instead of *one* difference operator $\mathscr{L}$, consider two, $\mathscr{L}_1$ and $\mathscr{L}_2$. Let C_1 and C_2 denote the corresponding solution operators that change $U(x, t)$ into the respective values of $U(x, t + k)$. Then it is plausible that, under certain conditions, an approximation to the true solution $u(x, t)$ may be obtained if we operate alternately with C_1 and C_2. In other words, we approximate $u(x, nk)$ at the grid points by

$$V(x, nk) = \begin{cases} (C_2 C_1)^{n/2} f(x), & \text{for even } n, \\ C_1 (C_2 C_1)^{(n-1)/2} f(x), & \text{for odd } n. \end{cases}$$

The reason for such a modification is that it is sometimes stable and convergent even though neither of the schemes based on $\mathscr{L}_1$ and $\mathscr{L}_2$ alone is stable.

The methods of Sec. 29 can easily be adapted to yield convergence and stability criteria for this new method. Let E_{1m} and E_{2m} be defined with respect to $\mathscr{L}_1$ and $\mathscr{L}_2$, as E_m was with respect to $\mathscr{L}$, and set

$$F_m(n) = \begin{cases} (E_{2m} E_{1m})^{n/2}, & \text{even } n, \\ E_{1m}(E_{2m} E_{1m})^{(n-1)/2}, & \text{odd } n. \end{cases}$$

Then the values of $V(x, nk)$ at the grid points are given by the infinite Fourier series

$$V(x, nk) = \sum_m e^{im \cdot x} F_m(n) c_m$$

analogous to (29.13), and also by the finite series

$$V(x, nk) = \sum_m e^{im \cdot x} F_m(n) c_m^*$$

corresponding to (29.23). In the second formula the components m_j of the vector m range over the integers $|m_j| \leq \pi/h_j$ only.

Just as in Sec. 29 it can be proved that, whenever

$$\|(E_{2m}E_{1m})^n\|_\infty \leq \text{const.}, \tag{30.1}$$

uniformly for all m and k and for $0 \leq n \leq T/2k$, the present scheme is stable and V tends to u, as $k \to 0$, at least at all even levels $t = 2nk$. In this statement we have, of course, assumed that the increments h_j are given functions of k tending to zero with k. A sufficient condition for (30.1) to be true is

$$\|E_{2m}E_{1m}\|_\infty \leq 1 + O(k). \tag{30.2}$$

As we shall see, there are cases where (30.1) is true even though neither E_{2m} nor E_{1m} satisfies such a condition.

30.2. Application to the Equation of Heat Flow in Two Dimensions

For the solution of the scalar differential equation

$$u_t = u_{xx} + u_{yy},$$

Peaceman and Rachford have proposed the following operators $\mathscr{L}_1$ and $\mathscr{L}_2$:

$$\mathscr{L}_1 V(x, y, t) = D_t V(x, y, t) - \delta_x^2 V(x, y, t + k) - \delta_y^2 V(x, y, t),$$

$$\tag{30.3}$$

$$\mathscr{L}_2 V(x, y, t) = D_t V(x, y, t) - \delta_x^2 V(x, y, t) - \delta_y^2 V(x, y, t + k).$$

Here we have used, for abbreviation, the symbols D_z and δ_z for the operators defined by

$$D_z\phi(z) = k^{-1}[\phi(z + k) - \phi(z)], \quad \delta_z\phi(z) = h^{-1}[\phi(z + h/2) - \phi(z - h/2)].$$

If V is already known at the level t, the equation $\mathscr{L}_1(V) = 0$ can be solved by simultaneously determining the values of V at the gridpoints on a grid line $y = \text{const.}$ at the level $t + k$. If the region R is the square $|x| < \pi$, $|y| < \pi$, one has to solve $\pi/h - 1$ linear systems of order $\pi/h - 1$ to find all values of $V(x, y, t + k)$. Each system has the same very simple tridiagonal matrix. In the solution of $\mathscr{L}_2(V) = 0$, the roles of x and y are interchanged.

For the present differential equation it is, of course, possible to formulate an implicit difference scheme analogous to (13.4) or (15.2). Such a scheme would have the same satisfactory stability and convergence properties as in one space dimension. However, its numerical application makes it necessary to solve at every step a system of $(\pi/h - 1)^2$ simultaneous linear equations, and the matrix of this system is not tridiagonal.

Therefore the method of Peaceman and Rachford, if it is stable and convergent, has great numerical advantages.

The scalars E_{1m} and E_{2m} can readily be calculated. According to the definition given in Sec. 29, the number E_{jm} is the solution of the equation

$$\mathscr{L}_j(e^{i(m_1 x + m_2 y)} E_{jm}^{t/k}) = 0, \qquad j = 1, 2.$$

A short calculation based on (30.3) shows that

$$E_{1m} = \frac{h^2 - 4k \sin^2 (hm_2/2)}{h^2 + 4k \sin^2 (hm_1/2)},$$

$$E_{2m} = \frac{h^2 - 4k \sin^2 (hm_1/2)}{h^2 + 4k \sin^2 (hm_2/2)}.$$

The numerical value of each of these quantities separately may very well exceed 1, but the modulus of their product is obviously never greater than 1. Hence condition (30.2) is satisfied, and stability and convergence are established for any manner of letting k and h tend to zero.

BIBLIOGRAPHY AND AUTHOR INDEX

The following list is intended to include all titles referred to in the text, and a number of additional recent titles which deal with our subject. There is no thought of its being even approximately complete. Where possible, the journal abbreviations follow the usage of *Mathematical Reviews*, vol. 17 (1956), pp. 1423–1435. The system of transliteration of Russian names follows that used in *Mathematical Reviews* since 1946, and thus differs somewhat from the Library of Congress system used in most United States libraries.

Numbers in italics following a reference give pages of this book where the reference is cited. Names of authors referred to personally apart from a publication also appear in this list. Names associated only with a subject will be found in the Subject Index.

A. A. Abramov [1953]: (А. А. Абрамов) О влиянии ошибок округления при решении уравнения Лапласа, Vyčisl. Mat. Vyčisl. Tehn., vol. 1, pp. 37–40. (A translation by R. and C. Mercer, entitled *On the influence of round-off errors in the solution of Laplace's equation*, has been reproduced at Space Technology Laboratories, Los Angeles 45, Calif.) *329*

A. C. Aitken. *370*

J. H. Alexander. *334, 351*

J. Albrecht and W. Uhlmann [1957]: *Differenzenverfahren für die Randwertaufgabe mit krummlinigen Rändern bei* $\Delta u(x, y) = r(x, y, u)$, Z. Angew. Math. Mech., vol. 37, pp. 212–224.

D. N. de G. Allen [1954]: *Relaxation Methods*, McGraw-Hill Book Co., New York, Toronto, London, 257 pp. *202, 365*

Anonymous [1958]: *Modern Computing Methods*, Philosophical Library, New York, 129 pp. (said to be written by L. Fox, E. T. Goodwin, F. W. J. Olver, and J. H. Wilkinson).

R. J. Arms [1957]: *Truncation errors involved in using special difference equations. Preliminary report*, Abstract, Bull. Amer. Math. Soc., vol. 63, p. 128. *368*

R. J. Arms and L. D. Gates, Jr. [1957]: *The computation of an axially symmetric free boundary problem on NORC, Part II*, NPG Report No. 1533, U. S. Naval Proving Ground, Dahlgren, Va., 8 pp.

R. J. Arms, L. D. Gates, and B. Zondek [1956]: *A method of block iteration*, J. Soc. Indust. Appl. Math., vol. 4, pp. 220–229. *243, 269*

F. Bagemihl, see Konrad Knopp.

N. S. Bahvalov [1957]: (Н. С. Бахвалов) Об одном способе приближенного решения уравнения Лапласа, Dokl. Akad. Nauk SSSR (N. S.), vol. 114, pp. 455–458. *213*

T. Banachiewicz [1938]: *Méthode de résolution numérique des équations linéaires, du*

415

416   BIBLIOGRAPHY AND AUTHOR INDEX

calcul des déterminants et des inverses, et de réduction des formes quadratiques, Bull. Intern. de l'Acad. Polonaise, Série A, Sci. Math., pp. 393–404. *209–211*

J. Barta [1937]: *Sur la vibration fondamentale d'une membrane*, C. R. Acad. Sci. Paris, vol. 204, pp. 472–473. *336*

Eduard Batschelet [1952]: *Über die numerische Auflösung von Randwertproblemen bei elliptischen partiellen Differentialgleichungen*, Z. Angew. Math. Physik, vol. 3, pp. 165–193. *202, 319*

F. L. Bauer. *218*

Edwin F. Beckenbach [1956] (editor): *Modern Mathematics for the Engineer*, McGraw-Hill Book Co., New York, Toronto, London, 514 pp.

Curtis D. Benster, see V. N. Faddeeva, L. V. Kantorovič, and V. B. Lidskiĭ. *206*

T. Bergeron, see V. Bjerknes.

Stefan Bergman and M. Schiffer [1953]: *Kernel Functions and Elliptic Partial Differential Equations in Mathematical Physics*, Academic Press, New York, 432 pp. *175*

Dorothy L. Bernstein [1950]: *Existence Theorems in Partial Differential Equations*, Annals of Mathematics Studies, No. 23, Princeton Univ. Press, 228 pp. *340*

Lipman Bers [1958]: *Mathematics Aspects of Subsonic and Transonic Gas Dynamics*, John Wiley & Sons, New York, 164 pp.

W. G. Bickley [1948]: *Finite-difference formulae for the square lattice*, Quart. J. Mech. Appl. Math., vol. 1, pp. 35–42. *195*

G. G. Bilodeau, W. R. Cadwell, J. P. Dorsey, J. G. Fairey, and R. S. Varga [1957]: *PDQ, an IBM-704 code to solve the two-dimensional few-group neutron-diffusion equations*, Report WAPD-TM-70, Bettis Plant, Westinghouse Electric Corp., Pittsburgh, Pa., 66 pp.

Garrett Birkhoff and Richard S. Varga [1958]: *Reactor criticality and nonnegative matrices*, J. Soc. Indust. Appl. Math., vol. 6, pp. 354–377.

Garrett Birkhoff and Richard S. Varga [1959]: *Implicit alternating direction methods*, Trans. Amer. Math. Soc., vol. 92, pp. 13–24. *272, 276, 277, 282*

V. Bjerknes, J. Bjerknes, H. Solberg, and T. Bergeron [1933]: *Physikalische Hydrodynamik*, J. Springer, Berlin. *388*

E. Bodewig [1956]: *Matrix Calculus*, Interscience Publishers, Inc., New York, 334 pp. *206, 214, 355*

H. C. Bolton and H. I. Scoins [1956]: *Eigenvalues of differential equations by finite-difference methods*, Proc. Cambridge Philos. Soc., vol. 52, pp. 215–229.

H. C. Bolton and H. I. Scoins [1957]: *Eigenvalue problems treated by finite-difference methods II. Two-dimensional Schrödinger equations*, Proc. Cambridge Philos. Soc., vol. 53, pp. 150–161.

Karl Borkmann, see D. J. Panow.

C. L. Bradshaw, see W. Robert Mann.

J. Brunings [1957]: *Discussion of iterative methods for solving certain mixed boundary value problems*, Report NN-71, Digital Computing Center, The Ramo-Wooldridge Corp., Los Angeles 45, 15 pp. Also *Addendum*, Report NN-71A, 2 pp. *259*

R. A. Buckingham [1957]: *Numerical Methods*, Sir Isaac Pitman & Sons, London, 579 pp.

W. R. Cadwell, see G. G. Bilodeau.

John W. Carr, III, see J. H. Wilkinson.

H. S. Carslaw [1930]: *Introduction to the Theory of Fourier's Series and Integrals*, 3rd ed., Macmillan and Co., London, 368 pp. *100*

H. S. Carslaw and J. C. Jaeger [1947]: *Conduction of Heat in Solids*, Clarendon Press, Oxford, 386 pp. *91, 99, 100, 111*

K. E. Černin, see L. V. Kantorovič.

S. Chandrasekhar [1943]: *Stochastic problems in physics and astronomy*, Rev. Mod. Phys., vol. 15, pp. 1–89. *91*

J. G. Charney [1949]: *On a physical basis for numerical prediction of large-scale motions in the atmosphere*, J. Meteorol., vol. 6, pp. 371–385. *387, 399*

J. G. Charney and A. Eliassen [1949]: *A numerical method for predicting the perturbations of the middle latitude westerlies*, Tellus, vol. 1, pp. 38–54. *392*

J. G. Charney, R. Fjörtoft, and J. von Neumann [1950]: *Numerical integration of the barotropic vorticity equation*, Tellus, vol. 2, pp. 237–254. *387–396*

J. G. Charney and N. A. Phillips [1953]: *Numerical integration of the quasi-geostrophic equations for barotropic and simple baroclinic flows*, J. Meteorol., vol. 10, pp. 71–99. *389, 393–398*

Ruel V. Churchill [1941]: *Fourier Series and Boundary Value Problems*, McGraw-Hill Book Co., New York, 206 pp. *3, 99*

L. Collatz [1933]: *Bemerkungen zur Fehlerabschätzung für das Differenzenverfahren bei partiellen Differentialgleichungen*, Z. Angew. Math. Mech., vol. 13, pp. 56–57. *200, 290*

L. Collatz [1938]: *Konvergenz des Differenzenverfahrens bei Eigenwertproblemen partieller Differentialgleichungen*, Deutsche Math., vol. 3, pp. 200–212. *349*

Lothar Collatz [1949]: *Eigenwertaufgaben mit technischen Anwendungen*, Akademische Verlagsgesellschaft, Leipzig, 466 pp.

L. Collatz [1950]: *Über die Konvergenzkriterien bei Iterationsverfahren für lineare Gleichungssysteme*, Math. Z., vol. 53, pp. 149–161. *221, 237*

L. Collatz [1951]: *Zur Stabilität des Differenzenverfahrens bei der Stabschwingungs-gleichung*, Z. Angew. Math. Mech., vol. 31, pp. 392–393. *133*

Lothar Collatz [1955]: *Numerische Behandlung von Differentialgleichungen*, 2nd ed., Springer-Verlag, Berlin, Göttingen, Heidelberg, 526 pp. *69, 127, 175, 195, 200, 304*

Lothar Collatz [1955a]: *Numerische und graphische Methoden*, vol. 2, pp. 349–470 of S. Flügge (editor), *Handbuch der Physik*, Springer-Verlag, Berlin, Göttingen, Heidelberg.

B. H. Colvin. *153, 154*

S. D. Conte and R. T. Dames [1958]: *An alternating direction method for solving the biharmonic equation*, Math. Tables Aids Comput., vol. 12, pp. 198–205.

A. F. Cornock [1954]: *The numerical solution of Poisson's and the biharmonic equations by matrices*, Proc. Cambridge Philos. Soc., vol. 50, pp. 524–535.

R. Courant [1934, 1936]: *Differential and Integral Calculus*, Blackie and Son, London and Glasgow, vol. 1, 568 pp., and vol. 2, 682 pp. (translated by E. J. McShane). *20*

R. Courant and K. O. Friedrichs [1948]: *Supersonic Flow and Shock Waves*, Interscience Publishers, Inc., New York, 464 pp. *38–44, 67, 72–79, 87*

R. Courant, K. Friedrichs, and H. Lewy [1928]: *Über die partiellen Differenzengleich-ungen der mathematischen Physik*, Math. Ann., vol. 100, pp. 32–74. (A translation by Phyllis Fox has been multilithed under the title *On the partial difference equations of mathematical physics*, Report NYO-7689, Institute of Mathematical Sciences, New York University, 1956. *25, 177, 310*

R. Courant and D. Hilbert [1937]: *Methoden der mathematischen Physik*, vol. 2, J. Springer, Berlin, 549 pp. *38–47, 89, 132, 166, 378, 380*

R. Courant and D. Hilbert [1953]: *Methods of Mathematical Physics*, vol. 1, Interscience Publishers Inc., New York, 561 pp. *3, 4, 89, 90, 155–167, 206, 314, 330–335, 347–353*

Richard Courant, Eugene Isaacson, and Mina Rees [1952]: *On the solution of nonlinear hyperbolic differential equations by finite differences*, Comm. Pure Appl. Math., vol. 5, pp. 243–255. *49, 61, 62*

Richard Courant and Peter Lax [1949]: *On nonlinear partial differential equations with two independent variables*, Comm. Pure Appl. Math., vol. 2, pp. 255–273. *38, 40, 44, 49*

J. Grady Cox, see W. Robert Mann.

Harald Cramér [1946]: *Mathematical Methods of Statistics*, Princeton Univ. Press, 575 pp. *289, 294*

S. H. Crandall [1951]: *Iterative procedures related to relaxation methods for eigenvalue problems*, Proc. Roy. Soc. London, Ser. A., vol. 207, pp. 416–423. *355*

Stephen H. Crandall [1954]: *Numerical treatment of a fourth order parabolic partial differential equation*, J. Assoc. Comput. Mach., vol. 1, pp. 111–118. *133*

Stephen H. Crandall [1956]: *Engineering Analysis, a Survey of Numerical Procedures*, McGraw-Hill Book Co., New York, Toronto, London, 417 pp.

Stephen H. Crandall [1957]: *Optimum recurrence formulas for a fourth order parabolic partial differential equation*, J. Assoc. Comput. Mach., vol. 4, pp. 467–471.

J. Crank and P. Nicolson [1947]: *A practical method for numerical evaluation of solutions of partial differential equations of the heat-conduction type*, Proc. Cambridge Philos. Soc., vol. 43, pp. 50–67. *102, 120, 141–143, 267*

Germund Dahlquist [1954]: *Convergence and stability for a hyperbolic difference equation with analytic initial-values*, Math. Scand., vol. 2, pp. 91–102. *25, 27, 101*

R. T. Dames, see S. D. Conte.

R. DeVogelaere. *242, 260, 334, 351*

J. B. Diaz and R. C. Roberts [1952]: *On the numerical solution of the Dirichlet problem for Laplace's difference equation*, Quart. Appl. Math., vol. 9, pp. 355–360.

J. B. Diaz and R. C. Roberts [1952a]: *Upper and lower bounds for the numerical solution of the Dirichlet difference boundary value problem*, J. Math. Phys., vol. 31, pp. 184–191.

J. B. Diaz, see also L. A. Lyusternik.

J. P. Dorsey, see G. G. Bilodeau.

A. S. Douglas [1958]: *On the numerical solution of a class of partial differential equations*, Proc. Cambridge Philos. Soc., vol. 54, pp. 214–218.

Jim Douglas, Jr. [1955]: *On the numerical integration of $\partial^2 u/\partial x^2 + \partial^2 u/\partial y^2 = \partial u/\partial t$ by implicit methods*, J. Soc. Indust. Appl. Math., vol. 3, pp. 42–65.

Jim Douglas, Jr. [1956]: *On the numerical integration of quasi-linear parabolic differential equations*, Pacific J. Math., vol. 6, pp. 35–42. *139*

Jim Douglas, Jr. [1958]: *The application of stability analysis in the numerical solution of quasi-linear parabolic differential equations*, Trans. Amer. Math. Soc., vol. 89, pp. 484–518. *139*

Jim Douglas, Jr. and H. H. Rachford, Jr. [1956]: *On the numerical solution of heat conduction problems in two and three space variables*, Trans. Amer. Math. Soc., vol. 82, pp. 421–439. *272, 282, 283, 375*

R. J. Duffin [1947]: *Lower bounds for eigenvalues*, Phys. Rev. (2), vol. 71, pp. 827–828. *336*

E. C. Du Fort and S. P. Frankel [1953]: *Stability conditions in the numerical treatment of parabolic differential equations*, Math. Tables Aids Comput., vol. 7, pp. 135–152. *127, 128, 133, 402*

Paul S. Dwyer [1951]: *Linear Computations*, John Wiley and Sons, Inc., New York, 344 pp. *206, 208*

W. J. Eckert [1940]: *Punched Card Methods in Scientific Computation*, The Thomas J. Watson Astronomical Computing Bureau, New York, 136 pp. *9*

R. P. Eddy [1952]: *A method for the numerical solution of a heat conduction problem*, NAVORD Rep. 2725, U. S. Naval Ordnance Laboratory, White Oak, Md. *143*

Milton C. Edlund, see Samuel Glasstone.

L. W. Ehrlich [1958]: *A numerical method of solving a heat flow problem with moving boundary*, J. Assoc. Comput. Mach., vol. 5, pp. 161–176.

A. Eliassen, see J. G. Charney.

J. Eve and H. I. Scoins [1956]: *A note on the approximate solution of the equations of Poisson and Laplace by finite difference methods*, Quart. J. Math. (2), vol. 7, pp. 217–223.

V. N. Faddeeva [1949]: (В. Н. Фаддеева) Метод прямых в применении к некоторым краевым задачам, Trudy Mat. Inst. Steklov, vol. 28, pp. 73–103.   *178*

V. N. Faddeeva [1950]: (В. Н. Фаддеева) Вычислительные Методы Линейной Алгебры, Gostehizdat, Moscow–Leningrad, 240 pp. (Translated by Curtis D. Benster under title *Computational Methods of Linear Algebra*, Dover Publications, New York, 1959, 252 pp.)   *206, 209, 237, 275, 404, 409*

J. G. Fairey, see G. G. Bilodeau.

William Feller and George E. Forsythe [1951]: *New matrix transformations for obtaining characteristic vectors*, Quart. Appl. Math., vol. 8 (1950–51), pp. 325–331.   *356*

Willy Feller, see also J. D. Tamarkin.

A. F. Filippov, see V. S. Ryaben'kiĭ.

R. Fjörtoft, see J. G. Charney.

S. Flügge, see Lothar Collatz.

Lester R. Ford [1933]: *Differential Equations*, McGraw-Hill Book Co., New York, 264 pp.   *55*

George E. Forsythe [1947]: *Speed of propagation of atmospheric waves with changing shape*, J. Meteorol., vol. 4, pp. 67–69.

G. E. Forsythe [1950]: *Round-off errors in numerical integration on automatic machinery*, Preliminary Report, Abstract, Bull. Amer. Math. Soc., vol. 56, pp. 61–62.   *34*

George E. Forsythe [1950a]: *Solution of the telegrapher's equation with boundary conditions on only one characteristic*, J. Res. Nat. Bur. Standards, vol. 44, pp. 89–102.   *391*

George E. Forsythe [1953]: *Solving linear algebraic equations can be interesting*, Bull. Amer. Math. Soc., vol. 59, pp. 299–329.   *215, 225*

George E. Forsythe [1954]: *Asymptotic lower bounds for the frequencies of polygonal membranes*, Pacific J. Math., vol. 4, pp. 467–480.   *334, 340, 341, 345, 352*

George E. Forsythe [1955]: *Asymptotic lower bounds for the fundamental frequency of convex membranes*, Pacific J. Math., vol. 5, pp. 691–702.   *341*

George E. Forsythe [1956]: *What are relaxation methods?*, pp. 428–447 of Beckenbach [1956].

George E. Forsythe [1956a]: *Difference methods on a digital computer for Laplacian boundary value and eigenvalue problems*, Comm. Pure Appl. Math., vol. 9, pp. 425–434.   *342, 361, 370*

George E. Forsythe and Theodore S. Motzkin [1952]: *An extension of Gauss' transformation for improving the condition of systems of linear equations*, Math. Tables Aids Comput., vol. 6, pp. 9–17.   *377*

George E. Forsythe, see also William Feller, C. F. Gauss, and Jörgen Holmboe.

L. Fox [1948]: *A short account of relaxation methods*, Quart. J. Mech. Appl. Math., vol. 1, pp. 253–280.   *241, 242*

L. Fox [1950]: *The numerical solution of elliptic differential equations when the boundary conditions involve a derivative*, Philos. Trans. Roy. Soc. London, Ser. A, vol. 242, pp. 345–378.

L. Fox, see also Anonymous.

Phyllis Fox, see R. Courant.

Werner Frank.   *235*

Stanley P. Frankel [1950]: *Convergence rates of iterative treatments of partial differential equations*, Math. Tables Aids Comput., vol. 4, pp. 65–75.   *242, 259, 272*

S. P. Frankel, see also E. C. Du Fort.

Bernard Fried, see George H. Shortley.

Bernard Friedman [1956]: *Principles and Techniques of Applied Mathematics*, John Wiley & Sons, New York, 315 pp. *174.*

Bernard Friedman [1957]: *The iterative solution of elliptic difference equations*, Report NYO-7698, Institute of Mathematical Sciences, New York University, 37 pp. *242, 243, 249, 269*

K. O. Friedrichs, see R. Courant.

G. Frobenius. *262, 272*

P. R. Garabedian [1956]: *The mathematical theory of three-dimensional cavities and jets*, Bull. Amer. Math. Soc., vol. 62, pp. 219–235. *153, 204*

P. R. Garabedian [1956a]: *Estimation of the relaxation factor for small mesh size*, Math. Tables Aids Comput., vol. 10, pp. 183–185. *263–266*

R. E. Gaskell, see D. Kirkham.

L. D. Gates, Jr., see R. J. Arms.

J. A. Gaunt, see L. F. Richardson.

C. F. Gauss [1823]: Brief an Gerling, 26. Dez. 1823, *Werke*, vol. 9, pp. 278–281. (Translated by G. E. Forsythe under title *Gauss to Gerling on relaxation*, Math. Tables Aids Comput., vol. 5 (1951), pp. 255–258). *241, 242*

C. L. Gerberich and W. C. Sangren [1957]: *Codes for the classical membrane problem*, J. Assoc. Comput. Mach., vol. 4, pp. 477–486. *334, 351*

S. Gerschgorin [1930]: *Fehlerabschätzung für das Differenzenverfahren zur Lösung partieller Differentialgleichungen*, Z. Angew. Math. Mech., vol. 10, pp. 373–382. *283–325, 367*

John H. Giese [1958]: *On the truncation error in a numerical solution of the Neumann problem for a rectangle*, J. Math. Phys., vol. 37, pp. 169–177. *204, 319*

Wallace Givens [1954]: *Numerical computation of the characteristic values of a real symmetric matrix*, Report No. 1574, Oak Ridge National Laboratory, Oak Ridge, Tenn., 107 pp. *353*

Wallace Givens [1957]: *The characteristic value-vector problem*, J. Assoc. Comput. Mach., vol. 4, pp. 298–307. *353*

Samuel Glasstone and Milton C. Edlund [1952]: *The Elements of Nuclear Reactor Theory*, D. Van Nostrand Co., Toronto, New York, London, 416 pp. *156*

Herman H. Goldstine and John von Neumann [1951]: *Numerical inverting of matrices of high order. II*, Proc. Amer. Math. Soc., vol. 2, pp. 188–202. (See first article under von Neumann.) *209*

Gene Howard Golub [1959]: *The use of Chebyshev matrix polynomials in the iterative solution of linear equations compared to the method of successive overrelaxation*, multilithed, Report No. 85, Digital Computer Lab., Univ. of Illinois, 133 pp.

E. T. Goodwin, see Anonymous.

S. H. Gould [1957]: *Variational Methods for Eigenvalue Problems. An Introduction to the Methods of Rayleigh, Ritz, Weinstein, and Aronszajn*, University of Toronto Press, Toronto, 179 pp. *167, 329*

William Gragg, Jr. *358*

L. E. Grinter [1949]: *Numerical Methods of Analysis in Engineering*, MacMillan, New York, 207 pp.

J. Grossman, see Wladimir Markoff.

William Gustin, see Jörgen Holmboe.

Jacques Hadamard [1923]: *Lectures on Cauchy's Problem in Linear Partial Differential Equations*, Yale University Press, New Haven, 316 pp. *4–6*

George J. Haltiner and Frank L. Martin [1957]: *Dynamical and Physical Meteorology*, McGraw-Hill Book Co., New York, 470 pp.

Douglas R. Hartree [1953]: *Some practical methods of using characteristics in the calculation of non-steady compressible flow*, Report LA-HU-1, Department of Mathematics, Harvard Univ., Cambridge, 41 pp.

D. R. Hartree [1958]: *A method for the numerical integration of the linear diffusion equation*, Proc. Cambridge Philos. Soc., vol. 54, pp. 207–213.

Jack Heller [1958]: *Ordering properties of linear successive iteration schemes*, Report NYO-7972, Institute of Mathematical Sciences, New York University, 40 pp.   *260*

J. Heller [1960]: *Simultaneous, successive, and alternating direction iteration schemes*, J. Soc. Indust. Appl. Math., vol. 8, 150–173.

P. Henrici.   *153n*

J. Hersch [1955]: *Équations différentielles et fonctions de cellules*, C. R. Acad. Sci. Paris, vol. 240, pp. 1602–1604.   *176, 339, 340*

Joseph Hersch, Albert Pfluger, and Andreas Schopf [1956]: *Über ein simultanes Differenzenverfahren zur Abschätzung der Torsionssteifigkeit und der Kapazität nach beiden Seiten*, Z. Angew. Math. Physik, vol. 7, pp. 89–113.   *176, 339*

Magnus R. Hestenes and Marvin L. Stein [1951]: *The solution of linear equations by minimization*, Report NAML 52-45, National Bureau of Standards, Los Angeles, 35 pp.   *239*

Magnus R. Hestenes and Eduard Stiefel [1952]: *Method of conjugate gradients for solving linear systems*, J. Res. Nat. Bur. Standards, vol. 49, pp. 409–436.   *214*

Thomas J. Higgins [1949]: *A survey of the approximate solution of two-dimensional physical problems by variational methods and finite difference procedures*, pp. 169–198 of Grinter [1949].

D. Hilbert, see R. Courant.

F. B. Hildebrand [1952]: *Methods of Applied Mathematics*, Prentice-Hall Inc., New York, 523 pp.   *40*

T. W. Hildebrandt [1955]: *On the reality of the eigen-values for a one-group, N-region, diffusion problem*, Report 55-6-35, Oak Ridge National Laboratory, Oak Ridge, Tenn., 6 pp.   *170, 173*

Urs Hochstrasser [1954]: *Die Anwendung der Methode der konjugierten Gradienten und ihrer Modifikationen auf die Loesung linearer Randwertprobleme*, Thesis, E. Truninger, Urania, Zürich, 45 pp.   *193*

Jörgen Holmboe, George E. Forsythe, and William Gustin [1945]: *Dynamic Meteorology*, John Wiley & Sons, New York, 378 pp.   *387*

Alston Householder [1953]: *Principles of Numerical Analysis*, The McGraw-Hill Book Co., New York, 274 pp.   *206, 214, 370, 409*

A. S. Householder [1954]: *On norms of vectors and matrices*, Report ORNL 1756, Oak Ridge National Laboratory, Oak Ridge, Tenn., 18 pp.   *206*

Alston S. Householder [1957]: *A survey of some closed methods for inverting matrices*, J. Soc. Indust. Appl. Math., vol. 5, pp. 155–169.   *213*

A. S. Householder [1958]: *The approximate solution of matrix problems*, J. Assoc. Comput. Mach., vol. 5, pp. 205–243.   *218, 242, 276*

Alfred Huber [1954]: *On the uniqueness of generalized axially symmetric potentials*, Ann. of Math., vol. 60, pp. 351–358.   *153*

Harry Huskey and Granino Korn [1960]: *Computer Handbook*, The McGraw-Hill Book Co., New York.   *7*

Morton A. Hyman, see George G. O'Brien.

Eugene Isaacson, see Richard Courant.   *397*

David Isherwood,   *148, 150*

C. G. J. Jacobi [1845]: *Ueber eine neue Auflösungsart der bei der Methode der kleinsten Quadrate vorkommenden lineären Gleichungen*, Astr. Nachr., vol. 22, No. 523, pp. 297–306. *220*

J. C. Jaeger, see H. S. Carslaw.

Earl Janssen [1956]: *I. An Analog Method for Solving the Hydrodynamic Equations for Two Dimensional Viscous Flow: II. Application of the Method to the Case of Flow Past a Flat Plate*, Dissertation, University of California, Los Angeles, 81 pp. *154, 155*

Fritz John [1952]: *On integration of parabolic equations by difference methods, I. Linear and quasi-linear equations for the infinite interval*, Comm. Pure Appl. Math., vol. 5, pp. 155–211. *94, 97, 112–137; 101*

M. L. Juncosa and D. M. Young [1953]: *On the order of convergence of solutions of a difference equation to a solution of the diffusion equation*, J. Soc. Indust. Appl. Math., vol. 1, pp. 111–135. *98, 101*

M. L. Juncosa and David Young [1954]: *On the convergence of a solution of a difference equation to a solution of the equation of diffusion*, Proc. Amer. Math. Soc., vol. 5, pp. 168–174. *101*

M. L. Juncosa and David Young [1957]: *On the Crank-Nicolson procedure for solving parabolic partial differential equations*, Proc. Cambridge Philos. Soc., vol. 53, pp. 448–461. *125*

S. Kaczmarz [1937]: *Angenäherte Auflösung von Systemen linearer Gleichungen*, Bull. Internat. Acad. Polonaise. Classe Sci., Math. Nat. (A), Sci. Math., 1937, pp. 355–357. *356, 357*

William Kahan [1957]: *The rate of convergence of the extrapolated Gauss-Seidel iteration*, Abstract, J. Assoc. Comput. Mach., vol. 4, pp. 521–522.

W. Kahan [1958]: *Gauss-Seidel Methods of Solving Large Systems of Linear Equations*, Thesis, Toronto, approx. 100 pp. *260, 262*

L. V. Kantorcvič and V. I. Krylov [1952]: (Л. В. Канторович и В. И Крылов) Приближен..ые Методы Высшего Анализа, 4th ed., Moscow–Leningrad, 695 pp. (There is an English translation by Curtis D. Benster, *Approximate Methods of Higher Analysis*, P. Noordhoff Ltd., The Netherlands, 1958, 681 pp.) *159, 178, 185, 194*

L. V. Kantorovič, V. I. Krylov, and K. E. Černin [1956]: (Л. В. Канторович, В. И. Крылов, и К. Е. Чернин) Таблицы для Численного Решения Граничных Задач Теории Гармонических Функций, Gostehizdat, Moscow, 462 pp.

Sidney Kaplan, see George G. O'Brien.

O. Karlqvist [1952]: *Numerical solution of elliptic difference equations by matrix methods*, Tellus, vol. 4, pp. 374–384.

Walter J. Karplus [1954]: *Electronic Analogue Solution of Free Surface Boundary Value Problems—Water Coning*, Dissertation, University of California, Los Angeles, 99 pp, *150*

Walter J. Karplus [1956]: *Water-coning before breakthrough—an electronic analog treatment*, Petroleum Trans. Amer. Soc. Mech. Engrs., vol. 207, pp. 240–245. *150–152*

H. B. Keller [1958]: *On some iterative methods for solving elliptic difference equations*, Quart. Appl. Math., vol. 16, pp. 209–226. *243, 267, 269*

A. Khintchine [1933]: *Asymptotische Gesetze der Wahrscheinlichkeitsrechnung*, Ergebnisse der Math., Springer, Berlin, 77 pp. *91, 292*

D. Kirkham and R. E. Gaskell [1951]: *The falling water table in tile and ditch drainage*, Proc. Soil Science Soc. of America, vol. 15, pp. 37–42. *150*

Konrad Knopp [1945]: *Theory of Functions. I. Elements of the General Theory of*

Analytic Functions, Dover Publications, New York, 146 pp. (translated from German by F. Bagemihl). *2*

Granino Korn, see Harry Huskey.

Gabriel Kron [1955]: *Solving highly complex elastic structures in easy stages*, J. Appl. Mech., vol. 22, pp. 235–244. *213*

V. I. Krylov, see L. V. Kantorovič.

J. Kuntzmann [1955]: *Evaluations d'erreur dans les réprésentations approchées de dérivées*, mimeographed, Société d'Electronique et d'Automatisme, 138, Boulevard de Verdun, Courbevoie (Seine), France, 49 pp.

Kaiser S. Kunz [1957]: *Numerical Analysis*, McGraw-Hill Book Co., New York, Toronto, London, 381 pp.

Pentti Laasonen [1957]: *On the behavior of the solution of the Dirichlet problem at analytic corners*, Ann. Acad. Sci. Fenn. A. I., vol. 241, pp. 3–13.

Pentti Laasonen [1957a]: *On the degree of convergence of discrete approximations for the solutions of the Dirichlet problem*, Ann. Acad. Sci. Fenn. A. I., vol. 246, pp. 1–19. *311, 312, 318*

Pentti Laasonen [1958]: *On the truncation error of discrete approximations to the solutions of Dirichlet problems in a domain with corners*, J. Assoc. Comput. Mach., vol. 5, pp. 32–38.

Pentti Laasonen [1958a]: *On the solution of Poisson's difference equation*, J. Assoc. Comput. Mach., vol. 5, pp. 370–382.

O. A. Ladyženskaya [1957]: (О. А. Ладыженская) Метод конечных разностей в теории уравнений с частными производными, Uspehi Mat. Nauk, vol. 12, no. 5 (77), pp. 123–148. (A translation has been prepared at the Institute of Mathematical Sciences, New York University, under title *The method of finite differences in the theory of partial differential equations*.) *177*

Cornelius Lanczos [1952]: *Solution of systems of linear equations by minimized iterations*, J. Res. Nat. Bur. Standards, vol. 49, pp. 33–53. *214*

C. Lanczos [1955]: *Spectroscopic eigenvalue analysis*, J. Washington Acad. Sci., vol. 45, pp. 315–323. *235*

Peter D. Lax [1954]: *Weak solutions of nonlinear hyperbolic equations and their numerical computation*, Comm. Pure Appl. Math., vol. 7, pp. 159–193. *84–87*

P. D. Lax and R. D. Richtmyer [1956]: *Survey of the stability of linear finite difference equations*, Comm. Pure Appl. Math., vol. 9, pp. 267–293. *94, 133–136, 400–410*

Peter Lax, see also Richard Courant.

Milton Lees [1957]: *Approximate solutions of parabolic and hyperbolic partial differential equations*, Technical Report 7, Department of Mathematics, University of California, Berkeley, multilithed, 83 pp. *139*

R. Sherman Lehman [1957]: *Development of the mapping function at an analytic corner*, Pacific J. Math., vol. 7, pp. 1437–1449. *341*

R. Sherman Lehman [1959]: *Developments at an analytic corner of solutions of partial differential equations*, J. Math. Mech., vol. 8, pp. 727–760. *311, 341*

D. H. Lehmer. *232*

Werner Leutert [1951]: *On the convergence of approximate solutions of the heat equation to the exact solution*, Proc. Amer. Math. Soc., vol. 2, pp. 433–439. *101*

Werner Leutert [1952]: *On the convergence of unstable approximate solutions of the heat equation to the exact solution*, J. Math. Physics, vol. 30, pp. 245–251.

Werner Leutert and George G. O'Brien [1952]: *On the convergence of approximate solutions of the wave equation to the exact solution*, J. Math. Physics, vol. 30, pp. 252–256.

Hans Lewy [1928]: *Über das Anfangswertproblem einer hyperbolischen nichtlinearen partiellen Differentialgleichung zweiter Ordnung mit zwei unabhängigen Veränderlichen*, Math. Ann., vol. 98, pp. 179–191. *43, 44*

H. Lewy, see also R. Courant.

V. B. Lidskiĭ [1950]: (В. Б. Лидский) О собственных значениях суммы и произведения симметрических матриц, Doklady Akad. Nauk SSSR (N. S.), vol. 75, pp. 769–772. (A translation by C. D. Benster has been prepared under the title *On the proper values of the sum and product of symmetric matrices*.) *347*

H. Liebmann [1918]: *Die angenäherte Ermittlung harmonischer Funktionen und konformer Abbildung (nach Ideen von Boltzmann und Jacobi)*, Sitzungsberichte der Bayer. Akad. Wiss., Math.-Phys. Kl., vol. 47, pp. 385–416. *236, 256*

Mark Lotkin [1959]: *The Calculation of Heat Flow in Melting Solids*, multilithed, Report TM-59-18, Avco Mfg. Corp., Wilmington, Mass., 18 March 1959, 13 pp.

G. Ludford, H. Polachek, and R. J. Seeger [1953]: *On unsteady flow of compressible viscous fluids*, J. Appl. Phys., vol. 24, pp. 490–495. *82–84*

Rudolf Lüneberg [1930]: *Das Problem der Irrfahrt ohne Richtungsbeschränkung und die Randwertaufgabe der Potentialtheorie*, Math. Ann., vol. 104, pp. 700–738. *292*

L. A. Lyusternik [1947]: (Л. А. Люстерник) Замечания к численному решению краевых задач уравнения Лапласа и вычислению собственных значений методом сеток, Trudy Mat. Inst. Steklov, vol. 20, pp. 49–64. *219*

L. A. Lyusternik [1954]: (Л. А. Люстерник) О разностных аппроксимациях оператора Лапласа, Uspehi Mat. Nauk (N. S.), vol. 9, no. 2 (58), pp. 3–66. (Translated by J. B. Diaz under title *On difference approximations of the Laplace operator*, Amer. Math. Soc. Translations (2), vol. 8 (1958), pp. 289–351.)

C. C. MacDuffee [1946]: *The Theory of Matrices*, American reprint, Chelsea Publishing Co., New York, 110 pp. *262*

R. H. MacNeal [1953]: *An asymmetrical finite difference network*, Quart. Appl. Math., vol. 11, pp. 295–310. *182*

W. Robert Mann, C. L. Bradshaw, and J. Grady Cox [1957]: *Improved approximations to differential equations by difference equations*, J. Math. Phys., vol. 35, pp. 408–415.

Wladimir Markoff [1916]: *Über Polynome, die in einem gegebenen Intervalle möglichst wenig von Null abweichen*, Math. Ann., vol. 77, pp. 213–258 (translated by J. Grossmann from Russian original of 1892). *227*

Harry M. Markowitz [1957]: *The elimination form of the inverse and its application to linear programming*, Management Sci., vol. 3, pp. 255–269. *211*

Frank L. Martin, see George J. Haltiner.

J. Massau [1899]: *Mémoire sur l'intégration graphique des équations aux dérivées partielles*, F. Meyer-Van Loo, Ghent, 144 pp. *64, 66*

W. H. McCrea and F. J. W. Whipple [1940]: *Random paths in two and three dimensions*, Proc. Roy. Soc. Edinburgh, Sect. A, vol. 60, pp. 281–298. *314, 317*

E. J. McShane, see R. Courant.

C. Mercer and R. Mercer, see A. A. Abramov.

Š. E. Mikeladze [1934]: (Ш. Е. Микеладзе) О численном интегрировании дифференциальных уравнений с частными производными, Izv. Akad. Nauk SSSR, Otd. Estest. Mat. Nauk, (vol. 1934), pp. 819–842.

Š. E. Mikeladze [1936]: (Ш. Е. Микеладзе) Численные Методы Интегрирования Дифференциальных Уравнений с Частными Производными, Moscow–Leningrad, 108 pp.

Sch. Mikeladze [1941]: (Ш. Е. Микеладзе) О численном интегрировании уравнений эллиптического и параболического типов, Izv. Akad. Nauk SSSR. Ser. Mat., vol. 5, pp. 57–74. *200*

William Edmund Milne [1949]: *Numerical Calculus*, Princeton Univ. Press, Princeton, 393 pp. *23, 69, 71*

William Edmund Milne [1953]: *Numerical Solution of Differential Equations*, John Wiley and Sons, New York, 275 pp. *199, 227, 274, 304; 178*

L. M. Milne-Thomson [1950]: *Theoretical Hydrodynamics*, 2nd ed., MacMillan and Co., New York, 600 pp. *155*

A. R. Mitchell [1954]: *Round-off errors in relaxational solutions of Poisson's equation*, Appl. Sci. Res. B., vol. 3, pp. 456–464. *323*

Halina Montvila [1958]: *On the convergence of the numerical solution for a certain partial differential equation of third order*, Report IMM-NYU 256, Institute of Mathematical Sciences, New York University, 72 pp. *399*

C. B. Morrey, Jr. and L. Nirenberg [1957]: *On the analyticity of linear elliptic systems of partial differential equations*, Comm. Pure Appl. Math., vol. 10, pp. 271–290. *340*

H. Motz [1946]: *The treatment of singularities of partial differential equations by relaxation methods*, Quart. Appl. Math., vol. 4, pp. 371–377. *204*

Th. Motzkin [1949]: *Approximation by curves of a unisolvent family*, Bull. Amer. Math. Soc., vol. 55, pp. 789–793. *279, 282*

T. S. Motzkin and W. Wasow [1953]: *On the approximation of linear elliptic differential equations by difference equations with positive coefficients*, J. Math. Phys., vol. 31, pp. 253–259. *181, 182, 299, 303*

Theodore S. Motzkin, see also George E. Forsythe.

Mervin E. Muller [1956]: *Some continuous Monte Carlo methods for the Dirichlet problem*, Ann. Math. Statist., vol. 27, pp. 569–589. *269*

M. Muskat [1946]: *The Flow of Homogeneous Fluids through Porous Media*, J. W. Edwards, Ann Arbor, 763 pp. *151*

Zeev Nehari [1952]: *Conformal Mapping*, McGraw-Hill Book Co., New York, 396 pp. *4*

John von Neumann and H. H. Goldstine [1947]: *Numerical inverting of matrices of high order*, Bull. Amer. Math. Soc., vol. 53, pp. 1021–1099. (See sequel under Goldstine.) *209*

J. von Neumann and R. D. Richtmyer [1950]: *A method for the numerical calculation of hydrodynamic shocks*, J. Appl. Phys., vol. 21, pp. 232–237. *78–84*

J. von Neumann, see also J. G. Charney. *10, 143, 395*

P. Nicolson, see J. Crank.

L. Nirenberg, see C. B. Morrey, Jr.

George G. O'Brien, Morton A. Hyman, and Sidney Kaplan [1951]: *A study of the numerical solution of partial differential equations*, J. Math. Phys., vol. 29, pp. 223–251. *125*

George G. O'Brien, see also Werner Leutert.

Rufus Oldenburger [1940]: *Infinite powers of matrices and characteristic roots*, Duke Math. J., vol. 6, pp. 357–361. *217*

F. W. J. Olver, see Anonymous.

Theodore A. Orlow [1958]: *Numerical solution of Laplace's equation for various three dimensional regions with axial symmetry*, NAVORD report 6038, White Oak, Maryland, approx. 25 pp.

James Ortega. *370, 371*

A. M. Ostrowski [1954]: *On the linear iteration procedures for symmetric matrices*, Univ. Roma. Ist. Naz. Alta Mat. Rend. Mat. e Appl. (5), vol. 13, pp. 140–163. *237 239, 261*

Alexander Ostrowski [1955]: *Über Normen von Matrizen*, Math. Z., vol. 63, pp. 2–18. *206*

A. M. Ostrowski [1958]: *On the convergence of the Rayleigh quotient iteration for the computation of the characteristic roots and vectors. I.*, Archive for Rational Mechanics and Analysis, vol. 1, pp. 233–241. *355*

A. M. Ostrowski [1959]: *On the convergence of the Rayleigh quotient iteration for the computation of the characteristic roots and vectors VI (usual Rayleigh quotient for nonlinear divisors)*, Archive for Rational Mechanics and Analysis, vol. 4, pp. 153–165. *355, 376*

D. J. Panow [1955]: *Formelsammlung zur numerischen Behandlung partieller Differentialgleichungen nach dem Differenzenverfahren*, Akademie-Verlag, Berlin, 134 pp. (translated from the Russian by Karl Borkmann and Werner Schulz).

D. Yu. Panov [1957]: (Д. Ю. Панов) Численное Решение Квазилинейных Гиперболических Систем Дифференциальных Уравнений в Частных Производных, Gostehizdat, Moscow, 216 pp.

D. W. Peaceman and H. H. Rachford, Jr. [1955]: *The numerical solution of parabolic and elliptic differential equations*, J. Soc. Indust. Appl. Math., vol. 3, pp. 28–41. *272–283, 375, 411–413*

I. Petrowsky [1934]: *Über das Irrfahrtproblem*, Math. Ann., vol. 109, pp. 425–444. *290, 292, 302, 313*

Albert Pfluger, see Joseph Hersch.

H. Phillips and N. Wiener [1923]: *Nets and the Dirichlet problem*, J. Math. Phys., vol. 2, pp. 105–124. *310*

N. A. Phillips, see J. G. Charney.

H. Poincaré [1890]: *Sur les équations aux dérivées partielles de la physique mathématique*, Amer. J. Math., vol. 12, pp. 211–294. *332*

H. Polachek, see G. Ludford.

G. Pólya [1954]: *Estimates for eigenvalues*, pp. 200–207 of *Studies in Mathematics and Mechanics Presented to Richard von Mises*, Academic Press, New York, 1954, 353 pp. *332, 335*

G. Pólya and G. Szegö [1951]: *Isoperimetric Inequalities in Mathematical Physics*, Princeton University Press, Princeton, 279 pp. *156, 265, 330, 335*

Mary Rita Powers [1955]: master's paper, University of California, Los Angeles. *259*

M. H. Protter [1958]: *Lower bounds for the first eigenvalue of elliptic equations and related topics*, mimeographed technical report, Dept. of Math., University of California, Berkeley, 25 pp. *336*

M. H. Protter [1959]: *Vibration of a nonhomogeneous membrane*, Pacific J. Math., vol. 9, pp. 1249–1255. *336*

H. H. Rachford, Jr., see Jim Douglas, Jr. and D. W. Peaceman.

Kenneth Ralston. *361, 363*

R. M. Redheffer [1957]: *On pairs of harmonic functions*, Proc. Amer. Math. Soc., vol. 8, pp. 450–457. *336*

Mina Rees, see Richard Courant.

Edgar Reich [1949]: *On the convergence of the classical iterative method of solving linear simultaneous equations*, Ann. Math. Statist., vol. 20, pp. 448–451. *237–240, 261, 355*

Hans Reichenbach. *179, 364*

Neal Reinders. *363, 374, 376*

Franz Rellich [1953]: *Perturbation Theory of Eigenvalue Problems*, mimeographed notes, Institute of Mathematical Sciences, New York University, 164 pp. *347*

L. F. Richardson [1910]: *The approximate arithmetical solution by finite differences of physical problems involving differential equations, with an application to the stresses in a masonry dam*, Philos. Trans. Roy. Soc. London. Ser. A, vol. 210, pp. 307–357, and Proc. Roy. Soc. London. Ser. A, vol. 83, pp. 335–336. *125–128, 224, 226–234, 307*

Lewis F. Richardson [1922]: *Weather Prediction by Numerical Process*, Cambridge University Press, 236 pp. *387*

L. F. Richardson and J. A. Gaunt [1927]: *The deferred approach to the limit*, Philos. Trans. Roy. Soc. London. Ser. A, vol. 226, pp. 229–361. *307*

Robert D. Richtmyer [1957]: *Difference Methods for Initial-Value Problems*, Interscience Publishers Inc., New York, 238 pp.

R. D. Richtmyer, see also P. D. Lax and J. von Neumann. *82*

B. Riemann. *45*

James D. Riley [1954]: *Iteration procedures for the Dirichlet difference problem*, Math. Tables Aids Comput., vol. 8, pp. 125–131.

R. C. Roberts, see J. B. Diaz.

Milton E. Rose [1956]: *On the integration of non-linear parabolic equations by implicit difference methods*, Quart. Appl. Math., vol. 14, pp. 237–248. *139*

R. L. Rosenberg, see P. Stein.

J. Paul Roth [1956]: *An algebraic topological approach to Kron's method. I.*, Institute for Advanced Study, Electronic Computer Project Report 56-03. *213*

V. S. Ryaben'kiĭ and A. F. Filippov [1956]: (В. С. Рябенький и А. Ф. Филиппов) Об Устойчивости Разностных Уравнений, Gostehizdat, Moscow, 171 pp.

Charles Saltzer [1958]: *Discrete potential theory for two-dimensional Laplace and Poisson difference equations*, N. A. C. A. Tech. Note 4086, 60 pp. *213, 314*

M. G. Salvadori [1951]: *Extrapolation formulas in linear difference operators*, Proc. 1st Congress Applied Mechanics, New York, pp. 15–18. *307*

W. C. Sangren, see C. L. Gerberich. *334, 351*

H. Sassenfeld [1951]: *Ein hinreichendes Konvergenzkriterium und eine Fehlerabschätzung für die Iteration in Einzelschritten bei linearen Gleichungen*, Z. Angew. Math. Mech., vol. 31, pp. 92–94. *237*

Robert Sauer [1952]: *Anfangswertprobleme bei partiellen Differentialgleichungen*, Springer-Verlag, Berlin, 229 pp. *44, 49, 64–67*

V. K. Saul'ev [1955]: (В. К. Саульев) К вопросу решения задачи о собственных значениях методом конечных разностей, Vyčisl. Mat. Vyčisl. Tehn., collection 2, pp. 116–144. (Translated by Abe Shenitzer under title *On the solution of the problem of eigenvalues by the method of finite differences*, Amer. Math. Soc. Translations (2), vol. 8 (1958), pp. 257–287.)

V. K. Saul'ev [1957]: (В. К. Саульев) Об оценке погрешности при нахождении собственных функций методом конечных разностей, Vyčisl. Mat., collection 1, pp. 87–115. *290*

Samuel Schechter [1959]: *Relaxation methods for linear equations*, Comm. Pure Appl. Math., vol. 12, pp. 313–335. *239*

M. Schiffer, see Stefan Bergman.

Werner Schmeidler [1949]: *Vorträge über Determinanten und Matrizen mit Anwendungen in Physik und Technik*, Berlin, 155 pp. *237*

Andreas Schopf, see Joseph Hersch.

Werner Schulz, see D. J. Panow.

H. I. Scoins, see H. C. Bolton and J. Eve.

R. J. Seeger, see G. Ludford.

Ludwig Seidel [1874]: *Ueber ein Verfahren, die Gleichungen, auf welche die Methode der kleinsten Quadrate führt, sowie lineäre Gleichungen überhaupt, durch successive Annäherung aufzulösen*, Abh. Math.-Phys. Kl., Bayerische Akad. Wiss. München, vol. 11 (III), pp. 81–108. *236, 241, 242*

C. B. Sensenig [1959]: *Existence and uniqueness for a third order non-linear partial differential equation*, Report IMM-NYU 258, Institute of Mathematical Sciences, New York University. *393, 397*

F. S. Shaw [1950?]: *An Introduction to Relaxation Methods*, Dover Publications, New York, 396 pp. *202*

J. W. Sheldon [1958]: *Algebraic approximations for Laplace's equation in the neighborhood of interfaces*, Math. Tables Aids Comput., vol. 12, pp. 174–186. *276*

Abe Shenitzer, see V. K. Saul'ev.

G. H. Shortley and R. Weller [1938]: *The numerical solution of Laplace's equation*, J. Appl. Phys., vol. 9, pp. 334–348. *198, 200, 201, 341, 362*

George H. Shortley, Royal Weller, and Bernard Fried [1940]: *Numerical Solution of Laplace's and Poisson's Equations with Applications to Photoelasticity and Torsion*, Ohio State University, Engineering Experiment Station, Bull. No. 107, 51 pp. (revised edition, January 1942).

S. L. Sobolev. *137*

Ivan S. Sokolnikoff and Elizabeth S. Sokolnikoff [1941]: *Higher Mathematics for Engineers and Physicists*, 2nd ed., McGraw-Hill Book Co., New York, 587 pp. *3*

I. S. Sokolnikoff [1956]: *Mathematical Theory of Elasticity*, 2nd ed., McGraw-Hill Book Co., New York, Toronto, London, 476 pp. *147*

H. Solberg, see V. Bjerknes.

Arnold Sommerfeld [1949]: *Partial Differential Equations in Physics*, Academic Press, New York, 335 pp. (translated by Ernst G. Straus). *4*

Walter W. Soroka [1954]: *Analog Methods in Computation and Simulation*, McGraw-Hill Book Co., New York, 390 pp. *7*

R. V. Southwell [1946, 1956]: *Relaxation Methods in Theoretical Physics*, Clarendon Press, Oxford, vol. 1, 248 pp.; vol. 2, pp. 250–522. *147, 241*

Marvin L. Stein, see Magnus R. Hestenes.

P. Stein [1951]: *The convergence of Seidel iterants of nearly symmetric matrices*, Math. Tables Aids Comput., vol. 5, pp. 237–240. *238*

P. Stein and R. L. Rosenberg [1948]: *On the solution of linear simultaneous equations by iteration*, J. London Math. Soc., vol. 23, pp. 111–118. *260*

E. Stiefel [1955]: *Relaxationsmethoden bester Strategie zur Lösung linearer Gleichungssysteme*, Comment. Math. Helv., vol. 29, pp. 157–179. *225*

Eduard L. Stiefel [1958]: *Kernel polynomials in linear algebra and their numerical applications*, pp. 1–22 of *Further Contributions to the Solution of Simultaneous Linear Equations and the Determination of Eigenvalues*, Nat. Bur. Standards Appl. Math. Ser., vol. 49, 81 pp. *227, 234, 235*

Eduard Stiefel, see also Magnus R. Hestenes.

Ernst G. Straus, see Arnold Sommerfeld.

J. L. Synge [1951]: *Approximations in boundary value problems by the method of the hypercircle in function space*, Rend. Circ. Mat. Palermo (5), vol. 10, pp. 24–47. *340*

J. L. Synge [1957]: *The Hypercircle in Mathematical Physics*, Cambridge Univ. Press, 424 pp. *340*

G. Szegö, see G. Pólya.

J. D. Tamarkin and Willy Feller [1941]: *Partial Differential Equations*, mimeographed, Brown University, Providence, 268 pp. *174, 330*

Olga Taussky [1949]: *A recurring theorem on determinants*, Amer. Math. Monthly, vol. 56, pp. 672–676. *221*

L. H. Thomas [1954]: *Computation of one-dimensional flows including shocks*, Comm. Pure Appl. Math., vol. 7, pp. 195–206. *68, 69, 71, 78*

John Todd [1949]: *The condition of a certain matrix*, Proc. Cambridge Philos. Soc., vol. 46, pp. 116–118. *228*

John Todd, see also David M. Young, Jr.

Charles B. Tompkins [1956]: *Methods of steep descent*, pp. 448–479 of Beckenbach [1956]. *164*

Leonard Tornheim [1950]: *On n-parameter families of functions and associated convex functions*, Trans. Amer. Math. Soc., vol. 69, pp. 457–467. *279*

L. R. Turner. *209*

W. Uhlmann [1958]: *Differenzenverfahren für die 1. Randwertaufgabe mit krummflächigen Rändern bei* $\Delta u(x, y, z) = r(x, y, z, u)$, Z. Angew. Math. Mech., vol. 38, pp. 130–139.

W. Uhlmann [1958a]: *Differenzenverfahren für die 2. und 3. Randwertaufgabe mit krummlinigen Rändern bei* $\Delta u(x, y) = r(x, y, u)$, Z. Angew. Math. Mech., vol. 38, pp. 236–251.

W. Uhlmann, see also J. Albrecht.

Richard S. Varga [1957a]: *A comparison of the successive overrelaxation method and semi-iterative methods using Chebyshev polynomials*, J. Soc. Indust. Appl. Math., vol. 5, pp. 39–46. *229*

R. S. Varga [1957b]: *Numerical solution of the two-group diffusion equation in x-y geometry*, Inst. Radio Engrs., Trans. Prof. Group Nuclear Sci., vol. NS-4, pp. 52–62. *198*

Richard S. Varga [1959]: *p-cyclic matrices: a generalization of the Young-Frankel successive overrelaxation scheme*, Pacific J. Math., vol. 9, pp. 617–628. *259*

Richard S. Varga [1959a]: *Orderings of the successive overrelaxation scheme*, Pacific J. Math., vol. 9, pp. 925–939. *259*

R. S. Varga, see also G. G. Bilodeau and Garrett Birkhoff.

R. V. Viswanathan [1957]: *Solution of Poisson's equation by relaxation method—normal gradient specified on curved boundaries*, Math. Tables Aids Comput., vol. 11, pp. 67–78. *202*

E. A. Volkov [1957]: (Е. А. Волков) К вопросу о решении методом сеток внутренней задачи Дирихле для уравнения Лапласа, Vyčisl. Mat., collection 1, pp. 34–61.

E. A. Volkov [1957a]: (Е. А. Волков) Исследование одного способа повышения точности метода сеток при решении уравнения Пуассона, Vyčisl. Mat., collection 1, pp. 62–80.

A. I. Vzorova [1957]: (А. И. Взорова) Таблицы для Решения Уравнения Лапласа в Эллиптических Областях, Izd. Akad. Nauk. SSSR, Moscow, 257 pp.

J. L. Walsh and David Young [1953]: *On the accuracy of the numerical solution of the Dirichlet problem by finite differences*, J. Res. Nat. Bur. Standards, vol. 51, pp. 343–363. *310*

J. L. Walsh and David Young [1954]: *On the degree of convergence of solutions of difference equations to the solution of the Dirichlet problem*, J. Math. Phys., vol. 33, pp. 80–93. *199, 310*

Charles H. Warlick [1955]: *Convergence rates of numerical methods for solving*

$$\frac{\partial^2 u}{\partial x^2} + \frac{k}{\rho} \frac{\partial u}{\partial \rho} + \frac{\partial^2 u}{\partial \rho^2} = 0,$$

Master's thesis, University of Maryland, 55 pp.

Charles H. Warlick, see also David Young.

Wolfgang Wasow [1951]: *Random walks and the eigenvalues of elliptic difference equations*, J. Res. Nat. Bur. Standards, vol. 46, pp. 65–73. *292*

Wolfgang Wasow [1951a]: *On the duration of random walks*, Ann. Math. Statist., vol. 22, pp. 199–216. *292, 302, 303* .

Wolfgang Wasow [1951b]: *On the mean duration of random walks*, J. Res. Nat. Bur. Standards, vol. 46, pp. 462–471. *292, 322*

Wolfgang Wasow [1952]: *On the truncation error in the solution of Laplace's equation by finite differences*, J. Res. Nat. Bur. Standards, vol. 48, pp. 345–348. *309, 319*

Wolfgang Wasow [1955]: *Discrete approximations to elliptic differential equations*, Z. Angew. Math. Phys., vol. 6, pp. 81–97. *307–309*

Wolfgang R. Wasow [1957]: *The accuracy of difference approximations to plane Dirichlet problems with piecewise analytic boundary values*, Quart. Appl. Math., vol. 15, pp. 53–63. *311, 314*

Wolfgang Wasow [1957a]: *Asymptotic development of the solution of Dirichlet's problem at analytic corners*, Duke Math. J., vol. 24, pp. 47–56. *311, 341*

Wolfgang Wasow [1958]: *On the accuracy of implicit difference approximations to the equation of heat flow*, Math. Tables Aids Comput., vol. 12, pp. 43–55. *124, 125*

W. Wasow, see also T. S. Motzkin.

H. F. Weinberger [1956]: *Upper and lower bounds for eigenvalues by finite difference methods*, Comm. Pure Appl. Math., vol. 9, pp. 613–623. *336–339, 349, 353*

H. F. Weinberger [1958]: *Lower bounds for higher eigenvalues by finite difference methods*, Pacific J. Math., vol. 8, pp. 339–368. *336, 349*

R. Weller, see G. H. Shortley.

H. Wielandt [1944]: *Bestimmung höheren Eigenwerte durch gebrochene Iteration*, Bericht der aerodynamischen Versuchsanstalt Göttingen, Report 44/J/37. *355*

Helmut Wielandt [1955]: *An extremum property of sums of eigenvalues*, Proc. Amer. Math. Soc., vol. 6, pp. 106–110. *347*

N. Wiener, see H. Phillips.

J. H. Wilkinson [1954]: *The calculation of the latent roots and vectors of matrices on the pilot model of the A.C.E.*, Proc. Cambridge Philos. Soc., vol. 50, pp. 536–566. *353, 355, 371*

J. H. Wilkinson [1958]: *The calculation of the eigenvectors of codiagonal matrices*, The Computer Journal, vol. 1, pp. 90–96. *105, 354*

J. H. Wilkinson [1959]: *Theory and practice in linear systems and the determination of characteristic values and characteristic vectors*, pp. 41–152 of John W. Carr, III (editor), *Application of Advanced Numerical Analysis to Digital Computers, an Intensive Course for Practicing Scientists and Engineers, Lectures given at the University of Michigan, Summer 1958*, Univ. of Michigan College of Engineering, Ann Arbor, Mich., 328 pp. *105, 209, 214*

J. H. Wilkinson, see also Anonymous.

S. S. Wilks [1943]: *Mathematical Statistics*, Princeton University Press, 284 pp. *326*

L. C. Woods [1953]: *The relaxation treatment of singular points in Poisson's equation*, Quart. J. Mech. Appl. Math., vol. 6, pp. 163–185. *204*

David Young [1954]: *On Richardson's method for solving linear systems with positive definite matrices*, J. Math. Phys., vol. 32, pp. 243–255. *105, 232–234*

David Young [1954a]: *Iterative methods for solving partial difference equations of elliptic type*, Trans. Amer. Math. Soc., vol. 76, pp. 92–111. *218, 242–272, 355, 394*

David M. Young [1955]: *ORDVAC solutions of the Dirichlet problem*, J. Assoc. Comput. Mach., vol. 2, pp. 137–161. *260*

D. M. Young [1956]: *Notes on an iterative method of Douglas and Rachford*, NN-32, Digital Computing Center, The Ramo-Wooldridge Corp., 8 pp. *281*

David M. Young, Jr. [1958]: *The numerical solution of elliptic and parabolic partial*

SUBJECT INDEX

The subject index includes names associated with a subject, like Hilbert space. Names mentioned with publications or in personal references will be found in the Bibliography and Author Index, pp. 415–431.

Abel's theorem, 100
Abbreviation of journal titles, 415
Absolute vorticity, 388, 392
Acceleration of convergence, 218, 370
Accuracy, *see* Discretization error, Round-off error
Adams' method, 68–71, 78
Adiabatic flow, 72–75, 386
  one-dimensional equations of, 41, 44, 72, 85
Adjoint problem, 170, 172
Admissible function, 163
Aitken's δ^2 process, 370
Algebraic language, 11, 364
ALGOL, 11
Almost symmetric matrix, 238
Alternating-direction method, 272–282, 375, 411–413
Analog computer, 7, 182, 184, 223, 224
Analytic continuation of solution, 204, 340
Analytic corner, 311
Analytic function, 146, 340, 351
Analytic initial conditions, 25, 27, 101
Angle, re-entrant, 311
Angles, region with, 301, 311, 340, 341
Approximation, by analytic function, 4
  formal, 17, 180, 405
Arithmetic operations, number of, 12–14, 208
Asymptotic equality of vectors, 216
Atmosphere, 386
Author index, 415–431
Automatic coding, 11
Automatic digital computer, 9–11
  experiments with, 86, 87, 334, 351, 358–363, 368–375
  used for large linear systems, 267
  used to solve Laplace's equation, 357–377

Average of harmonic function on circle, 175, 292

Backward difference, 50, 52, 69, 398
Banach space, 134, 135
Bessel function, 265
Bibliography, 415–431
Bidiagonal matrix, 212
Biharmonic operator, 153
Bilinear interpolation, 332
Block-iterative method, 269
Block-tridiagonal matrix, 210, 243, 268
Body equation, 200
Borel set, 289
Borel-measurable function, 289
Boundary, curved, 179, 199–202
Boundary conditions, at infinity, 155
  for elliptic equations, 147–159
  for heat equation, 99
  involving normal derivatives, 202–204
  mixed, 169
  natural, 162, 165, 166, 182
Boundary node, 362
Boundary-value problem, 147
  Neumann, 202–204, 259, 318, 319, 376, 377
  third, 169, 259
Bounded variation, 101, 310
Buffer, 10
Burroughs *220* computer, 374

C.P.C., 9, 223
Calculus of variations, applied to boundary-value problems, 159–165
  applied to eigenvalue problems, 165–167, 331, 335, 336
  used in forming difference equations, 182–184, 195–198, 366
Canonical blocks, 216, 257

433